EDINBURGH UNIVERSITY PUBLICATIONS

SCIENCE AND MATHEMATICS TEXTS

8

ELECTRICITY
AND
MATTER

an introductory survey by
NORMAN FEATHER FRS

AT THE UNIVERSITY PRESS
EDINBURGH

© Norman Feather 1968
EDINBURGH UNIVERSITY PRESS
22 George Square, Edinburgh 8
North America
Aldine Publishing Company
320 West Adams Street, Chicago
Australia and New Zealand
Hodder & Stoughton Ltd
Africa, Oxford University Press
India, P. C. Manaktala & Sons
Far East, M. Graham Brash & Son
Printed in Great Britain by
Robert Cunningham and Sons Ltd, Alva
85224 015 5

Library of Congress
Catalog Card Number 68-19878

PREFACE

For readers of *Mass, Length and Time* (1959), or *Vibrations and Waves* (1961), little is needed by way of preface to this third volume 'written for the beginning specialist in physics'—and generally addressed to anyone who, 'at this time, and with good reason, is looking for an answer to the question, What is physics all about?' However, some sort of a preface is customary, and for new readers it may even be informative.

First of all, then, the two quotations are taken from the original Preface of *Mass, Length and Time*. In that first volume the intention was to begin 'by examining . . . the bases of measurement of the fundamental physical quantities' enumerated in its title. Similarly, in this volume, the prolegomena to measurement receive attention first. And because, in electricity, the simplest measurement is one stage removed from common experience—for man has no electrical sense organ of his own—the matter is of some subtlety, and almost a third of the book is taken up with its discussion. Naturally, on the way, many facts are elicited and some theoretical viewpoints are established, but all this is merely the laying of foundations for what is to follow.

In what follows, of necessity much remains untold at the end. In the Preface to *Mass, Length and Time*, I wrote 'I am sufficiently old-fashioned to believe that a carefully-told story, starting at the beginning, is likely to be more satisfying to any serious questioner, whatever his speciality, than the most colourful [modern version which ignores the past] could possibly be. Even though much of the story must remain untold, I believe he will still find satisfaction in it.' That philosophy informs this book, also. Already, modern physics has four hundred years of history behind it. Inevitably, it is no easy task for the specialist student to assimilate the experience of those four centuries, within the brief span of an undergraduate career. Eventually, when he comes to his degree, he will be expected to have appropriated to himself the conquests of the great men of a dozen generations, and to have accepted the discipline which they have laid upon him; initially, however, he must start from the beginning, as Newton did in dynamics, or Ampère, or Faraday, in electricity, for he can start nowhere else. It is the aim of this book—along with its predecessors—to provide the starting ground for such an adventure. It is merely *An introductory survey*; what remains untold, at the end, is the end of the story.

Realistically, of course, the story has no end: continually, over the years, new theoretical insights are won, new questions are posed by carefully-contrived experiment, and some clear-cut answers are found. The serious student of physics will find abundant documentation of these later developments in the monographs and treatises of the experts. Obviously, he must pay due heed to them, for they point the way to the future, which is his ultimate concern. But in the beginning he will need to develop, first, a sense of direction, and in the end a perspective. This book was written for his early reading—and it was written in the hode that in later years what will remain to him from the reading of it will, at least, be a valid perspective, correcting the distortions of the too-close view, leaving the horizon open ahead.

Electricity and Matter has been more than three years in the writing. During that time successive chapters have been passed, in draft, to various colleagues for comment. Mr R. M. Sillitto has read them all in that way, and Dr P. S. Farago and Dr A. F. Brown have read some of them. From all three I have received criticism and encouragement on a generous scale. I wish to thank them most warmly for their help. Finally, I must thank Miss D. E. Brewster, who once more has been responsible for the final typescript. By her faithfulness in that task she has not only lessened the compositors' labour; she has been a constant source of support for the author, as well.

NORMAN FEATHER
14 April 1967

CONTENTS

CHAPTER 1

INTRODUCTION

It has been said that the first and last concern of the physicist is to attempt to understand 'the varied interactions of dead matter'. The quoted phrase is taken from the second paragraph of chapter 1 of *An Introduction to the Physics of Mass, Length and Time* (herein-after referred to as *M L & T*)—and in it the crucial word is 'interactions'. By use of this word, the validity of Newtonian dynamics is presupposed. In the earlier book, the development of that system was treated in detail. It was described how Newton gave precision to the concepts of mass and force, and, in doing so, formulated the axiom (or law of nature) that forces occur, in the real world, only as equal and oppositely directed 'action and re-action pairs', effective between the ultimate particles of matter.

In so far as this fundamental law, Newton's third law of motion, has been found to be consistent with experiment—and for more than two hundred years it was not seriously brought into question —it must be regarded as a generalisation of the very greatest sim-plicity and power. But it must also be understood that, of itself, the law contributes nothing to the physicist's attempt at 'under-standing'. That attempt approaches fulfilment only when the forces, which the Newtonian analysis reveals, are found to depend upon the physical qualities intrinsic to the particles, or systems of par-ticles, which give rise to them. Newton succeeded so far as to establish such a relation of dependence for the forces of gravitation (*M L & T*, chap. 10): gravitational attraction, so he asserted, is a universal attribute of matter, determined, for any two particles, directly by the product of their inertial masses and inversely by the square of their distance of separation. Once this empirical law had been accepted, a beginning could be made with an attempt to 'understand' the phenomenon of gravitation: it could not have been made without some such precise correlation as the law provided.

In Newton's day, other types of force, besides gravitational force, were recognised, at least descriptively. William Gilbert (1544-1603) had already done much to elucidate the more obvious phenomena of magnetic and electrical attraction between bodies, and a great deal of empirical knowledge had been won concerning the forces of elasticity. Magnetic forces, so it appeared at that time, were specific to a small class of substances, and were exhibited only in particular circumstances. Electric forces were much less specific in their mode of action: all materials, it seemed, were attracted indiscriminately to an electrified body. Any material which was available in thin flakes or small particles could be shown to exhibit the effect. Concerning elastic forces, Robert Hooke (1635-1703) had concluded, in the special case of the coiled spring, and John Wallis (1616-1703) more significantly, in relation to the forces brought into play in the impact of solid bodies generally, that these mutual forces depend upon the deformation of the bodies in question. But in respect of none of these types of force had any simple, all-embracing, law of action been formulated: there was no real quantitative basis, in Newton's day, for an incipient understanding of any of the phenomena concerned.

Nowadays, we believe that we have a secure basis for an understanding of these phenomena. We assert that all the forces (except the force of gravitation) already mentioned—indeed, all the forces which physicists had come to recognise, through the application of Newtonian dynamics, up to the year 1920—are essentially electrical in nature. We make this assertion because we regard the basic structure of matter itself as electrical: all matter constituted of atoms, each atom built of electric charges—of negatively charged electrons and a positively charged nucleus. At this level of analysis the only ultimate qualities of matter are electrification and mass (inertia). The forces of gravitation issue from the 'massiness' of matter; all other forces of interaction between material bodies issue from the electrification intrinsic to the electrons and atomic nuclei, which are the elementary constituent particles of the bodies concerned. At this level of analysis, the dichotomy is simple and complete.

In these last assertions we are repeating, and elaborating, a claim which has previously been made (*M L & T*, p. 2): 'We have claimed that physics is the basic science; in physics, it would appear, electricity is the fundamental subject.' And we have come up against the same natural occasion for warning: all forces, other than gravitational forces, are essentially electrical in nature—provided that we regard atomic nuclei as structureless particles, and so rule out of court any question of the forces which are responsible for their stability. In the earlier book we wrote (*ibid.*), more tersely, 'It would indeed appear [that electricity is the fundamental subject], if scientists were not already heavily involved in the physics of the atom nucleus. There is a new subject there, but that is for future understanding.' Throughout the present book the problem of nuclear forces will remain a matter 'for future understanding', but we shall make reference in passing (p. 287) to some of the observations which, from 1920 onwards, forced upon the attention of physicists the necessity to postulate the occurrence of modes of interaction of particles which are neither gravitational nor electrical in character. Since our title is specific—*Electricity and Matter*—we can make no claim to be concerned with these specifically nuclear forces, rather our aim will be adequately fulfilled if we are able to survey the more important phenomena of electricity and magnetism, experimentally, and to describe them consistently in terms of a simple atomic theory in which electrons and nuclei are regarded as the ultimate particles. Even this aim we shall realise only partially—for, as our title states, we are concerned merely with *An introductory survey*.

In 1913, N. R. Campbell (1880-1949) wrote 'The electrical science of the last century was concerned with the properties of electricity; modern electrical science is concerned with the relations between electricity and matter.' That was the opening sentence of a highly original book. *Modern Electrical Theory*, as the book was titled, gave a conspectus of the subject as it then appeared to the theorist, pointing to the unsolved problems—neither few in number nor inconsiderable in basic importance at that time. This forward-looking book was overtaken only by the experimental discoveries of the years that followed. Now, half a century later, the professional physicist is much better able than Campbell was to give an answer to the questions then in doubt, better able to offer a convincing account of the subject as a whole—in terms of the known properties of electrons and of atomic nuclei. So completely has our ability changed, in this particular, that a strong body of opinion has grown up in favour of a method of presenting the subject in which a knowledge of atomic structure is assumed from the outset. By common consent, successful exposition in science consists always in describing the less familiar in terms of the more familiar: the advocates of this particular approach to the teaching of electricity and magnetism maintain that, nowadays, atoms and electrons and nuclei are among the most familiar physical concepts of all. Obviously, there is some validity in this idea (and we shall in no way disdain to profit by accepting it, as occasion offers), but if, in relation to the basic concepts of our science, 'familiarity' in some way implies 'intuitive comprehension or understanding', as it certainly should do, we shall do well to proceed cautiously in this respect. In any case, we shall attempt to be realistic in our descriptions. If we think it pictorially advantageous to regard a body which is charged with positive electricity as a piece of matter from which electrons have been drawn, we shall attempt to keep the picture quantitatively in focus by reminding ourselves that the maximum degree of positive electrification which any body can sustain in normal air, under ordinary conditions, is that which corresponds very closely to the loss of a single electron from one atom in every hundred-thousand in the surface layer of atoms of the body (see footnote, p. 412), every other atom in the surface layer, and every atom in every lower layer, throughout the whole body, remaining electrically 'intact'. We shall not be carried away, to talk over-glibly of charged bodies as having an unspecified 'excess', or 'a deficit', of electrons; we shall try to remember that even in the most extreme case, with gross bodies, the degree of disequilibrium in this respect is numerically insignificant. In this book, then, we shall proceed without systematic use of atomic concepts to begin with. Before we reach the half-way stage, these concepts will come into prominence, naturally, in relation to the electrical phenomena that we shall then have under review. From that stage on, they will be in constant use.

But here another warning is appropriate. To use atomic concepts convincingly in an elementary textbook on electricity—even after these concepts have been introduced historically—presents the conscientious writer with a serious problem. The phenomena to be discussed are mostly such as may be demonstrated in laboratory-scale experiments. Newtonian dynamics is perfectly valid in respect of the behaviour of the equipment involved in the demonstrations. Indeed, we have already implied that all knowledge of electrical forces in their varied manifestations—in electrostatic and magnetostatic attraction, in the elastic resistance of solid bodies to deformation, in the mutual interactions of magnets and current-carrying conductors, and in many other situations—stems from our confident use of the laws of motion as set out in the *Principia*. Moreover, as long as we limit ourselves to the use of macroscopic electrical concepts—the concepts of charge, of magnetisation, of current, and the like—we have no difficulty in providing a consistent account of a majority of these phenomena within the same framework—albeit at a utilitarian level. It is only when we attempt the deeper interpretation, when we introduce the notion of the atomicity of electricity (obligatory, of course, in respect of certain phenomena), that Newton's laws fail us. We naturally wish to describe an electric current in a conductor as a flow of electrons through its substance, but detailed enquiry convinces us that any picture that we may make of this process in classical terms is fraught with inconsistencies. The same conclusion emerges time and again: we may construct a classical 'model', and we may use it with some show of success up to a point, but it fails us in the end. The truth is that the motions of electrons, within atoms, and among the closely-packed arrays of atoms in solids, has been satisfactorily described only through the mathematical formalism of wave mechanics. It is this truth that presents the problem to which we have referred. What, we may ask, are its possible solutions? Should the textbook-writer defer all attempts at 'deeper interpretation' until the student has mastered the formalism of the less familiar conceptual approach; should he use the classical models unashamedly, without mention of their limitations, abandoning the student to resolve his own future disillusionment (if, happily, he should pursue the subject farther); or should he introduce his reader cautiously to the 'correct' view of the matter by way of the classical model, its limitations openly admitted? Of these possible courses of action, the third undoubtedly makes the greatest demand on the writer—a demand on his integrity as a scientist; moreover, it is clearly open to misunderstanding and criticism by the theorist. In spite of these considerations, it is the course that we shall follow in this book.

In dealing with the properties of solid conductors and dielectric substances, and with magnetic materials, then, we shall be using, by and large, classical models, exposing their limitations as appropriate, and occasionally indicating the gist of a more acceptable mode of description. Only at the end of the book, in the last chapter, shall we introduce a topic which cannot be treated in this way. There we shall consider, briefly, the phenomena of 'field emission' and radioactivity. For these phenomena no classical model is of any avail. In relation to them the inadequacy of Newtonian dynamics is evident from the outset. The issue in each case concerns the principle of conservation of energy: it is a direct issue which cannot be avoided.

Obviously, having proceeded as far as the final chapter of the book on the assumption that the reader is unfamiliar with the formalism of wave mechanics, we shall not confront him with the use of that formalism there. Devoting that chapter to a qualitative account of these manifestly 'non-classical' phenomena, our aim will be rather to provide a clear-cut example of the failure of the classical approach, so that, in spite of the partial successes which have resulted from our adoption of that approach throughout the rest of the book, the reader may pay heed to the warning that has been given: though classical models may help in our understanding —as the argument from dimensions may help—a satisfactory description of the motions of electrons within atoms, or among the atoms of solid substances generally, can be given only in terms of wave mechanics.

In *An Introduction to the Physics of Vibrations and Waves* (hereinafter referred to as *V & W*), the last sentence of chapter 1 reads: 'Perhaps, when he has traversed the book, the reader may return with added profit to this introduction, finding in it, also, something of a summary—and a background against which to evaluate the significance of what he has read.' This sentence can, equally well, be taken as concluding chapter 1 of this book. It is just as relevant, now, as it was previously.

CHAPTER 2

INVERSE SQUARE LAW FORCES

2.1. INTRODUCTORY

A very brief summary has already been given, in an earlier book
(*V & W*, §9.1), of the quantification of the concepts 'electric
charge', 'magnetic pole', 'electric current', on the basis of laws of
force empirically established as valid in specific situations. On that
occasion we were concerned only incidentally with these fundamental interactions; now they are our primary object of study. In
this chapter, therefore, it will be our aim to elaborate our previous
account, looking back to the pre-quantitative era, and forward,
from the early nineteenth century, when these particular laws of
force were first established, to the present. Bringing the whole
subject into focus in this way, our object will be to indicate the
experimental observations which gave rise to the concepts in the
first instance, and to describe the more sophisticated investigations
on which the quantitative laws were eventually founded. At this
stage we shall be concerned more with facts than with theories,
and we shall not be over-specific in relation to units of measurement. The development of a 'single, self-consistent, system of
units which is applicable throughout the entire range of the unified
subject electricity-and-magnetism' (*V & W*, p. 262) occurred relatively late in the history of our science: it will be advantageous
if, in this book, we defer its consideration to the next chapter.
Here, we shall treat, in turn, electrostatic forces, magnetostatic
forces, and the forces of interaction between magnets and currents
—attempting to re-create something of the sense of exploration
which characterised the 'classical' investigations in these fields.

2.2. ELECTROSTATIC FORCES:
PRE-QUANTITATIVE OBSERVATIONS

For more than two thousand years, from the time when the
Greeks came to recognise the peculiar properties of amber (Gr.
ἤλεκτρον, L. electrum), the phenomena for which the adjective

'electrical' was first introduced into our language—by William Barlowe, archdeacon of Salisbury, in 1618—were seen as involving only forces of attraction. Thus seen, a piece of amber, rubbed in the palm of the hand or on dry cloth, acquires, for a time, the power of attracting small objects, such as fragments of straw (hence the oriental name, karabe*), bits of paper, or thin metal foil—and that is all.

During almost the whole of this long period, although amber remained an article of commerce in Europe, no new aspects of the phenomenon were noted, and only a handful of other substances were recorded as having similar properties. Then, at the end, in the sixteenth century, William Gilbert investigating the matter systematically, showed that the property was indeed widespread (to those substances exhibiting it, writing in Latin, he gave the name 'electrica'). But neither Gilbert, nor anyone else, paid any attention to the fact, which surely all must have observed, that the attraction was in general short-lived. In most cases, attracted objects do not adhere to an electrified body; once having made contact, they fall away again. The credit of having been the first to find significance in this fact probably belongs to Niccolo Cabeo (1585-1650); the first to give (1663) a connected account of it was Otto von Guericke (1602-1686). Cabeo was a Jesuit priest, who had been born in Ferrara at the time of its greatest magnificence; Guericke was born at Magdeburg in Saxony, and became mayor of that town (see *V & W*, p. 112). With the observations of Cabeo and Guericke it became clear that both forces of attraction and forces of repulsion were involved in the simplest of electrical effects: half a generation later, when the laws of Newtonian gravitation had been formulated, gravitational effects were seen to involve attractions only.

Within the context of this recognition of difference, a fundamental discovery was made by Charles Francois de C. du Fay (1699-1739). Du Fay, who was superintendent of gardens to Louis XV of France, posed himself the question (1733) 'do electrified bodies differ from each other in no respect save their intensity of electrification?' In order to examine the matter, he electrified a number of bodies, of glass, quartz, amber, copal, sealing wax, and similar substances. Presenting one of these electrified bodies to a piece of gold-leaf, he observed the attraction, contact and subse-

* Literally, 'that which attracts straw'.

quent repulsion, as Cabeo had done. Then, bringing the other electrified bodies in turn near to the gold-leaf, he discovered that their effects were diverse: some repelled the leaf, others tended to attract it. With whichever electrified body the experiment was started, the final demarcation was the same: the bodies which were 'vitreous' exhibited one behaviour with respect to the 'excited' leaf (attraction or repulsion), the bodies which were 'resinous' exhibited the other (repulsion or attraction). Du Fay wrote in conclusion: 'there are two electricities of a totally different nature. . . . Each of them repels bodies which have contracted an electricity of the same nature as its own, and attracts those whose electricity is of the contrary nature.' In these experiments, it should be stated, du Fay electrified his vitreous bodies by rubbing them with silk, his resinous bodies by rubbing them with flannel. And it should also be stated, as must be obvious, that his conclusion makes sense only if it be assumed that the gold-leaf, on contact with the first body presented to it, takes away some of the electrification of that body. That is the meaning to be attached to the term 'excited', as we have used it.

This last remark is of some importance: du Fay's observations were made within two years of the publication of the results of a series of experiments carried out by an Englishman, Stephen Gray (1696-1736). In 1729 Gray had communicated the first of these results to Jean Théophile Desaguliers (1683-1744), at that time Curator of the Royal Society of London. Gray claimed that he had been able to transfer 'the Electrick Virtue of a Glass Tube' to other bodies, merely by connecting these bodies to the electrified tube by metal wires or hempen string. Some materials would act as 'channels of transport' under these conditions; others, such as silk, would not. Desaguliers confirmed Gray's results (as did du Fay), and introduced the general term 'conductor' to describe a substance (or a body) which transports electricity in this way. Du Fay showed that even bodies which were conductors could be electrified by friction, provided that they were supported by non-conductors, and, more perspicacious than Desaguliers, he recognised from the beginning that the true antithesis is that between a conductor and an 'insulator' (non-conductor), rather than that between a conductor ('non-electric') and an electric (in the sense used by Gilbert, namely a body susceptible of electrification by friction).

EM B

By 1733, then, it was established that two 'portions' of electricity of the same kind are mutually repulsive, and that electricity of either kind is mobile throughout the volume (or over the surface) of certain bodies, that is, bodies that are conductors. These facts being accepted, it was not unnatural to conclude that the electrification of a conducting body should reside always on its surface. This conclusion, as we shall see (p. 16), was somewhat naïve, but, already in 1729, Gray had carried out experiments with similar conducting bodies, the one solid and the other hollow, to explore the situation, and had interpreted them in this way. Once predictions can be made which are confirmed by experiment, the beginnings of a scientific theory are clearly to be discerned. At this stage, therefore, the rudiments of a qualitative theory of electricity began to take shape. That it should have happened at this stage, was chiefly due to the work of Gray and du Fay, but it is only just to record the fact that, largely isolated from contact with European science, and unaware of the work that we have just described, Ebenezer Kinnersley (1711-1778) made similar advances independently, in Philadelphia, not many years later than this.

The work of du Fay brought qualitative order into contemporary knowledge concerning the attractions and repulsions of electrified bodies, but it thereby diverted attention from the still unsolved problem of the attractions which electrified bodies have for bodies which are unelectrified—the original problem of the properties of amber as known to the Greeks. The fact is that the older problem is the more subtle of the two; in 1733 the basic experimental observations on which its solution depended had still to be made. The first person to make them was John Canton (1718-1772), who, after five years apprenticeship to the master of a school in Spital Square, in London, spent the remainder of his working life as a schoolmaster himself. In 1753, Canton discovered the phenomenon of electrostatic induction: the fact that an unelectrified conducting body, brought near to a body which is electrified, itself exhibits regions of electrification—the region farthest from the electrified body developing electrification of the same kind as that of the electrified body; the region nearest to that body, electrification of the opposite kind. Four years later, this effect was rediscovered, independently, by Johann Karl Wilcke (1732-1796), a Swede then resident in Berlin. Wilcke published a preliminary account of his discovery at Rostock in 1757, and, having in the meantime returned to Sweden, described a long series of further experiments in a memoir which he presented to the Swedish Academy in 1762.

In 1763, Jean Antoine Nollet (1700-1770) wrote, in volume 6 of *Leçons de physique expérimentale* (see *V & W*, p. 6), 'It is greatly to be desired that we should have an accurate instrument, not merely to provide an indication whether or not a body is electrified, but by how much it is electrified more than another body, or more than it was itself, at another time, or in other circumstances. Such an instrument would be the true *Electrometer* for which we have been looking for so long, which some have deluded themselves into thinking that they have found, but which no one in fact possesses—if we speak the truth. Nothing that anyone can offer, for the purpose of measuring electrification, is any better than the two bits of thread that one hangs, one beside the other, on a body that is to be electrified, and which diverge, the one from the other, as they become electrified along with the body to which they are attached. . . .' The double-thread electroscope to which Nollet referred had been introduced—and used to good purpose— by Benjamin Franklin (1706-1790) in Philadelphia; in expressing the need for something that was better, Nollet was reflecting the scientific temper of the age in which he wrote. The pre-quantitative study of electrical phenomena had yielded all that could reasonably be expected of it: further advance depended on numerical evaluation.

2.3. ELECTROSTATIC FORCES : THE QUANTITATIVE LAW

Except for two years, Benjamin Franklin spent the period 1757 to 1772 in England, as agent for the General Assembly of Pennsylvania and, in the latter part of this period, for other of the American colonies. His own scientific work had already largely been concluded, owing to force of circumstance, but, having been elected F.R.S. in 1756, he served on various committees of the Society and maintained contact generally with the fellowship. By 1766 the electrical researches of Joseph Priestley (1733-1804) had attracted sufficient attention to secure his election, also, and Franklin communicated to the new Fellow a 'curious observation' that he had made some years previously. A small cork ball suspended on a silk thread and presented to the outside of a metal cup charged with electricity was strongly attracted; when it was presented to the inside surface of the cup it was not. Priestley, who was at that time classical tutor in a school at Warrington, repeated the experiment, with various modifications, confirmed the result, and concluded (1767): 'May we not infer . . . that the attraction of electricity is subject to the same laws with that of gravitation . . . since it is easily demonstrated that were the earth in the form of a shell, a body in the inside of it would not be attracted to one side more than another.'

In this brilliant deduction, Priestley was relying on a result that Newton had derived. In another place (*M L & T*, p. 205) we have given Newton's proof that a uniform spherical shell attracts an external particle as if the whole of the mass of the shell were concentrated at its centre: here we give the (simplest) proof that the resultant attraction is zero if the particle is situated within the shell. In either case, of course, the law of force is assumed to be the inverse-square law.

FIGURE 1

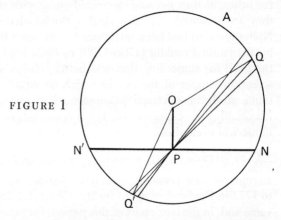

Let A (fig. 1) represent a uniform spherical shell of material, of mass σ per unit surface area, and negligible thickness. Let O be the centre of the sphere, and let there be a particle of mass m situated at P an arbitrary internal point. Let N'PN be the trace of the plane through P perpendicular to OP, and let Q'PQ be any line through P intersecting the surface A in Q and Q' Consider a cone of small solid angle $\Delta\omega$, having Q'PQ as axis, and terminated by elements of surface of the sphere of areas ΔS (about Q) and $\Delta S'$ (about Q'). Let $\angle OQP\ (=\ \angle OQ'P) = \theta$, PQ $= r$, PQ' $= r'$.

Then $\quad \Delta\omega = \dfrac{\Delta S \cos\theta}{r^2} = \dfrac{\Delta S' \cos\theta}{r'^2},$

and, consequently,

$$\frac{Gm\sigma\,\Delta S}{r^2} = \frac{Gm\sigma\,\Delta S'}{r'^2} \qquad (1)$$

Equation (1) is a formal result: if we interpret it by regarding G as the Newtonian constant of gravitation, the left-hand member is the measure of the force of attraction between the particle at P and the element of shell of area ΔS about Q; similarly, the right-hand member is the measure of the attraction between the particle and the corresponding element of the shell about Q'. It being established that these attractions are equal in magnitude and oppositely directed, the effect of the whole shell on the particle at P is obviously zero, since its entire surface may be broken up into pairs of corresponding elements, by elementary cones through P, as before. To be precise, the attraction due to that portion of the shell on one side of the plane N'PN exactly balances the attraction due to the portion on the other side of the plane. As Priestley insisted, this formal result must certainly be valid for any comparable situation in which inverse-square law forces are involved.

Though Priestley's deduction was indeed the result of brilliant intuition, it cannot be claimed that the experiments on which it was based were of more than qualitative validity. For that reason, perhaps, it did not convince his contemporaries—and it was lost sight of by historians. Writing in 1807, Thomas Young made no mention of Priestley in relation to the discovery of 'the true law of the electric attractions and repulsions': in this connection he gave credit only to 'Lord Stanhope' and 'Mr Cavendish'.

Charles Stanhope (1753-1816), born Viscount Mahon, succeeded to the earldom of Stanhope on the death of his father in 1786. He was elected F.R.S. at the age of nineteen, under a statute assigning special privileges to peers of the realm, and seven years later justified his election (if he did not fully justify the ground of it) by publishing a quarto volume entitled *Principles of Electricity*. His investigations concerning the law of force are described in this volume: they are of interest chiefly in that they provide possibly the first occasion on which a precise hypothesis in relation to electrical attraction was tested in terms of its more remote consequences. When a small electrified body is brought near to one end of a long insulated conductor, there is a fairly well-defined zone separating the distributions of induced electrification of opposite sign. These distributions are most intense at the two ends of the conductor: somewhere in between there is a region of zero charge. Earlier investigators, and Stanhope himself, had determined the position of this neutral zone experimentally. Stanhope calculated where it should be situated, if the law of force were the inverse-square law. His calculations tallied with his observations; he concluded, therefore, that his original assumption of inverse-square law forces was validated.

The 'Mr Cavendish' of Thomas Young's account was actively engaged throughout the ten years from 1771 to 1781 on electrical researches. For the present, we shall confine attention to two of these investigations—one in the manner of Stanhope, the other a refinement of the experiment of Priestley which eventually attracted to its author (posthumously) credit which he should at least share with his less methodical, but hardly less gifted, contemporary. The Honourable Henry Cavendish (1731-1810), nephew of the Duke of Devonshire and himself the inheritor of very considerable wealth, assiduously avoided contact with his fellow men (even with his domestic servants) throughout his adult life—except such contact as came to him within the fellowship of the Royal Society. From the time of his election, in 1760, until his death, he regularly attended the weekly meetings (and the club dinners which followed them), and he served the Society for twenty-seven years as a member of its Council. Occasionally he would present the results of his own researches for publication in the Society's *Transactions*—as he did in 1771, indicating then that he inclined to the view that the law of force between electric charges is an inverse-square law—but much more frequently he did not. Thus, almost the whole of his work during the ten-year period of which we are writing remained hidden away, among his personal papers, for nearly a century, until it was rescued from oblivion by Maxwell (see *V & W*, p. 254). An account of it appeared in print for the first time in 1879, in the year in which Maxwell died.

In the manner of Stanhope, but with more mathematical skill, Cavendish examined the problem of the sharing of charge between an insulated sphere and a circular disk of the same radius, when these are separated by a considerable distance and joined by a thin metal wire. By direct experiment he satisfied himself that, in actual fact, charge is shared in the way that is predicted by calculation, if the inverse-square law of force is assumed.

In succession to Priestley, Cavendish re-examined, next, the question of the force, or absence of force, on an electrified body placed within a hollow charged conductor of spherical form, matching his experimental arrangement more nearly to the theoretical ideal—and dispensing altogether with the need for an extraneous test body within the apparatus. It was a brilliant solution of a subtle problem in the design of experiment. Moreover, when the experiment was over, Cavendish was able to set limits to its sensitivity: he concluded that if the variation of electrostatic force with distance is expressible as a simple power law, then the negative index in that law cannot differ from 2 by more than $\frac{1}{59}$, either way. Were it otherwise, he would have observed an effect which, in fact, he did not observe.

Let us examine the method of experiment, and the arguments by which Cavendish reached his conclusions. We refer back to fig. 1 (p. 12), and to our previous result—translating it first into electrical terms, for sake of convenience. If the law of force is the inverse-square law, and if A is a uniformly electrified spherical shell, the force on a charged particle situated at an arbitrary internal point P is zero: we have shown that this force can be resolved, along the radius OP, into two equal and oppositely directed components, due, respectively, to the electrification on one side of the plane N'PN, and to that on the other.

We suppose, now, that the inverse-power law of electrostatic action has a different index, n ($\neq 2$). Then, in the same situation, exact balance of forces will no longer obtain: for $n > 2$, the effect of the electrification on the side of N'PN opposite to O will be greater than the effect of the electrification on the other side of the plane (this latter electrification being, on the average, farther from P); when $n < 2$, the reverse will be the case. Here is the basis of Cavendish's argument. Suppose that we have a spherical shell charged with electricity, and imagine that a second, uncharged spherical shell is fitted around it, the material of both shells being conducting material. Then, if the two shells are connected by a metallic wire, and whatever is the precise variation of electrostatic force with distance, the force on an electrified particle on the surface of the wire will be directed from the inner to the outer shell, initially, if the charge on the particle is of the same sign as the charge on the inner shell, and *vice versa*. The connecting wire allowing free passage of electricity, charge will begin to pass from the inner to the outer shell, in this arrangement—and the process will not be arrested until the force acting on an electrified particle in the surface of the wire has decreased to zero. If the law of force is the inverse-square law, this will be the case when the whole of the charge has passed from the inner to the outer shell; if $n > 2$, it will be the case at an earlier stage in the process, when some of the original charge still remains on the inner shell; if $n < 2$, it will not occur until later, until the inner shell has developed electrification opposite in sign to its original electrification, the outer shell having concurrently received a larger charge than was resident on the inner shell to begin with. If $| n - 2 | \ll 1$, the fractional amount of the original charge (of the same, or of opposite, sign) remaining on the inner shell can be calculated, assuming spherical symmetry.

Cavendish carried out the experiment, as nearly as possible as we have described it ideally. When the two hemispherical portions constituting the outer shell of his arrangement were removed, he could not detect any residual electrification, of either sign, on the originally electrified inner shell with which they had been in contact. Estimating the sensitivity of the pith-ball electroscope with which he made his observations, he assigned to $| n - 2 |$ the limiting value, $\frac{1}{59}$, that we have already quoted, on the basis of calculations such as we have indicated in the last paragraph.

That Cavendish is justly entitled to the major share of the credit for the Priestley–Cavendish derivation of the law of electrostatic action, though he must obviously concede strict priority in the matter, is evidenced by the way in which his experiment has been repeated, over a period of more than a century and a half, modified essentially only in relation to the final instrument of detection. Using a quadrant electrometer as this instrument, Maxwell (1878) obtained a limiting value of $4 \cdot 6 \times 10^{-5}$ for $| n - 2 |$; more recently Plimpton and Lawton (1936) obtained $1 \cdot 0 \times 10^{-9}$, using a valve amplifier, in an alternating-current arrangement, to detect any back-and-forth transfer of charge between the two spherical conductors. We may conclude that, on the macroscopic scale, the inverse-square law of electrostatic action has been repeatedly validated, by the method of Cavendish, whenever an improvement in the available methods of measurement has made possible any notable increase in the precision of the experimental investigation.

Traditionally, however, the inverse-square law of electrostatic action has for long been referred to as Coulomb's law. Charles Augustin Coulomb (1736-1806) was the first to verify the law, systematically, by the direct measurement of the mechanical force between two charged bodies. He employed the torsion balance for this purpose in 1785, essentially as Cavendish employed it thirteen years later (see *M L & T*, §10.5) in order to measure the force of gravitational attraction in a laboratory experiment. Fortunately, his problem was simpler than Cavendish's in nearly every respect. In almost any situation, when the charge on two bodies is above the lower limit for detection, the electrostatic force is enormously greater than the gravitational force acting between them (see p. 289)—and, in any case, the quantity of electricity that can be concentrated on a spherical body depends only on its surface area (see p. 36), and in no way on its mass. Cavendish was to experience very considerable difficulties in relation to strength of suspension and rigidity of support when he came to apply the torsion balance to the measurement of gravitational attraction; Coulomb experienced none of these difficulties in using it for the measurement of the electrostatic forces which his gold-coated pith balls exerted on one another when suitably charged.

Though it cannot be claimed that the torsion-balance investigations of Coulomb added anything of importance to the knowledge of his time in the matter of the variation of electrostatic force with distance (indeed, they involved a difficulty in this respect to which we must presently refer), they are nevertheless noteworthy for the fact that they provided a direct verification of an assumption that we have hitherto made implicitly, without clear justification. We have assumed that the electrostatic force between two elementary portions of electricity is proportional to the product of the 'quantities of electricity' involved in each. Here, obviously, with Priestley, we have been following blindly the analogy with gravitation. Coulomb examined this assumption experimentally: he used the device of sharing charge between two exactly similar conducting spheres, one initially charged, the other uncharged, in order to be able to work with a series of bodies the charges of which were in pre-determined ratios (known powers of two, to be precise). In this way he verified the fundamental assumption that we have drawn in question. Only on the basis of his experiments are we able to speak consistently of quantities of electricity—accepting for these quantities a law of conservation, without which mere quantification of charge is irrelevant in any wider context.

Arguing from real experimental bodies to ideal 'particles', then, and adopting suitable units of measurement, we may claim that Coulomb verified directly the basic force-law

$$F = \frac{q_1 q_2}{r^2} \tag{2}$$

Here F is the measure of the mutual force of electrostatic repulsion acting in the line of join of two 'particles' separated by a distance r, when q_1 and q_2 units of electricity are the magnitudes of the charges carried by the particles, respectively. For future reference we note that in this statement of the law the particles are assumed to be situated in vacuum, though in Coulomb's day any difference that there might be in the magnitude of the force when the surrounding medium is changed from air to vacuum, or to any other substance, was scarcely a matter for effective speculation. Furthermore, it is trivial to note, though necessary for precision, that equation (2) describes with equal fidelity electrostatic forces of repulsion and forces of attraction: when F, the measure of the mutual force, is positive, by conventional definition, this force is repulsive; when F is negative, an attractive force is implied. According to experiment, the force is attractive when the charges on the particles are of 'opposite' kinds, repulsive when they are of the 'same' kind (see p. 9); conventionally, then, we represent one kind of electricity ('vitreous') by a positive measure q, the other kind ('resinous') by a negative measure. We have already, elsewhere in this section, fallen into the conventional phraseology, speaking of the 'sign' of a charge. Henceforward, we shall use this phraseology without further ado.

At the beginning of this chapter (p. 7) we stated that, for the present, 'we shall not be over-specific in relation to units of measurement': here we remark, in passing, that the unit of charge which must be adopted if equation (2) is to be valid numerically, is the 'electrostatic unit'. Ideally, two such unit point charges of the same sign, situated in vacuum at unit distance of separation, would repel one another with unit force, and, if of opposite sign, would attract one another similarly. Later, we shall define another unit, more suited to take its place in a comprehensive system applicable alike to measurements of electrical and magnetic quantities generally (see p. 91); for the present we make do with equation (2) and the unit of charge which belongs to it.

For the present, more important than the question of units of measurement, are the physical implications of the experimental results which are subsumed in Coulomb's law. Let us review this matter very briefly, taking 1790 as our vantage point in time. 'Charge of electricity' has been established as a measurable physical quantity: it is almost as if 'electricity' has been established as an indestructible substance. We have recognised the distinction between vitreous and resinous electricities, and having adopted the device of sign of charge, we have accepted an algebraic law of conservation of quantity. But, within our experience, our electrical substance is always associated with gross matter; we postulate forces acting between elementary portions of electricity, but, effectively, we are aware of these forces only through the accelerations of the gross bodies which carry the charges. Certainly, we must postulate, also, forces of interaction between our hypothetical electrical substance and inert matter, in order to explain this effect, and we must assume that uncharged bodies naturally possess a latent store of the electrical substance, for single bodies may be electrified by induction, and we start always with uncharged bodies, originally, whenever electrification is produced by friction.

This is a very brief review, and we must be content to leave it so. It is not our intention in this chapter to record the history of the interplay of the rival electrical theories of the eighteenth century—the 'one fluid' theory of Franklin, Franz Ulrich Theodor Aepinus (1724-1802) and Cavendish, and the 'two-fluid' theory of Robert Symmer (d. 1763) and Coulomb. At the appropriate stage we shall have more to say of the modern theory, a theory of electrons and nuclei in which the conceptual distinction between the electrical substance and gross matter is finally abolished (see p. 158, and chap. 6): here we have merely drawn together some of the vague theoretical ideas which took shape about the time that

we have indicated—without assigning them to the various pro-
tagonists. Proceeding in this way, we have identified certain questions to which the nineteenth century failed to produce answers;
only the modern theory has succeeded in answering them satisfactorily. Deliberately, we fixed a precise date for an imaginary
survey—a date prior to the publication of Dalton's *New System
of Chemical Philosophy* (1808): in doing so we must confess to
having over-simplified the resulting picture. Forty years later
Michael Faraday (1791-1867) did not think that he was wasting
his time establishing more rigorously by experiment the law of
conservation of charge that we have regarded as already established. Indeed, he was not wasting his time: any empirical law in
physics must remain a target for the sceptical experimenter, per-
petually—only that way is the body of fundamental knowledge
progressively purged of insidious error.

Ideally, the laws of electrostatic and gravitational action are of
the same form, but there is one basic respect in which the two
sets of phenomena are different—so much so, that to argue
naïvely by analogy from one to the other is frequently to reap
nothing but confusion. The important difference is not that the
conservation law in relation to gravitating mass is an 'arithmetic'
law operating with positive quantities only, whereas the corresponding law in relation to electric charge is an 'algebraic' law
operating with quantities of both signs together. This is certainly
the case, but the difference is trivial. The significant difference is
that there is a whole class of bodies (conductors) such that electricity moves freely over their surfaces. To a very high degree of
accuracy it is true to say that, when two uncharged solid bodies
are brought together, the distribution of gravitating mass in each
remains constant. In consequence of this fact, two uniform
spherical bodies, of whatever size, attract one another, gravitation-
ally, with a force which is inversely proportional to the square of
the distance of separation of their centres of figure. But it is not
true to say that, when two charged conducting bodies are brought
together, the distribution of electric charge on each remains constant. If the two bodies have charges of the same sign, then the
tendency is for these charges to concentrate more and more on
the mutually remote parts of the bodies, when the bodies are
brought closer together, and *vice versa*, and there is the induction
of charge, also, ascribable to the fact that, over and above the

initial charge on each body, there is the effectively inexhaustible and perfectly balanced supply of electricity of both signs resident in the body in its uncharged state. The result is that, at distances of separation less than a few radii of the larger of two electrically charged spherical conducting bodies, the overall law of electro-static force is not precisely the inverse-square law, involving the distance of separation of the geometrical centres of the bodies, simply. This is the difficulty to which we referred (p. 17) in rela-tion to Coulomb's experiments. It is a difficulty of which Coulomb, himself, was fully aware.

2.4. GAUSS'S THEOREM : THE BASIC RESULT

In any situation in which forces varying inversely as the square of the distance are operative, a mathematical theorem, due originally (1839) to Karl Friedrich Gauss (1777-1855) (see V & W, p. 263), has important applications. Suppose there be a 'substance' (for example, gravitating matter, or electricity), such that any two 'particles' consisting of, or endowed with, the substance interact mutually according to an inverse-square law. Suppose that the measures of the quantities of substance, Q_1, Q_2, of the distance of separation of the particles, r, and of the repulsive force, F, are connected by the equation

$$F = \gamma \frac{Q_1 Q_2}{r^2} \tag{3}$$

where γ is a (dimensional) constant the magnitude of which (either positive or negative in sign) may depend upon the medium in which the particles are located. Then, in such a situation we define E, the measure of the 'field intensity' at a distance r from an isolated particle with which a quantity of substance Q is asso-ciated, by the related equation

$$E = \gamma \frac{Q}{r^2} \tag{4}$$

Physically interpreted, E is also the measure of the force which would act, from the specified particle, on a particle carrying unit quantity of the substance, if it were placed at a point at this distance. Clearly, according to this definition, E is in fact the measure of a vector quantity the direction of which, at any point, is that of the line drawn outwards from the 'source' particle through the point considered. Furthermore, if, instead of a single source particle, a distribution of many 'charged' particles were to be specified, the 'total' field intensity at any point would be uniquely determined by the Newtonian law of the composition of forces: it would be the vector sum of the intensities due to the individual particles separately considered.

Suppose, then, that in a field of 'charged' particles the (total) field intensity at any point is E. We define D, the flux density at that point, by the equation

$$D = \frac{E}{4\pi\gamma} \tag{5}$$

Now, let us consider any region of the field, bounded by a closed surface of which dS is an element of area. Let $\Sigma_i Q$ denote the (algebraic) sum of the quantities of substance ('charges') associated with the particles within this bounded region. Then Gauss's theorem states that

$$\int (D \cos \theta) dS = \Sigma_i Q \tag{6}$$

θ being the angle, at any point on the surface, between the outwards normal to the surface and the direction of the flux density at that point. In respect of the left-hand term of equation (6), integration is assumed to be over the whole surface and for that reason this term is said to give the 'total outwards flux' over the surface. In words, then, Gauss's theorem states that, in the situation specified, and independently of the medium, the total outwards flux is a measure of the total 'charge' enclosed by any arbitrarily drawn surface in the field.

In order to establish the truth of the theorem, let us first consider a single particle, with which is associated a charge Q, situated at the point P (fig. 2). About the axis PX let there be drawn an elementary cone, of solid angle $\Delta\omega$, and through points A_1 A_2, ... in PX, distant r_1, r_2, ..., respectively, from P, let oblique sections of the cone be drawn such that the outwards normals to these sections are inclined to PX at angles θ_1, θ_2. ... (In fig. 2 the situation is represented two-dimensionally: in general, the respective normals A_1N_1, A_2N_2, ... would not be co-planar.) Then ΔS_j, the area of the jth such section, is given by the equation

$$\Delta S_j = \Delta\omega \cdot r^2{}_j \sec \theta_j.$$

Now, in respect of the charge at P, the flux density at any point in PX is directed along PX, and its magnitude at A_j is given (see equations (4) and (5)) by

$$D_j = \frac{Q}{4\pi r^2_j}.$$

Thus, for the jth section,

$$D_j \cos \theta_j \, \Delta S_j = \frac{\Delta\omega}{4\pi} Q \qquad (7)$$

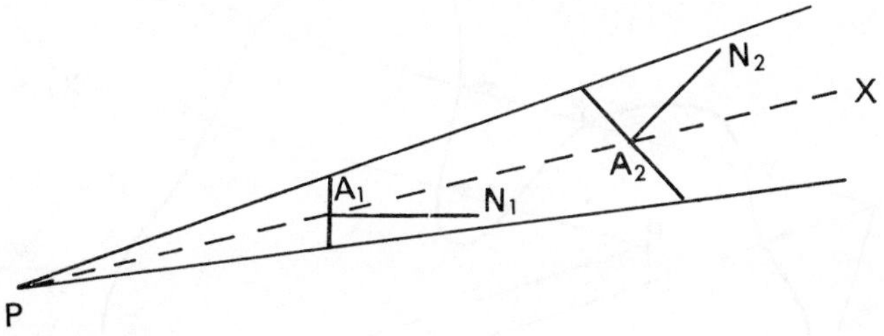

FIGURE 2

We translate equation (7) into words as follows: the outwards flux across every section of an elementary cone drawn from P is the same—it is that small fraction of the charge at P which is given by the ratio of the solid angle of the elementary cone to 4π, the solid angle subtended by a closed surface at an interior point. This basic result provides the first step in our proof.

Let us consider, next, a closed surface B of arbitrary form, represented two-dimensionally by its plane section B′ (fig. 3), and let P_1, P_2, be, respectively, points situated arbitrarily within and without this surface. Then inspection of the figure will confirm the following results: (i) any straight line P_1X_1, drawn from P_1, intersects the surface B an odd number of times; (ii) any straight line P_2X_2, drawn from P_2, intersects B an even number of times; (iii) in the former case, the outwards normal to B at the point of intersection nearest to P_1 makes an acute angle with P_1X_1; (iv) all the more distant intersections in the former case (an even number), and all the intersections in the latter, may be grouped in successive pairs, such that the angle between the outwards normal to B and the line P_1X_1 (or P_2X_2) is obtuse at the first intersection of any pair, and is acute at the second intersection of the pair.

Suppose, now, that there is a charge Q_1 located at P_1, and a charge Q_2 located at P_2, and that we consider the lines P_1X_1 and P_2X_2 as the axes of elementary cones of solid angles $\Delta\omega_1$, $\Delta\omega_2$, as in our previous discussion. Result (iv), which we have just obtained by inspection, implies that, as far as the paired intersections are concerned, the contributions, along either elementary cone, to the total outwards flux over B (due to the one charge, or the other) cancel out to zero. This is necessarily so, since, for any pair

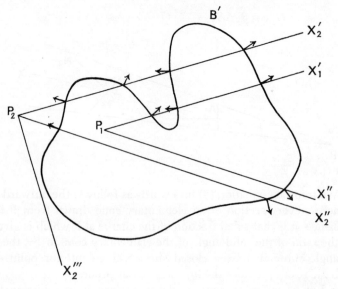

FIGURE 3

of intersections, the first contribution is always negative, the second positive, and equation (7) shows that these contributions of opposite sign are equal in magnitude ($\dfrac{\Delta\omega_1}{4\pi} Q_1$ at every intersection along the one cone, and $\dfrac{\Delta\omega_2}{4\pi} Q_2$, similarly, along the other). This conclusion already disposes of the case of the external charge (result (ii), above, being implicitly included in (iv)): obviously, over the whole surface of B, the total outwards flux from an externally situated point charge reduces to zero in all circumstances. In the same way, and in respect of our internally situated charge, the cancelling of the paired contributions along each elementary cone reduces the calculation of the total outwards flux

over B to the summation of the contributions (each of them positive according to (iii)) arising at the first (unpaired) intersection
of each such cone with the surface. The only variable in this summation is the element of solid angle itself, and since, by definition,

$$\int d\omega = 4\pi,$$

we conclude, precisely, that the measure of the total outwards
flux over B from a point charge Q_1, situated arbitrarily at P_1 within
the surface, is itself Q_1, the measure of the localised charge.

At this stage we have established two results, unambiguously.
In the first place, an 'external' charge contributes nothing to the
total outwards flux over a closed surface; secondly, the contribution from an 'internal' charge, localised in a point, is given by the
measure of the charge. Only one further step is required to
establish the truth of Gauss's theorem completely: we have to
show that, for a distribution of point charges, or, finally, for a
continuous distribution of charge, within the surface, each such
charge, or each element of charge, contributes independently to
the total flux.

Let us suppose that there are n discrete charges, Q_1, Q_2, ...,
Q_k, ..., Q_n, within the surface. Let A be an arbitrary point in
the surface, and AN be the outwards normal through A. Let the
direction of the total flux density at A, due to the n internal
charges acting together, make an angle θ with AN, and let its
measure be D. Let D_1, D_2, ..., D_k, ..., D_n be the measures of
the flux densities at A due, respectively, to each of the n charges
acting independently, the directions of these flux densities making
angles θ_1, θ_2, ..., θ_k, ..., θ_n with AN. Then, from the general
laws of composition of vectors (see p. 22)

$$D \cos \theta = \sum_{1}^{n} D_k \cos \theta_k$$

—and, in the context of equation (6),

$$\int (D \cos \theta)dS = \sum_{1}^{n} \int D_k \cos \theta_k \, dS \qquad (8)$$

Equation (8) is the formal statement that we were seeking to
validate: for a distribution of point charges within a closed surface,
each such charge contributes independently to the total outwards
flux over the surface. In the form of equation (6), therefore, the

EM C

truth of Gauss's theorem is completely established for this case. Here it is pertinent to remark that, if it is significant to distinguish between 'charges' of positive and negative sign, Gauss's theorem is still valid, since in all cases (independently of the sign of γ—see equations (4) and (5)) D_k (in equation (8), and so in equation (6)) has the same sign as Q_k. The final element of proof is to pass from 'a distribution of point charges' to 'a continuous distribution of charge' within the surface. Physically, no new principle is involved; all that is required is a trivial reformulation of the mathematics of the problem. Previously, in relation to equation (6) we defined $\Sigma_i Q$ as 'the (algebraic) sum of the charges associated with the particles' within the bounded region. Now, having established the validity of the equation by detailed argument on the basis of this definition, we may safely omit the qualifying phrase 'associated with the particles' from our previous statement.

Gauss's theorem, as we stated at the outset, is applicable alike to problems involving gravitational and electrical forces. Although, in this chapter, our concern is primarily with the latter, consideration of two simple examples of its application in the former field will not be out of place. We have already referred (p. 12) to Newton's two results concerning the gravitational attraction due to a uniform spherical shell of material—the attraction on an outside particle and the attraction on a particle situated within the shell, and we have noted Priestley's reliance on the second of these results to support his own assertion that electrical and gravitational interactions follow the same law of variation with distance. These two results of Newton may be derived very simply from Gauss's theorem: in each case nothing more than the mere symmetry of the situation need be stated to establish their validity. If we are concerned with the 'external' particle, situated at a distance R from the centre of a spherical shell of material of total mass M, then M is also the measure of the total outwards flux over a sphere of radius R concentric with the shell—and, because of the symmetry of the situation, the flux density is uniform over this sphere, and of magnitude $M/4\pi R^2$ everywhere on its surface. Precisely the same result would be true if the whole mass of the shell were concentrated at its central point. Thus Newton's first result is vindicated: a uniform spherical shell of material attracts an external particle as if the whole mass of the shell were concentrated at its centre. For the 'internal' particle the argument is entirely similar. If a spherical surface, concentric with the shell, and of smaller radius, is considered, since no matter is contained within the surface, the total outwards flux over the surface is zero. In conditions of spherical symmetry, this can only be the case if the flux density itself is everywhere zero over the surface. Hence Newton's second result: a uniform spherical shell of material exerts no force on an internal particle wherever such a particle is situated within the shell.

With complete justification, as it subsequently appeared, Priestley believed that Newton's results could be taken over directly, into the realm of electrostatics, by substituting 'a spherically symmetrical surface distribution of electrification' for Newton's 'uniform spherical shell of material'—and by replacing 'mass' by 'electric charge' (taking count of the sign of the charge), as appropriate, in the statement of the results. This justification, indeed, follows immediately, once the common relevance of Gauss's theorem is accepted. But the mere taking over of Newton's results into electrostatics does not exhaust the information which Gauss's theorem provides in this domain. As we have already indicated (p. 20) there is no phenomenon in gravitation corresponding to the free movement of electricity in, or over the surfaces of, bodies which are conductors. It is in this context, in relation to the forces arising from the equilibrium distributions of charge over conducting bodies, that further results of a more general character emerge, when Gauss's theorem is applied consistently in the electrical case. It must be our object to elicit the more important of these results, but, before we can do this, we must first discuss the concept of 'potential', as it relates to our subject.

2.5. ELECTRIC POTENTIAL

In another place ($M L \& T$, §11.2) we have already introduced —and briefly discussed—the concept of gravitational potential. This concept was first adumbrated by Joseph Louis Lagrange (1736-1813) in 1777. It was eventually given its currently accepted designation by George Green (1793-1841) in 1828. By 1828 Green was chiefly concerned to provide a mathematical description of electrical phenomena; however, the basic notion of potential is equally relevant in all situations in which the mutual forces between 'particles' do not depend upon the velocities of the particles, but only on their positions. Here we discuss it more fully than before, with particular reference to electrical forces, as is appropriate in this context.

For our present purposes, then, let us postulate an arbitrary distribution of electrically charged particles, and a very small 'test charge', Δq, with which we may explore the field arising from these charges. Let A and B be two points in this field, and let us imagine that the test charge is moved reversibly (see *M L & T*, p. 290) from A to B. If ΔW_{AB} is the measure of the work which must be done by an outside agency, in this process, against the electric forces resisting the motion, then, to be precise, we define $V_B - V_A$, the difference of electric potential between B and A (the excess of the potential of B over the potential of A) by the equation

$$\Delta W_{AB} = (V_B - V_A)\Delta q.$$

If A and B are neighbouring points, separated by an elementary distance Δs, and if E_s is the measure of the component of electric intensity, over this small interval, in the direction of motion of the test charge, clearly

$$\Delta W_{AB} = -E_s \Delta q \Delta s.$$

Then, in self-evident notation, we have

$$E_s \Delta s = -\Delta V,$$

and, in the limit, as applying at any point in the field,

$$E_s = -\frac{\partial V}{\partial s} \tag{9}$$

On the basis of equation (9), generally regarded, we are able both to add precision to our notion of potential, and also in a measure to justify what previously we merely asserted—that this new concept (as we have now defined it) is relevant in any situation in which the mutual forces between particles depend only on their positions (and not on their velocities). For, when this is the case (of necessity, any system of forces with which we may be concerned will depend upon the magnitudes of the 'charges' carried by the particles—this aspect of the matter is not in question), the total field intensity at any point will be so determined, and the component of intensity in any direction through the point will be given in a similar manner. The positional co-ordinates of the charges, and the measures of their magnitudes will enter as constants into the expressions defining the total intensity at the point, and the only variables in these expressions, if they be considered as general expressions describing the field as a whole, will be the positional co-ordinates of the arbitrary point to which they refer. For equation (9) to be valid in these circumstances, clearly the expression for V must include the magnitudes of the charges as constants, and we must at least require that it be continuous, and single-valued at every point in the field. Finally, we note that the potential must be a scalar quantity—as, indeed, is obvious from the form of the defining equation from which we started.

Our discussion, in the last paragraph, has been in general terms, but in relation to the arbitrary distribution of electrically charged particles which we originally postulated we can be more specific. If we imagine this distribution to be built up, particle by particle, we can deduce the precise form of the expression for the potential at any point in the field. And, in so doing, we shall be verifying what we have claimed in general—at least in one particular situation.

For a single particle, situated in empty space (or in any 'featureless' isotropic medium), and carrying a charge q_1 of electricity, clearly the whole field possesses full spherical symmetry, and any scalar quantity which describes it must be a function of the distance alone. This being the case, the expression for the electric potential at any point distant r_1 from the isolated charge can be written simply as $V_1(r_1)$—and equation (9) can be applied directly to its evaluation, writing the equation in the corresponding one-dimensional form

$$\frac{dV_1}{dr_1} = -\gamma \frac{q_1}{r_1^2}.$$

Solving this equation for $V_1(r_1)$, we integrate with respect to r_1, from r_1 to ∞, and obtain

$$V_1(\infty) - V_1(r_1) = \gamma q_1\left(0 - \frac{1}{r_1}\right).$$

Then, explicitly, if $V_1(\infty) = 0$ (it is always necessary, in problems of potential, to establish, conventionally, some convenient base of reference—see $M L \, \& \, T$, p. 229),

$$V_1(r_1) = \gamma \frac{q_1}{r_1} \tag{10}$$

Throughout this calculation, and in the final result, γ, the unspecified constant of equation (4) has been retained, for we have not as yet fully defined our units of measurement (see p. 19).

Let us suppose, now, that a second particle, carrying a charge q_2, is introduced into the region of space that we are considering. We wish to show that the resultant field due to the two particles is correctly described in terms of a potential V, where

$$V = V_1 + V_2 \qquad (11)$$

and V_2 is the potential which would describe the field due to the charge of the second particle, if this were effective alone, namely

$$V_2(r_2) = \gamma \frac{q_2}{r_2}$$

—analogously, as in the case of the first particle that we have already discussed.

The field which the potential V describes is given, at any point, in terms of the three rectangular components of the field intensity at that point. Formally, each of these components may be represented by the equation ($s = x, y, z$)

$$E_s = -\frac{\partial V}{\partial s},$$

and similar equations, namely

$$E_{1s} = -\frac{\partial V_1}{\partial s} \text{ and } E_{2s} = -\frac{\partial V_2}{\partial s},$$

give the three components, in each case, of the field intensities which would be effective at the point, if first the charge q_1, and then the charge q_2, were present alone in the region considered. On the basis of equation (11) we have

$$\frac{\partial V}{\partial s} = \frac{\partial V_1}{\partial s} + \frac{\partial V_2}{\partial s},$$

thus, at any arbitrary point,

$$E_s = E_{1s} + E_{2s} \qquad (12)$$

Equation (12) may be regarded a formal statement of the Newtonian law of the composition of forces, which we have already admitted as axiomatic (p. 22). That we should have derived this result, starting from the potential which equation (11) defines, shows that that potential indeed describes the actual resultant field in the present case correctly, as we hoped to show.

We have now considered in detail the first two steps in the building up of our originally postulated static distribution of electrically charged particles. Obviously, the procedure could be continued, step by step—and, equally obviously, nothing new in principle would emerge in the process. We may, therefore, with complete assurance, state the final result without further calculation. The electric potential V, at any point in the field of a static distribution of n particles, carrying charges $q_1, q_2, \ldots, q_k, \ldots q_n$ of electricity, respectively, is given by the expression

$$V = \gamma \sum_{1}^{n} \frac{q_k}{r_k} \tag{13}$$

where r_k is, in general, the distance of the charge q_k from the point in question. As in our previous problem (p. 26), it is once more a mere matter of mathematical reformulation, simply, to translate this result so that it refers to a static distribution of electrification which is spatially continuous, rather than discrete.

It is important, at this stage, to examine, somewhat more generally, the relation between potential and field intensity which is implicit in equation (9). At any point in a field, unless the field intensity is zero at the point, there is a unique direction, that of the total intensity. In any direction at right angles to this, the re-solved component of the intensity is zero, and, according to equation (9), the 'potential gradient' is zero, also. Indeed, in every direction, through any point, at right angles to the direction of the total field intensity at the point, the potential gradient is zero. On this basis we conclude that the loci of points of constant potential are in general continuous surfaces—'equipotential surfaces'—and that the direction of the field intensity at any point is along the normal to the equipotential surface through that point.

Now, let us examine the concept of electric potential in respect of any region of space which is occupied by a body which is a conductor. We have already identified the important properties of such a body (p. 9): electric charge is able to move freely over its surface (or throughout its volume) and there is an 'effectively in-exhaustible and perfectly balanced supply of electricity of both signs resident in the body in its uncharged state'. Suppose, then,

that we have such a body, charged or uncharged, isolated or subject to the actions of other charges external to it, our only condition
being that the whole distribution of charge is a static distribution,
so that the charges on the body are in equilibrium under the conditions obtaining. Then we must conclude that the electric intensity is everywhere zero throughout the body, for, if this were
not so, there would be further separation of the latent charge
(positive and negative charge) which is intrinsic to its substance,
and the equilibrium state which we have postulated could not
persist. If the intensity is everywhere zero throughout the body,
the potential is constant: the surface of the body is an equipotential surface under the conditions that we have specified, and
the potential at an internal point is the potential of the surface.
At any point immediately outside the body, the direction of the
total electric intensity is normal to its surface—whatever the distribution of charge over the body, or in the space surrounding it.

2.6. GAUSS'S THEOREM : SOME FURTHER APPLICATIONS

With the results of the last section established, we have the necessary basis for the further applications of Gauss's theorem which
earlier (p. 27) we were unable to pursue. As the first of these, let
us consider what conclusions we can draw concerning the electrostatic properties of a hollow conducting body of arbitrary shape.
Let A and B (fig. 4) represent the traces, in the plane of the diagram, of the exterior and interior surfaces of this body. We start
from the result (above) that the electric intensity is everywhere
zero within the material of the body. In this case, the flux density
is likewise zero throughout, and the total charge enclosed by any
surface (such as S), which is entirely contained within the material
of the body, is zero, also. This result is valid until, in the limit,
(we are imagining S to expand continuously) the surface S becomes congruent with A. It is valid, whether or not there are other
charged bodies within B (that is, within the hollow interior of the
conductor), and we therefore conclude that, if there is any unbalanced charge of either sign on the system as a whole (that is,
the system formed by the hollow conductor and any other bodies
which it may enclose), then there is charge, of the same amount,
resident on the outer surface of the conductor. Let us examine,
further and independently, the two possibilities regarding enclosed charges that we have indicated.

If there is no charge on any body enclosed within B, or if there is no body so enclosed, then any charge which the hollow conductor may possess must reside exclusively on its outer surface A. This is a generalisation of the result which Cavendish deduced, on the basis of Newton's calculations, for the spherical shell (p. 15). Alternatively, if there are bodies enclosed within B which together carry a net charge of electricity, then an exactly equal charge, of opposite sign, must reside on this interior surface (we imagine S to collapse continuously to become congruent with B, to establish this result). If, in this case, the net charge on the whole system is precisely the charge on the bodies enclosed within B, there will be an exactly equal charge of the same sign on the outer surface A.

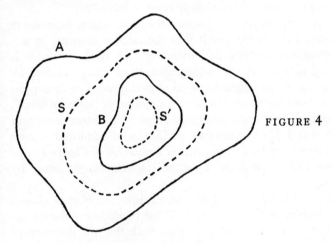

FIGURE 4

Let us now consider the field intensity within the hollow conductor—in the special case, when there are no charged bodies enclosed within it. Then the total outwards flux over any closed surface S', wholly within B, is zero. Let us imagine this surface to be chosen so that it lies close to B, and let us assume that, in this position, S' is an equipotential surface over which the electric potential is different from the potential over B (B is necessarily an equipotential surface, being the surface of a conductor). According to this assumption, the electric intensity over S' is everywhere directed along the normal to the surface, and is everywhere directed in the same sense along the normal (that is, outwards, over the whole surface, or inwards, over the whole surface, as the case may be). In either event, the total outwards flux is necessarily finite—therefore our assumption fails. The potential over S′ must, in fact, be the same as the potential over B. We repeat the argument indefinitely, allowing the surface S′ to collapse, stage by stage—and we finally conclude that the electric potential must be constant throughout the enclosure: it is the potential of the hollow conductor, precisely. The potential being constant throughout the enclosure when there are no charged bodies within it, we have the general result that the electric intensity is everywhere zero within the outer surface of a hollow conductor under these (static) conditions. This is a generalisation of the Newtonian result on which Cavendish relied, but it should be emphasised that it has no general counterpart in the theory of gravitational attraction, for reasons which have already been given (p. 20).

The second application of Gauss's theorem, which we make in this section, leads to the result that the electric intensity at any point immediately outside the surface of a charged conductor is determined directly by the surface density of charge carried by the conductor in the neighbourhood of that point. For this application it is convenient to introduce the notion of 'tubes of force'. This notion derives originally from Faraday. Its most consistent exponent was J. J. Thomson (see p. 158), who employed it with marked success, particularly in *Recent Researches in Electricity and Magnetism* (1893)—a large tome still much sought after by collectors.

Faraday had built many of his most fruitful arguments around the prior notion of 'lines of force'. A line of electric force (or intensity) is a continuous curve in space such that the direction of the electric intensity, at any point in the curve, is the direction of the curve at that point. A tube of electric force (or intensity) may then be defined as an elementary tubular element of space such that, for any point in the 'wall' of the tube, the line of force which passes through that point remains in the wall of the tube throughout its whole length. At every point in the wall of a tube of force, therefore, the component of intensity along the normal to the wall is zero. Moreover, at every such point, in a tube of small cross-section, the direction of the electric intensity is essentially parallel to the direction of the 'axis' of the tube as it crosses the section in question. If an electrostatic field is described in terms of equipotential surfaces and tubes of force, every section of a tube by such a surface is a right section of the tube. In particular, if a tube of force extends to the surface of a conducting body, of necessity it meets that surface orthogonally. It does not extend below the surface, since the intensity within the material of the conductor is zero.

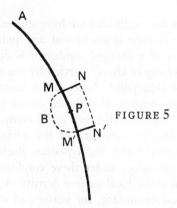

FIGURE 5

Suppose, then, that A (fig. 5) represents, two-dimensionally, a portion of the surface of a conducting body carrying a charge of electricity. Let the measure of the surface density of charge in the region of the point P be σ. Let us consider a small area, ΔS, of surface around P, and let MN, M'N', be elements of the out-wards normals from two points, M, M', in the boundary of ΔS. Then, close to the surface, these lines lie wholly in the wall of the tube of force which originates in the surface and has ΔS as its section of origin. Imagine, now, another right section of this tube, through N, N', separated from A by a distance small compared with the smaller principal radius of curvature of the surface at P. Then the area of this section differs insignificantly from ΔS. Let D be the measure of the flux density at any point in the section. We proceed to calculate D by applying Gauss's theorem to the elementary closed surface constituted of the right section of the tube of force through N, N', the wall of the tube of force between this section and A, and any arbitrary surface (represented by B in the figure), wholly within the material of the charged conductor, which completes the enclosure. We have the following results: the normal component of flux density over the right section through N, N' is D, the normal component of flux density at any point in the wall of the tube is zero, the flux density is everywhere zero over the terminating surface B. Also, the total charge contained within the elementary closed surface is $\sigma\Delta S$. We have, therefore,

$$D . \Delta S = \sigma\Delta S$$

or
$$D = \sigma \tag{14}$$

Equation (14) establishes the result that we have quoted already: the flux density—or the electric intensity—at any point immediately outside the surface of a charged conductor is determined directly by the surface density of charge carried by the conductor in the neighbourhood of that point. Indeed, the manner of its derivation gives further precision to that result, defining the term 'immediately outside' as 'within a distance small compared with the smaller principal radius of curvature of the surface in the neighbourhood of the point'—and the equation itself demonstrates that the electric intensity, under these conditions, is, in fact, directly proportional to the local surface density of charge.

On an isolated spherical conductor, for reasons of symmetry, any net charge carried by the conductor must be distributed uniformly over its surface. In view of the result that we have just obtained, it is interesting to enquire how the surface density of charge, σ, (or the total charge, Q) depends upon V, the potential of the conductor. Let the radius of the spherical conductor be r. Then (compare equation (10))

$$V = \gamma \frac{Q}{r} \tag{15}$$

and
$$\sigma = \frac{Q}{4\pi r^2} = \frac{V}{4\pi\gamma r} \tag{16}$$

The interest of equation (16), at the present stage of our discussion, is that, taken in conjunction with equation (14)—and equation (5) —it shows that the electric intensity at the surface of an isolated spherical conductor, at potential V, is inversely proportional to the (unique) radius of curvature of the surface of the conductor. This precise quantitative result gives us good reason to believe that with an isolated conductor of arbitrary shape, and of fixed potential, the equilibrium distribution of charge over the surface of the conductor will be such that the electric intensity at its surface will vary with the total curvature of the surface, being greatest where the total curvature is greatest, and *vice versa*. This qualitative conclusion is fully supported by experiment (see p. 161).

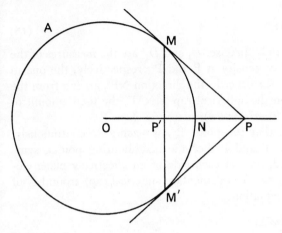

FIGURE 6

The result which is expressed formally in equation (14) can be followed up with profit in yet another direction. To do so, we again consider, first of all, the case of a spherical conductor, charged to surface density σ, and isolated in space. Let A (fig. 6) represent the surface of this conductor, of radius r, and let P be a point outside it. Let ON be the radius of the sphere which, produced, passes through P, and let $NP = x$. Let the tangent cone from P make contact with the spherical surface of the conductor over the small circle through M, M′, and let P′ be the centre of this circle. Now, consider the flux density at P. We may regard it as made up of two components, the one due to the charge situated on the spherical cap MNM′, the other due to the charge on the rest of the sphere. Because of the symmetry of the situation, the directions of the total flux density and of these two components are collinear: all three are radially outwards through P. If we denote the measure of the total flux density by D, and the measures of these two components by D_1 and D_2, respectively, we have, therefore,

$$D = D_1 + D_2 \qquad (17)$$

At P′, let the measures of the corresponding components of the total flux density be D_1' and D_2'. These components are oppositely directed in the line ON, and our previous discussion of the Newtonian problem of the uniform shell of gravitating material (p. 12) justifies the result

$$D_1' = D_2' \tag{18}$$

In this situation, to be precise, D_1 and D_1' are the measures of the components of flux density at P and P', respectively, the one in the direction NP, the other in the direction NP', arising from the charge situated on the spherical cap MNM', the total amount of this charge being $2\pi x r^2 \sigma/(r+x)$.

Suppose, now, that the point P approaches N continuously, until, in the end, P and P' become neighbouring points, symmetrically situated, one on each side of an effectively plane elementary region of surface (elementary spherical cap) around N of area given by the equation

$$\Delta S = 2\pi r \Delta x.$$

In the limit so attained, P and P' being separated by the infinitesimal distance $2\Delta x$, we must have

$$D_2 = D_2' \tag{19}$$

(the flux density in the direction ON due to the charge on the whole sphere, omitting only the charge, $\sigma \Delta S$, on the remaining elementary spherical cap around N, must, in the end, be the same at P and P'). And, we must also have

$$D_1 = D_1' \tag{20}$$

(the oppositely directed flux densities due to the charge $\sigma \Delta S$, on the effectively plane elementary region of surface ΔS around N, must be the same at P and P', corresponding points on opposite sides of this surface). Combining equations (14), (17), (18), (19) and (20), we have, finally,

$$D_2 = D_1 = \frac{D}{2} = \frac{\sigma}{2} \tag{21}$$

Now D_2 is the measure of the flux density, continuous across the element of surface ΔS, arising from the charge situated on the rest of the sphere. Thus, this charge acts on the charge $\sigma \Delta S$, situated on ΔS, with an outwards directed mechanical force, ΔF, given by

$$\Delta F = \sigma \Delta S \, . \, 4\pi\gamma D_2$$

(see equation (5)), or, if we substitute for D_2 from equation (21), by

$$\Delta F = 2\pi\gamma\sigma^2\Delta S.$$

But $\Delta F/\Delta S$ is the measure of a pressure, p. We have, therefore,

$$p = 2\pi\gamma\sigma^2 \tag{22}$$

and we interpret equation (22) by the statement that the mutual repulsion of the elements of charge on an isolated spherical conductor is such as to generate an outwards pressure of amount $2\pi\gamma\sigma^2$ over the surface of the conductor. Combining equations (16) and (22) we have an alternative expression for this pressure, namely,

$$p = \frac{V^2}{8\pi\gamma r^2} \tag{23}$$

As in the previous case (see equation (16)), we argue from this equation to the conclusion that with an isolated conductor of arbitrary shape, and of fixed potential, the mutual repulsion of the elements of charge, under equilibrium conditions, will be such as to generate an outwards pressure which will vary over the surface of the conductor, being greatest where the total curvature of the surface is greatest, and *vice versa*. A convenient method of investigating the pressure of electrostatic origin which equation (23) describes is to study the effect of charging a spherical soap bubble.

In our last two examples we have been evaluating some of the properties of that ideal body, an isolated conductor. Let us now consider a slightly more realistic situation. Let a conducting body of arbitrary shape have a spherical hole in its interior. Let r_2 be the radius of this hollow region and let it enclose a spherical conductor of radius r_1, symmetrically. This arrangement is represented two-dimensionally in fig. 7. Let the enclosed body carry a charge Q, and the outer conducting body an equal charge of opposite sign, $-Q$. Then we have already shown that the whole of this charge must reside on the inner surface of the hollow body. From the symmetry of the arrangement, electrostatically, it is clear that the distribution of charge over each of the two opposing surfaces (represented by A_1 and A_2 in the figure) must be uniform, and if σ_1 and $-\sigma_2$ represent the surface densities of charge over these surfaces, respectively, then

$$Q = 4\pi r_1^2 \sigma_1 = 4\pi r_2^2 \sigma_2 \tag{24}$$

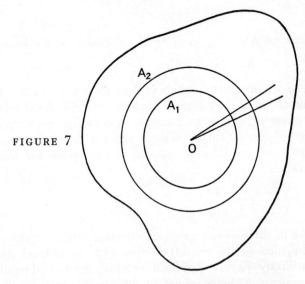

FIGURE 7

Let us imagine an elementary cone, of small solid angle $\Delta\omega$, drawn from O, the common centre of A_1 and A_2, and intersecting the two surfaces in areas ΔS_1 and ΔS_2. We wish to calculate the resultant forces acting on the equal and opposite charges $\sigma_1 \Delta S_1$ and $-\sigma_2 \Delta S_2$ situated on these elements of surface, respectively, when the areas ΔS_1, ΔS_2 are so small that the elements of surface are effectively plane. Let us denote the resultant outwards force on the charge on ΔS_1 by ΔF_1, and the resultant inwards force on the charge on ΔS_2 by ΔF_2. Then, from equation (22),

$$\Delta F_1 = 2\pi\gamma\sigma_1^2 \Delta S_1$$

(the charge $-Q$ on the inner surface of the hollow body exerts no force on any element of enclosed charge). In respect of ΔF_2, there are two components of this force: the attraction exerted on the charge $-\sigma_2 \Delta S_2$ by the total charge Q on the enclosed sphere, and the outwards force due to the repulsion of the rest of the charge

$-Q$ on the inner surface of the hollow conductor. We have, therefore,

$$\Delta F_2 = \gamma \frac{Q}{r_2^2} \sigma_2 \Delta S_2 - 2\pi\gamma\sigma_2^2 \Delta S_2$$

(the charge on the enclosed sphere attracts as if it were wholly concentrated at O). Writing $\Delta S_1 = r_1^2 \Delta\omega$, $\Delta S_2 = r_2^2 \Delta\omega$, and substituting for Q and σ_2 from equation (24), we obtain, finally,

$$\Delta F_1 = 2\pi\gamma\sigma_1^2 r_1^2 \Delta\omega$$
$$\Delta F_2 = 2\pi\gamma\sigma_2(2\sigma_1 r_1^2 - \sigma_2 r_2^2)\Delta\omega \qquad (25)$$
$$= 2\pi\gamma\sigma_1\sigma_2 r_1^2 \Delta\omega$$

Equations (25) are valid generally: in the special case when $r_2 = r_1 + x$, $x \ll r_1$, to a first-order approximation,

$$\Delta F_2 = \Delta F_1 \left(1 - \frac{2x}{r_1}\right).$$

In the limit, then, as $x \to 0$, these oppositely directed forces are equal in magnitude, and in that case the force per unit area acting on the charge on either surface is given by

$$p = 2\pi\gamma\sigma^2 \qquad (26)$$

($\sigma_1 = \sigma_2 = \sigma$), and V, the difference of potential between the two surfaces, being given by

$$V = 4\pi\gamma\sigma x \qquad (27)$$

we have $p = \dfrac{V^2}{8\pi\gamma x^2}$ \qquad (28)

In proceeding to the limit in this way, we have deduced an important practical result (hence our claim that the situation that we were considering was 'more realistic'!). If it can be ensured that the electric intensity between two parallel plane surfaces is everywhere the same (as the intensity between the two spherical surfaces that we have been considering is, in the limit), then, when the surfaces are separated by a distance x, when the potential difference between them is V, and the surface densities of charge on the two surfaces are σ and $-\sigma$, respectively, these three quantities are connected by equation (27), and equations (26) and

EM D

(28) give alternative expressions for the force of mutual attraction between the charges on the surfaces, reckoned per unit surface area. We have, in these results, the essence of the theory of the attracted-disk electrometer, a 'classical' instrument devised for the 'absolute' measurement of potential difference in terms of a mechanical force. Clearly, we must interpolate here a cautionary remark: before equation (28) can be applied specifically in this way, a decision must be taken on the value to be assigned to the constant γ. As already indicated (p. 30), we are postponing any statement of the value now conventionally given to this constant until we have considered the basic physical phenomena in relation to which the decision has been made.

Primitive forms of the attracted-disk electrometer were devised by Alessandro Volta (1745-1827), professor of natural philosophy at Pavia (see p. 69), and (in 1834) by William Snow Harris (1791-1867), a medical graduate of the university of Edinburgh. At the age of thirty-three Snow Harris had given up his practice in Plymouth to devote himself entirely to the study of electricity. Elected F.R.S. seven years later, and knighted in 1847, he eventually received from a grateful parliament an honorarium of £5000 in recognition of his invention of a new method of 'affixing lightning conductors on ships'. His attracted-disk electrometer, like that of Volta, consisted essentially of two circular conducting disks, one fixed and the other hanging from the arm of a sensitive balance. Having a crude method of measuring (in arbitrary units) the charge given to the insulated disk, Harris convinced himself that the attractive force, for a fixed separation, was proportional to the square of the charge (compare equation (26)), but we cannot suppose that this simple arrangement satisfied the conditions laid down in our theoretical treatment. The attraction between two circular, coaxial, conducting disks, of area S and separation x, is not given precisely by the expression

$$F = \frac{V^2 S}{8\pi\gamma x^2} \tag{29}$$

when the difference of potential between the disks is V, as we should expect if equation (28) were strictly applicable to this case. In conventional terms, the Snow Harris electrometer does not, in fact, make possible the 'absolute' measurement of potential difference that we have claimed, as a practical possibility. In order to understand how Kelvin (see p. 46) was able to modify it, so as to meet this claim, we must first consider in greater detail the characteristics of the original arrangement.

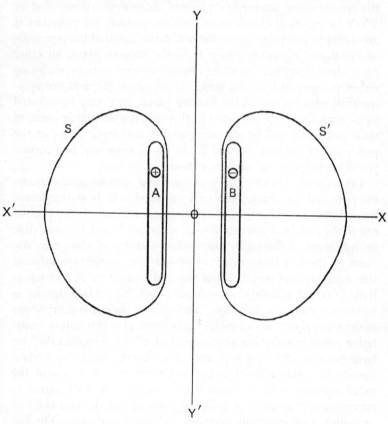

FIGURE 8

Let us suppose, then, that there are two circular disks of conducting material, placed coaxially, with their opposing surfaces separated by a distance x. Let r be the radius of either disk in its mid-plane, let d be its thickness, and let the edges of the disks be rounded in such a way that an axial section reveals semi-circular profiles of radius $d/2$. The arrangement is pictured two-dimensionally in fig. 8, X'X representing the axis of the system. Let us suppose that the disk A carries a charge Q, and the disk B a charge $-Q$ of electricity, and that V is the difference of potential between the disks. Then, because the potential is constant through-out the material of either disk, the complete surfaces of the two disks are equipotential surfaces, and, because of the symmetry of the arrangement, the median plane of the system (represented by Y'OY in fig. 8) is also an equipotential surface, the potential at any point in this plane being the arithmetic mean of the potentials of the disks. Moreover, apart from the median plane, all other equipotential surfaces must be closed surfaces, entirely enclosing either the one disk or the other. If two such surfaces are sym-metrical with respect to the median plane, they may be referred to as 'corresponding' surfaces: in this case the arithmetic mean of their potentials will be the same as the arithmetic mean of the potentials of the disks. S and S', in fig. 8, represent two corres-ponding equipotential surfaces defined in this way.

Let us now consider two corresponding equipotential surfaces the potentials of which differ only infinitesimally from the poten-tials of the disks. Each of these surfaces will completely enclose one of the disks and will nowhere be separated from it by more than an infinitesimal distance. The surface density of charge at any point on the disk being inversely proportional to the separation of this equipotential surface from the disk at that point (see equa-tions (14), (5) and (9)), we conclude that the surface density is nowhere zero over either disk—and that on each it is everywhere of the same sign.* We cannot, at this stage, give this purely quali-tative result any further precision. Indeed, the problem that we have been considering is a very complicated one: the surface density on either side of either disk must be a function of the radial distance, with the linear magnitudes r, d, and x entering as parameters; it must be a different function for the two sides of each disk, with matching over the mid-plane perimeter. The be-ginnings of a solution for the limiting case $(d/r) \to 0$ were first given by Maxwell in his monumental *Treatise on Electricity and Magnetism*, published in 1873. Here we can certainly be excused further comment on matters of detail.

The qualitative result that we have just derived is, however, entirely adequate for our particular purposes. It should be clear that, for disks of fixed separation (x) and given difference of potential (V), for any specified equipotential surface the more

---

* In strict logic we should have introduced a generalised version of this last result as a preliminary to the considerations of §2.6.

distant of its points of intersection with the axis X'OX must recede from O monotonically as r, the radius of the disks, is increased. With r the only remaining variable in the problem, therefore, the fraction of the total charge remaining on the outer surfaces of the two disks must steadily decrease as r increases. Ultimately, if the disks were infinite, the whole of the charge would be on the inner (opposing) surfaces, and the electric intensity would be uniform throughout the intervening space.

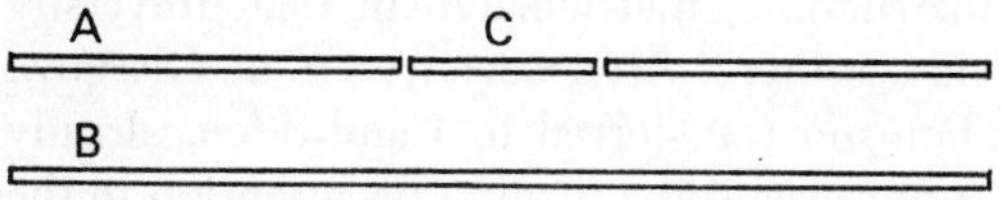

FIGURE 9

Kelvin's introduction of the 'guard-ring' into the design of the attracted-disk electrometer (*c.* 1865) simulated this last, limiting situation with adequate precision. For the various versions of the modified instrument incorporating this principle, therefore, equation (29) may be applied without serious error. The common principle of these instruments is illustrated in fig. 9. Here A and B represent two circular disks maintained at a difference of potential V. A small circular hole is cut in the centre of disk A and a circular disk C, of the same material and the same thickness as A, all but fills this hole. Metallic connection is made between the outer surfaces of A and C by a light, flexible wire. If C is precisely coplanar with A, and if the radius of A is large compared with its distance from B, the force on C—and this is what is actually measured—is given in terms of equation (29), as we have stated already.

2.7. ELECTRIC IMAGES AND ELECTRIC DOUBLETS

In the discussions of the last section we have become familiar with the general result that the equilibrium distribution of charge over a system of conductors, situated in an infinite, non-conducting medium, is describable in terms of the (infinite) family of equipotential surfaces which also specify the electric intensity at every point in the medium. The 'method of electric images' is the name given to a powerful, and specifically geometrical, approach to a large class of problems of charge distribution. Many of these problems were, in fact, first solved by this method, having previously defeated the persistent endeavours of the best analysts of the day. This elegant method of investigation was originally devised by William Thomson, First Baron Kelvin (1824-1907) in 1848.

At the age of twenty-four, William Thomson was in no sense an unknown investigator who had miraculously hit on a bright idea. When he was eight years old, his father had been appointed professor of mathematics in the University of Glasgow, and, two years later, the son, 'having acquired all his early education through his father's instruction', matriculated in that university and began to attend classes there. After seven years at Glasgow, the young William Thomson transferred to Cambridge, already sufficiently mature as a physicist to be turning his attention to the unsolved problems of the day. In his first year as an undergraduate in the older university, he published a paper on the analogy of the electric field in an infinite non-conducting medium to the flow of heat in an infinite conductor. By this paper, as Maxwell later insisted, a youngster of seventeen had made a contribution to our understanding of the nature of electrical action comparable with the massive contribution of Faraday, who was fifty-one years old at the time and the doyen of electrical scientists in Britain. A little more than three years later, within a few days of his twenty-first birthday, Thomson graduated from Cambridge, and he spent the following year in Paris, in Regnault's laboratory (see *M L & T*, p. 295). Then, in 1846, when he was twenty-two, he returned to Glasgow, to the chair of natural philosophy. Declining all offers of other appointments, he remained in his Glasgow chair until, in 1899, he resigned. He was knighted in 1866, and he was raised to the peerage in 1892. His contributions to electrical science—and they were only part of his contribution to science in general— were prodigious in range and originality: we have already mentioned two of them, others will appear in due course, as our survey of the subject proceeds.

There is one point that we should clarify, before we embark on a discussion of Kelvin's method of images. It is an essentially practical point, related to the fact that our discussions deal with abstractions (as so frequently in physics)—infinite media, isolated systems, infinite plane surfaces, and the like—when our real concern is with laboratory experiments, carried out with actual apparatus which is anything but isolated, in situations which are far more complex than any that we postulate in our theoretical treatment. In section 2.5 we adopted the convention (p. 29) that the reference surface of zero potential, in our formal analysis, is the surface at infinity. In laboratory practice we replace this convention by the convention that the whole earth is a conducting body of which the potential is zero. For problems in electrostatics this alternative convention is entirely acceptable: the material of the earth's crust in general, and the ocean waters, possess the requisite conductivity, and the radius of the earth is so large in comparison with that of any spherical body with which we are likely to be concerned in our experiments that its potential would be insignificantly changed if 'experimental' quantities of electricity were communicated to it (see equation (15)). If we connect any conducting body by a thin metal wire to a metal plate buried in the ground, then, according to our laboratory convention, the potential of the body is zero. Indeed, we shall use the terms 'earth potential' and 'zero potential' indiscriminately in future, adopting this convention. By this token, 'connecting to earth' becomes a significant operation in all experiments in electrostatics: if, in any case, the whole of the equipment for an experiment is enclosed in an earthed conducting 'screen', the experiment is effectively isolated—the electric intensity is zero in the surrounding space, if there are no charged bodies in the vicinity, and there is no charge on the outer surface of the screen.

Let us now consider—introducing the method of images formally—the general situation in which there is an unspecified distribution of charged conducting bodies in space. Let us consider the electric field due to these charges as described by its equipotential surfaces, and let us fix our attention on a (closed) equipotential surface of potential V. Let the distribution of charge outside this surface be described in terms of point charges Q_1, $Q_2, \ldots, Q_k, \ldots$, suitably situated, and the distribution of charge within the surface by point charges $Q_1', Q_2', \ldots, Q_k', \ldots$. Then, for a reason that we shall presently elaborate, we refer to the latter charges, collectively, as the electric image of the former charges in the surface in question.

Consider what the situation would be if this equipotential surface (a geometrical abstraction) were to be materialised as a very thin, uniform shell of conducting material, carrying no net charge. This shell would develop a charge $-\Sigma Q'_k$ over its inner surface, and an equal and opposite charge over its outer surface (see p. 33), the separation of charge being everywhere normal to the surface, and the precise distribution of charge over the shell being determined by the overall distribution of charge in space which we originally postulated. In relation to the description of the field in terms of tubes of force, what we are supposing is that we break these tubes by a continuous right section (the equipotential surface of potential V, which has been materialised as the thin conducting shell), and make good these breaks by the equal and opposite charges which develop on the two surfaces of the shell and so 'anchor' the tubes in their original dispositions. Except within the material of the shell, the thickness of which we have assumed to be negligible, we have in no way altered the field—either outside the shell or within its hollow interior. The potential of the shell is V, and σ, the surface density of charge at any point on its outer surface, is given by

$$\sigma = \frac{E}{4\pi\gamma} \tag{30}$$

E being the electric intensity at the point in question, due to the original distribution of point charges in the field (the conducting shell being absent), and reckoned in the direction of the outwards normal to the shell at that point. Furthermore, if dS is an element of area of the surface of the shell surrounding this arbitrary point,

$$\int \sigma dS = \Sigma Q'_k \tag{31}$$

as we have effectively stated already.

Let us now suppose that the hollow interior of the shell is progressively diminished in extent, through the addition of successive layers of uncharged, conducting material to its inner surface (an 'ideal' experiment in the best Galilean tradition—see $M L \& T$, pp. 28, 123). As each of the enclosed bodies is engulfed in this process, its charge is neutralised by a portion of the charge on the inner surface of the shell, and the charge remaining on the inner surface is redistributed appropriately. But at no stage is the charge on the outer surface of the shell affected: the electric intensity within the material of the shell remains zero permanently (if the process is carried out sufficiently slowly), and the charge on the outer surface experiences no force as a result of the changes taking place within the shell. Ultimately, when all the enclosed bodies have been engulfed, no charge remains within the shell, and we can imagine it to be completely filled with conducting material, so constituting a conducting body of potential V, having its surface congruent with the equipotential surface of that potential with which we began our discussion.

The upshot of our ideal experiment is the demonstration that, throughout the 'object space' occupied by the charges Q_k ($k = 1$, 2, ...), the field due to these charges, acting together with the image charges Q'_k, is precisely the same as that due to the object charges, acting together with a total charge $\Sigma Q'_k$ suitably distributed over the surface of a conducting body (solid or hollow), provided that the surface of the body occupies the position in space of the equipotential surface in which the charges Q_k are said to be imaged (at a specified potential) in the charges Q'_k. Indeed, in applying the method of images, we are normally relying on the converse of this proposition. We have a system of discrete charges, and an extended conducting body at a specified potential, and we wish to calculate the field in the region exterior to the body —and so, through equation (30), the distribution of charge over its surface. If we are able to determine the distribution of image charges appropriate to the case, we can achieve this result working with a set of discrete charges (object and image charges) only. We shall now consider, by way of example, some simple applications of this method of procedure.

Let A (fig. 10) represent part of the plane surface of a 'semi-infinite' conductor at earth potential, and let there be a point charge Q at P, distant x from A. We wish to determine the electric intensity throughout the region not occupied by the conductor, and the distribution of (induced) charge over its surface. Let PN be the normal through P to the surface, and let P' be the point, on PN produced, such that $P'N = PN$. (In this case P' is also the 'optical' image of P in A.) Then it is easy to see that a charge $-Q$ at P' is the electric image of the charge Q at P in the surface A at earth potential. For, if M is any point in this surface, $P'M = PM = x \sec \theta$, and the potential at M due to the two charges, being given by

$$\gamma\left(\frac{Q}{PM} - \frac{Q}{P'M}\right),$$

is necessarily zero. Having identified the image charge in this way, if X is an arbitrary point in the 'object' space, and the potential at X is V,

$$V = \gamma Q \left(\frac{1}{r} - \frac{1}{r'} \right) \tag{32}$$

where $PX = r$, $P'X = r'$. Also, if σ is the surface density of charge at M, from equation (30),

$$\sigma = -\frac{Q}{2\pi x^2} \cos^3 \theta \tag{33}$$

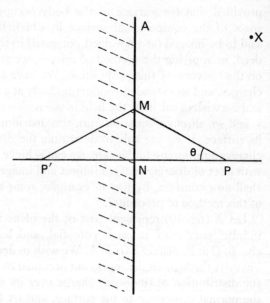

FIGURE 10

Equations (32) and (33) provide the complete solution to our problem. The total charge resident on the surface A is given by

$$\int_0^{\pi/2} \sigma 2\pi x^2 \tan \theta \sec^2 \theta \, d\theta,$$

that is by

$$-Q \int_0^{\pi/2} \sin \theta \, d\theta,$$

or

$$-Q.$$

We conclude that all the tubes of force originating in the charge Q

at P terminate on the plane surface A. In formulating the problem, we postulated that this surface was the surface of a semi-infinite earthed conductor. Obviously, the solution would be in no way changed if we were to postulate, instead, an infinite thin conducting sheet. We are not, in fact, concerned with the precise shape of the conducting body in the image space, provided that it presents a continuous plane surface to the object charge at P.

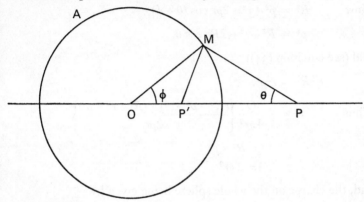

FIGURE 11

As providing our second application of the method of images, we consider the case of an object charge Q situated at a distance R from the centre of an earthed conducting sphere of radius ρ. The situation is represented two-dimensionally in fig. 11. Here O is the centre of the sphere A, and P is the position of the object charge. Let P' be the inverse point of P with respect to the sphere (see *M L & T*, p. 206), and M be any point on its surface. Let PM $= r$, P'M $= r'$. Then (*M L & T*, equation (84))

$$\frac{\rho}{r'} = \frac{R}{r} \tag{34}$$

and the potential at M, due to the object charge Q at P and a charge Q' at P', being given by

$$\gamma\left(\frac{Q}{r} + \frac{Q'}{r'}\right),$$

the potential over the whole spherical surface A would clearly be zero for

$$Q' = -\frac{\rho}{R}Q.$$

Thus, the electric image of Q, in the surface of the earthed conducting sphere of our problem, is the charge $-\rho Q/R$ situated at the inverse point as specified. If $\angle \mathrm{OPM} = \theta$, $\angle \mathrm{MOP} = \phi$, and if σ is the surface density of charge at M, from equation (30),

$$\sigma = -\frac{Q}{4\pi}\left(\frac{1}{r^2}\cos(\theta+\phi)+\frac{\rho}{Rr'^2}\cos\theta\right).$$

Now
$$R^2 = \rho^2 + r^2 + 2\rho r \cos(\theta+\phi),$$

$$\rho^2 = R^2 + r^2 - 2Rr \cos\theta,$$

and (see equation (34))

$$r'^2 R^2 = r^2 \rho^2.$$

Thus
$$\sigma = -\frac{Q}{4\pi r^2}\left\{\frac{(R^2-\rho^2-r^2)+(R^2+r^2-\rho^2)}{2\rho r}\right\}$$

$$= -\frac{Q}{4\pi}\frac{R^2-\rho^2}{\rho r^3},$$

and, the charge on the whole sphere being given by

$$\int_0^\pi \sigma 2\pi\rho^2 \sin\phi \, d\phi,$$

the total induced charge is

$$-\frac{Q\rho(R^2-\rho^2)}{2}\int_0^\pi \frac{\sin\phi \, d\phi}{(R^2+\rho^2-2R\rho\cos\phi)^{\frac{3}{2}}},$$

or
$$-\frac{Q(R^2-\rho^2)}{2R}\left[(R^2+\rho^2-2R\rho\cos\phi)^{-\frac{1}{2}}\right]_\pi^0,$$

or
$$-\frac{\rho}{R}Q,$$

as equation (31) would lead us to expect.

We note two results in relation to the case that we have just considered. First, that P′ is not the 'optical' image of P in A, and second, since the magnitude of the image charge Q' is smaller than that of the object charge Q, that not all the tubes of force originating in Q terminate on the earthed sphere A—the remainder terminate on 'charges at infinity'.

It is a simple matter to extend the solution that we have just completed to the case in which the conducting sphere A is not at earth potential, but at some arbitrary potential V. Because a charge $\rho V/\gamma$ (see equation. (15)) at O, acting alone, would establish this potential over the surface of the sphere, the electric image of the charge Q at P in the sphere, in this case, is the pair of charges, $-\rho Q/R$ at the inverse point, P', and $\rho V/\gamma$ at O, the centre of the sphere. The expression for the surface density of charge at an arbitrary point on the sphere is then

$$\sigma = -\frac{Q}{4\pi}\left(\frac{1}{r^2}\cos(\theta+\phi)+\frac{\rho}{Rr'^2}\cos\theta-\frac{1}{\gamma\rho}\frac{V}{Q}\right),$$

and the detailed evaluation of this solution proceeds as before. We note that if $\rho V/\gamma = \rho Q/R$, that is, if

$$V = \gamma\frac{Q}{R} \tag{35}$$

the net charge on the conducting sphere is zero. Now, equation (35) may be considered as giving the electric potential at a point distant R from an isolated point charge Q. We conclude, therefore, that, if an uncharged conducting sphere is brought into the neighbourhood of an isolated point charge, then the potential of the whole sphere is that originally characteristic of the point to which its centre has been brought.

There is a further extension of the problem of the induction of charge on a spherical conductor which is of considerable importance for our future discussions (see p. 368), and which leads immediately to the concept of the electric doublet—our secondary concern in the present section. It arises out of a consideration of the geometrically symmetrical case, in which an earthed conducting sphere of radius ρ is situated in the field of two point charges Q and $-Q$, located at P_1 and P_2, two points in a straight line passing through O, the centre of the sphere, and at equal distances, R, from O. This arrangement is represented diagrammatically in fig. 12. If P_1' and P_2' are the inverse points of P_1 and P_2, respectively, the image system in this symmetrical case consists of equal and opposite charges, $-\rho Q/R$ and $\rho Q/R$, at P_1' and P_2'. If $P_1'P_2' = x$, then (see $M L \& T$, p. 206)

$$x = \frac{2\rho^2}{R} \tag{36}$$

and E, the electric intensity at O in the absence of the sphere, is given by

$$E = \frac{2\gamma Q}{R^2} \tag{37}$$

the direction of this intensity being along $P_1'P_2'$. From equations (36) and (37) we have

$$\frac{\rho Q}{R} \cdot x = \frac{2\rho^3 Q}{R^2} = \frac{\rho^3 E}{\gamma} \tag{38}$$

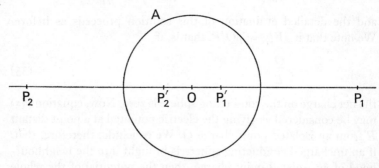

FIGURE 12

Equations (38) show that, in the symmetrical case here considered, the quantity given by the product of the measure of the separation of the equal and opposite image charges and the magnitude of either of them is determined only by the radius of the conducting sphere and the electric intensity, in the absence of the sphere, at the point occupied by its centre. If the object charges were withdrawn symmetrically and progressively from O, and were increased in magnitude continuously, so that the 'clear field' electric intensity at O remained constant, this product would not change.

The constancy of the product, under these conditions, suggests that the pair of equal and opposite image charges can profitably be considered as a single entity. We give to it the name 'electric doublet', and we refer to the constant product as the 'dipole moment' of this doublet. To be precise, in the situation that we have been considering, we say that, if an earthed conducting sphere of radius ρ is placed symmetrically between two equal and opposite charges, in respect of which the electric intensity is E at the point midway between them, then the charge induced on this sphere (being zero in net amount) will modify the electric field in the surrounding space exactly as would an electric doublet, re-placing the sphere at its centre, if p, the measure of the dipole moment of the doublet, were given by

$$p = \frac{\rho^3 E}{\gamma} \tag{39}$$

We have written, here, 'the measure of the dipole moment', since it will be clear that this physical quantity is a vector quantity—and that in this particular instance the direction of the dipole moment is the same as the direction of the electric intensity to which it is causally related.

Equation (39), as we have already emphasised, is valid whatever the distance, R, between the inducing (object) charges and the centre of the conducting sphere. If, in the limit, these charges were withdrawn symmetrically 'to infinity', the field at the origin remaining the same as before, our problem would be transformed, from that of an earthed conducting sphere in the field of two charges symmetrically placed, to the problem of such a sphere arbitrarily situated in a uniform electric field of intensity E. Nevertheless, equation (39) would still remain valid, in spite of this transformation. It is interesting to note that, at this extreme, it is unprofitable to ask, separately, the two questions, 'what is the magnitude and what is the separation of the image charges?': the former tends to infinity and the latter to zero, in the limit considered. Only the magnitude of the dipole moment continues finite, in accordance with equation (39). In more concrete terms, throughout the changes in the disposition and magnitude of the inducing charge that we have been considering, the distribution of induced charge over the surface of the earthed conducting sphere remains essentially constant once $R \gg \rho$.

Having introduced the concept of the electric doublet in this particular context, let us now consider, in its own right, the field originating in such an entity. Let X'OX (fig. 13) be the axis of an electric doublet consisting of charges $-q$ (at P') and q (at P), separated by a distance x and centred at the origin O. Let O be taken as the pole, and OX as the reference direction, with respect to which the polar co-ordinates of an arbitrary point M are (r, θ),

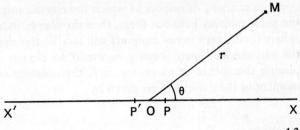

FIGURE 13

as shown in the figure. Then, if $r \gg x$, V, the electric potential at M is given by

$$V = \gamma \left(\frac{q}{r - \frac{x}{2} \cos \theta} - \frac{q}{r + \frac{x}{2} \cos \theta} \right),$$

or, in the limit, when $x \to 0$, $qx \to p$, by

$$V = \gamma \frac{p}{r^2} \cos \theta \tag{40}$$

Essentially, equation (40) provides a complete description of the field of the doublet, of dipole moment p. If we wish to describe the field, alternatively, in terms of the electric intensity at M, we have, for E_r and E_t, the radial and transverse components of the intensity, respectively, (the third rectangular component is necessarily zero)

$$E_r = -\frac{\partial V}{\partial r} = \gamma \frac{2p}{r^3} \cos \theta$$

$$E_t = -\frac{1}{r} \frac{\partial V}{\partial \theta} = \gamma \frac{p}{r^3} \sin \theta \tag{41}$$

and we note, as special cases, that

when $\theta = 0$, $E_t = 0$, $E_r = \gamma \frac{2p}{r^3}$

when $\theta = \frac{\pi}{2}$, $E_r = 0$, $E_t = \gamma \frac{p}{r^3}$ $\qquad$ (42)

—at equal distances, along the axis of the doublet and at right angles to it, the resultant intensities are in the ratio 2:1, the directions of these resultants being parallel and opposed.

In fig. 14, for sake of comparison, we give the traces of a series of equipotential surfaces (and the corresponding lines of force) for an ideal point charge (see equation (10)) and an ideal doublet (equation (40)). It will be noted how the equipotential surfaces form a single set in the former case, whereas, in the latter, they are constituted of two sets (corresponding to positive and negative values of the potential)* which mirror one another in the plane through the centre of the doublet and at right angles to its axis. In this connection the terms 'monopole' and 'dipole', sometimes applied to the fields illustrated in fig. 14, are seen to be appropriately descriptive.

2.8. MAGNETIC FORCES

The concept of the dipolar doublet that we have just elaborated is even more important in relation to the phenomena of magnetostatics than it is for the electrostatic phenomena considered in the last section. Indeed, we shall discover that it is the fundamental concept of our interpretative scheme, in magnetostatics, at least until we pass from the macroscopic to the sub-microscopic level, and seek to base our interpretations on notions of electrons and nuclei (see p. 4). At the macroscopic level of discussion, we shall be dealing largely with magnetic doublets—and equations (40), (41) and (42), suitably re-interpreted, will be significant for our enquiry.

In this brief summary, we are obviously anticipating conclusions still to be drawn: here our immediate aim must be to trace, in outline at least, the historical process by which these conclusions were reached. In relation to the basic concepts of electrostatics, we devoted sections 2.2 and 2.3 to such an historical sketch; now the salient events of the period can be dealt with in smaller compass.

In about the year 1180, a young Englishman, Alexander Neckam (1157-1217), then lecturing in the University of Paris, compiled a manual of the scientific knowledge of his day. In this compilation, *De naturis rerum*, there occurs the following passage: 'Mariners

---

* For the point charge, equipotentials have been drawn for potentials of 1, 2, 3, 4 and 5 units; for the doublet, for −3, −2, −1, 0, 1, 2 and 3 units of potential.

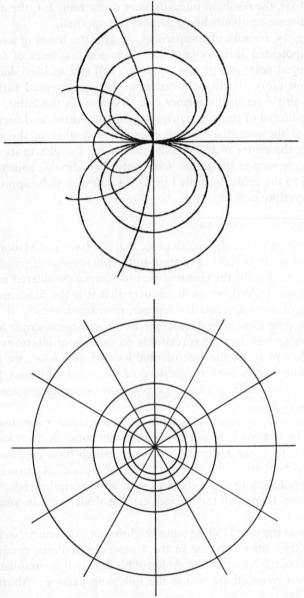

FIGURE 14

at sea, when, through cloudy weather in the day which hides the sun, or through the darkness of the night, they lose the knowledge of the quarter of the world to which they are sailing, touch a needle with the magnet, which will turn round till, on its motion ceasing, its point will be directed towards the north.' In this passage we have probably the earliest extant description of a navigational aid which, on the evidence of the passage itself, must already have been in fairly widespread use, around the coasts of western Europe, at the time of writing. The 'magnet' of the passage is obviously, 'the stone', of magnetite (Fe_3O_4). The property of attracting small pieces of iron, which this naturally occurring mineral frequently possesses, was known to the Greeks of 600 BC —and its property of inducing similar 'magnetism' in objects made of this metal had been recognised before the beginning of our present era. But with Neckam's account, the first that we have, we are inclined to place the first practical application of 'artificial magnets' at least a millennium later in time, and to assign to the same time, or thereabouts, the third significant discovery in our subject—the discovery of a pervasive field of magnetic influence belonging to the earth itself.

Some fifty years after the death of Neckam, Peter of Maricourt, a Frenchman, wrote, from Lucera, in Italy, for his master in Paris, *Epistola de magnete* (1269). In this letter, disregarded by most of his learned contemporaries, and soon generally forgotten, Maricourt described how (in modern parlance) he had used a magnetised needle to investigate the field near the surface of a large lodestone of roughly spherical shape. When he had covered the surface of the stone with 'lines of force' determined in this way, he found that the lines, being great circles of the sphere, converged towards two diametrically opposed points on the spherical surface, and, borrowing his phraseology from the geographers, he referred to these points of convergence as the 'poles' of the magnet. Through many experiments, he convinced himself that the mutual actions of magnetised bodies could be understood by regarding the magnetic force as a property of such poles, and in order to explain the setting of a freely suspended magnet in the meridian he made the picturesque suggestion that 'the heavens have poles' (see *M L & T*, p. 199). But all this, as we have said, was soon largely forgotten—though his manuscripts remained in the libraries, and a printed edition was produced at Augsburg in 1558:

more than three hundred years later, William Gilbert (see p. 2) had to re-establish what Maricourt had known, through his own investigations.

Gilbert's *De magnete* was published in the year 1600. Nineteen years previously, Robert Norman, an English instrument maker, had already recorded, in *The Newe Attractive*, his systematic observations on the effects of magnetic needles one on another, drawing attention, as he thought for the first time, to the repulsions as well as to the attractions which characterise these effects (we noticed, earlier, the lack of attention paid to electrostatic repulsions, until an even later date—see p. 8). Maricourt had, in fact, anticipated him, but Norman should at least share the credit for his observations. Jointly, these two are the authors of the empirical law, 'two north-seeking (or two south-seeking) poles repel one another; two poles of opposite character attract'.

Norman's work was done within the context of his trade; Gilbert's was the more disinterested, and the more original. He demonstrated clearly the difference between electrostatic and magnetostatic attraction in relation to the screening effect of interposed materials, noting the strong diminution of the former and the insignificant change in the latter attraction in such circumstances. He constructed a spherical lodestone (or 'terrella'), such as Maricourt had used, and, more systematically than his predecessor, he investigated its properties. His conclusion was not the semi-mystical conclusion that the heavens have poles, but the more mundane assertion that the earth is a great magnet. The full title of the treatise in which he recorded his investigations was *De magnete magneticisque corporibus et de magno magnete tellure physiologia nova*.

For reasons that are not difficult to understand—magnetised needles being more permanent objects, and more easily manageable, than bodies charged with electricity—the pre-quantitative stage in the development of the subject came to an end earlier in magnetostatics than it did in electrostatics. Newton made many experiments with magnets, and in book 3 of the *Principia* he wrote (1687) 'The power of magnetism . . . in receding from the magnet, decreases not in the duplicate, but almost in the triplicate proportion of the distance, as nearly as I could judge from some rude observations.' Brook Taylor (1685-1731), Secretary to the Royal Society from 1714 to 1718, made some more accurate measurements during this period, and had them published by the Society. George Graham, the London instrument maker (see *M L & T*, p. 24), who had been elected to the Fellowship in 1720, devoted much time in 1722 to a careful study of the behaviour of pivoted magnets, and put forward the suggestion that the period of oscillation of such a magnet provides the best 'method of computing the magnetic forces'—a suggestion which found little favour at the time (see p. 74). Peiter van Musschenbroek (1692-1761) included an account of his experiments with magnets in a collection of miscellaneous material published during his tenure of the chair of natural philosophy and mathematics at Utrecht (1729). None of these investigators claimed to have established any simple power-law of magnetic action, but, in a note on Newton's own statement, already quoted, that appeared in an edition of the *Principia* published in 1739 and 1742, there is to be found the claim that the effect of one magnet on another is essentially a turning effect, and that the magnitude of this effect is inversely as the cube of the distance between the magnets. This edition of the *Principia* is commonly referred to as the Jesuits' edition; its printing was supervised by G. L. Calandrini (1703-1758), professor of mathematics at Geneva, the first in a long line of European mathematicians to carry forward the Newtonian theory of gravitation as it applies in detail to the motion of the moon. But neither this note, imperfectly grounded in experimental observation as its oversimplified claim undoubtedly was, nor Graham's suggestion (which, in essence, was founded on a similar view of the basic response of a magnet to an external magnetic influence), appears to have received any wide recognition by the scientists of the day. Emphasis was on the magnetic influence as a 'virtue' resident in the poles of magnets, rather than on magnets as entities in themselves.

In 1750, John Michell (see *M L & T*, pp. 214, 217) achieved the first real success in formulating a law of force based on this 'traditional' point of view. He worked over the previous observations of Taylor and Musschenbroek, and made some further experiments of his own. He convinced himself that all the material at his disposal could be explained in terms of two hypotheses: that the simplest magnet is one which possesses two poles of equal strength but opposite character; that the law of mutual attraction or repulsion between magnetic poles is an inverse-square law.

Michell's conclusion found many adherents in the following years, but not until 1785 was there any real attempt to test the matter by direct experiment. Then Coulomb (see p. 17), making use of magnets that were very long and thin, and vertically disposed, was able to study the effects due to their uppermost poles almost in isolation, bringing these poles to different distances from one end of a magnet suspended horizontally by a vertical torsion wire. From the twist of the wire the force could be deduced in each case. In this way, adopting the direct approach, Coulomb came very near to establishing the law of magnetic action convincingly, but, as with the law of electrostatic action (p. 15), another and much less direct experiment eventually provided the unequivocal demonstration. The validity of the inverse-square law in magnetism must be considered to rest on the experiments of Gauss, in 1832, rather than on those which Coulomb made nearly half a century earlier.

In the intervening half-century, however, there were theoretical developments of importance which did not wait for the final demonstration of the validity of the law—and their initiation can be credited to Coulomb himself. It was accepted at the time (1789) that all attempts to obtain isolated magnetic poles had resulted in failure. If a long bar magnet is divided in two, new poles, equal and opposite in magnitude, appear across the surface of section, so that the two portions of the original bar become complete dipolar magnets in themselves. Before the advent of the Daltonian hypothesis, Coulomb pointed out that this fact, alone, requires an atomic theory of matter for its full comprehension. Only on the assumption that the ultimate unit of magnetic polarity is the individual atom,* was it possible, on his view, to make sense of the experimental results. Then, sixteen years after the publication of the first volume of the *New System of Chemical Philosophy*, but taking his notion of 'magnetic atoms' from Coulomb rather than from Dalton, S.D.Poisson (see *M L & T*, p. 256) developed (1824) a very elegant and thorough-going mathematical theory of magnetisation. Inevitably the basic notion of the atomicity of

---

* In a posthumously published work, *Magnetismus Magnus, or metaphysical and divine contemplations on the Magnet or Loadstone* (1695), Sir Matthew Hale (1609-1676), sometime Lord Chief Justice of England, drew attention to the fact (as he accepted it) 'That every smallest Particle of this Magnet, every little Dust thereof should have the same Conformation that the entire Magnet had, every little Particle having his Poles...perfectly Analogal to the great Magnet, whose Dust it is'.

matter was lost sight of in the mathematics of continuous functions, but for the first time the concept of the magnetic dipole moment per unit volume emerged as the significant concept in relation to a magnetised material. And, behind the mathematics, there was the underlying physical interpretation: that this new quantity, 'the intensity of magnetisation', was merely the resultant of the dipole moments of all the elementary particles, the 'magnetic atoms', in unit volume of the material. In this book, for convenience of presentation, we first introduced the notion of the dipole moment of a doublet in relation to electric charges (see p. 54). Historically, it belongs, by origin, to Poisson's theory of magnetisation: already, at the beginning of this section (p. 57), we have claimed its fundamental importance for the physics of magnetism.

The essence of Gauss's experimental verification of the inverse-square law for magnetic poles is to be found in equations (42), translated from their electrostatic form so as to be applicable to the new situation—and in the statement that follows them (p. 56), once it has been suitably modified. If we consider a short bar magnet as an ideal magnetic doublet of total dipole moment M, then the modified statement asserts that at equal distances from the centre of the magnet, along its axis and at right angles to this axis, the magnetic field intensities are in the ratio 2:1. This result is based directly on the assumption of an inverse-square law of force between magnetic poles. A more general calculation, assuming that the force between two poles varies inversely as the nth power of the distance ($n > 1$), leads to the result that the ratio of these intensities (of the 'end-on' and 'broadside' fields, at equal distances from an ideal dipole) is n, precisely. In the ideal case, then, a simple determination of the magnetic field intensities at two points, suitably chosen in the neighbourhood of a doublet, is sufficient to identify the index in the inverse-power law involved.

Gauss's experiment of 1832 was complicated only by the fact that 'real' magnets are demonstrably not ideal doublets: their poles are separated by finite distances. For a real magnet, then, we write, explicitly, $M = ml$, where l is the distance between the poles of the magnet, and m is the pole strength. In this case, the approximation which led to equation (40) in our earlier analysis is no longer admissible, and it is necessary to calculate the field intensities directly. In this way, we have, when $\quad \theta = 0, \quad H_r = \gamma' \left\{ \dfrac{m}{\left(r - \dfrac{l}{2}\right)^2} - \dfrac{m}{\left(r + \dfrac{l}{2}\right)^2} \right\},$

or $\qquad\qquad H_r = \dfrac{2\gamma' M r}{\left(r^2 - \dfrac{l^2}{4}\right)^2}$ (43)

when $\quad \theta = \dfrac{\pi}{2}, \quad H_t = 2\gamma' \dfrac{m}{r^2 + \dfrac{l^2}{4}} \cdot \dfrac{l}{2\left(r^2 + \dfrac{l^2}{4}\right)^{\frac{1}{2}}},$

or $\qquad\qquad H_t = \dfrac{\gamma' M}{\left(r^2 + \dfrac{l^2}{4}\right)^{\frac{3}{2}}}$ (44)

—if the inverse-square law is valid. On the basis of equations (43) and (44), it is now the experimentally determinable ratio $H_e \left(1 - \dfrac{l^2}{4r^2}\right)^2 : H_b \left(1 + \dfrac{l^2}{4r^2}\right)^{\frac{3}{2}}$, involving the end-on and broadside field intensities (H_e and H_b, respectively) at equal distances r from the centre of the magnet, which has the 'theoretical' value 2, rather than the simple ratio of the intensities of the ideal situation.

Gauss determined the ratio H_e/H_b by comparing each field intensity with the intensity of the horizontal component of the magnetic field of the earth effective in his laboratory. A small magnet, freely suspended through its centre of gravity by a vertical suspension, under the influence of the earth's field alone, takes up an equilibrium position with its axis along the direction of the horizontal component of the field. This statement could be taken as a truism—defining the direction of that component. Adopting the less realistic definition that the direction of any field is the direction of the force experienced by a 'test' pole placed in the field (compare p. 28), the statement is consequential—the suspended magnet is in equilibrium when the equal and oppositely directed forces acting on its two poles are collinear. On the basis of the second definition we can calculate the turning couple acting on a magnet when its axis is inclined to the direction of a uniform magnetic field at an arbitrary angle. Let NS (fig. 15) represent a bar magnet, of effective length l and pole strength m, of which the axis is inclined at an angle θ to the direction of a uniform mag-

netic field of intensity H. Then the magnitude of the force acting
on each pole of the magnet is mH, and the directions of the forces
are as shown in the figure. If G is the magnitude of the couple
constituted by the forces, we have

$$G = -mHl \sin \theta,$$

or $\qquad G = -MH \sin \theta \qquad\qquad\qquad (45)$

M being the total dipole moment of the magnet, and the positive
direction of G being taken as that of θ increasing. On this basis,
the equilibrium position, for a freely suspended magnet, is clearly
determined by the condition $G = 0$.

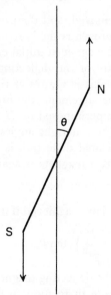

FIGURE 15

In respect of Gauss's experiment, let us regard H as referring
to the horizontal component of the earth's field in the laboratory.
We can imagine the experiment conducted as follows. We postulate a small freely suspended magnet initially in equilibrium in the
earth's field alone. Along the horizontal line through the centre
of this magnet and at right angles to its axis (in this initial equilibrium position) a short bar magnet is brought up until the distance
between the centres of the two magnets is r. The axis of the
approaching magnet is always directed along the line of approach.

Then superimposed on the horizontal component of the earth's field in the neighbourhood of the suspended magnet there will be the end-on field, H_e, of the 'deflecting' magnet, horizontally directed and at right angles to the direction of H. The suspended magnet will at each stage tend to take up a position of equilibrium in which the turning couples due to these two fields are equal and opposite. Finally let the deflection be θ_e. Then, from equation (45),

$$MH \sin \theta_e = MH_e \sin \left(\frac{\pi}{2} - \theta_e \right),$$

or $$H_e = H \tan \theta_e.$$

Next, the deflecting magnet is removed, and the procedure is repeated except that the line of approach is the horizontal line containing the axis of the suspended magnet in initial equilibrium in the earth's field alone. The centre of the deflecting magnet approaches along this line, and its axis is always at right angles to the line and horizontal. In this arrangement, the broadside field, H_b, of the deflecting magnet is superimposed on H in the neighbourhood of the suspended magnet, at right angles to that field and horizontally directed. If the final deflection is θ_b, when the separation of the centres of the two magnets is again r, we have

$$H_b = H \tan \theta_b.$$

Verification of the inverse-square law is achieved if it is found that

$$\left(1 - \frac{l^2}{4r^2} \right)^2 \tan \theta_e = 2 \left(1 + \frac{l^2}{4r^2} \right)^{\frac{3}{2}} \tan \theta_b,$$

where l is the effective length of the deflecting magnet.

Two last remarks must be made in relation to this 'classical' experiment, of which we have just given an obviously idealised account. The first is that, in applying equation (45) to Gauss's arrangement, we have tacitly assumed that the two fields which are superposed in the neighbourhood of the suspended magnet are, individually, uniform fields in that region. This is demonstrably not the case for H_e and H_b, the end-on and broadside fields of the deflecting magnet. In order that the experiment shall be acceptable, therefore, the length of the suspended magnet must be small—small, that is, compared with the length of the deflecting magnet. The second matter to be remarked upon is more subtle—and more easily overlooked. Fortunately, its practical neglect is of little consequence in this and in other similar experiments. It is that our derivation of equation (45) presupposes that the magnetisation of the magnet is entirely 'permanent' magnetisation: no account is taken of 'induced' magnetisation produced through the action of the field. Pedantically, it must be insisted that all materials which are capable of exhibiting permanent magnetisation are susceptible of magnetisation by induction. This complication is analogous to that to which we drew attention when we were considering Coulomb's experiments on the electrostatic forces between charged spherical conductors (p. 21).

We conclude this section with a final comment. As previously in this chapter (see, for example, pp. 19, 30), it is necessary to enter a caveat concerning units of measurement. It will be appreciated that our immediate object has been merely to survey the basic phenomena of magnetostatics qualitatively, and to show that their formal description in terms of the concept of poles acting on one another according to an inverse-square law of distance is an empirically valid description. This we have done with the minimum use of mathematical symbolism. But, of necessity, we have had to use some mathematics, and equations (43)-(45), having the form of precise statements, are clearly incomplete without precise definitions, particularly the definition of the unit of pole strength. It will be obvious from the way in which we have introduced the subject—taking over equations (40)-(42) from electrostatics into magnetostatics—that we are assuming here a definition of unit pole exactly analogous to the definition of unit charge which, in our discussion of Gauss's theorem and its consequences, we left imprecise (at least in relation to the constant γ). Now, we are being similarly imprecise concerning the constant γ'. We have already noted the fact (p. 19) that the electrostatic unit of charge was originally defined by writing, in respect of charges in vacuum, $\gamma = 1$ (and disregarding the dimensional character of this quantity); later, the 'electromagnetic unit' of pole strength was similarly defined by disregarding the true nature of the quantity represented by γ' in our present equations, and equating its magnitude to one for magnetic poles situated in vacuum (see, also, $V \,\&\, W$, p. 257). To retain the quantity γ', as we shall do, is a first step towards the possibility of a self-consistent system of units equally suited to electrostatic and to magnetic measurements, but when this system is finally developed (in chap. 3) it will not be on a basis so artificial as to require the notion of disembodied magnetic poles situated in vacuum, which was fundamental to the electromagnetic system of the early nineteenth century.

2.9. FORCES BETWEEN MAGNETS AND CURRENTS

We have not, so far, introduced the notion of a current of electricity. We have made the distinction between conductors and insulators (p. 9), and have discussed, at least in its end-results, the flow of charge through conducting bodies. We have interpreted this flow as a re-distribution of the positive and negative charges which we have assumed to be intrinsic to matter generally, and present in almost unlimited amount—and in exact balance, when any body is macroscopically uncharged. In this section we consider, for the first time, some of the effects associated with such flow of charge.

Eighteenth-century scientists were not altogether unfamiliar with some of these effects. Throughout the whole of that century frictional machines were available by which bodies could be electrified—and they were being constantly improved; furthermore, the invention of the 'Leyden jar' by E. G. von Kleist, in 1745, provided a composite body in which large quantities of electricity (equal quantities of separated positive and negative electricity) could be stored for subsequent use. Kinnersley (see p. 10), in 1763, described experiments on the elongation and eventual fusion of thin iron wires through which Leyden-jar discharges had been passed, and Cavendish made a very systematic study, which he did not publish at the time (1775-1781), of the passage of these discharge 'currents' through metal wires and columns of liquid contained in long glass tubes. In this matter, Cavendish had, indeed, to some extent been anticipated by Giovanni Battista Beccaria (1716-1781), professor of experimental physics at Palermo, Rome, and finally at Turin, who in 1753 had described his researches in a treatise *Dell'Elettricismo Naturale ed Artificiale*. This work had appeared in an English translation in 1776.

Early in the eighteenth century it was already common belief that certain magnetic effects could result from electrical discharges. There had been chance observations of the magnetisation of articles of iron during thunderstorms—and the view was gaining ground that these latter were essentially electrical phenomena on a grand scale. This view originated, in 1705, with Francis Hawksbee (d. 1713), instrument-maker, and sometime curator of experiments to the Royal Society, and had been subscribed to by Nollet (see p. 11). Eventually it was verified by Franklin, in 1752, in a series of experiments in which a Leyden jar was charged from a thundercloud through the string of a kite which the intrepid investigator had flown in the path of the cloud. In the previous year Franklin had reported the magnetisation of a steel needle by a Leyden jar discharge. However, this earlier clue proved misleading, or, at the least, elusive, and two generations had to pass before a precise laboratory experiment established conclusively the interrelation of magnetic and electrical phenomena. The breakthrough came with the invention of the electric pile by Alessandro Volta (see p. 42) in 1799 (or 1800).

The antecedents of Volta's discovery were as multifarious (see, for example, p. 226) as its end-result was simple: the first recipe for the production of a steady difference of electric potential between bodies by other than essentially frictional means. In 1782 Volta had very considerably increased the sensitivity of the electroscope (see p. 11) by the incorporation of a condenser (see p. 116), and in this way he established the fact that, when disks of two dissimilar metals are separated by a disk of cloth moistened with almost any dilute aqueous solution, a small permanent difference of potential is developed between the metal disks. His invention of 1799 issued directly from his further discovery that if a 'pile' of n such composite units is assembled, metallic contact being assured between the (dissimilar) metals of adjacent units, then between the extreme metal disks of the pile the permanent difference of potential is n times that developed by a single unit. Volta produced many variants of this, the first 'electric battery of simple cells' (a unique collection of original examples was totally destroyed by fire on the occasion of the centenary exhibition in Como in 1899), and within a year investigations employing voltaic piles were in process in a score of laboratories in western Europe. At first, chemical effects attracted all the attention. The experiments of Beccaria and Cavendish were repeated and greatly extended by William Nicholson (1753-1815) and Anthony Carlisle (1768-1840), William Cruikshank (1745-1800), W. H. Wollaston (see *V & W*, p. 142), and, most spectacularly, by Humphry Davy (see *M L & T*,

p. 271), in London, and by Jöns Jakob Berzelius (1779-1848) and Wilhelm Hisinger (1766-1852) in Stockholm. Even the more physical investigations, in this first flurry of excitement—hardly matched, again, until the discovery of X-rays by Röntgen in 1895 (see *V & W*, p. 273), were carried out in the main by chemists and medical men turned scientist: in Paris by Louis Nicolas Vauquelin (1763-1829) and Antoine François de Fourcroy (1755-1809), and Louis Jacques Thénard (1777-1857), their more famous protégé, by Martin van Marum (1750-1837) in Haarlem and Christian Heinrich Pfaff (1773-1852) in Kiel. Almost the only professional physicist who made any contribution at this early stage was Paul Erman (1764-1851), at that time teacher of science at the Military Academy in Berlin. He repeated and refined Volta's original observations with the electroscope.

The invention of the voltaic pile, so we have said, provided the means for the first successful demonstration of an interrelation between electric and magnetic phenomena. Yet, even with the pile available, the initial attempt to use it for this purpose proved nugatory. Indeed, the manner of the attempt affords striking comment on the general unpreparedness of men of science of the day for the developments that were to come. In 1805, Jean Nicolas Pierre Hachette (1769-1834), geometer and engineer, and Charles Bernard Desormes (1777-1862), in Paris, suspended a voltaic pile 'on open circuit' thinking that they might be able to detect some directive effect attributable to the magnetic field of the earth. They were not the first to remark on the apparent analogy between the polarity of the pile and that of a magnet, though they were, probably, the first to put the matter to systematic test. Their test produced nothing significant. Having this particular analogy in mind, Hachette and Desormes naturally made their test on open circuit—and there is no record that they made it in any other way. Voltaic piles, it is true, had already been used on closed (metallic) circuit, for short intervals of time, in experiments in which their efficacy had been assessed by their power of fusing thin metal wires connected across their terminals, but, when attention was largely focused on the action taking place within the pile itself, and the chemical effects that could be produced with its aid, there was little inclination to regard the wires leading from the terminals of the pile to the chemical cell as the seat of physical phenomena in their own right. In 1807, Thomas

Young (see *V & W*, p. 142) wrote 'An uninterrupted current of electricity, through a perfect conductor, would perhaps be also in every respect imperceptible, since the best conductors appear to be the least affected by it. . . . A constant stream of galvanic electricity, passing through an iron wire is, however, capable of exciting a considerable degree of heat. . . .' 'There is no reason to imagine any immediate connexion between magnetism and electricity, except that electricity affects the conducting power of iron or steel for magnetism, in the same manner as heat or agitation.' The two quotations are taken from different lectures (*A Course of Lectures on Natural Philosophy . . .* , nos. 54 and 55), but they fit together—and few natural philosophers of the period can have taken serious objection to the views which they express. Ten years later, as we shall see, even Oersted probably assented to them: after all, possible interrelations between phenomena of the two types had been sought for more than half a century, and nothing more specific had emerged. When, in 1819, the really fundamental connection was brought to light, the discovery was made almost by chance.

Hans Christian Oersted (1777-1851) was professor of natural philosophy in Copenhagen. He had received his doctorate in metaphysics, and in later years he spent much time in pure speculation, elaborating the evolutionary philosophy of Schelling; even when young he had the reputation of 'a very unhappy experimenter'. But he was a man of original ideas, and from an early stage he had contemplated making experiments with pivoted magnets and current-carrying wires. In 1819, according to Maxwell (*Treatise*, pt. IV, chap. 1), he was endeavouring 'to ascertain the effect [on a compass needle] of a wire *heated* by an electric current'. It was his custom to lecture 'privately' to a few advanced students, and to employ those 'of his auditors who had easy hands' to 'arrange' his experiments. One of them, in later life, described what happened (over a period of weeks?) towards the end of that year: 'Oersted tried to place the wire of his galvanic battery perpendicular (at right angles) over the magnetic needle, but remarked no sensible motion. Once, after the end of his lecture . . . he said, "Let us now once, as the battery is in activity, try to place the wire parallel with the needle"; as this was made, he was quite struck with perplexity by seeing the needle make a great oscillation. . . . Then he said, "Let us now invert the direction of the current", and the needle deviated in the contrary direction. . . . He had not before any more idea than any other person that the force should be *transversal*' (letter from Christopher Hansteen* to Michael Faraday, 30 December 1857). By his simple reversal of the current, Oersted had disposed, once for all, of the possibility that the effect that he had observed was in any way related to the electrical heating of the wire; more fundamentally, his observation itself had outmoded the conservative speculations of Young, which we have quoted as representative of informed opinion at that time.

During the months that followed, Oersted consolidated his discovery, convincing himself that the effect was in no way dependent upon the nature of the wire carrying the current, that the deflection was reversed equally on reversing the current or on transferring the wire from a position above to a position below the compass needle—and, consonant with these two results, that, if a long straight wire carrying a current above the needle were looped back so as to return under it, the deflection was increased. Then, in July 1820, he wrote an account of his researches (in Latin), and it was printed in Copenhagen. Later, Hansteen referred to Oersted's discovery as of the 'transversal' force on a compass needle (see above). Oersted was more precise: he wrote, 'We may likewise conclude that this conflict performs gyrations round the wire, for without this condition it seems impossible that one part of the wire when placed below the magnetic needle should drive its pole to the east, and when placed above it, to the west.' Nowadays, we should say that an electric current flowing through a long straight wire gives rise to a magnetic field in the surrounding space, the lines of force being everywhere circles about the wire as common axis. This is merely Oersted's statement in modern form.

In 1819 Oersted had made a fundamental discovery, and he had shown great physical insight in pursuing it, and in setting forth his findings, but his account of them had been purely qualitative. Within five months of the publication of that account, a strictly quantitative description was provided in full by Jean Baptiste Biot (1774-1862) and Félix Savart (1791-1841). Biot had

---

* b. 1784, d. 1873. Soon after his appointment as professor of astronomy and applied mathematics at Christiania (Oslo), Hansteen went some considerable way towards anticipating Gauss in the experimental verification of the inverse-square law for magnetic poles (see p. 63).

been appointed professor of physics at the Collège de France at the age of twenty-six; his colleague was a surgeon by profession. Because the five months that we have mentioned witnessed the birth of the modern science of electromagnetism, in Paris, spanning not only the experiments of Biot and Savart which are our present interest, but also the more remarkable investigations of Ampère with which we shall later be concerned (see pp. 82, 91), it is appropriate that we should devote some time to their consideration. For, in truth, the hundred and fifty days of the French Academicians of 1820 represent a turning point of history no less significant than the hundred days of Napoleon which brought him to Waterloo.

At the meeting of the Académie des Sciences on 4 September 1820, Arago (see *V & W*, p. 144) gave an account of Oersted's experiments, and reported that the observations of 'the Danish philosopher' had since been repeated* in Geneva 'with complete success'. He was thereupon charged to demonstrate the experiments, himself, at the next meeting, in a week's time. On Monday, 11 September 1820, therefore, Arago duly 'repeated before the Academy the experiments of M. Oersted'. Seven weeks later, Biot and Savart presented the first of two memoirs 'On the laws according to which metal wires joining the poles of a galvanic pile act on magnetised needles'. Their second memoir was read before the Academy on 18 December—seven weeks later again.

In their first memoir, Biot and Savart described how they had suspended a small magnetised needle, in a region where the horizontal component of the earth's field was effectively neutralised by an auxiliary magnet, and had measured the period of free oscillation of the needle when a vertical wire, forming part of the external circuit of a voltaic pile, was brought to different distances from its centre. The vertical wire, symmetrically disposed above and below the plane of oscillation of the needle, was some 2·5 metres long, and the range of distances from wire to needle was from 1·5 cm to 12 cm. Because, in such an arrangement, the position of equilibrium of the suspended needle is tangential to the circular right section of a cylindrical surface having the wire as

* By Auguste Arthur de la Rive (1801-1873), the brilliant student son of the then professor of pharmaceutical chemistry at the Geneva Academy. Three years later, still only twenty-two, the young man was appointed professor of natural philosophy at the Academy (in the same year in which his father became Rector).

axis (provided there is no constraint in the suspension), the requirement that the length of the needle be small compared with its mean distance from the wire is not a particularly onerous requirement (the length of the needle need not be 'very small' compared with this distance), and conditions are, therefore, favourable for an accurate experiment.

Biot and Savart, it will be noted, were using the method of oscillation which had been suggested by George Graham almost a century earlier (see p. 61). The theory of the method may be stated quite simply. According to equation (45), the restoring couple acting on a suspended needle of total magnetic dipole moment M, when the axis of the needle is inclined at angle θ to a uniform magnetic field of intensity H, is $MH \sin \theta$. For small inclinations, the restoring couple being thus proportional to the angular displacement, the period of free oscillation is given by

$$\tau = 2\pi \sqrt{\frac{I}{MH}} \tag{46}$$

where I is the moment of inertia of the needle about the axis of suspension. Combining their observations in such a way as to take account of a slow decay of current in their vertical wire, Biot and Savart deduced the empirical result $\tau^2/r = $ constant. Here r denotes the distance from the wire to the centre of the needle. Interpreted in terms of equation (46), this result leads directly to the conclusion $Hr = $ constant. This, then, is the conclusion that Biot and Savart reported to the Academy of Sciences on 30 October 1820: the magnetic field varies inversely as the distance from the wire.

When Oersted showed that the deflection of his compass needle was increased when the long straight current-carrying wire was looped back on itself, so that it passed both above and below the needle, it was immediately evident that different elements of length of the wire, in such circumstances, contribute individually to the overall effect. If we ascribe this effect, in general terms, to the magnetic field associated with the current in the wire, we are naturally led to the view that the intensity of this field, in the neighbourhood of the needle, is the resultant of infinitesimal components, each of which may be independently ascribed to the instantaneous current in an infinitesimal length of the wire. This is essentially the point of view from which Biot and Savart considered their empirical results in their second memoir (though the basic notion of 'current in the wire' had not been fully developed at the time—see p. 94). Let us, therefore, explore its consequences, in relation to the 'infinite' straight wire, as Biot and Savart did.

Necessarily, we must make some tentative assumptions. In relation to fig. 16, let AB be a portion of an 'infinite' straight wire carrying a constant current. Let P be an external point where the magnetic field due to the current in the whole wire is of resultant intensity H. The direction of H is at right angles to the plane of the diagram, and we have the empirical result that $Hr = \beta$, r being the perpendicular distance of P from the wire, and β being constant under the conditions specified. Our first tentative assumption is that the directions of all the infinitesimal components of H are the same, namely the direction through P at right angles to the plane of the diagram. Then, we require three assumptions concerning the magnitudes of these components: we assume (as is almost axiomatic) that they are proportional to the elementary lengths of current-carrying wire to which they are severally ascribed, that they are proportional to some inverse power of the distance of the external point from the various elements of the wire, and, finally, that they may depend on the angle between the direction of the current in a wire-element and the join of that element to the external point.

Now, in fig. 16, let QR be an element of the wire of length ds, and let θ, as shown, be the angle between the direction of the current in this element and the join to the external point P. If N is the foot of the perpendicular from P on the wire, and if $\angle NPQ = \phi$,

$$PN = r,$$
$$NQ = r \tan \phi,$$
$$QP = r \sec \phi,$$
$$QR = r \sec^2 \phi \, d\phi = ds,$$

and, giving formal expression to the assumptions that we have specified, we may write

$$H = \beta' \int_{-\pi/2}^{\pi/2} f(\theta) \frac{r \sec^2 \phi \, d\phi}{(r \sec \phi)^n} \tag{47}$$

Here $f(\theta)$ represents the possible angular dependence of our last assumption, n is the inverse power of the distance involved in the last-but-one, and β' is a constant (which clearly depends upon the current flowing in the wire). Moreover, since $\theta = \dfrac{\pi}{2} + \phi$, we may re-write equation (47) in the form

$$H = \frac{\beta'}{r^{n-1}} \int_0^{\pi} f(\theta) \sin^{(n-2)} \theta \, d\theta \tag{48}$$

The definite integral in equation (48) is necessarily a pure number, thus for a given current in the wire, according to this result, $Hr^{n-1} = \text{constant}$.

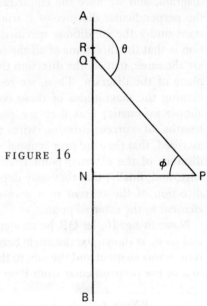

FIGURE 16

Empirically, as we have seen, $Hr = \text{constant}$, for a given current. Thus, if our assumptions are accepted, $n = 2$. We say 'if our assumptions are accepted'—but we note that we have not needed to make use of all of them in reaching this conclusion. The empirical fact, that the magnetic intensity due to a steady current in a long straight wire varies inversely as the distance from the wire, can be accounted for on the basis of an inverse-square law of action of individual elements of the current-carrying wire, provided that the elementary components of the intensity are proportional to the lengths of the elements of wire—and are co-directional, whatever the angular dependence represented by $f(\theta)$

in our equations. In this connection, the only condition which must be satisfied is that

$$\int_0^\pi f(\theta)\, d\theta \neq 0.$$

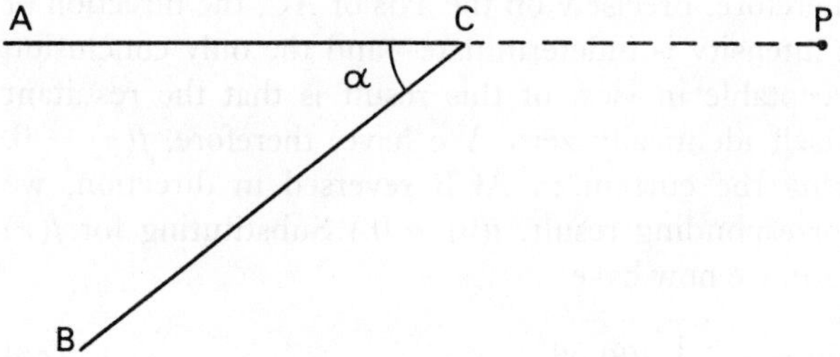

FIGURE 17

In order to investigate the angular dependence function $f(\theta)$, Biot and Savart used, instead of a long straight wire, a wire formed of two straight portions including an angle α which could be varied. This wire, ACB (fig. 17) was set up in a vertical plane passing through P, the centre of the suspended compass needle, towards which one arm of the bent wire pointed directly. This arm, AC, was arranged horizontally, and remained fixed when α was varied. If H now represents the resultant magnetic intensity at P for a constant current in the wire, if $CP = r'$, when $n = 2$, equations (47) and (48) as applied to this case become

$$
\begin{aligned}
H &= \frac{\beta'}{r' \sin \alpha}\int_0^\alpha f(\theta)\, d\theta + \beta' f(\pi)\int_{r'}^\infty \frac{ds}{r^2} \\
&= \frac{\beta'}{r'}\left\{\frac{1}{\sin \alpha}\int_0^\alpha f(\theta)\, d\theta + f(\pi)\right\}
\end{aligned}
\tag{49}
$$

In this formal expression, as will be obvious, the first term represents the contribution to H due to the current in BC, the second term the contribution due to the current in CA. Within the framework of our assumptions, we can evaluate the latter contribution on the basis of symmetry considerations alone. We have assumed that all the individual contributions to the resultant intensity, due to elementary sections of a long straight current-carrying wire, have, at any exterior point, the same direction as the resultant intensity at that point. Now, if AC (fig. 17) had been extended through P as an infinite wire, the lines of force of the magnetic field around P would have been circles centred at P in a plane at right angles to the wire. The assumption quoted above implies that, when only the 'semi-infinite' segment AC is in question, the lines of force around P are, similarly, circles centred at P. At P itself, therefore, precisely on the axis of AC, the direction of the resultant intensity is indeterminate—and the only conclusion physically acceptable in view of this result is that the resultant intensity is itself identically zero. We have, therefore, $f(\pi) = 0$. (By considering the current in ACB reversed in direction, we obtain the corresponding result, $f(0) = 0$.) Substituting for $f(\pi)$ in equation (49), we now have

$$H \sin \alpha = \frac{\beta'}{r'} \int_0^\alpha f(\theta)\, d\theta \qquad (50)$$

or, in respect of measurements made at a constant distance r',

$$\frac{d(H \sin \alpha)}{d\alpha} = \frac{\beta'}{r'} f(\alpha) \qquad (51)$$

Equation (51) shows how, from sufficiently accurate relative measurements of H, over a range of values of α from 0 to $\frac{\pi}{2}$, it is possible to deduce the form of $f(\alpha)$—the angular dependence function which we postulated in our assumptions. Biot and Savart, though they did not analyse their experimental results in precisely this way, satisfied themselves that, writing $\sin \theta$ for $f(\theta)$ in equation (50), they could describe them with considerable accuracy. They found that, in the arrangement of fig. 17, the field at P varied as $1/r'$ when α was constant, and as $\tan \alpha/2$ when r' was constant, as nearly as they could determine—and it will be obvious that, with $f(\theta) = \sin \theta$, this is precisely the variation which equation (50) would predict.

We have now shown that the assumptions which we adopted at the beginning are capable of providing the basis for a self-consistent analysis of the resultant intensity due to an infinite straight current-carrying wire in terms of individual contributions from elementary sections of the wire. We have not shown that this is the only set of assumptions on the basis of which such a result could be achieved; thus we have not proved that the final result itself represents a unique solution to our problem. Suffice to say that our assumptions have been in no way artificial—and that in fact the law of Biot and Savart has stood the test of time, becoming merged in a much wider synthesis in the theories of Ampère which were to follow. With these we shall be concerned in the next chapter; here we content ourselves with expressing the present law in its precise form. We may state the law as follows: let P be a point, and at a distance r from P let there be an elementary section QR of a current-carrying conductor, of length ds, and making an angle θ with QP (as shown in fig. 18). Then the current in this element of conductor contributes to the resultant magnetic intensity at P an infinitesimal component the direction of which is perpendicular to the plane PQR and the magnitude of

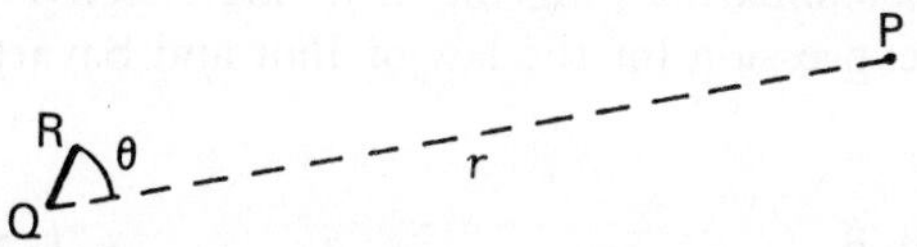

FIGURE 18

which is proportional to $(ds/r^2) \sin \theta$. Our only further comment, in this connection, is that $ds \sin \theta$ is the projection of the length of the current element at right angles to the line QP. Thus, if we write, instead of $(ds/r^2) \sin \theta$,

$$\frac{1}{r^3}(ds \sin \theta \cdot r),$$

we have an expression in which the quantities within the bracket are effectively the magnitudes of two mutually perpendicular vectors (lengths) multiplied together. In this respect the Biot–Savart law involves a vector product (see *M L & T*, p. 177). Now, in many cases, vector products refer essentially to situations involving rotations (in the most general sense): in this case it is the magnetic intensity which 'performs gyrations round the wire', as Oersted originally concluded. Conventionally, we adopt the right-handed screw rule (see *M L & T*, p. 81) to relate the positive direction of the current in the wire to the positive direction of the magnetic intensity at P; this we can do independently of any conventional decision as to what is meant by the positive direction of the current. As a matter of history, 'positive' electricity was identified with the 'vitreous' electricity of du Fay (see pp. 9, 18), and, consonant with this identification, positive current in the external circuit of Volta's pile flows from the copper to the zinc.

As soon as he began to consider the implications of Oersted's discovery, Ampère realised that in the couple experienced by a pivoted compass needle, when an electric current is passed through a loop of wire coplanar with the needle (and its axis of rotation), there is the basis for a practicable method of current measurement. Previously, no such method had been available. The word 'galvanometer', which we now use for a current-measuring instrument embodying this basic idea, dates in fact from 1820: it was introduced into the vocabulary of physics in the course of the paper which Ampère presented to the Academy of Sciences on 18 September of that year. If, with such an instrument, we decide to measure the current in the wire in terms of the couple experienced by the needle in a standard arrangement, we are effectively completing the formal expression for the law of Biot and Savart, giving it the form

$$dH = \gamma'' i \frac{ds}{r^2} \sin \theta \qquad (52)$$

Here i is the measure of the current (in some units which we need not now specify) and γ'' is a (possibly dimensional) constant.

We introduced the discussions of this section (p. 68) by speaking of an electric current as a flow of charge. This notion was entertained by all the investigators, of the late eighteenth and early nineteenth centuries, whose work we have been considering. Moreover, by the time of which we are now writing it had been abundantly shown that there is no essential difference between the effects produced in, and in the neighbourhood of, a wire, when it is employed, on the one hand, to connect the coatings of a Leyden jar charged with 'frictional' electricity or, on the other, to connect the poles of a voltaic pile. Only, the effects are transient effects in the former case, and persistent effects in the latter. Thus the way was indeed open for a theory of the electric current as a transfer of charge. However, the original 'fluid' theories of electricity (see p. 19) were still so much in vogue that it did not occur to anyone to follow this idea to its logical conclusion, and to think in terms of the motion of discrete units of electricity rather than of the flow of a continuous electric fluid. It was not until 1846 that a suggestion made in the previous year by Gustav Theodor Fechner (1801-1887) was worked out in detail by W. E. Weber (see *V & W*, p. 263), who had succeeded Fechner in the chair of

physics at Leipzig in 1843.* Fechner's was a two-stream hypothesis. He had supposed that every current consists of oppositely
directed streams of discrete charges of positive and negative electricity: later, Weber had given this hypothesis mathematical form
and precision. Nowadays, we are convinced that a one-stream
hypothesis is nearer to physical reality (the discrete charges in
motion in a metal wire being, as we believe, negative electrons—
see chap. 7): here, therefore, we comment briefly on equation (52)
from this modern viewpoint.

Suppose that our metallic conductor is a cylindrical wire of
cross-sectional area A, the material of which contains n discrete
charge-carriers per unit volume. Let e be the magnitude of the
charge on each carrier, and suppose that, when a current i is
flowing in the wire, the streaming-velocity of the carriers is v.
Then

$$i = Anev.$$

If the number of carriers in a length ds of wire is dN, clearly

$$dN = An\,ds,$$

and equation (52) may be rewritten

$$dH = \gamma'' \frac{ev}{r^2} \sin \theta \,.\, dN \tag{53}$$

According to equation (53) it appears that each single carrier, of
charge e, moving with velocity v through the element of wire QR
represented in fig. 18, contributes at the external point P its own
component of magnetic field intensity of magnitude

$$\gamma'' \frac{ev}{r^2} \sin \theta.$$

Here we have penetrated as far as is possible, at this stage, into
the physical significance of the empirical law of Biot and Savart
We may merely note, in conclusion, that if we re-state our result
in the alternative form

$$\gamma'' \frac{e}{r^3} (v \sin \theta \,.\, r)$$

* Fechner had held the chair since 1834, but had resigned through failing
eyesight. Subsequently, he achieved even wider recognition as an experimental
psychologist than he had done as a professor of physics.

we again have an expression in which the quantities within the bracket refer essentially to a vector product (cf. p. 79), only in this case the vector quantities involved are a length and a velocity, rather than two lengths.

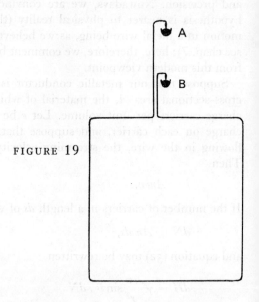

FIGURE 19

Hitherto, we have been speaking exclusively of the action of a current in a wire on a magnetic needle in its vicinity. From the first, in discussing Oersted's experiments, Ampère referred to 'the mutual action of a current-carrying wire and a magnet'. His intuition in this respect was unerring, and he was quick to devise experiments by which his anticipations were verified. Forming a loop of wire into a rectangle, as illustrated in fig. 19, he provided his loop with connecting elements which dipped into mercury cups A and B arranged one above the other along a vertical axis. The connecting element dipping into the one cup was terminated in a sharp steel point which, in the conical cup, served as a pivot and bearing for the whole system. The other connecting element dipped into the other cup without touching the bottom. The mechanical balance of the wire loop having been finely adjusted, connections were made through the mercury cups with the poles of a voltaic cell. Then a bar magnet was brought up into a position parallel to the lower horizontal side of the rectangular loop—and the whole loop was observed to turn about its vertical axis, to take up a position at right angles to the length of the magnet. Reversing the current in the loop (or turning the magnet through 180° about the vertical axis) resulted in a reversal of direction of deflection of the loop. By taking particular precautions to avoid extraneous effects, Ampère was able to demonstrate that a current-carrying loop suspended as we have just described is orientated in the magnetic field of the earth, as if it were a magnet having its axis permanently at right angles to the plane of the loop. Having demonstrated this result, he was led to suggest—and it is not surprising in view of his discoveries as a whole (see § 3.2)—that there is no such thing as magnetism *sui generis*, only 'voltaic' currents circulating in closed loops in planes at right angles to the axis of a magnetised body. We shall have more to say of this suggestion in a later chapter (see p. 455)—here, in order to clarify our ideas, we confine attention to one particular aspect of it, only. We calculate the magnetic field intensity, at large distances from a small rectangular current-carrying loop, at points (i) along the axis of the loop, (ii) in the plane of the loop.

Let ABCD be a rectangular conducting loop, centred at the origin O (fig. 20) and lying in the plane XOY. Let i be the measure of the current in the loop, and let P, P' be points in OX, OZ, respectively, distant d from O. Let BA $= 2a$, CB $= 2b$, and suppose that $d \gg a, b$. Under these conditions we may apply equation (52) to each of the four sides of the current-carrying loop in turn, and so calculate the magnetic field intensity at P (or P') as the resultant of four elementary components.

For the field at P' (a point on the axis of the loop), the elementary component corresponding to the current in AB is directed at right angles to the line joining P' to the mid-point of AB, clockwise in the plane YOZ. Its magnitude is $2\gamma''ia/(d^2+b^2)$. This is also the magnitude of the component corresponding to the current in CD, which is correspondingly directed (anticlockwise) in the quadrant Y'OZ. Combining these two components, we have a contribution to the axial intensity (in the direction OZ) of magnitude

$$\frac{4\gamma''ia}{d^2+b^2} \cdot \frac{b}{(d^2+b^2)^{\frac{1}{2}}}.$$

Likewise, combining the elementary component intensities at P'

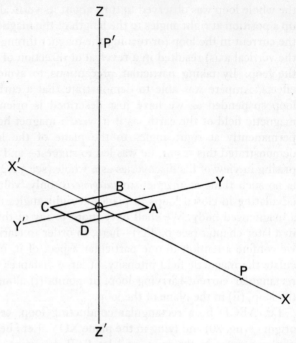

FIGURE 20

corresponding to the currents in BC and DA, we obtain a contribution of magnitude

$$\frac{4\gamma''iab}{(d^2+a^2)^{\frac{3}{2}}}$$

to the axial intensity at P′. When $d \gg a, b$, as we have supposed, these two contributions are essentially equal in magnitude, and, if we write H_e for the magnitude of the resultant magnetic field intensity at P′, we have, simply,

$$H_e = \frac{8\gamma''iab}{d^3},$$

or $\qquad H_e = \dfrac{2\gamma''iS}{d^3}$ $\qquad\qquad(54)$

where $S(=4ab)$ represents the area of the loop ABCD.

Proceeding in the same way, in respect of the resultant intensity at P (of magnitude H_b), we note, first of all, that the directions of all four elementary component intensities are at right angles to the plane XOY. In particular, each of the components corresponding to the currents in AB and CD is directed parallel to OZ, and each is of magnitude

$$\frac{2\gamma''ia}{d^2+b^2} \cdot \frac{b}{(d^2+b^2)^{\frac{1}{2}}};$$

the component corresponding to the current in BC is directed parallel to OZ and is of magnitude

$$\frac{2\gamma''ib}{(d+a)^2};$$

finally, the component corresponding to the current in DA is directed parallel to OZ' and is of magnitude

$$\frac{2\gamma''ib}{(d-a)^2}.$$

On this basis we have

$$H_b = 2\gamma''ib\left\{\frac{1}{(d-a)^2} - \frac{1}{(d+a)^2} - \frac{2a}{(d^2+b^2)^{\frac{3}{2}}}\right\},$$

or, making the same approximation as before,

$$H_b = \frac{4\gamma''iab}{d^3},$$

that is $\quad H_b = \frac{\gamma''iS}{d^3}$ \hfill (55)

The results that we have just obtained (equations (54) and (55)) show that, at large distances from a rectangular current-carrying loop, the resultant magnetic field intensities along the axis and in the plane of the loop are anti-parallel, and that, at equal distances, the magnitude of the former intensity is twice that of the latter. These are precisely the results that would obtain (see equations (43) and (44)) if the current-carrying loop were replaced by a magnetic doublet centred at O and having its axis along Z'OZ, and in this respect the loop and the doublet would be completely equivalent if M, the dipole moment of the doublet, were given, in terms of the current in the loop and its area, by the expression

$$M = \frac{\gamma''}{\gamma'} iS \qquad (56)$$

More detailed calculations show that, equation (56) being satisfied, the equivalence of current-carrying loop and doublet holds good throughout the whole of the space surrounding them (provided that the condition $d \gg a$, b is fulfilled)—and that, indeed, the equivalence holds good whatever the shape of the loop (provided that it is planar).

In this section, our treatment has been largely historical—and in particular, we have been concerned with the history of a few months in Paris in the autumn of 1820. Possibly, then, an historical postscript, inessential though it is to our main theme, may not be entirely uninstructive.

On 30 October 1820, having listened to the paper presented by M. Biot, the Académie des Sciences proceeded to ballot for the vacant place of 'correspondent' in the Physical Section of that body. On the previous Monday the list of six candidates chosen by the Section had been presented to the meeting. Oersted was one of the six nominees. In the upshot, when the result of the ballot was announced, 'M. Leslie, of Edinburgh' was declared elected by 33 votes out of 37.

John Leslie (1766-1832) had been an Edinburgh professor since 1805 (see *M L & T*, p. 336); first, professor of mathematics, and then, from 1819, professor of natural philosophy. He had already received the Rumford medal of the Royal Society of London for his *Experimental Inquiry into the Nature and Properties of Heat* (1804). He had also been a contributor to the sixth edition of the *Encyclopaedia Britannica*—and, when preparatory work on the seventh edition was begun in 1827, he was commissioned to write the last of four 'dissertations' which, collected together in the first volume of that publication, were to provide 'a general map of the various departments of human knowledge'. The realisation of this ambitious prolegomenon was incomplete when the volume went to press, but two dissertations covering certain aspects of philosophy, and two dealing with the progress of mathematical and physical science, were assembled. Of these latter two, the first was from the pen of John Playfair (1748-1819), whom Leslie succeeded, first in one university chair and then in another, the second was

Leslie's own. Playfair had followed the history of the matter to the end of the epoch of Newton and Leibnitz; Leslie was concerned chiefly with the eighteenth century. But the eighteenth century did not wholly contain him, and in prose of elaborate contrivance he attempted to bring his survey up-to-date. In section 4 (Magnetism) he wrote 'The remarkable discovery of Oerstedt has greatly enlarged the field of magnetic influence. A wire of any kind of metal being laid horizontally and at right angles [sic] to the magnetic meridian, to connect the opposite conductors of a Galvanic battery, a needle either below or above it is drawn considerably to the one side or the other. Instead of bewildering the imagination with the vagaries of invisible streams, a sufficient explication of the phenomena may be deduced from two leading principles:— 1. Magnetism is in some proportion diffused through all metallic substances, owing either to their peculiar constitution or the universal dissemination of ferruginous molecules: 2. The cross wire, from its position with regard to the Terrestrial Magnet, acquires induced magnetism, but extending transversely; the under side having the virtue of a north pole, and the upper side that of a south pole. The copious infusion of that virtue is occasioned probably by the duration of the internal tremor, excited by intense electrical action, and analogous to the effects on a bar of iron or steel subjected to hammering, twisting, heating, or the fulminating shock. Hence are easily explained the diversified phases of attraction, rotation, or impressed magnetism.'

Our quotation hardly needs comment—but that the title-page of the dissertation should describe its author as 'Corresponding Member of the Royal Institute of France', in the circumstances savours of imposture: the eminent professor cannot have profited much, over a period of seven years, from his scientific contacts with the savants of the Academy!

CHAPTER 3

PRECISION IN THE MATTER OF UNITS

3.1. INTRODUCTORY

One of the most important tasks of the physicist is the framing of 'concepts which do not derive directly from common sense' (*M L & T*, p. 3). In the reference quoted, the rules which should govern this process are set out in some detail. It will be advantageous here to make a brief abstract of them. First, then, '[the physicist] will not introduce any such concept unless from its adoption there issues the possibility of measurement . . .'. Secondly, 'he will not introduce a new concept unless his consideration of observations already made forces it on his attention'. At our present level of discussion, therefore, a concept is valueless unless it is represented by a physical quantity, the magnitude of which, in a practical situation, can be deduced from experiment and so given expression in terms of a number (measure) and a unit. 'The introduction of new concepts will involve definitions —qualitative definitions, and quantitative definitions relating to the measurement which the concepts imply' (*ibid.*). When the quantitative definitions take the form of algebraic expressions connecting the measures of the different physical quantities significant in a particular class of situations, then, clearly, not more than one new unit can be defined by each such expression—and, equally clearly, definition in such a case being in terms of other units previously defined, the new unit can properly be referred to as a 'derived' unit (see *M L & T*, pp. 31, 64). But all units cannot be so derived. There must be some 'primary' or 'fundamental' units.

For a large part of physics, experience has shown that it is both necessary and sufficient to accept the units of three physical quantities as fundamental. Formally, a fairly wide range of choice is open, but by common consent the three units chosen are those of mass, length and time. On the basis of this choice the whole of macroscopic physics, leaving aside electric and magnetic phenomena at the macroscopic level, can be dealt with conceptually with entire success. In making this claim, we should enter, perhaps, a faint reservation concerning the concept of temperature, but that would be all. With that reservation, and within the limits specified, we can apply the method of dimensional analysis to our problems (see, for example, $M\ L\ \&\ T$, pp. 259-62), admitting only three 'exponents of dimension', those associated with the three units that we have chosen as fundamental.

When electric and magnetic phenomena are in question, when we are framing our rudimentary concepts of electric charge, magnetic dipole moment, electric current, and the rest, we cannot, however, make do with the system that we have described. Intuitively, we come to the conclusion that electrification, for example, cannot be described in terms of the 'massiness' of bodies, or elementary constituents of bodies, acting in space and time (gravitational phenomena are so described)—and, if we attempt to force our observations into this framework of description, formal difficulties inevitably appear. Some of these difficulties have been briefly exhibited in another place ($V\ \&\ W$, p. 259). If we override our intuition, and naïvely suppose that equation (2) (p. 18) represents all the factors which determine the mechanical force arising from the electrification of two particles of matter, we reach the conclusion that the physical quantity 'charge of electricity' is measurable in terms of a unit having dimensions $M^{\frac{1}{2}}L^{\frac{3}{2}}T^{-1}$—that is, in terms of a unit entirely 'mechanical' in character. If we pay heed to our intuition, we look to the possibility of introducing some other 'electrical' quantity (that is some quantity other than electric charge) into the equation. This we did, as a matter of prudence, so as to secure generality, when we introduced Gauss's theorem on the basis of equation (3) (p. 21). If Coulomb's law is written

$$F = \gamma \frac{q_1 q_2}{r^2},$$

where γ is a quantity 'the magnitude of which . . . may depend upon the medium in which the particles are located', then the corresponding dimensional conclusion,

$$[\gamma q^2] = M^1 L^3 T^{-2} \tag{57}$$

arouses no undue suspicion: the unit of charge, and the unit of the quantity represented by γ, can each be such that a purely

EM G

mechanical prescription is inadequate for it, but that does not rule out the prescription which equation (57) requires for the unit of the 'composite' quantity which γq^2 represents.

We have here been exploring the alternatives of following our not-yet-rationalised 'feeling' for the essential physics of a situation —or disregarding it, and venturing no farther than the empirical knowledge of the time allows (a choice which frequently confronts the researcher): in the present context it is merely to record historical fact to say that the quantity γ was introduced into the expression for Coulomb's law, not on the basis of any 'hunch' of a theorist, but, more than fifty years after the law had first been enunciated, as an empirical result, by Michael Faraday, prince of experimenters (see p. 117).

We are agreed, then, that over and above the three fundamental units of mass, length and time, at least one other such unit is required before a satisfactory system of measurement of electric and magnetic quantities becomes possible. If, for example, we were to choose the unit of charge as fundamental, defining unit charge so that two such charges in vacuum at unit separation interacted with unit force, then, on the basis of our modified Coulomb's law, we should conclude that the measure of γ for free space was unity, and that the dimensions of this unit were $M^1L^3T^{-2}Q^{-2}$, Q representing the unit of charge in this notation. In fact, this is not the most satisfactory choice of fundamental unit. The phenomenon on which it is based, the repulsion of elementary charges of the same sign, is a purely electrostatic phenomenon: it would appear much more appropriate that we should base our fundamental definition on a phenomenon in which both electric and magnetic features appear—for our aim is nothing less than the development of a system of measurement equally applicable in these two fields.

At first sight, the criticism that we have just brought against the adoption of the unit of charge as a fundamental unit might appear equally valid when directed against the choice of unit magnetic pole as fundamental. Historically, the subjects of electrostatics and magnetostatics developed independently, the one of the other, and the interaction of two poles, as seen in that context, is an entirely magnetostatic interaction. However, we must not forget Ampère's speculative conclusion (p. 83) that there is no such thing as magnetism *sui generis*—only electric current flowing in elementary circuits in material that is magnetised. If there is truth in this speculation, our criticism loses much of its cogency. Yet, we reject this possible choice, also—but on another count entirely. An isolated magnetic pole is a theoretical fiction (see p. 62): to adopt a physical situation as basic which is essentially unrealisable in practice (the mutual presentation of isolated poles in vacuum) is surely unsatisfactory, when the aim is to develop a system of precise measurement for practical use.

Ampère's ideas regarding magnetisation might be dismissed as pure speculation—though they merit more respect than this, as we shall later discover (see p. 456)—but they arose out of his consideration of Oersted's experiments, and they were not seriously maintained until he had himself discovered the mechanical force which is developed between two neighbouring conductors when each is traversed by an electric current. The forces between magnets may not arise simply in this way, but two current-carrying loops certainly exert a force, one on the other, and the effect is indubitably 'electromagnetic' in character. No criticism of basic impracticability can be brought against the definition of a fundamental unit which uses this effect for purposes of measurement: indeed it has much to commend it. Without further ado, therefore, we shall proceed to consider the physical phenomenon of the 'force between currents', and to show how it provides a satisfactory basis for the definition of the fourth fundamental unit (of electric current), which, taken together with the units of mass, length and time, affords an adequate ground for the development of a thoroughgoing system of measurement of electric and magnetic quantities generally.

3.2. FORCES BETWEEN CURRENTS

Ampère demonstrated 'the mutual action of two voltaic currents' before the Académie des Sciences for the first time on Monday, 25 September 1820 (here we take up the history of the hundred-and-fifty days at the point where we left it on p. 83). It was only three weeks since Arago had first reported Oersted's discovery (see p. 73), and already on the previous Monday Ampère had addressed the Academy, telling them of his newly developed views on the nature of magnetisation and of the many experiments he had in mind to perform in order to test his assumptions. In these circumstances it is perhaps natural that Ampère's first demonstration of the mutual action of two currents should have been made with long, slender coils of wire, so formed as to simulate, in some degree at least, the character of magnetised needles. Then, at the session of the Academy on 9 October, 'M. Ampère showed [by experiment] that two rectilinear currents behave in the same way as the currents in spiral wires that he had used on 25 September'.

Ampère's 'theoretical' ideas raced ahead of his experimental investigations—even though he did not deny himself the time to keep his colleagues thoroughly informed of their progress, as the weeks passed by. As we have seen, he made communications to the meetings of the Academy on 18 and 25 September, and on 9 October. He also spoke on 2 and 30 October, on 6 November, and on 4, 11 and 26 December (Christmas Day 1820 fell on a Monday, but there was a meeting on the day following—and, as it would seem, a quorum of auditors). As early as 9 October he outlined 'the method he proposed to follow in calculating the actions of two finite electric currents, once the experiments on which he is now engaged have disclosed the law of attraction and repulsion for indefinitely small lengths of such currents'. In the upshot, the matter was not to be determined as summarily as the enthusiasm of the early days gave hope for. Ampère's definitive theoretical *Mémoire* was not published until 1825, and his *Théorie des phénomènes électro-dynamiques* not until November 1826. After that date, however, for a quarter of a century, 'no one paid much attention to this branch of electricity, in which it appeared that nothing further remained to be done' (A. A. de la Rive, *Traité d'électricité*, 1854).

In one respect, the details of Ampère's investigations have little more than historical interest, at this remove of time, for the expression which he finally deduced for the force between two current elements is now superseded (though it gives the correct result when integrated over a closed circuit carrying a constant current). In another respect, however, they are as important now as they were originally. Ampère was investigating a complex phenomenon in a previously unexplored field of fundamental physics, and his method of approach was novel and of great subtlety and penetration. It was as if, de la Rive pointed out, in this particular field, one man had set himself to do what, independently, Kepler and Newton had done for the phenomenon of universal gravitation. In that case, Kepler had elicited the empirical regu-

larities, Newton had discerned the 'law of nature' which under-
lay them. Ampère was resolved to do both, for the large-scale
phenomena of electrodynamics.

The empirical regularities for which Ampère first sought, by
most ingenious experiments, were of the nature of hardly-more-
than-qualitative generalisations. Of two such generalisations he
had convinced himself within three months of starting work on
the subject in September 1820; to these he eventually added a
third, and before he finally gave precision to his theory, in 1825,
a fourth. We may express Ampère's four 'statements of equilibrium' as follows:

(i) if a straight wire carrying a current is bent back on
itself at its mid-point, so that the two portions of the wire
are parallel and indefinitely close together, then the double
current-carrying conductor so formed exerts no action on
any portion of an exterior circuit;

(ii) if a straight wire carrying a current is bent back on
itself at a point other than its mid-point, and the longer
portion is coiled up in any arbitrary fashion, so that it
matches the shorter portion in overall length and is nowhere by more than a little distant from it, then the double
current-carrying conductor so formed exerts no action on
any portion of an exterior circuit;

(iii) if current is flowing in a conductor having the form of
a circular arc, and if this conductor is free to move only in
its own plane around its centre of curvature, then it shows
no tendency so to move when it is acted on by an exterior
current-carrying circuit in the form of a closed loop of
arbitrary shape;

(iv) if the same current flows through three geometrically
similar circuits, A, B and C, and if the circuits are so disposed that the system formed by A and B together is geometrically similar to that formed by B and C together, then,
the circuits A and C being fixed, and B free to move, the
circuit B remains in equilibrium under the joint action of
the other two.

Obviously, no single experiment, carried out in relation to a particular situation, can establish that an action is precisely zero in
magnitude (compare our discussion of Cavendish's experiment,
p. 15, and the deduction of the law of force between charges

from its empirically null result); nor can general statements such as Ampère's be accepted as universally valid on the basis of a finite number of experiments of this kind. The statements were, rather, intuitively apprehended in the light of limited experiment, but they were of the type of statement for which Ampère was searching—just as Kepler's laws (see *M L & T*, §7.2) exemplified the type of mathematical regularity which he believed that the motions of the planets must surely exhibit. In each case the intuition of genius was undeniably fruitful. Newton discovered the inverse-square law of gravitation implicit in the empirical regularities of Kepler (*M L & T*, §§7.3 and 10.2), and Ampère himself extracted a significant law from his own statements of equilibrium which only narrowly failed to go to the heart of the matter. We shall not follow Ampère in detail through the steps of his mathematical analysis, but some comment on his statements will certainly be profitable.

From the point of view of the twentieth century, Ampère's first statement may appear entirely trivial. To the physicist accustomed to regard an electric current as a uni-directional flow of charge (electrons) it would appear self-evident that equal and opposite streams in essentially the same linear conductor can exert no external action (after all, even when the circuit is broken, and there is no 'current' in the conductor, the charge-carriers, if they take part in the general thermal motion, have, in any element of the conductor and at any time, velocities which are just as likely to be in one direction or the other parallel to the axis of the conductor). However, in Ampère's day the notion of an electric current was novel, and still ill-defined (see p. 80). Ampère, himself, inclined to the view that there was movement of electricity in each direction (positive charge in one direction and negative in the other), but de la Rive, writing thirty years later, commented more cautiously: 'Following what is admittedly a mere convention, Ampère has assumed that this current has a direction—that it leaves the positive pole [of the voltaic pile] to traverse the conductor, arrive at the negative pole, and return through the pile to its point of origin, the positive pole. . . . For the rest, nothing establishes the fact that this direction is the true direction of the current, or even that the movement of electricity takes the form of a current. We repeat: it is no more than a convention, a convenient way of describing a physical phenomenon. . . .' It was, therefore, in 1825, a non-trivial conclusion, that the effects of equal and oppositely directed steady 'currents' in a linear conductor cancel at all exterior points.

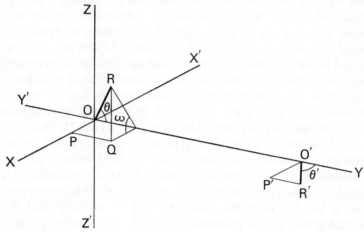

FIGURE 21

Ampère's second statement of equilibrium is more readily acceptable as non-trivial. Taken together with the first, it implies that the ordinary law of resolution of vectors (the so-called parallelogram law) is applicable in relation to the interaction of current elements. If OR (fig. 21) is an element of a conducting circuit, of length ds and carrying a current i, and O'R' an element of another such circuit, of length ds' and carrying a current i', then, in relation to the figure as drawn (where, without loss of generality, O'R' is assumed to lie in the plane XOY), the mutual action of the two current elements can be decomposed into the six components representing the mutual actions of the three sub-elements OP, PQ, QR (each carrying a current i) and the two sub-elements O'P', P'R' (each carrying a current i'). We shall return to this figure, from time to time, as our discussion proceeds.

To comment on Ampère's third statement (necessary as it was for the development of his analytical argument) would take us too far from our purpose, but his fourth statement is of direct and simple relevance. Ampère assumed, as basic for his calculations, that the mutual action of two current elements is always proportional to the product of the lengths of the elements of conductor concerned. (He also assumed that such mutual action is proportional to the product of the corresponding current strengths—though that assumption is irrelevant in the present context.) His fourth statement, in our version lengthy only because it was intentionally cast in the form of a statement of equilibrium, may be expressed more tersely as follows: 'In geometrically similar systems, traversed by a given current, corresponding forces are equal.' We see at once that this statement implies (or, at least, would follow from the assumption) that the force between current elements is proportional to the inverse square of their distance of separation. In similar systems corresponding lengths bear a constant ratio; only if $n = 2$ would $ds\, ds'/r^n$ be the same for two such systems. In this connection, in relation to fig. 21, $OO' = r$.

We have traversed Ampère's exploration of his problem, so far, without committing ourselves to his cardinal assumption—an assumption which in the end proved to be unnecessary, and which, in retrospect, is seen as the root cause of his failure to provide a wholly acceptable solution. Ampère assumed that the mutual action of two current elements always consists of a pair of equal forces, oppositely directed along the line joining the centres of the elements. On this basis he concluded that four of the six component actions which we have identified with the help of fig. 21 are identically zero. Having reduced his problem in this way, Ampère eventually concluded that the magnitude of the force between the two current elements represented in the figure (fig. 21) is, in appropriate units,

$$\frac{i\, i'\, ds\, ds'}{r^2} (\sin\theta \sin\theta' \cos\omega - \tfrac{1}{2}\cos\theta \cos\theta').$$

In this expression—and as indicated in the figure—θ and θ' are the angles between the individual current elements and the line joining their centres, and ω is the angle between the two planes which, intersecting in the line joining the elements, contain, respectively, the one element and the other. It may be noted that this particular formulation, whether or not it provides a solution of the basic problem which is acceptable on all counts, is open to criticism, 'internally', in that when the value of either θ or θ' is zero (or π), the value of ω is indeterminate. For this reason an alternative formulation using ϕ, the angle between the directions of the two current elements, instead of ω, is preferable. Since

$$\cos\phi = \sin\theta \cos\omega \sin\theta' + \cos\theta \cos\theta',$$

the preferred formulation of Ampère's expression becomes

$$\frac{i\,i'\,ds\,ds'}{r^2}\left(\cos\phi - \tfrac{3}{2}\cos\theta\cos\theta'\right).$$

It has been said that Ampère reduced the six component actions identified on the basis of fig. 21 to two—thereby simplifying his problem. As illustrating the kind of argument which may legitimately be made in this connection, consider the mutual action of two elements, 1 and 2, centred at O and O′ (fig. 21), the first directed along Z′OZ and the second along OY (these elements are not actually drawn in the figure). Suppose, as Ampère did, that the force exerted by element 1 on element 2 acts along OY. Imagine the physical system to be rotated through 180° about Y′OY. Then an observer must still report a finite component of force acting from element 1 on element 2 in the direction OY. But, looking at the system as a whole, the observer might justifiably say that the net effect of the rotation could have been achieved if the direction of the current in element 1 had simply been reversed, while that of the current in element 2 had been left unchanged. According to Ampère's first statement of equilibrium (or the deduction from it) this should have had the result of changing the direction of the force on element 2. Clearly, these two estimates of the situation are irreconcilable, unless the original assumption of a finite force along OY is abandoned.

As we have seen, there were two independent investigations going forward in Paris, in the last months of 1820: both stemmed from the discovery of Oersted, and both were of great importance. Biot and Savart had set themselves the direct task of elucidating the phenomenon of the action of a current on a magnet which Oersted had discovered; Ampère had discovered another phenomenon and had himself embarked on its elucidation. More ambitiously, being convinced that magnetisation was no more than a manifestation of electric currents established in elementary circuits throughout the material magnetised, Ampère was seeking to formulate a theoretical description which would be equally valid as an 'explanation' of Oersted's experimental discovery and his own. We have now sketched the history of both these investigations. We recorded how Biot and Savart successfully concluded their analysis of the action of a current on a magnet within a matter of four months, whereas Ampère, in the end, took five years to provide what appeared to be a satisfactory theoretical description of the mutual action of two currents. In each case the basic element in the formulation could be considered as a mathematical statement of a law of force. In the law of Biot and Savart the statement gives, in effect, the force experienced by an elementary magnetic pole situated in the neighbourhood of a current element (see equation (52)); in Ampère's law the statement relates to the force experienced by one current element situated in the neighbourhood of another. When we express the matter in this way we are, somewhat artificially, stressing the similarities of the two results. In fact, Ampère totally disregarded the analysis of Biot and Savart; in the full conviction of the correctness of his own approach to the physical problem, he put on one side any consideration of the action of a current on a magnet until he should have elicited, first, the law of action of one current on another. And he set himself to do this in the most obvious way which would ensure that the laws of Newtonian mechanics were respected. He set himself to construct a system in which the mutual interaction of current elements was, by assumption, of the form of equal and oppositely directed forces acting along the line joining the centres of the elements. Biot and Savart, on the other hand, were inhibited by no such over-riding concern for the Newtonian scheme. They were perfectly content to accept, at its face value, Oersted's conclusion that 'the conflict performs gyrations round the wire' (p. 72), and they set themselves the limited task of deriving a mathematical formula by which the intensity of this (transverse) 'conflict' could be calculated in terms of infinitesimal (transverse) components ascribable to the current in successive elements of the current-carrying wire. Because they accepted the phenomenological description of the object on which the 'conflict' operated, aspiring to no deep understanding of the nature of magnetisation, Biot and Savart identified Oersted's 'conflict' as a magnetic field—and their theory became essentially a field theory. The effect on the magnet was given in terms of the magnetic field intensity in its neighbourhood: the current-carrying conductor was at one stage farther removed; its disposition, and the strength of the current flowing in it, determined the magnetic field intensity —that was all. By contrast, Ampère's formulation of the force between current elements carried no implication of physical process, the force which it described was an action at a distance, as inscrutable as the force of gravitation described by the formula of Newton. Only, Ampère's formula, in its details, involving angles as well as distances, was even more 'mysterious' than Newton's.

When the suspicion began to take root, among men of science, that Ampère's formula was not, perhaps, the only one which would describe adequately the mutual actions of current-carrying conductors in the various dispositions in which they could, in fact, be investigated experimentally (the interactions of ideal current elements could not be so investigated), there was a general inclination in many quarters to pay attention to the properties of the medium and to think in physical rather than formal terms concerning the forces operating between one material system and another.

From this point of view let us look at the law of Biot and Savart again, paying attention now to the force acting from the magnetic pole on the current element, rather than *vice versa*. As we have seen (p. 82), Ampère was quick to show, by direct experiment, that there is such a force, since a suitably suspended current-carrying wire tends to set at right angles to the axis of a permanent magnet brought into its vicinity. In the ideal situation represented by fig. 18 (p. 79), we have seen that the force acting on a magnetic pole at P is given by

$$\gamma'' m i \frac{ds}{r^2} \sin \theta,$$

m being the strength of the pole (see equation (52)). If the direction of the current i is from Q to R in the element QR, then this force acts away from the reader and in a direction perpendicular to the plane of the figure through P. Now the intensity of magnetic field at Q due to the pole at P is $\gamma' m / r^2$. If we write H_m for this quantity then an alternative expression for the force on the pole at P is

$$\frac{\gamma''}{\gamma'} H_m i \, ds \sin \theta.$$

Our intention is to relate the force on the current element QR to some attribute of the magnetic field in its neighbourhood. We examine the possibility that the force is in fact equal in magnitude and opposite in direction to the force on the pole at P in the situation that we are discussing. This assumption does not fulfil the Newtonian condition as obviously as the assumption on which Ampère based his analysis: taking the system of the pole and the current element together, we are postulating, not a pair of oppositely directed equal and collinear forces as Ampère postulated in the case of two current elements, but a pair of equal and oppositely directed parallel forces constituting a couple. At this elementary level, clearly, we have not satisfied the Newtonian condition: we are offering a hostage to fortune, gambling on the chance that in the outcome, when real, finite systems are involved (rather than idealised elements of current, and isolated poles) the conservation laws will be found to apply. Suppose, then, that in the situation represented by fig. 18 the force on the element QR is perpendicular to the plane of the figure, towards the reader, through the mid-point of the element and of magnitude

$$\frac{\gamma''}{\gamma'} H_m \, i \, ds \sin \theta.$$

Let us re-write this expression in the form

$$i(ds \, . \, \sin \theta \, . \, B_m),$$

in this way effectively defining a new vector quantity associated with the magnetic field intensity H according to the general specification

$$B = \frac{\gamma''}{\gamma'} H \tag{58}$$

and emphasising the fact that on our present assumption the force on the current element of fig. 18 is given by the vector product of ids and B (see p. 79, noting that $\sin \theta = \sin (\pi - \theta)$). That the force should be directed along the normal to the plane containing the current-carrying element QR and the direction of B at its mid-point is, of course, implicit in the last statement—and it is, indeed, the assumption from which we started.

The physical quantity represented by our new vector B is referred to as the 'magnetic induction' or the 'magnetic flux density' at a point in the field. By definition (equation (58)) B has the same direction as the magnetic field intensity H, in an isotropic medium, but because we anticipate that the multiplying factor γ''/γ' is the magnitude of a dimensional quantity characteristic of the medium (see pp. 67, 80) we conceive of the magnetic induction as distinct, physically, from the field intensity. It will be noted that we have previously identified two similarly related but physically distinct quantities (E and D—see p. 22) in respect of the electrostatic field.

Our introduction of a new quantity, the magnetic induction, through consideration of the special case of the interaction of an ideal current element and an isolated pole would not make sense unless we were prepared to carry forward our assumption, and to assert, generally, that in all cases the mechanical force dF acting on a current element situated in a magnetic field of whatever origin is given by the expression

$$dF = i(ds \cdot \sin \theta \cdot B) \tag{59}$$

B being the magnitude of the magnetic induction at the centre of the element ds, θ the angle between the direction of B and the direction of the current in the element, and the direction of dF being normal to the plane in which θ is measured—and related to the directions of current and induction as the positive axis of z is conventionally related to the positive axes of x and y, respectively, in a set of right-handed axes. On the basis of equation (59) and with the help of fig. 21 we are now in a position to formulate, for consideration, the alternative to Ampère's expression for the force on one current element due to another. Let us calculate, on this basis, the force on the current-carrying element OR due to the current in O'R' (see p. 95).

For the magnetic field intensity at O due to the current i' in O'R', we have (see equation (52))

$$dH = \gamma'' \frac{i'}{r^3} (ds' \cdot \sin \theta' \cdot r),$$

the direction of this intensity being along OZ'. Thus, for the magnetic induction at O, we obtain (see equation (58))

$$dB = \frac{\gamma''^2}{\gamma'} \frac{i'}{r^3} (ds' \cdot \sin \theta' \cdot r) \tag{60}$$

and for the magnitude of the force on the element OR, the formal result

$$dF = \frac{\gamma''^2}{\gamma'} \frac{ii'}{r^3} \{ ds \cdot \sin \psi \cdot (ds' \cdot \sin \theta' \cdot r) \} \tag{61}$$

where $\angle ZOR = \psi$, and, more particularly, where

$$\sin \psi = (1 - \sin^2 \theta \sin^2 \omega)^{\frac{1}{2}} \qquad (62)$$

In equations (61) and (62) we have the expressions that we are seeking. Remembering that in this case the direction of the magnetic induction dB is along OZ', we may interpret the first of them, as we interpreted equation (59), and conclude that the direction of dF is perpendicular to the plane ORQ (fig. 21), away from O in the quadrant X'OY.

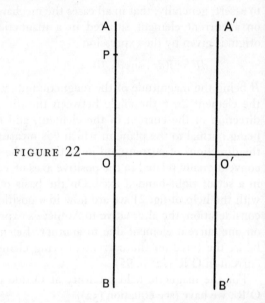

FIGURE 22

As we have calculated the force on the element OR due to the current in O'R', we may similarly calculate the force on O'R' due to the current in OR. A little consideration will show that in the general case represented in the figure this second force is neither equal to the former in magnitude nor is it in a direction parallel (and opposed) to the direction of that force. We disregard this somewhat disturbing result (persisting with the 'gamble' to which we are committed—see p. 100), and concentrate attention on a situation of simple symmetry in which it does not emerge. With the help of fig. 22 we consider the ideal case of two parallel infinite wires in which currents i, i' flow in the same direction. In the figure, OO' is a common perpendicular to the two wires, portions of which are represented by AB, A'B'. The directions of current flow is assumed to be from B to A (and B' to A'). We wish to calculate the force on an element of A'B' of length ds' centred at O'. We note, in the first place, that there is no force on ds' due to the current in other elements of the wire A'B'. Ideally, (see p. 77) the magnetic field intensity (and therefore the magnetic induction) due to the current in any element of A'B' is zero at O'.

Consider now the force on ds' due to the current i in an element of AB of length ds centred at P. Let $OO' = r$, $\angle PO'O = \alpha$, then, adapting equation (60) to give the magnitude of the magnetic induction at O' due to this current element, we have

$$dB = \frac{\gamma''^2}{\gamma'} \frac{i \, ds \cos \alpha}{r^2 \sec^2 \alpha},$$

and we note that the direction of dB is perpendicular to the plane of the figure, and away from the reader, through O'. In the case that we are considering, $\omega = 0$ (fig. 21), thus $\sin \psi = 1$ (equation (62)), and we have (equation (61))

$$dF = \frac{\gamma''^2}{\gamma'} \frac{ii'}{r^2} \frac{ds \, ds' \cos \alpha}{\sec^2 \alpha}.$$

Now, we may write

$$ds = r \sec^2 \alpha \, d\alpha$$

(compare p. 75), thus

$$dF = \frac{\gamma''^2}{\gamma'} \frac{ii'ds'}{r} \cos \alpha \, d\alpha.$$

—and, since the direction of dF is along O'O, we may obtain the force on ds' due to the current in the whole wire AB by simple integration. This resultant force, which we represent by Tds', is clearly itself directed along O'O, and its magnitude is given by the expression

$$T = \frac{\gamma''^2}{\gamma'} \frac{ii'}{r} \int_{-\pi/2}^{\pi/2} \cos \alpha \, d\alpha,$$

or $$T = \frac{2\gamma''^2}{\gamma'} \frac{ii'}{r} \qquad (63)$$

Obviously, we should have obtained a precisely similar result if we had calculated the force on a current element at O due to the current in the whole wire A′B′. On the basis of the formulation of equations (60), (61) and (62) we therefore conclude that two infinite parallel wires carrying similarly directed currents should exert a mutual attraction one on the other, directly, the magnitude of the force per unit length of either wire being T, as given by equation (63) above.

Our first object is now to show that (once units are correctly specified) we obtain exactly the same result on the basis of Ampère's formulation. Previously (p. 96) we have given Ampère's expression for the mutual force of direct attraction between current elements without precise regard to units. If we re-write that expression (in its general form) as follows

$$dF = \frac{2\gamma''^2}{\gamma'} \frac{ii'\,ds\,ds'}{r^2} (\cos\phi - \tfrac{3}{2}\cos\theta\cos\theta') \tag{64}$$

—the extra initial factor of 2 is necessary, as we shall presently discover—then, in relation to the current elements centred at P and O′, respectively, (fig. 22) we have $\phi = 0$, $\theta = \theta' = \dfrac{\pi}{2} + \alpha$,

and for r in the general expression we must write $r\sec\alpha$. Obviously, with direct forces between current elements, the resultant force on ds' due to the current in the whole wire AB must be directed along O′O, but according to Ampère the force represented by equation (64) acts along O′P. Writing in an extra factor of $\cos\alpha$ to take count of this fact, we finally have, as the contribution to the resultant force on ds' arising from the element ds,

$$\frac{2\gamma''^2}{\gamma'} \frac{ii'\,ds\,ds'}{r^2\sec^2\alpha}(1 - \tfrac{3}{2}\sin^2\alpha)\cos\alpha,$$

and, substituting for ds as before, and integrating, we obtain

$$T = \frac{2\gamma''^2}{\gamma'} \frac{ii'}{r} \int_{-\pi/2}^{\pi/2} (1 - \tfrac{3}{2}\sin^2\alpha)\cos\alpha\,d\alpha$$

$$= \frac{2\gamma''^2}{\gamma'} \frac{ii'}{r},$$

as we set out to show.

The attraction which occurs between long straight parallel

wires carrying similarly directed currents had been discovered by Ampère—and he had investigated it experimentally. His formulation of the law of action of current elements (equation (64)) was developed to describe that attraction, and other similar effects. We have now seen that the formulation of equations (61) and (62) leads to the same prediction, in the case of the system of parallel wires, as Ampère's does, and for all other systems open to experiment the conclusion is the same. As we have already pointed out (p. 98), Ampère's formulation relies on 'action at a distance'; the alternative formulation involves action through a field (of magnetic induction) of which the physical characteristics are to some extent specified. The present-day choice of the alternative approach exemplifies the general attitude that a deeper understanding is to be reached through field theories than through the bare formalism in which notions of action at a distance must necessarily be expressed. Henceforward, then, we adopt equations (61) and (62) as basic for our discussions, and abandon Ampère's equation (64). As long ago as 1888, this course was seen as the only practical one by Oliver Heaviside (1850-1925): 'It has been stated, on no less authority than that of the great Maxwell, that Ampère's law of force between a pair of current elements is the cardinal formula of electrodynamics. . . . I would . . . transfer the name of cardinal formula to another . . . expressing the mechanical force on an element of a conductor supporting current in any magnetic field—the vector product of current and induction. There is something real about it; it is not like [the] force between a pair of unclosed elements; it is fundamental. . . .'

It should be stated, as a fact of history, that a formulation essentially identical with that of our equations (61) and (62) was first given, somewhat speculatively, by Hermann Gunter Grassmann (1809-1877) in 1845. Grassmann pointed out that, according to Ampère's formula (equation (64)), when the current elements are parallel ($\phi = 0$, $\theta = \theta'$) the force changes sign as θ decreases from $\frac{\pi}{2}$ to 0, being zero when $\cos^2 \theta = \frac{2}{3}$. Intuitively, Grassmann declined to accept this conclusion as credible, in the physical context.

3.3. THE UNIT OF CURRENT

Having established the formal result given in terms of equation

EM H

(63), we now have—at long last—the basis for a satisfactory definition of the fundamental unit of current measurement, albeit in
a situation still somewhat idealised. Within the framework of the
'rationalised M.K.S.A. system' of units, we say that unit current
is such that two infinite parallel wires separated by unit distance
(1 metre) in vacuum attract one another with a force of 2×10^{-7}
newton for each unit of length, when unit current (1 ampere)
flows in the same direction in each. This definition effectively
assigns a value of 10^{-7} newton per ampere[2] to the magnitude of
the quantity (γ''^2/γ') in relation to free space ('vacuum'), as equation (63) confirms. The choice of this particular numerical assignment is rooted in the history of earlier systems of electrical
measurement, and need not concern us here.

If we are not concerned with the precise magnitude assigned to
$\gamma''_0{}^2/\gamma'_0$ (we use the subscript zero, henceforward, to denote a
quantity having reference to free space), we are at least concerned
to decompose the composite quantity to which this magnitude has
been assigned into its constituent factors, for these were introduced into our discussion quite separately, representing 'factors
of ignorance' in relation to two entirely different situations. Accepting the assumption that we should be able to construct a
comprehensive system of derived electrical units with the aid of
only one fundamental unit in addition to the mechanical units of
mass, length and time (see p. 90), we might expect some degree
of latitude in making this decomposition.

It will be recalled that γ' was introduced as a factor of ignorance
into the expression for the law of force between magnetic poles
(p. 67), just as γ had been introduced earlier (p. 21) into the
corresponding expression for the law of force between electric
charges. Effectively, in the one case this led to an expression for
the magnetic field intensity due to an isolated pole, and in the
other to an expression for the electric field intensity due to an
isolated charge. These expressions may be written, formally, in
order of their introduction:

$$E = \gamma q/r^2, \ H = \gamma' m/r^2.$$

In developing Gauss's theorem, as an expression of Coulomb's
law, it became natural, in the electrostatic case, to define a quantity
D, the electric flux density, given (p. 22) by

$$D = E/4\pi\gamma.$$

In the electromagnetic case, also, we later introduced (p. 100) a second field quantity which we called the magnetic flux density (or magnetic induction). This quantity B was related to H through the expression

$$B = \gamma'' H / \gamma'.$$

It is clearly a matter of interest to consider whether we may make our representation of electric and magnetic quantities formally symmetrical, without inconsistency, by writing $\gamma'' = 1/4\pi$, whatever the medium—for it must be remembered that our factors of ignorance were introduced explicitly to take count of any 'hidden' effect of the medium on the phenomena under consideration.

So far as γ'' is concerned, reference to equation (52) shows that it was introduced (p. 80) into the expression for the magnetic field intensity due to a current element: γ', as we have just recalled, was introduced into the expression for the magnetic field intensity due to an isolated pole. If we make γ'' a pure number then γ' must be a dimensional magnitude, for B and H are self-evidently quantities of a different kind (p. 100). But we have flexibility in our choice: we could make γ' a pure number and γ'' a dimensional magnitude. In either case a self-consistent system of units could be evolved. As between these possibilities, there is no cause for internal inconsistency in our system, whichever we choose. Naturally, therefore, we choose to make γ'' a pure number—$1/4\pi$ to be precise, thereby achieving the symmetry that we have indicated. We may note, in relation to this choice, that, as followers of Ampère, we intuitively regard the concept of an electric current as one degree more concrete or 'real' than that of an isolated pole. In this context, therefore, it is not surprising that we prefer to assign physical dimensions to the factor of ignorance that we associated with the measure of the pole strength m in the expression for H, rather than to the factor that we associated with the measure of the current strength i in the analogous expression.

Writing $\gamma'' = 1/4\pi$ in equation (63), we see that our definition of unit current implies that the value of γ''_0/γ'_0 is $4\pi \times 10^{-7}$ newton per ampere². This quantity, generally denoted by μ_0, is referred to as the absolute magnetic permeability of free space.* In relation

* Conventionally, the fourth primary unit of the rationalised M.K.S.A. system is the ampere, defined as we have defined it on p. 106. Quite clearly, this is an 'arbitrary' unit (of current). However, it is equally justifiable, and it is perhaps more significant, physically, to regard the fourth fundamental unit of

to any material medium, γ''/γ' is referred to as the absolute magnetic permeability of the medium. We shall use the symbol μ for this quantity. On this basis we have the general result*

$$B = \mu H \qquad (65)$$

It has been said—and it is obvious—that our formal definition of unit current has been based on a physical situation that is still somewhat idealised. In practice, no one would seriously attempt an absolute determination of current strength using 'infinite parallel wires' as the essential feature of his experimental arrangement. The practical instrument—the ampere balance of Kelvin and others—was designed, instead, so that the force of attraction between coaxial circular current-carrying coils could be measured. We cannot profitably discuss the design and functioning of this instrument at this stage; later (p. 137) we shall return to its consideration, when we have developed the necessary theoretical ideas.

3.4. DERIVED UNITS IN RELATION TO STEADY-CURRENT PHENOMENA

One of the earliest effects observed with voltaic piles was that thin wires could be fused by being connected across their terminals (p. 70)—just as it had been observed by Kinnersley, forty years previously, that such an effect could be obtained by using a thin wire to discharge a large battery of Leyden jars (p. 68). It soon became evident that this effect was merely an extreme example of the general phenomenon of the production of heat in conductors of all kinds when current is passing. We have already quoted Thomas Young (1807): 'A constant stream of galvanic electricity, passing through an iron wire is . . . capable of exciting a considerable degree of heat.'

Precise experiments on the rate of production of heat under these conditions were first made by J. P. Joule in 1840. As we have

this system as a 'natural' unit of permeability, of magnitude $10^7/4\pi$ of the magnetic permeability of free space. From this point of view the ampere, rather than the unit of permeability, is the derived unit of the pair.

* Some authors use μ to denote the 'relative permeability' of the medium. In this case μ is a pure number, and equation (65) becomes $B = \mu\mu_0 H$. This complication appears to be wholly unnecessary, directly at variance with accepted practice in relation to physical magnitudes generally, and a latent source of confusion to students. We shall accord it no place in our discussions.

elsewhere recorded ($M\,L\,\&\,T$, p. 271), these experiments were the earliest of a long series, covering some thirty-five years, in which Joule was to establish conclusively the equivalence of heat and work in a wide variety of circumstances. Here we shall accept that equivalence without question, and adopt the view that when a current passes through a conductor work is done by electric forces, originating in the battery (or other source of current), in moving the charges which constitute the current against forces of resistance arising in the conductor. In this way the motion of the charges is effectively unaccelerated overall (in the macroscopic sense) and the energy which the charges derive from the electric action is continuously dissipated as heat in the conductor. Introducing the concept of electric potential in relation to the electrostatic field (see §2.5), we defined the increase of potential as between one point and another as numerically given by the work which must be done by an outside agency to move unit charge from the first point to the second against the electric forces resisting the motion. In the case of the current in the conductor, each element of charge (electron) whose motion contributes to the current has that motion promoted (rather than hindered) by the electric forces acting. The work which it, in turn, is able to do in increasing the thermal agitation of the atoms of the conductor, is derived from this electric action, as we have already indicated. In conformity with our definition in electrostatics, we may therefore equate the mechanical equivalent of the heat generated in the conductor to the product of the charge and the difference of electric potential between the ends of the conductor. In conditions of steady current, the measure of the current is the rate of transport of charge, and the corresponding rate of generation of heat is the power developed. If we measure this power in mechanical units, we have, in consequence, an equation providing a definition of the derived unit of potential difference:

$$P = iV \tag{66}$$

In the rationalised M.K.S.A. system, when the current i is measured in amperes, and the power P in watts, the potential difference V is given in volts. A current of 1 ampere, flowing in a conductor between the ends of which the difference of potential is 1 volt, generates heat in the conductor at the rate of 1 joule per second (power = 1 watt).

We have just ascribed the potential difference which is maintained between the ends of a conductor conveying current to an electric action originating in the battery (or other source of current) with which the conductor is in circuit. It was Georg Simon Ohm (1787-1854) who first gave precision to this view, introducing, as we should now say, the concept of the 'electromotive force' of the source in a pamphlet published in Berlin in 1827 and entitled (in translation) 'The galvanic circuit: a mathematical treatment'. We shall later discuss the physical processes which are responsible for the action of voltaic cells, and the development of electromotive force in other sources of current; here we merely note that this quantity is of the same nature as potential difference: it is measured in volts in our system.

Ohm's pamphlet is generally regarded—and is widely quoted— as providing the first formal definition of 'electrical resistance'. This, indeed, it does—and the 'mathematical' statement of the relation between current, potential difference and resistance which it postulates will be used in what follows for precisely that purpose. However, before we use it in that way, it will be profitable to trace the history of the concept of resistance-to-current-flow in some detail, for it stretches back for almost a century before Ohm's pamphlet was published.

We have already seen (p. 9) that the empirical distinction between electrical conductors and insulators had been established, about 1730, by the investigations of Gray, Desaguliers and du Fay. It soon became evident that all conductors were not equally effective, and by 1753 Beccaria had reported experiments on the dependence of the intensity of shock on the cross-sectional area of tubes of water of constant length which were used as conductors to discharge Leyden jars. He found the shock to be more powerful when the cross-sectional area was increased. Independently, though some twenty years later, Cavendish carried out similar but more systematic experiments, comparing the effects observed with conductors in the form of metal wires and tubes of liquid of different dimensions (see p. 68). In 1775 he reported briefly to the Royal Society that 'electricity meets with no more resistance in passing through a piece of iron wire 400,000,000 inches long than through a column of [distilled] water of the same diameter and only one inch long. Sea-water . . . conducts 100 times . . . better than rain-water.' By 1807, Thomas Young could entertain the ideal notion of a perfect conductor (see p. 71) through which 'An uninterrupted current of electricity . . . would perhaps be also in every respect imperceptible'. By that time the first experiments with conductors carrying steady currents of voltaic electricity had already been performed.

In 1821 Davy (see p. 69) published the results of experiments which were classic in their simplicity. For many years previously he had been studying the chemical effects attending the passage of currents through solutions and molten salts. The simplest of these effects is the decomposition of water into its constituent elements (see chap. 5). Davy discovered that this process takes place only when, in modern parlance, the difference of potential between the metal plates ('electrodes') inserted in the liquid exceeds a critical value. He therefore arranged a battery of voltaic cells to pass current through a water-decomposition cell, and he studied the effect of 'short-circuiting' the cell by a metallic wire providing an alternative ('parallel') path for the current. He found that, in general, as the length of this wire was decreased, a stage was reached at which the decomposition of the water ceased. Assuming that all other relevant factors remained constant, Davy in this way identified lengths of wire of different material and different cross-section which were in some way equivalent in relation to the conduction of current. For wires of the same metal he found that this condition of equivalence was most simply expressed by the requirement that the quantity l/A should be constant. Here l is the length of the (uniform) wire and A is its cross-sectional area (of whatever shape). He concluded that the conducting power of a wire is inversely proportional to its length and directly proportional to its cross-sectional area. Davy even studied the effect of temperature on conductivity with this arrangement, and demonstrated conclusively that with most metals the conductivity decreases as the temperature is raised. Five years later, then, when Ohm embarked on his 'mathematical treatment', much was known experimentally concerning the factors determining the conducting power (or, inversely, the electrical resistance) of metal wires.

Ohm based his treatment of the galvanic circuit on the then recently published mathematical theory of the conduction of heat, which was due to Fourier (see V & W, p. 27). In the ideal case of the flow of heat along a uniform rod, without loss to the surrounding medium, the rate of transport of heat across any right section of the rod is given by the product of the longitudinal temperature gradient (which is constant), the cross-sectional area of the rod (whatever its shape) and the coefficient of thermal conductivity of the material of which the rod is made. Ohm became convinced that the electrical situation in a uniform wire forming part of a galvanic circuit is precisely analogous to this. He considered the electric current to be the analogue of the (rate of) flow of heat, and he postulated that difference of electric potential must be the analogue of difference of temperature. In this way he was led to the formal result

$$i = \frac{\sigma A}{l} V.$$

Here V is the difference of potential between the ends of a uniform conductor of cross-sectional area A and length l, i is the current, and σ is the measure of the electrical conductivity of the material of the conductor. It will be noted that Davy's empirical findings are faithfully reproduced in this expression, which may be regarded, once units of current and potential have been defined, as defining the derived unit of measurement of electrical conductivity.

If attention is concentrated on the characteristics of the conductor, rather than on the properties of the material of which it is made, the more appropriate form of Ohm's equation is

$$i = \frac{V}{R} \qquad\qquad (67)$$

This expression gives the measure of the electrical resistance of the conductor (here denoted by R) in terms of the difference of potential which must be maintained between its ends if unit current is to flow steadily in it. Combining equations (66) and (67) we have for the power expended in the resistance, and appearing as heat under steady conditions, the alternative expressions

$$P = Ri^2 = \frac{V^2}{R}.$$

In the system that we are developing the unit of electrical resistance (volt per ampere) is named, after G.S. Ohm, the ohm. If, comparing the two forms of Ohm's equation which we have just given, we write $R = \rho l/A$, rather than $R = l/\sigma A$, we are effectively defining a quantity ρ, the 'resistivity' (or specific resistance) of the material of the conductor. Obviously, the unit in which this quantity is measured is the ohm metre.

3.5. DERIVED UNITS IN ELECTROSTATICS

The basic unit in electrostatics is the unit of charge. This unit has effectively been predetermined, in the last section, in the statement (p. 109) 'the measure of the current is the rate of transport of charge'. We have, therefore, as defining equation, simply

$$ i = \frac{dq}{dt} \tag{68} $$

—and the unit of charge becomes the ampere second. Traditionally, the unit is named after C.A.Coulomb (see p. 17), the coulomb.

We have also, in the last section, explicitly identified the concept of electrostatic potential difference with the concept of electric potential difference as appropriate to steady-current phenomena. Potential difference in electrostatics, then, is measured in volts, and this unit we have already defined.

On the other hand, we have not, so far, even obliquely, adumbrated the concept to which our next unit refers. This concept is that of 'electrical capacity', and the unit is the unit of 'capacitance'. Consider the ideal situation in which a conducting body of arbitrary shape is isolated in an infinite non-conducting medium. If a charge q is given to the body, this charge will distribute itself over the surface of the body in a unique manner, determined by the requirement that the surface of the body shall be an equipotential surface (see p. 32). In principle, the electric potential at any point in the medium can be calculated from this distribution of charge, using equation (13) (p. 31). If the charge on the body is increased n times, the surface density of charge at any point on the surface of the body is likewise increased by a factor n, and the electric potential at an arbitrary point in the medium is similarly increased n-fold. Now, equation (13) is based on the convention that the potential is zero at infinity: on the basis of this convention, therefore, and the argument that has just been given, we conclude that when charge is communicated to an isolated conducting body, the potential of the body is raised by an amount V which is proportional to the charge q, proportional to our factor of ignorance γ, and is otherwise determined by a purely geometrical factor relating to the size and shape of the body. If we combine the two last mentioned factors (inversely) in a single quantity C, we may write formally

$$V = \frac{q}{C} \qquad (69)$$

The quantity C, of which equation (69) defines the measure, in this ideal case, is the electrical capacitance of the isolated conducting body under consideration. We have seen that its magnitude depends upon the size and shape of the body and (hypothetically, at least) upon the nature of the medium surrounding it. Clearly, on our system, according to equation (69), capacitance is measured in coulombs per volt—or, traditionally, in farads, after Michael Faraday, to whose work in this connection we shall later refer.

An ideal case of more relevance to real situations than the one just considered is that in which an indefinite number of conducting bodies are situated in an infinite non-conducting medium. Let these bodies be numbered $1, 2, \ldots, k, l, \ldots$ In deriving equation (13) we have already justified a principle of superposition in relation to the contributions which individual members of a system of point charges make to the resultant potential at any point in the region in which they are situated. In relation to our present case there is a more general principle of superposition (which we shall not justify in detail) which states that if there are two distributions of charge on the bodies in question, each distribution being an equilibrium distribution, then the distribution that would result if these two were superposed would likewise be an equilibrium distribution of charge. Let us suppose that in one equilibrium state the charges on the bodies are $q_1, q_2, \ldots, q_k, q_l, \ldots$ In this state the potential of body k is given, by an extension of equation (13), by an expression of the form

$$V_k = p_{1k}q_1 + p_{2k}q_2 + \ldots + p_{kk}q_k + p_{lk}q_l + \ldots,$$

and the potential of the body l by a similar expression,

$$V_l = p_{1l}q_1 + p_{2l}q_2 + \ldots + p_{kl}q_k + p_{ll}q_l + \ldots.$$

In these expressions the coefficients p naturally involve the factor γ directly; otherwise each is a purely geometrical factor relating to the size and shape, and the separation, of the pair of bodies to which its two subscripts refer (one coefficient in each expression for V has identical subscripts: obviously, in relation to that coefficient, only the size and shape of a single body is in question).

Suppose, now, that bodies k and l are momentarily connected by a thin conducting wire, so that their potentials become equalised, a charge q passing from body k to body l in the process. Let the final common potential of these bodies be V. Then we have

$$V = p_{1k}q_1 + p_{2k}q_2 + \ldots + p_{kk}(q_k - q) + p_{lk}(q_l + q) + \ldots,$$
$$V = p_{1l}q_1 + p_{2l}q_2 + \ldots + p_{kl}(q_k - q) + p_{ll}(q_l + q) + \ldots.$$

The distributions of charge and potential represented by the two sets of equations (for each set we have written down only the equations relating to the bodies k and l) being equilibrium distributions, any distribution obtained by superposition is also an equilibrium distribution. Let us make the superposition, therefore, changing the signs of all the charges (and potentials) in our second set of equations. So far as the bodies k and l are concerned, in the new distribution so derived, the situation is represented by the equations

$$V_k - V = p_{kk}q - p_{lk}q,$$
$$V_l - V = p_{kl}q - p_{ll}q.$$

Formally, from these two equations, we obtain the result

$$V_k - V_l = q(p_{kk} - p_{lk} - p_{kl} + p_{ll}) \qquad (70)$$

Equation (70) has a simple and important interpretation: it is that, whatever the charges on the other bodies may be, the quantity of electricity q which passes when the two bodies k and l are 'discharged' (by being connected momentarily by a thin metal wire) is dependent only on the difference of potential between the two bodies themselves and on a factor $(p_{kk} - p_{lk} - p_{kl} + p_{ll}$, in our notation) determined by the geometrical configuration of the two bodies and the properties of the surrounding medium. Indeed, equation (70) shows that the notion of capacitance is equally valid for a system of two bodies as it is for the isolated conductor of our earlier discussion. Comparing equations (69) and (70), we may write, for the two-body system,

$$C_{kl} = (p_{kk} - p_{lk} - p_{kl} + p_{ll})^{-1} \qquad (71)$$

A system of two conductors so disposed in a non-conducting medium that when they are at a relatively small difference of potential a relatively large quantity of electricity passes on their discharge, is referred to as an electrical condenser (or 'capacitor'). The original Leyden jar of 1745, devised by its originator (see p. 68) on intuitive rather than on strictly rational grounds, provides the prototype of all such arrangements.

It has been stated that the quantities p of equation (71) involve the factor γ directly. This being the case, the capacitance defined by that equation (as also that defined by the equation (69)) is inversely proportional to this factor of ignorance, which, as we recall, was originally introduced (into the expression for the law of force between charges: see p. 21) to take count of any possible effect of the medium.

In November 1837, during the course of his eleventh series of *Experimental Researches on Electricity*, Faraday investigated the influence of the medium on the capacitance of condensers by direct experiment. He constructed two exactly similar condensers, formed of concentric spherical conductors, so devised that the space between the inner and outer spheres could be filled by non-conducting substances, whether in the form of gas, liquid or solid. The outer conducting sphere of each condenser was formed of two closely fitting halves, for ease of dismantling and re-assembly, and the inner sphere was supported by an insulating rod which was so tapered as to fit snugly into the conical end of a hollow tube projecting vertically from the upper of the two outer half-spheres. The electrical lead to the inner sphere passed along the axis of the insulating rod. When solid non-conductors were used to fill the space between the spheres, these non-conductors were also moulded as hemispherical shells. Faraday used his condensers with the outer spheres connected to earth and the inner spheres isolated. He proceeded by the method of sharing of charge (as we shall describe) and he used a 'proof plane' in the form of a sphere of elder-wood pith covered with gold leaf, in conjunction with a torsion balance having a similar sphere at the extremity of the balance arm, for the estimation of potential.

The method of sharing of charge is a method of comparison of capacitances which can be illustrated as follows. Suppose that two bodies of capacitance C_1 and C_2, respectively, are originally uncharged. The first is given a charge q, then the two bodies are momentarily connected by a long thin wire, then isolated again. At the end of the first stage of this process the potential of the first body is $q/C_1 (= V_1)$. Eventually the bodies are at a common potential V, the first carrying charge VC_1 and the second VC_2. Since $VC_1 + VC_2 = q$,

$$\frac{V}{V_1} = \frac{C_1}{C_1 + C_2}.$$

When the second body is a proof plane of capacitance C_2 very small compared with C_1, V is essentially equal to V_1 and the proof plane carries away a charge $V_1 C_2$ determination of which (in arbitrary units) gives a relative measure of V_1.

Faraday's experiments, based on the principles outlined in the last paragraph, gave the following results. Whatever the potential used in the investigation, the capacitance of the condenser having a given solid (or liquid) non-conducting substance completely filling the space between the spherical 'plates' was greater than that of the exactly similar condenser having air between the plates in a constant ratio characteristic of the 'dielectric substance' concerned. (Within the accuracy of the measurements, the capacitance of the test condenser was the same whatever gas was used as dielectric substance, at whatever temperature and pressure, within the range investigated.) Faraday gave the name 'specific inductive capacity' or 'dielectric constant' to this constant ratio, relating the relevant property of a given non-conducting material to the corresponding property of normal air. Nowadays, we should relate the specific inductive capacity of a material substance to that of free space ('vacuum'). On that basis it would be given by γ_0/γ, by an obvious extension of our accepted formalism. (More accurate experiments than those of Faraday have since shown that for the simple gases, at ordinary densities, specific inductive capacities, referred to vacuum, are greater than unity, the excess over unity for each gas being proportional to the density.)

In the rationalised M.K.S.A. system of units, Faraday's non-dimensional quantity 'specific inductive capacity' is abandoned in favour of an 'absolute' (dimensional) quantity 'permittivity'.* In order to maintain the symmetry that we have been attempting

---

* Some authors use the term 'relative permittivity' to denote the numerical ratio defined by Faraday's experiments. For comments on the unnecessary complication of such a convention, see footnote p. 108

to achieve between the definitions of electric and magnetic quantities in this system (p. 107), we define the (absolute) permittivity of the medium by the equation

$$\epsilon = \frac{1}{4\pi\gamma}.$$

Consider, now, the units in which permittivity is measured on the basis of this definition. We take the simplest case, that of the isolated conducting sphere of radius a. When the charge on this spherical conductor is q, its potential is $\gamma q/a$ (equation (15), p. 36), and if C is its capacitance,

$$C = \frac{a}{\gamma} = 4\pi\epsilon a \tag{72}$$

Obviously, ϵ, the permittivity of the medium, is measured in farads per metre, in our system.

Having considered the question of unit, we turn next to numerical values. Ideally, equation (69) (p. 114) provides a general specification whereby the capacitance of any system can be determined on the basis of measurements of charge and potential difference, in units which have been uniquely defined. The radius of a sphere may also be measured in terms of a well-defined unit. In relation to equation (72), therefore, the numerical values of two of the three quantities, C, a and ϵ, being experimentally determinable, the value of the third follows by simple calculation. Equation (72), in fact, provides the necessary specification for the experimental determination of ϵ. If the experiment were made in relation to a spherical conductor in vacuum, we should obtain, empirically, the value of ϵ_0, the permittivity of free space in farads per metre.

In practice, there are other methods of determining the capacitance of a condenser in farads, less idealised than the one that has been indicated here. These we cannot profitably discuss in this context; suffice to say that the experimental determination of the measure of the permittivity of free space, in rationalised M.K.S.A. units, is an entirely practical possibility. The appropriate experiments have been done, and the result turns out to be

$$\epsilon_0 = 8\cdot854 \times 10^{-12} \text{ farad/metre.}$$

When we adopted the unit of current as the fourth fundamental unit in the rationalised M.K.S.A. system, we noted (p. 107) the degree of flexibility that we had in fixing the magnitude of that unit and concurrently fixing the magnitude of the magnetic permeability of free space. Having chosen the magnitude of unit current, we defined unit permeability in such a way that

$$\mu_0 = 4\pi \times 10^{-7} \text{ newton/ampere}^2$$

$$= 1\cdot2566 \times 10^{-6} \text{ newton/ampere}^2.$$

We may note that if these choices had been differently made, then, of necessity, the size of the farad would have been different, and the experimental value of ϵ_0 would have been different, also.

In a later section we shall be developing the concept of 'inductance' (see p. 134), and on that basis arriving at a specification of magnetic permeability in henries per metre. This alternative specification will re-emphasise the symmetry underlying our definitions of ϵ and μ. Here, from a somewhat different point of view, we consider the mutual relevance of these two quantities by evaluating the dimensions of the units in which they are measured. In this connection we note the obvious fact that four fundamental units are involved in any such dimensional equation: we are seeking dimensions in terms of mass, length, time and current. For μ, the specification of the magnitude in newtons per ampere^2 gives the dimensional equation directly; it is

$$[\mu] = M^1L^1T^{-2}I^{-2} \tag{73}$$

For ϵ, according to the specification that we have established, we must work back through the dimensions of the farad and the volt. We have

$$[\epsilon] = [C]L^{-1},$$
$$[C] = I^1T^1[V^{-1}],$$
$$[V] = I^{-1}M^1L^2T^{-3}$$

(the second and third of these equations are based on equations (69) and (66), respectively, by which the units were defined). For ϵ, therefore,

$$[\epsilon] = M^{-1}L^{-3}T^4I^2 \tag{74}$$

Combining equations (73) and (74), we note that

$$\left[\left(\frac{1}{\mu\epsilon}\right)^{\frac{1}{2}}\right] = L^1T^{-1},$$

and, substituting the numerical values already quoted for μ_0, ϵ_0, in relation to this result, we obtain

$$\left(\frac{1}{\mu_0\epsilon_0}\right)^{\frac{1}{2}} = 2\cdot998 \times 10^8 \text{ metre/second}.$$

We note that this velocity is precisely the velocity of light in free space. Elsewhere we have discussed the background to this observation in greater detail (V & W, pp. 259-69); we shall not repeat that discussion here. We merely record that it is a result of the electromagnetic theory of Maxwell that ('long') electromagnetic waves are propagated through a non-conducting medium with a phase velocity given by

$$v = \left(\frac{1}{\mu\epsilon}\right)^{\frac{1}{2}}.$$

We are now in a position to conclude our survey of the derived units of electrostatics very briefly. E, the intensity of the electrostatic field is measured in volts per metre (see equation (9)), and D, the electric flux density (or 'electric displacement') in coulombs per metre^2 (see equation (6)).

3.6. DERIVED UNITS IN MAGNETOSTATICS

Now that we have identified the factor of ignorance which we originally included in our expression for the inverse-square-law force between magnetic poles, we may re-write that expression, explicitly,

$$F = \frac{m_1 m_2}{4\pi\mu r^2} \tag{75}$$

This equation still refers to a physical situation which is strictly unrealisable in practice, but it allows us to specify the unit of measurement of magnetic pole strength for use in situations in which that concept is significant. From equation (75) we have the dimensional result

$$[m^2] = L^2[\mu F].$$

But　　　$[\mu] = I^{-2}[F],$

thus　　　$[m] = I^{-1}L^1[F].$

We conclude, therefore, that magnetic pole strength is measured in joules per ampere, in our chosen system.

The defining relation, in magnetostatics, between magnetic field intensity H and magnetic pole strength m, being

$$F = mH \tag{76}$$

(see p. 65), obviously, the dimensional equation for the unit of H is

$$[H] = I^1 L^{-1},$$

and the unit of magnetic field intensity is the ampere per metre. We note that we already have this result in terms of equation (52) (p. 80), once we have decided (p. 107) to regard the factor γ'', which was originally introduced into that equation, as a pure number.

The unit of magnetic moment (defined as the product of pole strength and distance, see p. 63) is the joule metre per ampere: it could alternatively be regarded as the newton per ampere per square metre (a unit of force per current density). Either form might equally well have been deduced from equation (56) (p. 86).

Intensity of magnetisation of a material (p. 63) is defined as the magnetic moment per unit volume. The simplest designation of the unit in this case is clearly the newton per ampere metre.

3.7. MAGNETIC FLUX

We have already defined a vector quantity B, which we have referred to as the magnetic flux density (or magnetic induction), and which is related to the magnetic field intensity through equation (65) (p. 108). On the basis of this equation, and the results of the last section, we conclude that the appropriate unit for the measurement of B in the rationalised M.K.S.A. system is the newton per ampere metre. We note, at once, that this is the same unit as that which we have just found appropriate for the measurement of intensity of magnetisation, J.

Let us now define what we mean by magnetic flux. Let there be a small plane area dS around a point where the magnitude of the magnetic flux density is B. Let the direction of B make an angle θ with the 'outwards' drawn normal to dS. Then the outwards magnetic flux through the area dS is given by the expression

$$d\Phi = B \cos \theta \, dS \tag{77}$$

From this expression, and our last result, it is clear that the unit of flux measurement on our system is the joule per ampere (see, also, p. 130). This is the same unit as that of magnetic pole strength which we derived in the last section. We should not be surprised by this result. We have successfully contrived to frame our definitions so as to ensure formal symmetry as between the fundamental expressions relating, respectively, to the electrostatic and magnetostatic fields. The vector quantities E and H are corresponding quantities in this context, and so are the quantities D and B. On the basis of Gauss's theorem, for the electrical case, we proved that the total outwards flux over any closed surface is equal to the total charge enclosed (see equation (6), p 22.): the theorem is equally valid for the magnetic case—and it gives the result that the total outwards flux is equal to the total pole strength enclosed by any arbitrarily drawn surface in the field. Such a result would be meaningless unless the unit of magnetic flux measurement were also the unit of measurement of pole strength. Because, in actual fact, magnetic poles have never been obtained in isolation, it is general to accept as a 'law of nature' that the total outwards magnetic flux over any closed surface whatsoever is always zero.

The notion of magnetic flux has particular relevance to the discovery, by Faraday, of the phenomenon of electromagnetic induction. Michael Faraday made his first original contribution to experimental electromagnetism in September 1821, a few days before his thirtieth birthday. By a most ingenious arrangement he demonstrated the mutual action of a magnet on a current, in a form in which a flexible element of a current circuit was caused to rotate continuously around one pole of a bar magnet, for as long as current was passing in the circuit. Only nine years previously, having served his apprenticeship as a bookbinder, and become a journeyman in his trade, he had secured the post of laboratory assistant at the Royal Institution in London (see *M L & T*, p. 271), as a result of his own importuning. During those first nine years he had acted in many capacities: as amanuensis and technician to Sir Humphry Davy, the professor of chemistry, even as his valet during his travels abroad. Then, in 1823 Davy's health began to worsen (he died in 1829, at the age of fifty), and from that stage onwards Faraday was effectively his own master, free, within the confines of his strict sense of duty, to follow the bent of his remarkable genius. Somewhat sporadically until 1831, then almost continuously until 1855, with utter singleness of purpose, he devoted himself to the 'experimental researches on electricity', which, more than the endeavours of any of his contemporaries, provided the point of departure for the advances that were to come. In 1825 he was appointed director of the laboratory, and in 1833 professor of chemistry in the Royal Institution, with life-long tenure and the minimum of duties.

Such electrical researches as Faraday was able to undertake in the period 1824 to 1831 were not attended by any very marked success. All the time he was assailed by the conviction that it ought to be possible to observe, with electric currents, effects analogous to the phenomenon of induction of charge (see p. 10) in electrostatics; moreover, as early as 1822 he had set himself the grandiose aim to 'convert magnetism into electricity'. In December 1824 an essay in the latter direction had been unsuccessful, then, in November 1825, and again on two later occasions, he had devised elaborate, but unrewarding, experiments as a result of which he had hoped to produce a current in one wire by means of a current in another wire or by a magnet. Arago (see p. 73), on the other hand, had, during the same period, discovered a new phenomenon, almost by accident. In 1824, noticing that an oscillating compass needle came to rest sooner when placed in a copper can than when in free air, he had studied the effect using sheets of copper and other substances placed at different distances below the oscillating needle. He found that the metals were much more effective than the non-metals in this connection, and then, by a happy inspiration, he tried rotating a copper disk just below a suspended needle (shielded from the viscous drag of the intervening air by an interposed sheet of glass). When the axis of rotation of the disk was made to coincide with the axis of suspension of the needle (which was initially at rest), Arago found that the needle took up a new position of equilibrium, deflected from the meridian in the direction of rotation of the disk. As the speed of rotation of the disk was increased, so the deflection of the needle increased, until a stage was reached at which the needle was set in permanent rotation.

Arago's observations were almost immediately confirmed by Thomas Johann Seebeck (1770-1831), an Esthonian, then working in Berlin, and before long the phenomenon of 'magnetism of rotation' had attracted the attention of many distinguished men of science. In Britain, alone, Peter Barlow (1776-1862), mathematical master in the Woolwich Academy (F.R.S., 1823), Charles Babbage (1792-1871), soon to become Lucasian professor of mathematics at Cambridge (F.R.S., 1816), Sir John Frederick William Herschel (1792-1871), Secretary to the Royal Society at the time (F.R.S., 1813), and William Snow Harris (see p. 42) (F.R.S., 1831), all contributed towards its investigation. In Paris, Ampère and J.D. Colladon observed that the magnet in Arago's experiment could be replaced by a long thin solenoid activated by a current: if such a solenoid were suspended horizontally, so that it could rotate about a vertical axis through its centre, it could be put into rotation merely by spinning a disk of copper placed immediately underneath it, provided that the latter motion were sufficiently rapid.

Within a few years, then, a great deal of information had been collected concerning 'magnetism of rotation', but no simple theory had been put forward to account for the effect. Poisson (see p. 62) had introduced certain arbitrary assumptions into his mathematical theory of magnetisation with the aid of which he claimed to have provided a formal description of the phenomenon, but time was to show that the elegant mathematics upon which this claim depended was entirely irrelevant to the physical situation involved.*

That Faraday did not directly concern himself, during the period 1824 to 1831, with the phenomenon of 'magnetism of rotation', that, indeed, his electrical researches during that period were somewhat sporadic, is to be ascribed largely to his involvement in work on behalf of a committee of the Royal Society which had been set up to investigate the possibilities of improvements in the manufacture of optical glass. Faraday accepted responsibility for the preliminary chemical investigations, and the ensuing small-scale manufacture of new types of glass—and for three years from 1827 he operated a series of special glass furnaces, which he had installed at the Royal Institution, with no other help than that of Sgt Anderson of the Royal Artillery, the only member of his 're-

---

* Writing in 1854, de la Rive commented (here we translate somewhat freely), 'So we spend no further time discussing the matter, only to say that the mathematical analysis by which this theory was developed may still, with some advantage, be studied by those who, with other hypotheses to follow, rather than that which M. Poisson took as the starting point of his theory, wish to submit them to the test of calculation'.

search and development' team. In 1831 the committee recommended to the Council of the Royal Society that Faraday should be asked to continue this work, but Faraday demurred: 'obliged as I have been to devote the whole of my spare time to the experiments already described, and consequently to resign the pursuit of such philosophical inquiries as suggested themselves to my own mind, I would wish, under present circumstances, to lay the glass aside for a while, that I may enjoy the pleasure of working out my own thoughts on other subjects'.

Faraday's letter to the Secretary of the Royal Society was written on 4 July. On 29 August his recently resumed 'philosophical inquiries' bore fruit, possibly beyond expectation, in the results of a simple experiment. Faraday had taken a soft-iron ring, of 6 inches external diameter and had wound 'many coils of copper wire . . . separated by twine and calico', some 130 feet of wire in all, in two 'windings' on opposite sides of the ring. He had connected the ends of one of these windings 'by a copper wire passing to a distance and just over a magnetic needle (3 feet from iron ring)'. When the other winding had been connected in circuit with a battery ('of 10 pr. plates 4 inches square'), 'immediately a sensible effect on the needle. It oscillated and settled at last in original position. On breaking connection . . . with Battery again a disturbance of the needle.' These excerpts are taken from Faraday's diary. On the following day, 30 August,* he wrote 'May not these transient effects be connected with causes of difference between powers of metals in rest and in motion in Arago's expts. ?'

Assuredly, it would not have occurred to many investigators, presented with the results of Faraday's simple experiment of 29 August, to connect them in any way with the so-called phenomenon of magnetism of rotation which Arago had discovered. Faraday's apparatus involved no moving parts—except the contact with the battery, and the galvanometer needle with which the transient currents were detected. But he was already beginning to think in terms of physical phenomena taking place throughout the medium, and was developing for himself a picture in terms of lines of force to describe such phenomena. For Faraday, the relative motion in Arago's experiment was the relative motion of the lines of force of the magnet and the material of the conducting

* On 30 August 1871, Ernest Rutherford was born; on 30 August 1940, J. J. Thomson died.

disk; in his own experiment there was no essential material element that was in motion, but the lines of force (or induction, as we should now say) in the soft-iron ring were in motion when the current in the 'primary' winding was increasing from zero, as contact was made with the battery, or decreasing to zero again, as that contact was broken. This must be so, for, essentially, there were no lines of induction through the iron when there was no current in the winding, and, when there was current, then there were lines of induction threading the circuit. Faraday's 'secondary' winding, then, the one in which his compass needle demonstrated the existence of the transient currents, could reasonably be compared with the rotating copper disk in the experiments of Arago. In those experiments there must have been 'induced' currents in the copper disk.

Faraday pressed forward with his experiments on the induction of currents, with unerring instinct, on the basis of this simple picture of the essential phenomenon. On 24 November 1831 he presented an account of his investigations to the Royal Society. Qualitatively, the matter had been fully explored as a result of a few weeks' concentrated effort. By realising, one after another, the appropriate situations in the laboratory, Faraday was able to state that an induced current flows in a closed circuit whenever the current in a neighbouring circuit changes in magnitude (or starts, or stops), whenever the distance or orientation of a neighbouring permanent magnet is altered, whenever another circuit in which a steady current is flowing is made to approach or recede from the circuit in question. All these were situations in which, in Faraday's terminology, the number of lines of magnetic force that were enclosed by the 'secondary' circuit was in process of change—and he had clear evidence for the claim that the effects observed in every case were the more pronounced as the rate of that change was the greater. Faraday had also another 'practical' observation to report: he had rotated a copper disk between the poles of the large compound steel magnet belonging to the Royal Society, and then on loan to S.H.Christie (1784-1865) of Woolwich, and had been able to obtain a steady induced current by making connection with the axle and rim of the disk through 'sliding' contacts.

Faraday made the first quantitative studies of the phenomenon of electromagnetic induction in the following year. By using wires of different materials, and different diameters, for the construction of his secondary circuits, he showed that, in otherwise similar circumstances, the magnitude of the induced current was inversely proportional to the resistance of the wire. Hence, he concluded, the essential phenomenon was the generation of electromotive force in the wire—and because, when this is said, the only significance remaining to the wire itself is to delineate a closed path in space for the mind to contemplate, he asserted that there is electromotive force around any closed path in space when the number of lines of magnetic force encircled by the boundary of the path is changing.

In 1833 Faraday turned his attention chiefly to studies relating to the passage of electricity through liquids (see chap. 5), and it was not until 1850 that he again made systematic quantitative experiments concerning the induction of currents. Then he showed, what he had expected from the first, that the induced electromotive force is directly proportional to the rate of change of the number of lines of force threading the circuit. In these investigations Faraday's outstanding ingenuity as an experimenter stood out as clearly as ever before, but by the time that the investigations were undertaken it would indeed have been utter confusion if his results had been otherwise. For, by that time, the mathematicians had shown that the conclusions to which Faraday had been led by inspired and patient experiment could be deduced by general reasoning from the law of Ampère.

The first connection between Ampère's results and those of Faraday was formulated as an empirical rule by H. F. Emil Lenz (1804-1865) in 1834. Lenz's rule states that when a closed circuit is moved in a magnetic field, so that induced current flows in the circuit, the direction of this current is such that, at any instant, the resultant mechanical force acting on the current-carrying circuit, by virtue of the magnetic field in which it is instantaneously situated, is in a direction such as to oppose the motion of the circuit. Franz Ernst Neumann (1798-1895), professor of mineralogy and physics at Königsberg from 1829 to 1876, adopted this qualitative statement of experimental fact as the starting point of a quantitative theory in 1845. In the following year, though from a somewhat different starting point, Wilhelm Eduard Weber (1804-1891) developed an alternative theory (see *V & W*, p. 263). In 1851 yet another mathematical approach was used by H. L. F. von Helmholtz (1821-1894), and for the first time the idea of the general conservation of energy was explicitly shown to be relevant to the problem. It will be recalled (see *M L & T*, p. 274) that in 1847 Helmholtz had gone farther than any of his contemporaries in greatly extending the notion of the equivalence of heat and work, which was beginning to take shape at that time as a result of the experiments of Joule (see p. 108) and others.

To the modern eye, Lenz's rule, in its original form, invites immediate translation into terms of heat and work: in order to obtain an induced current in a closed circuit through the steady motion of that circuit in a magnetic field it is necessary that an external agency shall do work against forces of electromagnetic origin acting on the circuit, otherwise it would be difficult to account for the energy which is dissipated as heat in the resistive circuit by the current that flows in it. In 1834, however, the publication of Lenz's rule evoked no such immediate interpretation: the relevant conservation law had yet to be formulated.

In 1851, even, von Helmholtz's own account of the matter had been incomplete in certain respects, but the ambiguities affecting it did not remain unresolved for long. Kelvin (see p. 46), in the same year, had been the first clearly to distinguish between the two magnetic field vectors which we have denoted by B and H (which he termed 'the magnetic force according to the electromagnetic definition' and 'the magnetic force according to the polar definition'—and which we have called the magnetic induction, or flux density, and the magnetic field intensity, respectively). In making this distinction, which von Helmholtz did not recognise, Kelvin pointed out, what we have implied already (p. 126), that it is the surface integral of the normal component of B (rather than of H), the magnetic flux as we have defined it (see equation (77)), which is to be identified with Faraday's total number of lines of force through a bounded area. Later in the same year he dealt, with complete rigour, with the general problem of the induction of currents from the standpoint of energy conservation. We cannot here follow the niceties of Kelvin's treatment; let us, instead, consider a simple case from first principles—that will be sufficient for present purposes.

In a previous section (p. 83) we calculated the magnetic field intensity at certain points in the neighbourhood of a rectangular current-carrying loop, using fig. 20 to represent the geometry of the problem. On the basis of the same figure, let us now consider the steady rotation of a rectangular conducting loop (containing no 'internal' source of e.m.f.) in a uniform magnetic field at right angles to its axis of rotation. Let the loop, ABCD (fig. 20), be maintained in rotation, with constant angular velocity ω, in the positive direction about X'OX as axis. Let there be a uniform magnetic field established in the region of the rotating loop, let Z'OZ be the field direction and let the magnetic flux density be B. At time t, when the loop has rotated through an angle θ ($= \omega t$) from the position shown in the figure, Φ, the magnitude of the magnetic flux through the loop is given (equation (77)) by

$$\Phi = 4abB \cos \theta.$$

At that instant let the magnitude of the induced current in the loop be i. In this connection positive direction of current flow in the loop is taken to be in the sense ABCDA—the direction of positive rotation around Z'OZ at $t = 0$. Then, at time t, the forces acting on the four sides of the loop are as follows (see equation (56)):

$$\text{on AB,} \quad 2aiB, \quad \text{parallel to OY,}$$
$$\text{on BC,} \quad 2biB \cos \theta, \text{ along OX',}$$
$$\text{on CD,} \quad 2aiB, \quad \text{parallel to OY',}$$
$$\text{on DA,} \quad 2biB \cos \theta, \text{ along OX.}$$

These forces combine to form a couple G, effective about X'OX, the axis of rotation of the loop, of magnitude (and direction) given by the expression

$$G = -2aiB \cdot 2b \sin \theta.$$

In order that the loop shall be maintained in steady rotation as we have assumed, an external agency must do work against this couple. At the instant in question the power which must be generated by this agency is given by $-G\omega$; that is

$$P = 4abiB\omega \sin \theta.$$

We may express this power (see equation (66)) in terms of the current i, and V, the instantaneous magnitude of the induced electromotive force effective in the rotating loop. In this way we have

$$iV = 4abiB\omega \sin \theta.$$

Remembering that $\theta = \omega t$, we now have the following results:

$$\Phi = 4abB \cos \omega t,$$

$$V = 4abB\omega \sin \omega t.$$

We may eliminate B, and $4ab$, the area of the loop, and we finally obtain

$$V = -\frac{d\Phi}{dt} \tag{78}$$

In equation (78) the two empirical generalisations of Lenz and Faraday (concerning, respectively, the direction and magnitude of the induced e.m.f.) are exemplified in relation to the simple case that we have considered. We shall leave the matter there, without further discussion: henceforth we shall assume that the equation is applicable generally, however the variation in the magnetic flux linked with a conducting circuit is produced. (Indeed we shall accept the equation as valid when a conducting circuit is not in question, only a closed curve in a non-conducting medium —see p. 127). And we shall take it for granted that the result, in the general case, derives directly from 'Ampère's law' for the 'ponderomotive' force on a current element in a magnetic field— and the law of conservation of energy.

Having accepted equation (78) in its general context, we note that it provides an alternative defining equation for the unit of magnetic flux. On the basis of equation (77) we identified that unit as the joule per ampere. Equation (78) shows that it is equally appropriate to refer to the unit as the volt second. However, magnetic flux being a physical quantity of great practical (technological) importance, a particular designation was assigned to it by decision of the Ninth General Conference of Weights and Measures in 1948. The unit of magnetic flux in the rationalised M.K.S.A. system is thus officially known as the weber. In conformity with this decision it is general to refer to the unit of magnetic flux density (magnetic induction) as the weber per metre^2.

3.8. MUTUAL INDUCTANCE AND SELF INDUCTANCE

On the basis of the law of Biot and Savart, and knowing the geometrical form of any current-carrying circuit and the magnetic permeability of the medium in which it is situated, we can, in principle, calculate the magnetic flux density at any point in the medium. In particular, if there were a second closed circuit in the neighbourhood of the first, we could, in principle, calculate the flux density at all points in a (finite) surface which had this second circuit as boundary. In that way we could obtain the total flux threading the second circuit and attributable to the existence of the steady current in the first. It is implicit in the form of the Biot–Savart law that the total magnetic flux so calculated should be directly proportional to the magnitude of the current to which it is due. In self-evident notation, then, we may write

$$\Phi_2 = {_2}M_1 i_1,$$

where the quantity ${_2}M_1$ depends only upon the permeability of the medium (it is obviously directly proportional to μ) and the geometrical configuration of the two circuits concerned.

Suppose, now, that we have a precisely similar system of two circuits in which all linear dimensions are n times greater than before. Suppose that the same current flows in the 'first' circuit as previously. Then, according to the Biot–Savart law (equation (52)), the magnetic flux density at any point within the 'second' circuit is $1/n$ times the value that it had at the corresponding point within the second circuit of the original arrangement. However, the area of the 'second' circuit is now n^2 times the previous area. We conclude that the quantity ${_2}M_1$ is n times greater than before. If it were the case that the purely geometrical ('configurational') factor in ${_2}M_1$ were derivable from a double integration of an expression giving the elementary contribution to that factor arising from an element ds_1 of the first circuit considered in relation to an element ds_2 of the second, the two elements being separated by a distance r, then, so far as lengths (as distinct from angles) are concerned, obviously the simplest form of such expression, consistent with this result, would be $ds_1 ds_2/r$. When Kelvin came to consider the matter, he recognised that a formula due to Neumann gave the quantity ${_2}M_1$ precisely. In our units, Neumann's formula may be written

$$ {_2}M_1 = \frac{\mu}{4\pi} \int_1 \int_2 \frac{ds_1 ds_2 \cos \phi}{r} \tag{79}$$

Here ϕ is the angle between the directions of the two elements

ds_1 and ds_2, and the integrations are taken round the two closed circuits in turn.

Considering the form of equation (79) we note immediately that it is entirely symmetrical in relation to the two circuits involved. If, in respect of our original configuration, we had started by calculating the total magnetic flux threading the first circuit and due to current i_2 in the second, we should have been led to the formal result

$$\Phi_1 = {}_1M_2 i_2.$$

Neumann's formula obviously gives the same value for ${}_1M_2$ as for ${}_2M_1$. For a system of two closed circuits, the total magnetic flux through either circuit, due to unit current flowing in the other, is the same. For such a system, then, we have no need to distinguish between the two coefficients ${}_1M_2$ and ${}_2M_1$; we replace them by a single coefficient M. Kelvin referred to this quantity as the 'coefficient of mutual induction' of the two circuits; more generally, nowadays, it is referred to as the 'mutual inductance' of the system.

Clearly, at this stage, we are accepting the uniqueness of the coefficient M, for a pair of closed circuits, on circumstantial evidence, only. We have not established Neumann's formula, though we have given plausible reasons for its general form. However, we shall leave the matter there for the moment, to return to it later (see p. 137). Meanwhile, we note that if μ is constant for the medium (that is, independent of the value of H, see equation (65)), and if there is in one circuit of a pair a current i which is varying, there is in consequence an induced e.m.f. in the other circuit of instantaneous value

$$V = -M\frac{di}{dt}$$

(see equation (78)).

During the year 1834, a certain William Jenkin, a young man who had been warned by his father not to waste his time on scientific pursuits, was one of many who called on Faraday with 'suggestions, hints for discovery, and propositions of various kinds . . . for my exclusive investigation and final honour'. As Faraday also recorded, 'but for [this] one exception . . . [such suggestions] have all been worthless'.

William Jenkin reported to Faraday that he had succeeded in giving himself a very appreciable electric shock, using no more powerful source of current than a single voltaic cell. He had wound a long piece of copper wire round a cylinder of soft iron, then holding the two ends of the wire, one in each hand, he had connected them to the two plates of the voltaic cell. Still holding both ends of the copper wire, he had next broken the contact with the cell. At that instant he had experienced the shock—and he had noticed a spark pass between the wire and the plate terminal, as the connection was broken. There was no shock, and no spark, if the same procedure were repeated using a short length of copper wire, instead of the iron-cored coil, for the external circuit of the cell.

Faraday immediately recognised the non-trivial nature of Jenkin's discovery, and for the next few months devoted much of his time to a detailed investigation of the phenomenon. On 29 January 1835, he presented an account of his results to the Royal Society in a paper entitled 'On the influence by induction of an electric current upon itself'. Precisely a week later, Joseph Henry (1797-1878), professor of natural philosophy in the New Jersey College at Princeton, reported his researches, 'On the influence of a spiral conductor in increasing the intensity from a galvanic arrangement of a single pair', before the American Philosophical Society in Washington. It might appear (from this account) as if the phenomenon of self induction of current, through some strange chance, had forced itself on the attention of these two experimenters in England and in America at the same hour! Facts do not bear out this romantic gloss: early in 1832 Henry had made his first observations of the effect (comparable with those of Jenkin), and he had published a brief account of them in the *American Journal of Science* in the same year.

Whatever may be written regarding priority, the basic explanation of the observations of Henry and Jenkin is simple enough. When current is flowing in any circuit, the circuit itself encloses magnetic flux due to the current; when the circuit is broken this flux must sink to zero. Consider the closed loop consisting of the material of the original circuit and the small gap which is rapidly opening as the circuit is broken. During this phase the flux through this loop is changing, so there is induced e.m.f. effective in it. According to Ohm's law, this induced e.m.f. operates preferentially in the region of greatest resistance, that is across the gap. Under ordinary conditions a spark passes through the residual gas as the gap is opening (see chap. 4)—it could even be initiated if the break were in vacuum (see chap. 10).

Obviously, when a conductor is first connected across the terminals of a battery a similar situation obtains: initially there is no current and no magnetic flux; eventually there is a steady current with its associated flux linking the circuit. But the phenomena on 'make' are not as spectacular as those on the 'break' of the circuit. Essentially, at 'make' there is no current until metallic contact has been achieved; the process of growth of current takes place in the complete circuit, there is no spark across the gap—at 'break' the process of decay of current involves the bridging of the gap, or some other channel of leakage. A person holding both ends of the wire experiences a shock, and a spark is seen.

Kelvin defined the 'coefficient of self induction' ('self inductance') of a closed circuit, by analogy with the corresponding quantity for a pair of circuits, through the formula

$$\Phi = Li.$$

Here Φ is the magnetic flux linked with the circuit and attributable to the steady current i which flows in it. Clearly, self inductance and mutual inductance are quantities of the same nature. Each involves the product of the permeability of the medium and a configurational factor having the dimensions of a length. In the rationalised M.K.S.A. system the unit of inductance is the henry; on the basis of our last statement we can now say that the unit of magnetic permeability is the henry per metre. Previously (p. 107) we concluded that the unit of permeability is the newton per ampere[2]. Our new (alternative) specification has already been referred to in anticipation (p. 119) when it was compared with that of the unit of permittivity, the farad per metre. This comparison was then said to 're-emphasise the symmetry underlying our definitions of ϵ and μ'; here it may be added that it also emphasises the symmetry which exists between the quantities capacitance and inductance. Each of these, indeed, is given by the product of a quantity characterising the medium and a configurational factor having the dimensions of length. If the permittivity and the permeability of the medium are known, the capacitance of a condenser and the inductance of a coil (or of two coils) immersed in the medium can be calculated merely on the basis of measurements of length.

The fact that the mutual inductance of a pair of coils can be calculated in this way has an important bearing on the realisation of a practical method of giving effect to our fundamental definition of the unit of current. We have already pointed out that the formal definition of this unit is based on a physical situation that is 'still somewhat idealised' (p. 106). Let us consider a system of two coils, carrying steady currents i_1 and i_2, respectively. Let the total

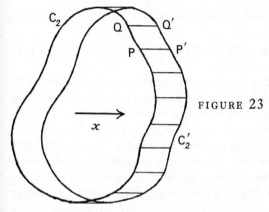

FIGURE 23

magnetic flux through the 'second' coil be represented by $_2\Phi_1 + _2\Phi_2$, $_2\Phi_1$ being the flux through this coil due to the current i_1 in the 'first' coil and $_2\Phi_2$ the flux due to the current i_2 in the second coil itself. We may write

$$_2\Phi_1 = Mi_1, \; _2\Phi_2 = L_2 i_2,$$

where M is the mutual inductance of the two coils in the arrangement considered and L_2 is the self inductance of coil 2. Coil 1 being held fixed, suppose that coil 2 moves parallel to itself through a small distance dx (see fig. 23) in an arbitrary direction. On the assumption that the currents through the coils remain the same (so that, in particular, $_2\Phi_2$ remains constant), the increase in the total magnetic flux through coil 2 is given by

$$\frac{\partial {_2\Phi_1}}{\partial x} dx = i_1 \frac{\partial M}{\partial x} dx \qquad (80)$$

In terms of fig. 23, where C_2 represents the original and C'_2 the final position of coil 2, this increase in flux (traversing the loops C_2, C'_2 in the general sense of x increasing) is obviously equal to the total inwards flux, due to the current in coil 1, through the strip-like surface, between the boundaries of C_2 and C'_2, generated by the motion of coil 2 from position C_2 to C'_2. If $_2B_1$ is the magnitude of the magnetic flux density at the centre of the element PQ attributable to the current i_1 in coil 1, and if the direction of $_2B_1$ makes an angle ϕ with the inwards drawn normal to the element of area PQQ'P' then we have

$$\frac{\partial_2 \Phi_1}{\partial x} dx = dx \int_2 {}_2B_1 \cos \phi \sin \psi \, ds \qquad (81)$$

Here ds is the length of PQ, $\angle$ P'PQ $= \psi$, and integration is performed round the boundary C_2.

Consider, now, the ponderomotive force on the element PQ when coil 2 is in position C_2. We assume that current is flowing in the direction from Q to P (so that the components of flux, $_2\Phi_1$ and $_2\Phi_2$, traverse the loop C_2 in the same sense). We are concerned only with the component of force in the direction PP' (the direction of x increasing). In order to calculate this force component we need to know the component of magnetic flux density at the mid-point of PQ in a direction normal to the elementary plane area PQQ'P'. So far as the flux density attributable to the current in coil 1 is concerned, there is a normal component of magnitude $_2B_1 \cos \phi$ along the inwards normal, as we have stated above. For the flux density attributable to the current in coil 2, in the ideal case, when the cross-section of the current-carrying conductor is indefinitely small, we have, at any point in the conductor itself, $_2B_2 = 0$, precisely. This result has already been established (p. 77) for the ideal case of a long straight conducting wire: it is true generally when the wire is indefinitely thin. In the next section we shall be considering certain aspects of the problems of definition introduced when the finite cross-sections of real conductors are taken count of; here we confine attention to ideal conditions. On this basis, then, the current i_2 flowing from Q to P in the element PQ experiences ponderomotive force in the plane PQQ'P' on account of the component of flux density $_2B_1 \cos \phi$ normal to this plane. This ponderomotive force is of magnitude $i_2 \, _2B_1 \cos \phi \, ds$, and since it acts in a direction at right angles to PQ (and generally towards P'Q' according to the directions that

we have specified for i_2 and $_2B_1$) the component of force along PP'
may be written

$$dF_x = i_2 \,_2B_1 \cos \phi \sin \psi \, ds.$$

On the whole coil then, in the direction of x increasing, we have
ponderomotive force of amount F_x given by

$$F_x = i_2 \int_2 \,_2B_1 \cos \phi \sin \psi \, ds.$$

Substituting from equation (81) we obtain

$$F_x = i_2 \frac{\partial_2 \Phi_1}{\partial x}$$

and, from equation (80), finally

$$F_x = i_1 i_2 \frac{\partial M}{\partial x} \tag{82}$$

Before proceeding, we may note the essential symmetry of
equation (82). The equation gives the x-component of ponderomotive force on coil 2, and if we had been strictly cautious we
should have derived it in terms of $_2M_1$, rather than M, as we did
originally (p. 135). Then a similar equation, involving $_1M_2$,
would have given the x-component of ponderomotive force on
coil 1, in the specified arrangement. That having been done, we
should have been led to the conclusion that these two forces
could not be equal in magnitude (and opposite in direction), as
they assuredly must be, unless $_2M_1 = {}_1M_2$, generally. In these
considerations we have a second indication of the validity of the
concept of a unique coefficient of mutual induction relative to a
pair of coils. Previously we have been content to accept Neumann's
formula (equation (79)) on trust, and to interpret it in this way.

Let us now consider equation (82) in relation to the design of
a current balance ('ampere balance'), the standard instrument in
which effect is given to the formal definition of unit current in the
rationalised M.K.S.A. system. In such an instrument the same
current is passed through two coils (or two systems of coils), the
resultant force acting on one coil (or system of coils) is measured
(almost certainly in gravitational units, initially), the quantity
$\partial M / \partial x$ is evaluated by measurements of length and subsequent
computation, then finally the magnitude of the current is deduced
on the basis of equation (82). The problem of the design of the

balance focuses chiefly on the properties of the derivative quantity $\partial M/\partial x$. We separate out the two factors involved in this quantity: the magnetic permeability of the medium and the configurational factor which depends only on measurement of length. Ideally, the arrangement should operate in vacuum—then the value of the permeability is given by definition (as $4\pi \times 10^{-7}$ henry/metre); when it operates in air the permeability is very little different, but the 'correction' must obviously be known. It is the configurational

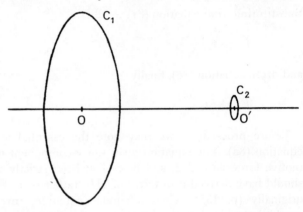

FIGURE 24

factor that is such as to give scope for ingenuity in design. We note, first of all, that since the configurational factor in M is of the dimension of length, the configurational factor in $\partial M/\partial x$ is a pure number (as Ampère originally concluded, the force between current carrying coils is unchanged if all linear dimensions are similarly modified, the currents remaining the same). The configurational factor in $\partial M/\partial x$ is, then, a 'shape' factor rather than a 'size' factor—and the problem is to choose the most advantageous shape. For practical—and intuitive—reasons, we limit consideration to axially symmetrical systems: in respect of such systems the problem reduces to the question of the relative diameters of the coils and their relative axial separation. Here, to simplify calculation, whilst providing an instructive example of relevant considerations, we shall confine attention to a coaxial system of two coils, one very much larger than the other.

Let C_1, C_2, fig. 24, represent the large and small coils, arranged along OO' as common axis. Let the radii of the coils be a and fa

($f \ll 1$), and let the separation of their centres be x. Then we may consider the flux density due to unit current in C_1 to be constant over the area of C_2. Evidently, the direction of this flux density will be along OO', and on the basis of the Biot–Savart law, and on this approximation, its magnitude will be

$$\frac{\mu}{4\pi} \cdot \frac{2\pi a}{a^2 + x^2} \cdot \frac{a}{(a^2 + x^2)^{\frac{1}{2}}}.$$

The mutual inductance M is obtained by multiplying the flux density per unit current by the area of C_2; thus

$$M = \frac{\pi}{2} \mu f^2 \frac{a^4}{(a^2 + x^2)^{\frac{3}{2}}},$$

and $$-\frac{\partial M}{\partial x} = \frac{3\pi}{2} \mu f^2 \frac{a^4 x}{(a^2 + x^2)^{\frac{5}{2}}} \qquad (83)$$

(Note that the sign of this expression, taken in conjunction with equation (82), implies that when the currents are in the same sense in C_1 and C_2 the resulting ponderomotive force is one of mutual attraction, as we have learned to expect.)

In the matter of design, the important aspect of equation (83) is that the absolute magnitude of $\partial M / \partial x$ is a maximum when $x = a/2$. Substituting this maximum value in equation (82), and assuming that the same current flows through each of the two coils, we have

$$F_{max} = \frac{24\pi}{25\sqrt{5}} \mu f^2 i^2$$
$$= 1 \cdot 349 \, \mu f^2 i^2 \qquad (84)$$

Equation (84) shows that, in this case, if the separation of the coils is chosen so that the attractive force is a maximum, the only configurational factor involved is the ratio of the radii of the coils. In an instrument designed by Rayleigh, making use of this result, the ratio f was itself determined by an electrical method. The smaller coil was moved so as to be coplanar (and coaxial) with the large one, then oppositely directed currents were passed through the two coils and adjusted in relative magnitude until the magnetic field at the centre of the system was zero. The ratio of the currents was then the required ratio of the radii effective in the main experiment.

It is worth while now considering in greater detail the problem of growth of current in an inductive circuit to which we have already made brief reference (p. 134) in relation to the experiments of Jenkin and Henry. At time $t = 0$, suppose that a battery of electromotive force V is connected through an external conducting system. Let R be the total resistance of the completed circuit, and let its self inductance be L. (In practice, if the external system is a large coil of fine wire, the major part of the resistance and the self inductance of the circuit will be external to the battery.) Let i be the value of the current in the circuit at any later time t. Then, according to Ohm's law,

$$V - L\frac{di}{dt} = Ri \tag{85}$$

Two results of interest follow from this equation. In the first place, if we solve the equation as it stands, we obtain the result

$$i = \frac{V}{R}(1 - e^{-Rt/L}) \tag{86}$$

Secondly, if we multiply through by i and integrate with respect to t, we have

$$V\int_0^t i\,dt - L\int_0^t i\frac{di}{dt}\,dt = R\int_0^t i^2 dt$$

or $$Vq = \tfrac{1}{2}Li^2 + R\int_0^t i^2 dt \tag{87}$$

According to equation (86), we see that, independently of the value of L the current in the circuit ultimately reaches the steady value $i_0 = V/R$ (as given by equation (67)), but that the characteristic growth time (the time required for the current to approach to within $1/e$ of its final value) is directly proportional to L (being given precisely by L/R). According to equation (87), we see that the total energy developed in the circuit (as a result of chemical action in the battery, or otherwise), in any time t (this total energy is represented by Vq in the equation), is not all dissipated in producing heat in the material circuit (the quantity of heat is given by the second term on the right-hand side of the equation, see p. 112), but some (the amount $\tfrac{1}{2}Li^2$, to be precise) has to be accounted for in some other way. We note that whereas the evolution of heat continues as long as current continues to flow, the term $\frac{1}{2}Li^2$ in equation (87) does not increase any further once the current has become steady. Whatever, then, the interpretation of this term may prove to be, it represents an energy transaction which is confined to the initial period during which the current is growing to its final value.

In line with Faraday's insistence on the importance of the medium, Kelvin and later theorists interpreted $\frac{1}{2}Li^2$ as the measure of the electromagnetic energy given to, and stored in, the medium as the current is established in the circuit. When the circuit is broken, this stored energy is reabsorbed and dissipated as heat in the circuit by the 'extra current at break' (as Faraday termed the current evidenced by the sparks observed in the experiments of Jenkin and Henry). We may formalise this statement as follows. We start again from equation (85), taking the zero of time as the time at which the resistance of the circuit begins to increase, and the current to decrease. We write $R(t)$ for the resistance at any subsequent time, and we assume that the resistance has become infinite, and the current zero in a time T. We assume further that the self inductance of the circuit does not change significantly during this time. Carrying through the previous procedure of multiplying through by i and integrating with respect to t, we now have

$$V\int_0^T i\,dt - L\int_0^T i\,\frac{di}{dt}\,dt = \int_0^T R(t)i^2 dt,$$

or

$$Vq - \tfrac{1}{2}L[i^2]_{i_0}^0 = \int_0^T R(t)i^2 dt,$$

that is

$$Vq + \tfrac{1}{2}Li_0{}^2 = \int_0^T R(t)i^2 dt \qquad (88)$$

Equation (88) shows that the energy dissipated as heat in the circuit during the break time T is greater than that supplied by the battery during that time by the quantity $\frac{1}{2}Li_0{}^2$—the energy that we have postulated as having been stored in the medium.

It is a simple matter to extend the discussion that we have just given to the case of a pair of 'coupled' circuits. Consider an arrangement of two circuits having self inductance L_1 and L_2, respectively, mutual inductance M, resistance R_1 and R_2, and containing individual sources of e.m.f. V_1 and V_2. Let the two circuits be completed at the same time, $t = 0$, and at any time thereafter let the currents in the two circuits be i_1 and i_2. Then we have

$$V_1 - L_1 \frac{di_1}{dt} - M \frac{di_2}{dt} = R_1 i_1$$

$$V_2 - M \frac{di_1}{dt} - L_2 \frac{di_2}{dt} = R_2 i_2$$

(89)

Multiplying the first of these equations by i_1 and the second by i_2, adding, and integrating with respect to t, we obtain

$$\int_0^t (V_1 i_1 + V_2 i_2)dt = L_1 \int_0^{i_1} i_1 di_1 + M \int_0^{i_1, i_2} (i_1 di_2 + i_2 di_1) + L_2 \int_0^{i_2} i_2 di_2 + $$

$$+ \int_0^t (R_1 i_1{}^2 + R_2 i_2{}^2)dt,$$

or, since

$$i_1 di_2 + i_2 di_1 = d(i_1 i_2),$$

in our previous notation,

$$V_1 q_1 + V_2 q_2 = \tfrac{1}{2} L_1 i_1{}^2 + M i_1 i_2 + \tfrac{1}{2} L_2 i_2{}^2 + \int_0^t (R_1 i_1{}^2 + R_2 i_2{}^2)dt \quad (90)$$

If we interpret equation (90) in the same way as we interpreted equation (87), we shall conclude that, for a pair of coupled circuits in which steady currents i_1 and i_2 have been established, the amount of electromagnetic energy stored in the medium is

$$\tfrac{1}{2} L_1 i_1{}^2 + M i_1 i_2 + \tfrac{1}{2} L_2 i_2{}^2.$$

In the case of the single circuit we considered the reabsorption of the stored energy during the process of breaking the circuit, equation (88) showing that this energy reappears as heat along with an amount of energy provided by the battery (and depending on the length of the break time T). Here it is instructive to consider the energy changes involved when the configuration of a pair of coupled circuits is altered, each circuit remaining intact in the process. Suppose that in the initial state (at $t = 0$) the currents in the two circuits are steady (i_{10} and i_{20}) and the mutual inductance is M, and that in the final state (at $t = T$) the currents are again steady (and unchanged in value) and the mutual inductance is M'. Suppose, further, that the only configurational change that has taken place has been in the relative positions of the two circuits: the circuits themselves have not been altered in size or shape in any way. Then we can say, at once, that an amount $(M - M')i_{10}i_{20}$ of stored energy has been lost by the medium. For sake of precision, let us suppose that this quantity is positive—that, indeed, we are considering the case of two circuits, carrying similarly directed currents, the separation of which has been increased. In this case the configurational change that we have postulated has been such as to reduce the total magnetic flux through each circuit, so that a positively directed (time-varying) e.m.f. has been induced in each—and, hence, a positively directed, time-varying 'extra' current. If we denote by i_1 and i_2 the instantaneous values of total current in the two circuits at any time whilst the configuration is changing, we can make use of equations (89), as before, but these equations must now be written

$$V_1 - L_1 \frac{di_1}{dt} - \frac{d(Mi_2)}{dt} = R_1 i_1,$$

$$V_2 - \frac{d(Mi_1)}{dt} - L_2 \frac{di_2}{dt} = R_2 i_2.$$

We multiply the first equation by i_1 and the second by i_2, as previously, but this time we integrate separately with respect to t. We have

$$\int_0^T V_1 i_1 dt - L_1 \int_{i_{10}}^{i_{10}} i_1 di_1 - \int_M^{M'} i_1 i_2 dM - \int_{i_{20}}^{i_{20}} i_1 M di_2 = \int_0^T R_1 i_1{}^2 dt,$$

$$\int_0^T V_2 i_2 dt - \int_M^{M'} i_2 i_1 dM - \int_{i_{10}}^{i_{10}} i_2 M di_1 - L_2 \int_{i_{20}}^{i_{20}} i_2 di_2 = \int_0^T R_2 i_2{}^2 dt.$$

Let us consider the situation when the change is carried out reversibly ($T \to \infty$). In this case i_1 and i_2 never differ more than infinitesimally from i_{10} and i_{20}, respectively, and the integrals with respect to i_1 and i_2 do not differ significantly from zero. In each equation, the integral with respect to M gives rise to a term which is indistinguishable from $(M - M')i_{10}i_{20}$, but the integrals with respect to t cannot be so simply evaluated. Postponing this evaluation to a later stage in the discussion, we write in the meantime

$$V_1q_1 + (M - M')i_{10}i_{20} = \int_0^T R_1i_1{}^2dt$$

$$V_2q_2 + (M - M')i_{10}i_{20} = \int_0^T R_2i_2{}^2dt$$
(91)

According to equations (91) the energy dissipated as heat in each circuit is greater than that supplied by the battery in that circuit (which energy is represented by V_1q_1 or V_2q_2, as the case may be) by the amount $(M - M')i_{10}i_{20}$. Hitherto we have identified the source of only one-half of this extra energy—the energy originally stored in the medium has decreased by precisely $(M - M')i_{10}i_{20}$. In order to identify the source of the rest of the energy we must investigate the work done by the external agency which is responsible for separating the circuits. As we have seen, the force from one circuit on another, in any direction, is given by $i_1i_2\dfrac{\partial M}{\partial x}$ (equation (82)). In the case that we are considering this force is attractive, and the work which the external agency must do, in the 're-versible' limit, in the process of separating the circuits is clearly $-i_{10}i_{20}\displaystyle\int_M^{M'} dM$, or $i_{10}i_{20}(M - M')$—exactly the amount that we had to find. We therefore conclude that when the circuits are separated reversibly, in the way that we have postulated, so that the total magnetic flux through each decreases, energy derived equally from the mechanical work performed by the external agency, and from the electromagnetic energy stored in the field, is dissipated as heat in the two circuits, the same amount in each.

We now return to the integrations with respect to t which previously we postponed. We have already stated that during the separation of the circuits a positively directed extra current flows in each. In the 'reversible' limit, although these extra currents are vanishingly small, the quantities of electricity which they carry, during the full process of separation, are finite. Let us consider the first circuit and write $i_1 = i_{10} + i_1'$. Then, with an extension of notation which requires no further explanation, the first of equations (91) becomes

$$V_1q_{10} + V_1q_1' + (M - M')i_{10}i_{20} = \int_0^T R_1(i_{10} + i_1')^2dt,$$

and, on the assumption $T \to \infty$, $i_1' \to 0$, we have

$$V_1 q_{10} + V_1 q_1' + (M - M') i_{10} i_{20} = R_1 i_{10} q_{10} + 2 R_1 i_{10} q_1'.$$

But $i_{10} = V_1 / R_1$, since i_{10} is the steady current in the initial configuration, thus

$$V_1 q_1' + (M - M') i_{10} i_{20} = 2 R_1 i_{10} q_1' = 2 V_1 q_1' \qquad (92)$$

Equations (92) may now be interpreted as follows. The quantity $2 R_1 i_{10} q_1'$ is the total additional energy dissipated as heat in the first circuit during the change of configuration that we have considered. Half this quantity, represented by $(M - M') i_{10} i_{20}$, we have already identified as to origin—it comes jointly from the mechanical work done in separating the circuits and from the electro-magnetic energy stored in the field. The other half, represented by $V_1 q_1'$, originates in the battery. As a consequence of the relative movement of the circuits, the battery in each, in the case that we have considered, liberates more energy in a given time (uses up more of its chemical constituents) than would have been the case if the circuits had remained stationary during that time. Moreover, as a little consideration will show, the additional energy so provided, over the whole process of separation of the circuits, is the same for the two batteries. Overall, then, in each circuit additional energy in total amount $2(M - M') i_{10} i_{20}$ is dissipated in heat—and, to be precise, there are three distinct contributions to this energy, by the battery in the circuit, by the existing electro-magnetic field, and by the external agency which performs the work of separation.

3.9. REAL CONDUCTORS

Throughout the whole of the discussions of this chapter—save in the matter of Ohm's law (p. 110)—we have consistently disregarded the fact that an electrical conductor in the form of a metal wire has a finite cross-section. We have persisted in the (generally undeclared) approximation according to which such a wire is represented by a geometrical line, and our use of the concept of 'current element' has given an appearance of respectability to this convention. Naturally, there are various situations in which this approximation is unacceptable on purely practical grounds, but in relation to the concept of the inductance of circuits it is open to more serious criticism. The fundamental definition of the self inductance of a circuit, as the magnetic flux linked with the circuit per unit of current flowing in the circuit (p. 134), is clearly imprecise unless the geometrical circuit is precisely delineated. Similarly, the notion of the area of a plane circuit is ill-defined (see p. 86) if the physical boundary is a real wire of non-zero radius.

The difficulty to which we have just drawn attention appears less obviously if we define the self inductance of a circuit as the e.m.f. developed in the circuit per unit rate of change of current in the circuit (p. 140). This, indeed, is a form of definition more directly related to experimental methods of comparing inductances, and so might be regarded as preferable to the other. But the definition is unambiguous only if the distribution of current over the cross-section of the wire forming the circuit is uniform in all situations. It is a matter of fact, that we cannot here pause to substantiate, that this is not inevitably the case: ultimately, if the rate of change of current is great enough, the current tends to avoid the axial filaments of the wire and be concentrated in the surface layers. And, in any case, this definition $\left(V = -L \dfrac{di}{dt} \right)$ is ultimately derivative from the other—moreover, it is on the basis of the other definition ($\Phi = Li$) that we have earlier claimed (p. 134) that the magnitude of an inductance can be calculated in absolute units in terms of the permeability of the medium and the geometrical dimensions of the coil (or pair of coils) of which the inductance is required. Fundamentally, it is more important that our definition* should provide the basis for the development of a procedure of standardisation (as with the current balance, see p. 137) than that it should merely relate to a method of comparing one inductance with another.

In order to carry our discussion farther, it is necessary to derive a general result that we have not hitherto required. We start from the proposition which we have already accepted (though we have verified it only in a particular case, see p. 83) that the magnetic field due to an elementary current loop of area dS, at any 'external' point, is indistinguishable from that of an elementary

---

* A third definition, favoured by the theorists, is in terms of the energy stored in the medium, $W = \frac{1}{2}Li^2$ (p. 140). We shall not pursue this definition in detail here.

doublet of moment dM, centred in and having its axis along the normal to the loop, provided that

$$dM = \mu i\, dS \tag{93}$$

Here i is the magnitude of the current in the loop and μ is the permeability of the surrounding medium (see equation (56), and p. 108 for the identification of γ''/γ' with μ).

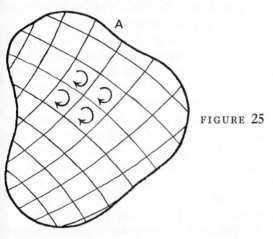

FIGURE 25

Consider, now, a finite current loop, A (fig. 25), of arbitrary shape. Let i be the magnitude of the current in the loop. Consider any continuous geometrical surface of which the loop is the boundary, and imagine this surface to be subdivided into elements of area by a grid of mutually intersecting lines, as shown. Then it is clear, on the basis of the first of Ampère's statements of equilibrium (p. 93), that the external magnetic field due to the current i in loop A can be regarded as the resultant of the fields due to currents of the same magnitude, i, circulating in the same sense on all the elementary loops into which the arbitrarily chosen surface bounded by A has been subdivided. For, except when the boundary of one of these elementary loops coincides (in part) with the boundary of the finite loop A, it is immediately adjacent to the boundary of a neighbouring elementary loop, and over each such region of congruence equal currents are flowing in opposite directions, so cancelling one another externally.

We have accepted the result that the external magnetic field due to an elementary current loop is indistinguishable from that of an elementary magnetic doublet, suitably placed and orientated, and of moment directly proportional to the area of the loop and the strength of the current (equation (93))—and now we have shown that the magnetic field due to a finite loop can be decomposed (in an infinite number of ways) into component fields due to the same current circulating in a set of elementary loops completely covering a surface of which the finite loop is the boundary. Combining these two results, we conclude that the external magnetic field due to a current i in a finite loop is indistinguishable from the field due to a uniform distribution of magnetic doublets so disposed that their centres lie on any surface of which the loop is the boundary, their axes being normal to this surface (and in the appropriate sense), provided that the surface density of magnetic dipole moment is μi, everywhere on the surface. This conclusion identifies the magnetic field due to a finite current loop with the external field due to a 'uniform magnetic shell' of strength given by μi, i being the current in the loop and μ the permeability of the medium in which it is situated. If we regard a 'magnetic shell' as a real physical entity (which we are under no obligation to do), we think of it as a thin sheet of magnetisable material magnetised everywhere in a direction normal to its surface, and we define the 'strength' of such a shell as the magnetic moment per unit surface area.

Let us now calculate the magnetic potential at a point external to a uniform magnetic shell of arbitrary form. We suppose that the surface of the shell is not a closed surface, but rather that it is bounded by the curve AA' (fig. 26), itself not necessarily a plane curve. P, in the figure, is an external point, and BN is the normal to the surface of the shell through B. If the strength of the shell is λ, the magnetic dipole moment associated with an area dS around B is λdS. BN is the axis of this elementary moment, and if $\angle$PBN $= \theta$, BP $= r$, the contribution to the magnetic potential at P due to the moment associated with dS is given by

$$d\phi = \frac{\lambda dS \cos \theta}{4\pi\mu r^2} \tag{94}$$

Here we have taken over equation (40), p. 56, replacing the electric dipole moment in that equation by the magnetic dipole moment of our present problem, and we have written $\gamma' = 1/4\pi\mu$ as is appropriate to the case (see p. 120). In using this form we have, in effect, deliberately accepted a definition of magnetic potential exactly analogous to that of electric potential elaborated in section 2.5. We record this acceptance in brief by writing, as defining equation, and as the analogue of equation (9), p. 28,

$$H_s = -\frac{\partial \phi}{\partial s} \tag{95}$$

Examining equation (94), we see at once that it can be simplified geometrically by our writing $d\omega$ for $(dS \cos \theta)/r^2$. Clearly, $d\omega$ is

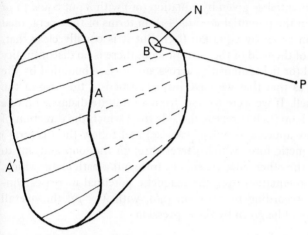

FIGURE 26

the solid angle subtended at P by the area dS around B. On this basis, equally clearly, the magnetic potential at P due to the whole shell is given by

$$\phi = \frac{\lambda \omega}{4\pi \mu} \tag{96}$$

where ω is the solid angle subtended at P by the curve AA′, the boundary of the shell. We note that equation (96) is already in the conventional form in which 'the potential at infinity' is directly given as zero. Only one further remark is relevant here: obviously we must devise a convention regarding the sign of the potential. We do this naturally by saying that when the radius vector from P strikes the surface of the shell (as at B) first on the positive (or north-seeking) face, then the elementary area of shell around the point in question makes a positive contribution to the potential at P. In terms of this convention, and equation (96), we have the necessary result that as between any two points along a common normal and on opposite faces of the shell there is a constant difference of magnetic potential of λ/μ—however thin the shell may be.

Our next enquiry concerns the relevance of equation (96) to the case of the current loop. If AA' (fig. 26) had been a conducting loop carrying a steady current i, it is clear from our earlier discussion that the magnetic field at P would have been derivable from the potential ϕ, given by equation (96) with λ put equal to μi (that is from the potential $\phi = i\omega/4\pi$), in terms of the operational specification given by equation (95). But it is equally clear that, in the case of the field of the current loop, there is no discontinuity of potential (or field intensity), across any surface bounded by the loop, such as that that we have just identified in the case of the uniform shell. If we were to start from an infinite distance on one side of the loop (to be precise, the side from which the direction of current flow appears as anti-clockwise) and follow the ('central') line of magnetic force which passes through the loop and out to infinity on the other side, we should trace out a path along which, according to equation (95), the magnetic potential increases continuously. According to equation (96), with $\lambda = \mu i$, the overall increase would be given by the expression

$$\phi_{-\infty} - \phi_{\infty} = i \qquad\qquad (97)$$

(ω would have increased monotonically from zero to 4π along the infinite path). Conventionally, we do not expect to have to deal with a potential which has different values at different 'points at infinity'. Indeed, equation (97) is sufficient evidence to show that the magnetic field due to a current loop cannot strictly be described in terms of a scalar potential (as the external field of a uniform magnetic shell can be). On the other hand, equation (97) is a significant statement, if otherwise interpreted. If we re-introduce the notion of the disembodied magnetic pole (for purely didactic purposes!) it refers to the work that must be done by an external agency to move a unit pole, along the path indicated, against forces due to the current in the loop. And, quite apart from this attempt to conjure up a picture of a physical process (in terms of an un-real object), we may re-formulate the result, in terms nearer to equation (95) than before,

$$\int_{-\infty}^{\infty} H_s ds = i \qquad (98)$$

(provided that the path of integration passes through the loop).

It is characteristic of any 'well behaved' potential (as we have already remarked) 'that it should be single-valued (conventionally, zero) over the whole 'surface at infinity'. This is a particular aspect of the requirement that the potential should have a unique value at each point in a space. Another way of stating this general requirement is that the force field to which the potential relates should be a conservative field—that the 'line integral' of the force intensity over any closed curve should be zero. Equation (98) gives the line integral of the magnetic field intensity along an infinite ('unclosed') path which passes through a current-carrying loop. If we had considered, instead, a finite, closed path passing through the loop, following an argument exactly similar to that which led us through equation (97) to equation (98), we should have noted the monotonic increase of ω along the path as before, and we should have concluded that for one traversal of the path the overall change in ω is precisely 4π, as in the earlier case. For any closed path threading the current loop, therefore, we have

$$\oint H_s ds = i \qquad (99)$$

—and we recognise equation (98) as representing a special (and extreme) case of this general result. We recognise also, that around a closed path which does not thread the loop the line integral is necessarily zero (under no convention as to sign can ω increase monotonically around a closed path which does not thread the loop). Finally, reversing the emphasis in our interpretation of equation (99), we can state our conclusions as follows: when a magnetic field is due entirely to currents, the line integral of the magnetic field intensity around any closed path is equal to the algebraic sum of all the currents threading the path. In respect of this statement, the direction of integration around the path, and the positive direction of current flow through it, are related conventionally by the right-handed screw rule, the normal mathematical convention in such cases. In the present century, equation (99), rather than equation (64), p. 104, to which we have previously given that designation, has come to be known as Ampère's formula. Modern usage in this matter at least has this to be said in its favour, that equation (99) provides a regularly used, and fully substantiated, basis of numerical calculation, whereas equation (64) has been largely abandoned for computational purposes (and its fundamental validity is suspect).

We embarked on the development of Ampère's formula (p. 146) in order to be able to carry farther our discussion of the concepts of self inductance and mutual inductance in relation to real circuits formed of conductors of finite cross-section. We shall use it to treat a particular case in some detail, thereby exemplifying the general problem. Even so, we shall not be able to achieve a full measure of realism: the only cases for which the complication of the mathematical analysis is not prohibitive are those of a pair of infinite parallel wires and of an infinite wire surrounded by a co-axial conducting sheath. Here, then, we shall consider the self inductance of a length l of a system of two infinite, parallel, cylindrical wires of radius a situated in vacuum, the axes of the wires being separated by a distance r ($r \gg a$). Treating this infinite system as a current-carrying circuit, we suppose that equal currents flow in opposite directions in the two wires, the current being uniformly distributed over the cross-section of each wire. Moreover, when we speak of the self inductance of a finite length of such an infinite system we refer to the total magnetic flux linked with the current through that finite length, per unit current in the whole circuit. Clearly, the system that we are to discuss is idealised, in some degree, but at least we assume a finite cross-section for the wires.

Let us begin by considering a single infinite straight wire carrying a current i, the circuit being completed 'at infinity'. Let A (fig. 27) be a right section of the wire, and let O be the centre of this section. We wish to calculate the magnetic flux density at P and Q, representative points outside and inside the wire. We assume that the wire is situated in vacuum (permeability μ_0) and that the permeability of the material of the wire is μ. If OP $= p$, OQ $= q$, we may calculate the magnetic field intensity at the two points in question by means of equation (99), taking the line integral around circular paths in the plane of the diagram and centred in O, the first path having radius p, and the second path radius q. The direction of the magnetic field at P is certainly tangential to the former path, and from general considerations of symmetry the magnetic lines of force within the material of the wire must also be circles centred in the axis. We have, then, in the first case, the simple result

$$2\pi p H_P = i.$$

In the second case, the total current threading the circular path of radius q is $q^2 i/a^2$. In this case, therefore, we have

$$2\pi q H_Q = \frac{q^2 i}{a^2}.$$

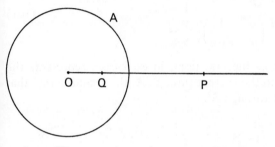

FIGURE 27

On the basis of these results, we obtain the magnitude of the magnetic flux density at the points P and Q as follows:

$$B_P = \frac{\mu_0 i}{2\pi p}$$

$$B_Q = \frac{\mu q i}{2\pi a^2}$$

(100)

We are now in a position to consider the system of two infinite parallel wires which is our main concern. Fig. 28 shows a right section of the system, with $OO' = r$.* We shall assume that current flows away from the reader through A and towards him through A'. We are concerned to know the resultant magnetic flux density at all points in OO'. Because the direction of the magnetic field intensity due to the current through A', at any such point, is the same as that due to the current through A at the same point (being perpendicular to OO' and downwards in the

* The wires are shown close together in the diagram for sake of convenience. As already stated, however, our formal considerations refer specifically to the situation in which $r \gg a$.

EM L

figure), superposition of the two fields is represented by simple addition of the magnitudes of field intensities, for all points in the range of interest. Furthermore, the right section being symmetrical about C, we may confine attention to points in the range OC. Let Q be a representative point inside the wire of which A is a section, and P be a point outside the wire and nearer to it than C. Then, making appropriate use of equations (100), we have

$$B_P = \frac{\mu_0 i}{2\pi}\left(\frac{1}{p} + \frac{1}{r-p}\right)$$

$$B_Q = \frac{\mu i}{2\pi}\left(\frac{q}{a^2} + \frac{1}{r-q}\right)$$

(101)

In these expressions the first term, in each case, represents the contribution due to the current through A, the second term* that due to the current through A'.

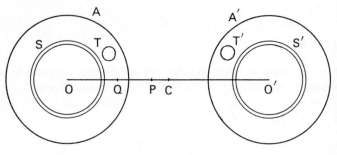

FIGURE 28

Equations (101) provide the basic results in terms of which the total magnetic flux through any rectangle having OO' (or part of OO') as base, and height l perpendicular to the plane of the figure, may be calculated. In this way we propose to obtain an effective value for the self-inductance of a length l of the parallel-wire system that we are considering. We have already made use of the assumption that the current is uniformly distributed over the cross-section of each wire; let us now sharpen that assumption by supposing that the current which passes parallel to the axis of the first wire through any small area T of A returns through the corresponding area T' of A' (T' being the mirror image of T in the

* The second term in the expression for B_Q issues from an approximation which is valid only when $r \gg a$.

line through C perpendicular to OO'). Clearly, as T varies in position in A, the magnetic flux linked with a length l of the elementary circuit defined by T and (T') varies—being greater, for example, when T is centred at O than when it is centred at Q. We have to decide how to define the effective self inductance in this case. If there were no ambiguity such as we have exposed, we should write $Li = \Phi$, Φ being the total flux linked with the current. When the total flux varies from one current filament to another, we need to define a suitable average value. We shall define the self-inductance in these circumstances by the equation

$$Li = \frac{\int \Phi \, di}{\int di} \tag{102}$$

Here Φ is the flux (due to the whole current) linked with the elementary current filament of strength di, and integration is carried out in such a way as to include all the elementary filaments which go to make up the whole circuit.

The specification of equation (102), if taken quite strictly, would imply a double integration over the cross-section of the wire. Taking the elementary current filament as one passing through A in a small area such as T (fig. 28), and fixing the position of T by two co-ordinates, we should have to integrate with respect to both in order to cover the whole cross-section. Except when the two wires are very close together, however, the lines of resultant magnetic force within the wires are effectively circles centred in the axes of the wires and lying in planes at right angles to those axes. Except in this limit, therefore, we shall make very little error if we take as our elementary current filament one which intersects the section A in the annular zone S. We represent by σ the radius of this zone (centred in O) and we denote its radial thickness by $d\sigma$. In this way we dispense with one of the two integrations which equation (102) strictly requires—and more importantly we do not need to know the values of the magnetic flux density elsewhere than at points in the line OO'. We know these values (but not any others!) already: equations (101) give them explicitly.

Having made these decisions concerning procedure, and taking L to refer to a length l of the infinite system, as we originally intended, we now have directly, in terms of equations (101) and (102), always provided that $r \gg a$,

$$\tfrac{1}{2}Li^2 = \int_0^a l \left\{ \int_a^{r/2} B_P dp + \int_\sigma^a B_Q dq \right\} \frac{2i\sigma d\sigma}{a^2}$$

$$= li \left[\int_a^{r/2} B_P dp + \int_0^a \frac{\mu i}{2\pi} \left\{ \frac{(a^2 - \sigma^2)}{2a^2} + \log_e \frac{r-\sigma}{r-a} \right\} \frac{2\sigma d\sigma}{a^2} \right]$$

$$= \frac{li^2}{2\pi} \left\{ \mu_0 \log_e \frac{r-a}{a} + \frac{1}{4}\mu + \mu \int_0^a \log_e \frac{r-\sigma}{r-a} \cdot \frac{2\sigma d\sigma}{a^2} \right\}.$$

The last term in this expression represents the contribution to L on account of the flux in either wire due to the current in the other. We imposed the condition $r \gg a$ so that this contribution should be small compared with that arising from the flux in either wire due to the current in it (represented by $\frac{1}{4}\mu$ in the expression above)—and so that our approximate treatment should be valid. Under this limitation, then, we may evaluate the term in question, to the first order in a/r, and obtain, finally,

$$L = \frac{l}{\pi} \left\{ \mu_0 \log_e \frac{r-a}{a} + \frac{\mu}{4} \left(1 + \frac{4}{3} \frac{a}{r-a} \right) \right\} \qquad (103)$$

If we had made the assumption that the current in the wires was confined to the surface of the wires, we should have obtained the result

$$L = \frac{l\mu_0}{\pi} \log_e \frac{r-a}{a}.$$

When, as is generally the case, the current is uniformly distributed over the cross-section, the self inductance is greater than this, the more so as μ/μ_0 is greater. For most 'non-magnetic' metals which are good electrical conductors (gold, silver, copper, etc.) μ/μ_0 is not significantly greater than 1, but for pure iron this ratio may be of the order of 1000. Taking, as an example, $r = 21a$ ($\log_e 20 = 3 \cdot 0$), for a parallel circuit of copper wires the ratio of the 'external' to the 'internal' self inductance is roughly $11:1$: for a similar circuit of soft iron wires it is about $1:90$.

In this section we have concentrated attention on the ambiguity inherent in the simple definition of self inductance and mutual inductance in relation to real circuits formed out of conductors of finite cross-section. That the definition of resistance is not without its subtleties, under similar scrutiny, may be seen by considering a single example. Suppose that fig. 28 were to represent, not a right section of a pair of infinite parallel wires, but a diametral section of a conducting anchor-ring (or quoit) made of material of resistivity ρ. The current filament through T, T′ would then be a circular filament in a plane at right angles to the plane of the figure. If the same e.m.f. were effective for all such circular filaments (the lengths of which are not the same), the current would not be uniformly distributed over the cross-section —and calculation would show that the effective resistance of the whole ring was given by

$$R = \frac{2r\rho}{a^2}\left(1 - \frac{1}{4}\frac{a^2}{r^2}\right),$$

to second-order accuracy in a/r. In such a case the effective resistance is not precisely in the inverse ratio of the cross-sectional area of the conductor, as we have hitherto supposed it to be (see p. 112).

3.10 SUMMARY

By way of summary we bring together, in the following table, the various units to the definition of which we have given precision in this chapter.

TABLE 1

Quantity	Rationalised M.K.S.A. Unit	Dimensions	Reference (page)
Current	ampere (A)	I^1	106
Electric Potential	volt (V)		
	(joule/coulomb)	$M^1L^2T^{-3}I^{-1}$	109
Electric Field Intensity	— volt/metre	$M^1L^1T^{-3}I^{-1}$	120
Resistance	ohm (Ω) (volt/ampere)	$M^1L^2T^{-3}I^{-2}$	112
Charge	coulomb (C)		
	(ampere second)	T^1I^1	113
Electric Flux Density (Displacement)	— coulomb/metre^2	$L^{-2}T^1I^1$	120
Capacitance	farad (F)		
	(coulomb/volt)	$M^{-1}L^{-2}T^4I^2$	114
Electric Permittivity	— farad/metre	$M^{-1}L^{-3}T^4I^2$	118
Magnetic Field Intensity	— ampere/metre	$L^{-1}I^1$	121
Magnetic Flux	weber (Wb)		
	(joule/ampere)	$M^1L^2T^{-2}I^{-1}$	130
Magnetic Flux Density (Induction) Intensity of Magnetisation	— weber/metre^2	$M^1T^{-2}I^{-1}$	130
Self (Mutual) Inductance	henry (H)		
	(weber/ampere)	$M^1L^2T^{-2}I^{-2}$	134
Magnetic Permeability	— henry/metre	$M^1L^1T^{-2}I^{-2}$	134
Magnetic Dipole Moment	— weber metre	$M^1L^3T^{-2}I^{-1}$	121

CHAPTER 4

STEADY CURRENTS IN GASES AND 'IN VACUUM'

4.1. INTRODUCTORY

The period from the publication of Ampère's *Théorie des phéno-mènes électro-dynamiques* (see p. 92) to the appearance of Maxwell's *Treatise* (see p. 44) was just short of fifty years. During that period the elaborate, and in the end highly successful, theories of the mathematical physicists of France, Germany and Britain eventually provided a complete formal description of the large-scale phenomena associated with the passage of electricity through metallic conductors—or so, at least, it seemed at the time. How-ever, almost in measure as these theories were successful, so the basic question concerning the nature of electricity receded into the background of the argument: by and large, the mathematical formalism could be interpreted equally well in terms of imponder-able fluids or material carriers of charge. In 1862 Thomson (Lord Kelvin) challenged his friend and co-author P.G.Tait, 'Tell me what electricity is, and I'll tell you everything else', but the challenge was a generation ahead of its time and was largely in jest: the promise that it made was no less extravagant than the prior question, on the answer to which that promise depended. Had not Thomson, more notably than most of his contemporaries, for the previous fifteen years or more, been prolific in writings bringing order and consistency and 'understanding' into the mathematical theory of electrical phenomena generally? In terms of what categories, or concepts, in 1862, did he imagine that further clarification was to be found? A vague prescience there may then have been in his words, but Kelvin lived on into the twentieth century without providing himself the answer that he sought. As he celebrated his eightieth birthday (1899), his name-sake J.J.Thomson (see *V & W*, p. 277) was following up the dis-covery of the electron, and so banishing for ever the concept of the imponderable fluid—and, not long after Kelvin was dead

(1907), Thomson's pupil Rutherford (see p. 252) was discovering the nucleus. Out of that discovery grew the first clear recognition that much more than a knowledge of 'what electricity is' is required if we are to know 'everything else' about the material world (see p. 3). However, with these comments we are racing ahead of our theme. The present chapter is concerned largely with the electron; the atomic nucleus will not enter into our considerations for some while yet.

Michael Faraday, many years before Kelvin, had posed a more direct, and less ambitious question: 'Admitting that a vacuum can be produced, it would be a very curious matter indeed to know what its relation to electrical phenomena would be' (1838). Faraday had experimented with currents in metallic conductors, with currents through liquids and gases (at atmospheric pressure, and to the modest limit of rarefaction which the air-pumps of the time would allow), and he had convinced himself that 'the current connected with these actions, when it occurs, appears in all cases to be the same.' He commented, 'This constancy in the character of the current . . . is exceedingly striking and important; and its investigation and development promise to supply the most open and advantageous road to a true and intimate understanding of the nature of electrical forces'. Faraday's undramatic assessment had been lost sight of in the glamour of success which attached to the theories of the mathematicians, but when J. J. Thomson's partial answer to Kelvin's question was at last given, it was by following the 'open and advantageous road' to which Faraday had pointed the way. In this chapter we consider the discoveries that resulted from the study of the passage of electricity through gases, and, in the limit, 'through vacuum'—and we reserve for the next chapter the hardly less fundamental (and mostly earlier) discoveries, many of which Faraday himself made, in relation to conduction through liquids.

The first begetter of the new discoveries was a German glass-blower Heinrich Geissler (1814-1879). When he was aged forty he settled in Bonn, and from then until the end of his life he designed and produced the apparatus, and took part in the actual experiments, of the physicists and chemists of the university in that city. In 1868 he received the honorary degree of doctor of philosophy from his adopted university as a mark of the general esteem in which he was held. For our present purposes, his main contribution was the improvement of the air-pump, and his main collaboration that with Julius Plücker (1801-1868), professor of physics since 1847. Plücker had a most remarkable career. Until the year of his appointment as professor of physics, he had published nothing in that subject—though he had already achieved international reputation as one of the founders of modern analytical geometry. *Privat-dozent* in mathematics at the age of 24, at the age of 27 he had been made professor extraordinary at Bonn; five years later he had moved to Berlin; he had been called to Halle as ordinary professor of mathematics in the following year; then, after only two years, in 1836 he had returned to Bonn, to the premier chair in mathematics in his own university. Having fulfilled the duties of that office for a decade, he brought out in 1846, a new version of some of his earlier mathematical works in a volume entitled *System of the geometry of spaces according to the new analytical methods*—and straightway he became an experimental physicist. Eighteen years later, at the age of 64, he turned once again to pure mathematics, inventing, and going far to develop, the new subject of 'line geometry'; he was awarded the Copley medal of the Royal Society of London—as a pure mathematician—in 1866. Immersed in his work in this new field, he died in 1868.

Plücker's excursion into experimental physics led to many discoveries in relation to the magnetic properties of materials (see p. 455), and in optical spectroscopy. Geissler was developing the sealed-off discharge tube, and it was Plücker's suggestion to include, between the wider portions containing the electrodes, a narrow capillary section in which the brightness of the discharge might be expected to be enhanced. The conditions necessary for the realisation of this expectation were explored, and with such tubes, containing various gases at appropriate pressures, Plücker effectively laid the foundation of spectrum analysis, some years before his countrymen R.W. von Bunsen (1811-1899) and G.R. Kirchhoff (see *V & W*, p. 188), at Heidelberg, established this technique as the powerful tool that it was destined to become. In that way, at long last, the original observation of the luminous discharge in rarefied air, which, in 1752, had so charmed Sir William Watson (1715-1787) that he wrote at length of 'the most delightful spectacle', was put to practical use. But, for our purposes, the more important of Plücker's observations on the luminous discharge were made, not on the brilliant light emitted from the capillary section of his tubes, but on the less intense luminosity which was to be observed in the wider sections around the electrodes. Plücker found that the disposition of this luminosity could be influenced considerably by the simple procedure of bringing the pole of a bar magnet into the vicinity of the tube. In 1858 he studied the effect in some detail, then in the following year he described the observation, in a highly exhausted discharge tube, of a spot of bright phosphorescence on the glass wall of the tube in the neighbourhood of the cathode. He found that the position of this phosphorescence, also, could be changed by bringing a magnet close to the tube, and he concluded that the phosphorescence was produced by 'currents of electricity' issuing from the cathode. From these seemingly trivial observations, after a period of nearly forty years, issued the discovery of the electron.

4.2. CATHODE RAYS AND THE DISCOVERY OF THE ELECTRON

Plücker's discovery of a feature of asymmetry in the luminous discharge in rarefied gases (he observed no patches of phosphorescence on the glass wall of the tube in the neighbourhood of the positive electrode) recalls the asymmetries earlier observed, and investigated in great detail by Faraday, in 'disruptive' (spark) discharges from metallic bodies, of various shapes and sizes, in free air and other gases. Summarising these results in 1838, Faraday had remarked, 'The results connected with the different conditions of positive and negative discharge will have a far greater influence on the philosophy of electrical science than we at present imagine, especially if, as I believe, they depend on the peculiarity and the degree of polarised condition which the molecules of the dielectrics concerned acquire.' So, literally, it proved to be, but the experimental 'conditions' had to be greatly refined and simplified before any effective advance in understanding could be achieved. Geissler's air-pump, and Plücker's observation of phosphorescence, when the gas pressure was as low as the pump could maintain, pointed the way, and in the forty years that followed, further technical improvements, in the air-pump, itself, and in ancillary equipment generally, largely determined the rate of progress overall.

The first step in advance resulted from the observations of

Johann Wilhelm Hittorf (1824-1914) and Eugen Goldstein (1850-1930), who showed that whatever agent is responsible for the phosphorescence, it proceeds from the cathode of the discharge tube normally, in straight lines, wherever the anode is situated in the tube. In 1869 Hittorf observed the shadows cast on the walls of the tube by solid bodies placed in front of a pointed cathode, and in 1876 Goldstein made the more convincing observation that small bodies placed close to a large plane cathode likewise cast shadows. It was from Goldstein's unexpected discovery that the term 'cathode rays' ('kathodenstrahlen') took on a definite descriptive meaning: we shall use it consistently in what follows.

Making use of the result that the cathode rays are emitted normally from the negative electrode, various later workers used concave cathodes so as to concentrate the rays on metal targets and other objects placed in their path. In this way it was shown that thin pieces of glass could be fused, and thin foils of metal raised to incandescence, by the 'impact' of the rays. Some time previously less spectacular examples of the heating effect of the rays had been noticed, and measurements of the amount of heat developed had been undertaken (1891) by Eilhard Ernst Gustav Wiedemann (1852-1928) professor of physics in the university of Erlangen, in collaboration with Hermann Ebert (1861-1913).

In the experiments of Wiedemann and Ebert, just mentioned, some indications were found, with very thin foils, that more heat was developed in thicker than in thinner foils. It was as if the incident rays were not wholly absorbed in the thinnest foils which these experimenters employed. More direct evidence of the penetration of thin foils by the rays was provided in the following year by Heinrich Rudolf Hertz (see *V & W*, p. 271), and in 1894 Philipp Eduard Anton Lenard (*ibid*, p. 277) constructed a special discharge tube having an aluminium foil of about 0.7 mg/cm^2 thickness covering a hole of 1.7 mm diameter in one end. By suitable design he was able to ensure that the cathode rays impinged on this thin aluminium window, and when that was the case, and the gas pressure within the discharge tube was sufficiently low, he observed in the air outside the window a diffuse glow, and on pieces of glass and certain other substances brought within the region of the glow the characteristic phosphorescence which these substances emit when subject to the action of the cathode rays within the tube. The most direct interpretation of the experiments just cited was that cathode rays may pass through thin layers of material, whether that material is transparent or opaque to visible light.

Almost all the workers quoted so far regarded the cathode rays as an immaterial radiation, 'waves in the ether'. At the times of which we are writing it could be held that there was much (negative) evidence in support of this view. Emanating in straight lines from the cathode, wherever the anode might be situated in the tube, they could not be involved in any direct way in transporting current between the electrodes. They were not abruptly stopped (or reflected) by solid objects placed in their path, but penetrated through measurable thicknesses of even the heaviest metals. Only the effect of a magnet, examined by Plücker, was difficult to reconcile with this hypothesis. Hertz, one of its strongest adherents, failed, in 1883, to observe any electrostatic deflection of the rays, when the field was applied transversely to the discharge tube by condenser-plates positioned inside the tube—and he was the more ready to disregard the obvious implications of Plücker's results when he also failed to find any reciprocal effect, any magnetic field external to the tube which could be attributed to the cathode rays themselves.

But the workers that we have been quoting were all of the German school of physics. On the matter of the crucial importance of the positive effect of an applied magnetic field on the paths of the rays, cleavage of opinion was markedly on national lines. Almost all British men of science took the 'obvious' view that the only entity which could be acted on in the way that the cathode rays were acted on in Plücker's experiments was a moving charged particle. The electrical engineer C. F. Varley (1828-1883) committed himself to this view unhesitatingly in 1871, and Sir William Crookes (1832-1919), chemist first and physicist afterwards, spent nearly ten years (sandwiched between an eight-years' study of the chemistry of thallium, and a period of twice that length when he was investigating the rare earth elements) bringing forward experimental evidence in its favour. Somewhat later, from 1884 to 1890, Arthur Schuster (see *V & W*, p. 235) carried out a series of experiments which were motivated by the same idea. Of these investigations, Crookes' have better stood the test of time. The main results which they yielded were described in three papers published in 1879. Crookes' chief discovery was of another cathode phenomenon, distinct from but related to the rays whose nature is in question. He found, in all gases, a sharply delimited region of negligible luminosity surrounding the cathode. As the pressure in the discharge tube was decreased, so the thickness of this 'Crookes' dark space' increased in roughly inverse ratio. The whole phenomenon had the appearance of a gas-kinetic effect in which the thickness of the dark space represented the mean free path of a particle liberated at the surface of the cathode. Crookes did not know it at the time, but an investigation of Hittorf four years later gave support to this view. Hittorf was the first to investigate how the electric field in a steady discharge varies along the length of the discharge, and he found that the field intensity near the cathode was much greater than elsewhere, also that in a given gas under a wide variety of conditions the difference of potential between the cathode and the further boundary of the Crookes' dark space was constant. British physicists of the day were predisposed to see in the situation disclosed by the observations of Crookes and Hittorf circumstances appropriate to the generation of streams of fast-moving charged particles rather than streams of ethereal waves of rather peculiar properties. However, in 1894, or thereabouts, despite the vaguely grandiloquent words of Crookes regarding a possible 'fourth state of matter', no one was bold enough to consider the possibility that the hypothetical cathode-ray particles might be other than charged atoms of the gas (or the electrode), and Schuster, who came nearest to an experimental result indicating that it might, indeed, be otherwise, shrank from the responsibility of accepting his preliminary results (1890) as a challenge, and adopted the conventional view. On that view, of course, the experiments of Hertz and Lenard on the passage of cathode rays through thin foils presented the ultimate difficulty. In the face of this difficulty, J. J. Thomson (1893) made a last ineffectual gesture to the logicians. He suggested that the 'particles' which emerged from the far side of Hertz's foils were not the same particles as were incident upon them, but merely particles having similar properties, generated in the foils by the incident beam. Clearly, the suggestion was mere word-spinning, and entirely unconvincing word-spinning at that.

The first sign of a break in the impasse came in 1895 when Jean-Baptiste Perrin (1870-1942) showed for the first time by direct experiment that the cathode rays transport negative electricity from the region of the cathode. The rays were received in a hollow metallic cylinder situated in the discharge tube, and the accession of negative charge was registered by an electroscope to which the cylinder was connected by a wire sealed through the glass wall of the tube. All of those who had investigated the magnetic deflection of the rays, from Plücker to Schuster, had been agreed that the general sense of the deflection was that which would be appropriate to a positive electric current following the path of the rays and directed towards the cathode, but Perrin's observation was something new. Previously, the opponents of the particle interpretation had been able to maintain that the statement concerning the sense of deflection was a mere formal statement—'true', but insignificant until it was shown to be correlated with some other statement of independent validity. Perrin's results provided the basis of just such a statement.

In relation to the cathode rays, the year 1895 is regarded, in general estimation, not so much as the year of Perrin's discovery, important as that was, but as the year of Röntgen's more spectacular discovery of the production of X-rays. In December of that year Röntgen reported that from the bright patch of phosphorescence which cathode rays produce on the wall of a discharge tube there proceeds a 'dark' radiation of unusual penetrating power, itself capable of producing phosphorescence on a suitable screen placed several feet away from the tube in a darkened room (see *V & W*, pp. 116, 273). A full historical account of this discovery has been given elsewhere (*Alembic Club Reprint*, No. 22, Edinburgh, 1958); here it suffices to say* that for almost the whole of the following year the energies of physicists with any interest in the general phenomena of gaseous discharge (and of many other persons, also) was largely devoted to the further study of the Röntgen phenomenon. Admittedly it had to do with the cathode rays, but the primary investigation of those rays was, for

---

* One remark might be added, without prejudice, to the previous account. More than a year before Röntgen made his discovery, Thomson had published a paper, 'On the velocity of the cathode-rays', in the *Philosophical Magazine*. There he wrote 'It is perhaps worth while to observe, in passing, that the light produced in an ordinary discharge-tube by an intense discharge is very rich in phosphorogenic rays. I have been able to detect phosphorescence in pieces of ordinary German-glass tubing held at a distance of some feet from the discharge-tube, though in this case the light had to pass through the glass walls of the vacuum-tube and a considerable thickness of air before falling on the phosphorescent body'. It is fairly clear that it was not ordinary ultra-violet light which produced the phosphorescence which Thomson observed 'in passing'!

a season, hindered rather than advanced by this exciting new discovery. It appeared to be universally agreed that the radiation that Röntgen had found must be of the nature of an ether-wave (or pulse train), but while British physicists tended to attribute the origin of this radiation to the sudden stopping of the charged cathode ray particles in the wall of the discharge tube, the Germans, having adopted the view that the cathode rays were themselves ether-waves of peculiar properties, were in no way embarrassed by the necessity of having to imagine that such waves might be transmogrified into other waves having yet other peculiar properties, merely by passage through a millimetre of glass. The participants in the Liverpool meeting of the British Association in September 1896 heard both these views advanced, at a joint discussion of the Physics and Chemistry Sections. Lenard opened the discussion, maintaining the German opinion, and was heavily criticised by Sir George Stokes (see *V & W*, pp. 256, 274), George Francis Fitzgerald (1851-1901), professor of physics at Trinity College, Dublin, and, less severely, by many others. In the following week Lenard was due to present a paper on the cathode rays before the German Association, meeting at Frankfurt-on-the-Main. There, no doubt, he delivered his prepared address, unchanged as a result of anything that had been said at Liverpool— and to a generally approving audience. So much, then, for the interlude of 1896; we shall return later (p. 182) to the important practical contribution which the discovery of the X-rays made towards the investigation of gaseous conduction at normal pressures and under small applied fields, for the present our concern is with low-pressure phenomena, and with the cathode rays in particular.

When J.J. Thomson returned to the investigations of the cathode rays in the autumn of 1896, his first objective was to make measurements of the magnetic deflection of the rays under as wide a range of conditions as possible. For that purpose he used the magnetic field generated by the current in a pair of large circular coils placed coaxially and with the discharge tube located in the space between them. With such a system of coils a fairly uniform field can be obtained over a reasonably large volume, and the apparatus was so designed that the cathode-ray beam traversed this region of uniform field in a plane perpendicular to the field direction. Viewing the deflection of the rays along the field direction,

Thomson photographed the luminosity marking the path of the cathode rays under the influence of the field. He used various gases in the discharge tube, adjusting the pressure in each case so that the potential difference necessary to maintain the discharge was always the same, then, with the magnetic field adjusted to the same value throughout, he found the surprisingly simple result that the path of the deflected rays was precisely the same in all the gases employed. 'The photographs could hardly be distinguished from one another', he wrote, 'even the details, such as the distribution of the bright and dark spaces, were the same.'

How the adherents of the ether-wave hypothesis would have interpreted Thomson's results we do not know; on the contrary assumption that the cathode rays are constituted of streams of moving charged particles, the interpretation was obvious. In its lowest terms it can be stated as follows. The potential difference between the electrodes being the same in all cases, the kinetic energy of the particles, at corresponding points in the discharge, will likewise be the same, whatever the gas employed. Then, because the magnetic deflection is the same (for the same field), unless this deflection is determined by the kinetic energy simply (independently of the mass of the particles), it is almost necessary to conclude that the particles must be of the same mass, in whatever gas they are produced. This last possibility (indeed, near certainty, as Thomson interpreted his results) was a far cry from the previous view that the cathode-ray particles must be negatively-charged atoms or molecules of the gas employed in the discharge tube. In Thomson's experiments the gases ranged from hydrogen (molecular weight 2) to methyl iodide (molecular weight 142). Using one of these gases, a few months later, Thomson also confirmed that, other conditions being as previously stated, the deflection of the cathode rays was the same whether the cathode were made of aluminium or of platinum—that is of a very light or a very heavy element.

Having given the charged-particle-stream interpretation of Thomson's experiments of 1896-7 'in its lowest terms', it is necessary that we should now be more precise concerning the conditions of magnetic deflection effective in those experiments. In so doing we shall explain the parenthesis 'indeed, near certainty' of the last paragraph. It was almost certain, in Thomson's view, that his experiments required that the cathode-ray particles should be the same whatever the gas, just because he believed that the magnetic deflection of moving particles (of a given charge, in a given field) is determined by their momentum simply, not by their kinetic energy. It is this point that we have now to elaborate.

In section 2.9 we discussed equation (52), expressing the law of Biot and Savart for the magnetic field intensity due to a current element at an external point, in terms of the notion that the current in a conducting wire is carried by discrete charges of unique magnitude e moving through the conductor with streaming-velocity v. We found that if we replaced *ids*, the strength of the current element, which occurs as a factor in the equation, by the product ev, we obtained an expression which could be interpreted as giving the external magnetic field due to a single charge moving with an arbitrary velocity. We accepted this interpretation without, at the time, having the benefit of Ampère's first and second statements of equilibrium (p. 93) with which to buttress it. Clearly Ampère's statements are significant in the earlier context (see p. 94), and equally clearly their acceptance provides something in support of our conclusion, in that connection, that the external magnetic field intensity due to a charge e moving with velocity v is given by

$$H = \frac{1}{4\pi} \frac{e}{r^3} (v \sin \theta . r) \qquad (104)$$

As we interpreted equation (52), so in the same way we can interpret equation (59), formally, deriving an expression which we might be prepared to accept as giving the mechanical force experienced, by virtue of its charge, by an elementary particle moving in a magnetic field with velocity v. This expression is obtained, by the same transformation as before, in the form

$$F = e(v \sin \theta . B) \qquad (105)$$

It will be evident that equations (104) and (105), if we take them at face value, are in some way interdependent: the former implies the existence of a force acting on an ideal magnetic pole from a moving charge, the latter the existence of a force acting on a moving charge from a magnetic pole. This is satisfactory, for in such a situation we are all the time inclined to look for paired forces, being conditioned in our thinking by the third law of Newton. But it should also be stressed that in the argument from the macroscopic to the sub-macroscopic, from the current element to the elementary charge in motion, the two cases are not strictly of the same simplicity. In arguing from equation (52) to equation (104) the only complication to be overcome was the disentangling of the drift velocity ('streaming velocity') of the carriers from the randomly-directed velocities of thermal motion in the conducting wire. In the other case, however, in the argument from equation (59) to equation (105), the transition is not so obvious. The force which equation (59) describes is an action the evidence for which is a tendency to motion of the conducting wire as a whole; the implication of equation (105) is that this macroscopic force is the resultant of the elementary forces acting on all the charges in motion in the wire. If the 'material' of the wire is essentially uncharged, or being charged is essentially motionless, then the hypothetical charged current carriers alone are subject to these forces—and they must in some way be capable of communicating the momentum which the forces generate to the material of the wire as a whole.

We cannot, within the scope of this book, do more to justify acceptance of equations (104) and (105) than we have already done (pointing out some of the points at which our argument is logically insecure). The problem of the magnetic effect of a freely moving charge, and that of the force experienced by such a charge moving through a magnetic field, attracted the attention of the leading mathematical physicists of the day from about 1875 to the close of the century. The first to formulate equation (105), and to support it on grounds which have since proved to be thoroughly acceptable, was Oliver Heaviside (in 1889); in respect of equation (104), even at the end of the period, there was still active discussion in progress. Theorists were agreed that the equation provides a sufficiently good approximation to the truth provided that the velocity of the moving charge is small compared with the velocity of light, but in order to evaluate the correction required when this condition is not satisfied they had first to make assumptions regarding the 'structure' of the moving charge which at that stage were entirely arbitrary. Not only the theorists were involved in the problems at issue—for they were, indeed, fundamental problems. At least over the period 1876 to 1903 many experimenters devoted much labour and ingenuity to the measurement of the magnetic fields due to 'static' electricity maintained in motion by mechanical means. The first of these was H. A. Rowland

(1848-1901), professor of physics at the Johns Hopkins University in Baltimore. All this said, we accept equations (104) and (105), with the interpretations that we have given them, with the single caution that, unless otherwise stated, we shall assume that all velocities are small compared with the velocity of light.

It will be recalled that the reason for our latest digression was to prepare the ground for a more detailed discussion of the magnetic deflection of the cathode rays (assuming the particle hypothesis). According to equation (105), if $\theta = \dfrac{\pi}{2}$, as in Thomson's arrangement—that is if the cathode-ray stream is moving in a plane perpendicular to the field direction—the force on the moving charge is of magnitude evB, and its direction is perpendicular to the directions of both v and B. Such a force, generating only transverse momentum, is without influence on the speed of the particle, and the resulting path is circular. If ρ is the radius of curvature of this circular path, and m is the mass of the particle, obviously

$$evB = \frac{mv^2}{\rho},$$

or
$$B\rho = \frac{mv}{e} \tag{106}$$

We wrote previously (p. 168) that Thomson believed (in 1896) 'that the magnetic deflection of moving particles (of a given charge, in a given field) is determined by their momentum simply'. Equation (106) exhibits the basis of that belief.

Other workers, besides Thomson, were independently making measurements of the magnetic deflection of cathode rays, and interpreting them in terms of equation (106), in the autumn of 1896. Both Johann Emil Wiechert (1861-1928), in Königsberg, and W. Kaufmann (1871-1947), in Gottingen, published preliminary accounts of their work early in the following year, before Thomson reported the experiments that we have already described. The object in each case was the restricted one of examining the relevance of the charged-particle hypothesis in relation to the properties of the cathode rays in a single gas. Neither investigator, at that time, had carried out comparative observations in several gases as Thomson was doing. Each made some assumption regarding the relation between the kinetic energy acquired by the particles and V, the voltage applied to the discharge tube, and in so doing obtained a second relation involving the unknown quantities e, m and v and a quantity that was experimentally measurable. Kaufmann made the forthright assumption that the majority of the cathode-ray particles in his arrangement had acquired the maximum possible kinetic energy eV; Wiechert merely assumed that the particles whose magnetic deflection he observed had an energy somewhere in the range between eV and $eV/10$. If, for sake of simplicity, we formalise Kaufmann's bolder assumption, we have

$$\tfrac{1}{2}mv^2 = Ve \qquad\qquad (107)$$

then, combining equations (106) and (107),

$$\frac{e}{m} = \frac{2V}{B^2\rho^2} \qquad\qquad (108)$$

On the basis of equation (108) Kaufmann reported that, for the cathode rays in air, the quantity e/m of the charged-particle hypothesis appeared to have the value $1{\cdot}86 \times 10^{11}$ coulomb/kg; allowing the uncertainty of a factor of 10 that we have indicated, Wiechert placed the value of e/m for these particles as between 4×10^{11} coulomb/kg and 4×10^{10} coulomb/kg.

It will be realised that in Thomson's first comparative experiments he also made an assumption regarding the relation between the kinetic energy of the cathode-ray particles and the voltage applied to the discharge tube. His assumption (justified pragmatically because of the great uniformity which issued out of diversity, following its adoption) was that when the difference of potential between the electrodes was the same the kinetic energy of the cathode-ray particles was the same, whatever the gas. This was a non-numerical assumption, which did not provide a second relation involving e, m and v, as Kaufmann's or Wiechert's assumption did. Obviously requiring such a relation, Thomson sought to obtain an independent measure of the kinetic energy of the particles without reference to the discharge-tube voltage. He arranged a thermo-junction of known heat capacity inside a hollow metal collector, suitably screened electrostatically and connected to an electrometer (as in Perrin's experiment, see

p. 164). The cathode rays were concentrated on the entrance-slit of this dual-purpose detector, and the rates of dissipation of energy as heat in the thermo-junction and of collection of negative charge by the system were measured simultaneously. Essentially, then, the experiment determined a quantity S, given by

$$S = \tfrac{1}{2} \frac{mv^2}{e} \qquad\qquad (109)$$

Combining this measurement with the measurement of the magnetic deflection (equation (106)), Thomson obtained for e/m a mean value of $1\cdot17 \times 10^{11}$ coulomb/kg.

Thomson's first public announcement of his results was in a lecture before the Royal Institution in London on 30 April 1897.* He reported in detail on the comparative experiments in various gases which we first described (p. 166), gave a brief account of some early results using the thermo-junction technique (giving a preliminary value of e/m of $0\cdot6 \times 10^{11}$ coulomb/kg), and, most importantly, was able to demonstrate, qualitatively, for the first time, the electrostatic deflection of the rays. In this matter he had at last succeeded, where Hertz had failed (see p. 163), by reducing the gas pressure in the discharge tube to the limit attainable with the methods at his disposal—and by positioning his deflection plates in the region of the cathode dark space where, as he rightly surmised, they were likely to have the greatest effect.

Once he had obtained qualitative evidence that the cathode rays could be deflected by an electrostatic field, Thomson proceeded to use this effect quantitatively so as to determine their velocity on the particle hypothesis. Suppose that a cathode-ray particle is traversing a region in which electric and magnetic fields have been established in directions at right angles to one another. If the direction of motion of the particle is perpendicular to the two field directions, the particle will experience a force of electrostatic origin of magnitude Ee (E being the electric field intensity) in the direction of that field, and a force of electromagnetic origin of magnitude Bev (B being the magnetic flux density) at right angles to the directions of both B and v. The line of action of this latter force will, therefore, be the same as that of the former, and by a

* He had given a preliminary account to the Cambridge Philosophical Society on 8 February.

suitable choice of the relative directions of E and B the two forces can be made to be opposed. By a suitable choice of the magnitudes of E and B these forces can be made to cancel one another completely. A little consideration will show that the necessary conditions are, first that the directions of v, E and B should be related (in that order) as the axes of a right-handed set, and secondly that

$$\frac{E}{B} = v \qquad (110)$$

We have so far considered the situation at a single point in the path of the particles. If the longitudinal velocity of the particles is constant over a long section of path, and if the deflecting fields are similarly uniform over this section (and abruptly terminated at its limits), then, when the above conditions are satisfied, the particles will traverse the region of the fields entirely undeflected.

Thomson sought to realise this situation, as nearly as possible, by arranging that the cathode rays generated in a small discharge tube should pass through the anode (in the form of a hollow cylinder with a defining slit at each end) into a much larger highly evacuated tube across a region in the centre of which the electrostatic field was applied between parallel metal condenser plates. Current in a double coil system (see p. 166) provided the magnetic field effective over the same region. The deflection of the rays could be observed through the phosphorescence which they produced in the glass at the far end of the tube. Having established the result that each field, separately, gave rise to a deflection proportional to the field intensity, Thomson was able to arrange these intensities so that the deflection was zero when both fields were effective simultaneously. In this way he evaluated the velocity of the particles, using equation (110). With the velocity of the particles known, measurement of the deflection in either field could be used to give a value of e/m. In respect of the magnetic deflection, which Thomson, in fact, used for this purpose, equation (106) may be re-written in the form

$$\frac{e}{m} = \frac{v}{B\rho}.$$

In October 1897 Thomson published the results of experiments by this method in three different gases, and at various pressures, which gave a mean value of $7 \cdot 7 \times 10^{10}$ coulomb/kg for e/m. Agreement with the earlier value (see p. 172) was not as good as might have been hoped for, but the general convergence of many observations, and in particular the successful demonstration of an electrostatic deflection of roughly the appropriate magnitude, told overwhelmingly in favour of the charged-particle hypothesis. Already, by the end of 1897, even Lenard was planning experiments the conception of which would have been without significance in terms of the ether-wave concept to which he had still resolutely subscribed in the previous year. Indeed, by the end of 1897, the problem was not so much the nature of the cathode rays —the conclusion was generally accepted that these were streams of negatively-charged particles; the problem was rather that of the position of these particles in the scheme of things, for their properties appeared to be the same in whatever gas, or with whatever electrodes, they were produced.

As we shall see in the next chapter, the study of the phenomena associated with the passage of steady currents through aqueous solutions had already led, some years previously, to the view that the carriers in the simplest cases are charged atoms (ions) of the chemical elements, the charge on any ion being a small integral multiple of a fundamental unit. On this view of the matter, it was necessary only to determine, macroscopically, the charge conveyed through the electrolytic cell, when unit mass of any element was liberated at the appropriate electrode, in order to obtain a measure of the specific charge (e/m) of the ion in question. This had been done repeatedly, and the largest value of this quantity which had been identified was that belonging to the (positive) hydrogen ion—the positive ion of smallest mass, according to the evidence of the chemists. For this ion, e/m was $9 \cdot 65 \times 10^7$ coulomb/kg (see p. 224). Furthermore, on the basis of all the evidence, it had been concluded that the hydrogen ion carried precisely one fundamental unit of positive charge.

Broadly speaking, then, the specific charge of the cathode-ray particles, as found by Thomson, was about one thousand times greater than the specific charge of the electrolytic hydrogen ion —in whatever gas (including hydrogen) the rays were produced. If this constancy of specific charge meant anything, it was difficult to resist the conclusion that it implied that both e and m were the same—that is, that the cathode-ray particles were essentially identical in nature—whatever the source of the particles. So far as the value of e was concerned, the simplest intuitive assumption was that this charge was the same as the fundamental unit (negative) charge on a simple ion in electrolysis (and so equal, except for sign, to the charge on the electrolytic hydrogen ion). If this assumption were accepted, then the mass of the cathode-ray particle was smaller than that of the hydrogen ion by a factor of the order of a thousand. This was Thomson's tentative conclusion at a very early stage. The suggestion of the existence of particles of mass very much smaller than that of the lightest chemical atom was admittedly a revolutionary suggestion, but at least it pointed the way to an understanding of the facts: the cathode rays are constituted of particles of the same nature, whatever their origin, just because the atoms of all elements contain these particles ('corpuscles', as Thomson first called them) as structural units. To fulfil such a role, the corpuscles must of necessity be of mass smaller than that of the lightest atom.

It should be added that the tentative identification of the charge on the cathode-ray particles with that on the simplest electrolytic ion was not, in 1897, such a rash identification as might be imagined. In the previous year Thomson and Rutherford had elucidated a particular type of gaseous conduction (see §4.4), which involved the transport of charged ions of both signs through gases at ordinary pressures, in a manner superficially very similar to the transport of electrolytic ions through aqueous solutions. If Thomson's corpuscle were, indeed, a common constituent of all atoms, capable of being set free under certain conditions, it was natural to regard an atomic ion, whether in a gas or a liquid, as an atom which had one or more corpuscles in excess, or in defect, of the normal complement required for electrical neutrality. In relation to the phenomena of electrolysis, the notion of a natural unit of charge had first been explicitly formulated by G. Johnstone Stoney (1826-1911) at the Belfast meeting of the British Association in 1874. Later, in 1891, Stoney had suggested the name 'electron' for this unit. After 1897, by slow degrees, Thomson's name 'corpuscle' was abandoned, and Stoney's 'electron' was adopted in its place. In this transition the meaning was changed: using the term 'negative electron' today, we no longer signify merely a unit of charge, but a sub-atomic particle, a common constituent of all matter.

4.3. CURRENTS OF NEGATIVE ELECTRICITY 'IN VACUUM'

Thomson's claim to be the essential discoverer of the negative electron, already strong by the end of 1897, was further consolidated by his investigations in the following years. Whilst others, Lenard, Kaufmann and Wiechert, in particular, made more detailed studies of the properties of the cathode rays, Thomson showed that particles having the same value of e/m as the cathode-ray particles were produced in other circumstances than in a gas at low pressure under the influence of an intense electric field. Indeed, the other modes of production which he identified did not involve the action of macroscopic fields of any kind. The effective agencies were heat, and light of very short wavelength.

The fact that the incidence of ultra-violet light on a metal surface could facilitate the discharge of negative electricity from the surface was, at the time, a fairly recent discovery (see V & W, p. 276); that there was a discharging effect due simply to intense heat (and possessed by the gases rising from flames) had been known since 1725, or thereabouts. In 1853 Alexandre Edmond Becquerel (1820-1891), professor of physics at the Conservatoire des Arts et Métiers in Paris,* showed that the air in the neighbourhood of a white-hot metal acted as a conductor when the potential gradient was only a few volts per centimetre. Prior to the work of Thomson, however, the only investigations—of the electrical effects of intense heat or of ultra-violet light—with which we need be seriously concerned were those of Elster and Geitel.

Julius P. L. T. Elster (1854-1920) and Hans F. K. Geitel (1855-1923) formed a lasting friendship and laid the foundations for a lifelong collaboration in scientific research, when they were fellow pupils at the secondary school in Blankenburg in Brunswick. Later they were together as teachers on the staff of a school at Wolfenbüttel, in the same duchy. For a large part of their adult lives they were members of a common household—Elster lived in the home of Geitel's parents until he married, afterwards Geitel joined the Elsters when his own mother had died. Finally, the two scientists built themselves a large house, furnished with a well-equipped laboratory, and there, ministered to by Frau Elster,

---

* A.E.Becquerel followed his father, Antoine César (1788-1878), as professor of physics at the Musée d'Histoire Naturelle, and on his death was succeeded in that post by his son, Antoine Henri (1852-1908), who, in 1896, discovered the phenomenon of radioactivity (see V & W, p. 273).

they carried out their researches without interruption until Elster died. Almost without exception their publications were joint publications; individually each turned down the offer of more than one professorship (jointly, on one occasion, they declined the offer of a dual chair!); never, perhaps, in the history of western science has there been another case of such single-minded collaboration between equal partners of such eminence.

The very first of the long series of investigations undertaken by these truly remarkable men was on the conductivity of gases in the neighbourhood of metallic wires heated electrically to incandescence. Elster and Geitel worked on this subject from 1882 to 1889 and slowly brought order into the observations of a very complicated phenomenon. For our purposes their essential demonstration was that at the lowest pressures, and with incandescent metals (and, indeed, with carbon filaments), an electric current would pass from the heated wire to a cold electrode, but only when the potential of the cold electrode was positive with respect to that of the wire. When the difference of potential between the wire and the cold electrode was reversed, no current was observed.

In 1889 the two scientists turned their attention to the effect discovered in the preceding two years by Hertz and Hallwachs (see $V \& W$, p. 276), the action of ultra-violet light in promoting the leakage of negative electricity from metal electrodes. In a qualitative sense this was an effect in many ways analogous to that which they had been investigating with incandescent solids when the gas pressure was low. In 1890 they discovered that the photo-current could be greatly reduced by the application of a magnetic field parallel to the illuminated surface. This discovery provided the starting point for Thomson's investigation of the nature of the negative carriers, both in the photoelectric effect and in the emission from heated metals ('thermionic effect').

Consider rectangular axes OX, OY, OZ, and let OACB (fig. 29) represent a metal surface, lying in the plane XOY, from which (negatively) charged particles, of charge e and mass m, are emitted, either on account of the incidence of ultra-violet light on the surface, or because the metal is maintained at a high temperature. Suppose that a uniform electric field of intensity E is established parallel to OZ, and a uniform magnetic field of flux density B parallel to OX. Consider one of the emitted particles situated instantaneously at P(x, y, z) in the evacuated region close to OACB.

The component accelerations of the particle are given by the equations

$$m\ddot{x} = 0$$
$$m\ddot{y} = Be\dot{z}$$
$$m\ddot{z} = Ee - Be\dot{y}$$

(III)

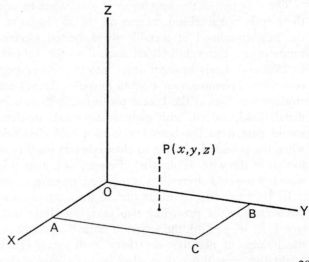

FIGURE 29

Clearly, the situation is simplest, analytically, if the particle at P was originally emitted from the surface with negligible velocity. Let us consider this simplest case first. Then, integrating the first of equations (III), we see that the motion of the particle is confined to a plane parallel to YOZ (for $\dot{x} = 0$ throughout the motion), and from the second equation we obtain

$$m\dot{y} = Bez$$

(112)

If we substitute this result in the third equation, we have

$$\ddot{z} = \frac{Ee}{m} - \left(\frac{Be}{m}\right)^2 z,$$

and, reckoning the time t from the instant of emission of the particle from the surface, we derive the solution

$$z = \frac{Em}{B^2e}\left(1 - \cos\frac{Be}{m}t\right) \qquad (113)$$

The solution for y is obtained by combining equations (112) and (113) and integrating; it is

$$y = y_0 + \frac{Em}{B^2e}\left(\frac{Be}{m}t - \sin\frac{Be}{m}t\right) \qquad (114)$$

where $(x_0, y_0, 0)$ are the co-ordinates of the point of emission of the particle from the plane surface OACB. In equations (113) and (114), together with the equation $x = x_0$, we have a full description of the path of the particle under the conditions that we have imposed.

The path described by equations (113) and (114) is in fact a cycloid (and in theory the path is of indefinite extent in the y-direction, the particle returning with zero velocity to the surface at each cusp of the curve), but for our purposes the important result is contained in equation (113), rather than the other. According to this equation we see that the whole motion of the particle is confined within a distance d of the emitting surface, where

$$d = \frac{2Em}{B^2e} \qquad (115)$$

If, therefore, a plane metal surface is illuminated by ultra-violet light and the photo-current is collected by a parallel electrode situated at a distance d, and if the collecting potential difference is V, a magnetic field of flux density just greater than B will completely suppress the current, provided that the field is applied parallel to the surface of the electrodes, the initial velocity of the emitted particles is negligible, and

$$B^2 = \frac{2Vm}{d^2e} \qquad (116)$$

Thomson carried out experiments on the negatively-charged carriers of the photoelectric and thermionic currents 'in vacuum', by a procedure suggested by the above analysis, in 1899. It was not at that time known to what extent the approximation of negligible initial velocities was valid (the first reasonably accurate determination of the velocities of the photoelectric carriers was made by Lenard in 1902), but having regard to the other ways in which the experimental arrangement was far from ideal (non-uniformity of the applied fields, presence of residual gas, etc.) the general nature of the results suggested that this approximation was sufficiently good in the circumstances. Making that assumption then, Thomson obtained values of e/m of 0.73×10^{11} coulomb/kg for the photoelectric carriers and 0.87×10^{11} coulomb/kg for the thermionic carriers under the same general conditions of experiment. Comparing these not very precise values with the values (1.17×10^{11} and 0.77×10^{11} coulomb/kg) which he had previously determined for the cathode-ray particles (see pp. 172, 174), he justifiably concluded that he had identified two other situations in which his 'fundamental particles much smaller than atoms'—the negatively-charged corpuscles of the cathode-ray tube—were to be found in the free state. The view of the negative electron as an essential constituent of all matter was never seriously challenged from that time on.

It has been stated that the first reasonably accurate determination of the velocities of emission of the photo-electrons was made by Lenard in 1902. The first comparable investigation in respect of the electrons emitted from incandescent metals was not made until six years later. In 1908 Owen Willans Richardson (1879-1959), then professor of physics at Princeton university, published an account of the latter investigation (part of it in collaboration with F. C. Brown). In each case it was shown that a negative (electron) current could be collected even though the potential of the collecting electrode was slightly negative with respect to the emitter. By investigating the diminution of the current as this 'retarding' potential was increased, Lenard and Richardson were able to obtain information concerning the spectrum of kinetic energy characterising those electrons which were emitted normally to the plates in their respective experiments. In so far as these later results are relevant to Thomson's investigations of 1899, we may compare 0·5 volt, a representative value for the retarding potential sufficient to suppress 95 per cent of the photoelectric (or thermionic) currents of Lenard and Richardson, with a value of the order of 100 volts for V, the 'accelerating' potential in equation (116). Arguing after the event, then, in view of the wide disparity of these two values, we may confidently conclude that none of the major uncertainties in Thomson's experiment are to be attributed to the assumption of negligible initial velocities on which its analysis was based.

In this section we have stressed—it may be hoped not too extravagantly—the claim of J.J.Thomson to have been the essential discoverer of the negative electron in its role as the first of the 'elementary' particles of modern physics. In postscript we must, however, record that the value of the specific charge of the electron is now known to be 1.759×10^{11} coulomb/kg. This is almost exactly twice the mean of Thomson's four determinations which we have recently summarised (p. 180), and which appeared to be mutually consistent within plus or minus 25 per cent. of the mean. From today's vantage point it must appear as a curious circumstance that there could have been such a discrepancy. But there were two determinations by Lenard, in 1898, which also yielded concordant values (0.64×10^{11} and 0.68×10^{11} coulomb/kg)—and these were even smaller than Thomson's. Only Kaufmann's (1897) value of 1.86×10^{11} coulomb/kg, which we have already quoted —though it cannot be said with any great conviction (see p. 171) —amongst the early determinations, came anywhere near to what we now know to be the truth. Possibly we should have paid more attention to Kaufmann's determination, for the criticism that we made of it was adequately disposed of by his collaborator S.Simon in 1899. Simon obtained essentially the same value as Kaufmann had done, using many different values of the potential difference applied to the cathode-ray tube. In order to mantain our previous doubts regarding the result of these experiments we should have to assume that the cathode-ray particles acquired the same fraction (say about one-half) of the maximum possible energy, whatever the voltage applied to the tube. Such an assumption would be extremely difficult to justify.

Thomson, then, discovered the electron—and Kaufmann (a few months earlier!) was the first to determine its specific charge with reasonable accuracy. Kaufmann, we may probably conclude, had the edge over his competitors, at the crucial time, in the matter of experimental 'vacuum technique'.

4.4. STEADY CURRENTS THROUGH IONISED GASES

In this section we are concerned essentially with such conductivity as gases may exhibit when the applied electric field intensity is small (say, of the order of a few volts per centimetre, when the gas pressure is atmospheric). We have already mentioned A.E. Becquerel's study of an effect of this nature in which the conductivity was to be ascribed to an action of a lump of white-hot metal on the ambient air in its vicinity (p. 176). Much earlier, Volta had introduced the method of discharging a charged nonconducting body by passing a flame over its surface, and Coulomb (1785) had convinced himself that, even at normal temperatures, there is a slow leak of charge from an insulated charged conductor through the surrounding air. In 1820 Ampère had written of 'the gradual loss of electricity which can take place across . . . the air . . . for it seems that there is no body which is a perfect insulator'. Carlo Matteucci (1811-1868), professor of physics at Bologna at the age of twenty-one—and at Ravenna and Pisa before he was thirty—showed (in 1850) that the rate of leak was less when the pressure was low than when it was high. All these were qualitative observations made on a phenomenon that was not understood. The understanding came dramatically as a result of a single investigation by Thomson and Rutherford in 1896. We have already made brief reference to this investigation on two occasions (pp. 166, 175); it is necessary now to describe it in detail.

The investigation of Thomson and Rutherford arose directly out of the discovery of the X-rays by Röntgen in December 1895 (see p. 165). On 27 January 1896 Thomson had reported to the meeting of the Cambridge Philosophical Society his then very recent discovery that electrified bodies lose their charge under the action of the rays. The same discovery must have been made almost simultaneously in Paris, for L. Benoist and D. Hurmuzescu were able to give a more detailed account of the same effect on 3 February before the Academy of Sciences. In Cambridge Thomson immediately set J.A.McClelland* to study the phenomenon. On 13 February preliminary results were reported at a meeting of the Royal Society in London. Thomson appears to have been in no doubt that the essential action of the rays was on the air surrounding the charged conductor, rather than on the conductor itself. At this early stage he even hazarded a guess as to the nature of that action: 'The passage of these rays through a substance seems . . . to be accompanied by a splitting up of its molecules, which enables electricity to pass through it by a process

* John Alexander McClelland (1870-1920) later occupied the chair of experimental physics at University College, Dublin.

resembling that by which a current passes through an electrolyte.'
Less than a month later (9 March) a full account was given to the
Cambridge society. For the first time plane parallel electrodes had
been used, by design, for the study of the leakage of charge, and an
attempt had been made, so far as possible, to shield these electrodes from the action of the X-rays, only the gas between the
plates being exposed to the main beam. Thomson reported '[Com-
paring the] rate of leak through different gases under similar conditions as to pressure and potential gradient . . . in general . . . the
greater the molecular weight of the gas the more rapid the leakage. . . . The most remarkable thing . . . is that the rate is almost
independent of the potential difference. Thus, when the high
potential plate was 5 volts above that of the low, the rate of leak
was appreciably greater than when the potential difference was
1 volt, but the rate was no greater when the potential difference
was 500 volts than when it was 5.' Within the next few weeks it
was found that the leakage current increased when the distance
between the plates was increased, provided that the width of the
X-ray beam was correspondingly increased, and the collecting
voltage was not too low. Then, early in April, Rutherford took
over from McClelland, and the systematic investigation went forward without interruption throughout the summer months.
(McClelland was transferred to an investigation of the absorption
of X-rays in solids.)

The work was finished in time for it to be reported to the meeting of the British Association at Liverpool on 18 September. It
was published in full as a joint paper by Thomson and Rutherford
in the *Philosophical Magazine* for November 1896. The current
between parallel plates situated in air, hydrogen, chlorine, coal
gas, hydrogen sulphide and mercury vapour had been studied
quantitatively in its dependence on the collecting voltage and the
distance between the plates, and qualitatively in relation to the
intensity of the X-rays. Other experiments had been made in an
arrangement in which gases had been drawn through a vessel in
which they were exposed to the radiation, then tested for residual
conductivity in another vessel, having been subject to various
treatments in the tube connecting the two vessels. In this way it
had been established that a gas loses its conductivity, after removal from the radiation vessel, progressively with the passage
of time, or when it is passed through a plug of glass wool, or

between electrodes maintained at a considerable potential difference, or when it is bubbled through water. On the other hand, the loss of conductivity had not been significantly accelerated when the irradiated gas was passed through a white-hot porcelain tube. There had been many other observations, too, more detailed than can be reported here.

Out of the ancillary experiments with the gas-flow apparatus Thomson and Rutherford developed the theoretical concepts of *ionisation, recombination* and *mobility* (though they did not use the last two terms explicitly in their paper) in order to give a quantitative account of the more precise measurements which they had made on the variation of current with voltage under controlled conditions. In its most general terms their point of view was expressed by Thomson at the Liverpool meeting as follows, 'When a current is passing through a gas exposed to the rays, the current destroys and the rays produce the structure which gives conductivity to the gas.' They regarded that structure as involving the presence in the gas of equal numbers of positively and negatively charged 'conducting particles' (*ions*), produced from the uncharged gas molecules, under the action of the X-rays, at a rate, per unit volume of gas, proportional to the intensity of the X-rays at the point in question—and they considered that these ions, left to themselves would recombine in pairs, so neutralising their charges and diminishing the conductivity of the gas, at a rate, per unit volume, proportional to the square of their concentration. Once the main premises had been adopted, this last was an obvious assumption to make on the basis of simple kinetic theory arguments.

We may evaluate one of the consequences of this view of the matter right away. If we write n as the number of ions of each sign per unit volume at any time t, when no fresh ions are being produced, and if α is the 'coefficient of recombination' (as it later came to be called), then, by definition of α,

$$\frac{dn}{dt} = -\alpha n^2 \qquad (117)$$

Consider the case when the initial concentration of ions is n_0. By integration we have

$$\frac{1}{n} - \frac{1}{n_0} = \alpha t$$

—and, if the number of ions has fallen to half the initial value in time T, then

$$T = \frac{1}{\alpha n_0} \qquad (118)$$

Thomson and Rutherford derived equation (118) as we have done and concluded, from their gas-flow experiments, 'with the intensity of radiation we generally employed, T was of the order of $1/10$ of a second'. We note that, other things being equal, the characteristic decay time T is inversely proportional to the initial concentration of ions—or to the intensity of the radiation which produced them.

A second consequence of the point of view of Thomson and Rutherford may be exposed by discussing the equation

$$\frac{dn}{dt} = q - \alpha n^2, \qquad (119)$$

This equation clearly refers to the state of affairs when an external source of radiation (X-rays) produces q pairs of ions per unit volume of gas per unit time, and the only loss-mechanism is the natural process of recombination that we have already described. Clearly, the concentration of ions does not increase indefinitely, but reaches a steady value n_∞,

$$n_\infty = \left(\frac{q}{\alpha}\right)^{\frac{1}{2}} \qquad (120)$$

We have not, so far, formalised the notion of 'ionic mobility'— and we have stated that Thomson and Rutherford did not do so either. Making a composite sentence out of two half-sentences occurring several pages apart in their paper (and suitably changing their symbols), we can, however, approximate to a definition. We find 'If V is the difference of potential between the plates [and l is their separation], k the sum of the velocities of the positively and negatively electrified particles when the potential gradient is unity, [then] kV/l is the sum of the velocities of the positively and negatively charged particles in the electric field.' It is the quantity k to which the name 'mobility' was later applied—or, rather, in order to preserve generality, k was eventually defined as the sum of the mobilities of the positive and negative ions concerned. It will be clear now what the assumption was that Thomson and

EM N

Rutherford were making. They were saying that, macroscopically, in the conditions of their experiments, the effect of the application of an electric field E was to cause the positive ions in a gas to drift in the direction of the field with a steady velocity proportional to the field intensity, and the negative ions, likewise, to drift in the opposite direction with a steady velocity proportional to E. They made no comment on this implicit assumption (which, indeed, later research showed to be well founded), though behind it there must have been considerable thought regarding the nature of the collisions between accelerated ions and the neutral molecules of the gas, and underlying assumptions regarding the efficiency of energy transfer in such encounters. Apart from such collisions, of course, the ions must be continuously accelerated by the applied field.

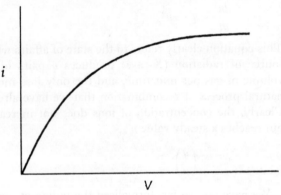

FIGURE 30

We are now in a position to consider the main quantitative experiments of Thomson and Rutherford, in terms of the theoretical concepts which they developed. Fig. 30 shows, schematically, the general way in which they found the current i between plane parallel electrodes of area A, separated by a distance l in a gas, to vary with the potential difference V, when the whole region between the plates was subject to ionisation by a parallel beam of X-rays of constant intensity. We shall imagine that conditions are uniform over the plates, and that the electric field is abruptly terminated around their periphery. Then, if e is the magnitude of the electric charge on an ion, in the steady state, when the current is i, the rate of discharge of negative ions at the positive electrode is i/e, and the rate of discharge of positive ions at the negative electrode has the same value. In order to maintain the current, then, i/e ion-pairs must be removed per unit time from a volume Al of irradiated gas. On the assumption that this steady loss of ions takes place uniformly throughout the gas, using the same symbols as before, we have, for any point in the gas, when the conditions are steady,

$$\frac{dn}{dt} = q - \alpha n^2 - \frac{i}{Ale}$$

$$= 0.$$

Also, considering the transport of charge across any plane in the gas parallel to the electrodes, we have

$$i = Ank\frac{V}{l}e \qquad \qquad (121)$$

Thus, under steady conditions,

$$\alpha n^2 + \frac{kV}{l^2}n - q = 0 \qquad \qquad (122)$$

Equations (122) and (121) allow us to solve for n and i in terms of α and k, the parameters describing the behaviour of ions in the gas irradiated, q which depends on the nature of the gas as well as (proportionately) on the intensity of the X-ray beam, l the separation of the parallel electrodes and V the difference of potential maintained between them.

It will be seen that, all the parameters being positive, equation (122) has just one positive root under all physically possible circumstances. It will also be clear that, as V is increased from zero, the other parameters remaining fixed, two approximations to this solution become valid successively:

when $V \ll (2l^2/k)\,(\alpha q)^{\frac{1}{2}}$, to a good approximation,

$$n = \left(\frac{q}{\alpha}\right)^{\frac{1}{2}}, i = A\left(\frac{q}{\alpha}\right)^{\frac{1}{2}}\frac{ke}{l}\,V;$$

when $V \gg (2l^2/k)\,(\alpha q)^{\frac{1}{2}}$, similarly,

$$n = \frac{ql^2}{kV}, i = Alqe.$$

In these approximations the significant features of the experimental curve of fig. 30 are faithfully reproduced—the initial feature showing 'ohmic' behaviour, with the current through the gas proportional to the difference of potential between the electrodes (and the steady concentration of ions scarcely diminished from its equilibrium value by the current—compare equation (120)), and the final feature of 'saturation', when all the ions produced in the gas are removed so rapidly that recombination is insignificant.

Having reproduced the general form of the saturation curve in terms of their basic assumptions, Thomson and Rutherford went on to discuss the differences observed when different gases were employed in their apparatus. There were differences in the magnitude of the saturation current, as McClelland had previously observed, and there were differences in the voltage required to produce effective saturation. Their assumptions had nothing to say regarding differences of the former kind, but they proved entirely adequate as a basis for the understanding of the latter kind of difference, as we shall now proceed to show. We shall do this by transforming equations (121) and (122) into numerical relations involving non-dimensional quantities only.

Let us write i_s for the value of the saturation current under the conditions we have specified, let us denote by V_c the quantity $(l^2/k)\,(\alpha q)^{\frac{1}{2}}$, and, in the present context, let us write n_0 for $(q/\alpha)^{\frac{1}{2}}$. We note that $2V_c$ is the characteristic potential difference in terms of which the range of validity of our approximate solutions has been defined—and our change of notation in respect of $(q/\alpha)^{\frac{1}{2}}$, from that adopted in equation (120), reflects the fact that this quantity now represents the ionic concentration at zero field intensity, rather than that at infinite time as previously was the case. With these formal designations accepted, it becomes a matter of simple algebraic manipulation of the original equations to show that

$$\frac{i}{i_s} = \frac{n}{n_0}\frac{V}{V_c} \tag{123}$$

$$\left(\frac{n}{n_0}\right)^2 + \frac{V}{V_c}\frac{n}{n_0} - 1 = 0 \tag{124}$$

From equations (123) and (124) it is again a straightforward exercise to express i/i_s explicitly in terms of V/V_c. We do not need the explicit form of the expression; we may write simply

$$\frac{i}{i_s} = f\left(\frac{V}{V_c}\right) \tag{125}$$

The implication of equation (125) is that the form of the function f is the same for all gases, whatever the dimensions of the parallel-plate ionisation chamber used for their investigation, and whatever the intensity of the ionising radiation to which they are exposed. In simple practical terms: the ratio of the actual current to the saturation current is the same, in all cases, when the ratio of the applied potential difference to the characteristic potential difference V_c is the same. Thomson and Rutherford convincingly argued that the differences (of the second kind mentioned above) which they found with different gases in their apparatus could be understood in terms of different values of V_c in the different experiments. We have written $V_c = (l^2/k) \, (\alpha q)^{\frac{1}{2}}$. Alternatively, we may write

$$\frac{l}{(kV_c/l)} = \frac{1}{(\alpha q)^{\frac{1}{2}}}.$$

We recognise the left-hand side of this equation as giving the time taken by a pair of ions to separate by a distance equal to the distance between the plates when the potential difference between the plates is V_c. The right-hand side of the equation we recognise as $1/\alpha n_0$, when $n_0 = (q/\alpha)^{\frac{1}{2}}$—and, with the help of equation (118), as the time necessary for the equilibrium concentration of n_0 ions per unit volume to decrease to one-half on account of recombination alone. As Thomson and Rutherford pointed out, then, the characteristic potential difference of our definition is that potential difference corresponding to which the ionic transport time is the same as the minimum time for half recombination in the conditions of the experiment. Saturation is effectively reached when $V \gg V_c$, that is when the ionic transport time is very small compared with the recombination time, as we have already implied. In an apparatus of constant dimensions, V_c is proportional to $(\alpha q)^{\frac{1}{2}}/k$; Thomson and Rutherford showed conclusively that for a given gas under these conditions saturation required higher collecting fields when the incident radiation was strong than when it was weak.

So far we have dealt non-numerically with the results which Thomson and Rutherford presented in their paper. To do no more than this, in a novel situation, is to run the risk of being carried away by the formal 'success' of a theory, without ever achieving an appreciation of the order of magnitude of the physical quantities involved. Thomson and Rutherford did not neglect this aspect of the situation. They argued from the fact that the saturation current which they measured between parallel plates of 10 cm^2 area at 1 cm separation in hydrogen of normal density was characteristically of the order of 3×10^{-11} ampere. A current of this order, they said, would in one second liberate approximately 3×10^{-12} cm^3 of hydrogen at s.t.p. in the electrolysis of water. If, therefore, the charge on the gaseous ions was the same as that on the ions in the electrolyte, the rate of production of ions in the 10 cm^3 of hydrogen gas in their ionisation chamber must have been such that the number of molecules 'destroyed' in this way per second would occupy a volume of 3×10^{-12} cm^3 at normal density. This is equivalent to saying that, under the conditions of their experiment, the ionising effect of the X-rays consisted in no more than the break-up of about one molecule in every 3×10^{12} molecules, per second. If the characteristic time for half recombination, relative to the same conditions of irradiation, but in the absence of a collecting field, be set arbitrarily at 0·3 second (see p. 185), we obtain a rough estimate of 1 in 10^{13} as the equilibrium ratio of numbers of ion-pairs to molecules, on the basis of equations (118) and (120). As Thomson and Rutherford wrote, 'It is not surprising that some experiments we made to see if any alteration in pressure was produced when a gas was transmitting Röntgen rays should have given negative results.'

Let us now return, briefly, to the earlier observations which we recorded at the beginning of this section, and of which we said that an understanding came only with the investigations of Thomson and Rutherford which we have now described. The point of view issuing from these investigations was that whenever a gas (free of suspended matter) exhibits electrical conductivity under the influence of an electric field of small intensity, there must be present in the gas positive and negative ions which have been formed from the gas molecules by the action of some 'external agent'. Because these ions inevitably recombine if left to themselves (albeit very slowly if the concentration is minute), it was further necessary to suppose that such an agent must be still operative (or, that it must only recently have ceased to operate) whenever such conductivity is found. If they could be obtained in the purely molecular state, all gases would, on this view, be perfect insulators in relation to electric fields of small intensity.

We cannot here particularise concerning the mode of action of ionising agents such as the white-hot bodies and flames to which we made earlier reference, but we should at least refer to Ampère's opinion that normal air is not, in fact, a perfect insulator—and to the century's work which followed, substantiating that opinion beyond all reasonable doubt. The investigation of Matteucci to which we referred (p. 182) was only one in a long line of investigations dealing with this aspect of the matter: towards the end of the century Elster and Geitel (see p. 176), in particular, increased our knowledge of the subject, in relation to the free atmosphere, by many years of systematic endeavour.

For present purposes it will suffice to state that the residual conductivity of the atmosphere is now known to be due to two main causes. First, there is the radiation originating in the radioactive materials (see p. 241) widely distributed in small concentration in the earth's crust; secondly, there is the even more penetrating radiation (the 'cosmic rays') entering the atmosphere from extra-terrestrial space. The mode of action of these radiations is very closely the same as that which we have ascribed to the X-rays in the experiments of Thomson and Rutherford. Their combined intensity, naturally, varies with locality (being small over the oceans, because of a large reduction in the terrestrial component); a representative value for the rate of production of ions at a land-based station might well be of the order of 20 ion pairs per cm^3 per second. We assess the smallness of this rate by reference to Loschmidt's 'number', $2 \cdot 7 \times 10^{19}$ molecules per cm^3 at s.t.p.—and we compare it with the corresponding rate which Thomson and Rutherford estimated for the ionisation in hydrogen in their laboratory experiments (approximately 10^7 ion pairs per cm^3 per second—see p. 190).

We should not be altogether honest if we were to conclude this section, giving a detailed account of the joint work of Thomson and Rutherford, without a final postscript. We have intentionally based our account very closely on the original paper of November 1896, and we have presented the theory of the effect essentially as it was given by the authors. Very obviously, the theory achieved all that was required of it at the time; moreover, there is abundant 'physical sense' in the limiting approximations for small and large field intensities which we have quoted and discussed. However, we have to admit that there is a technical flaw in the development —an assumption that was made casually without justification, and which cannot strictly be justified in a logical analysis. We made the assumption (p. 187)—following our authors, who did not so much as draw attention to the fact—that the 'steady loss of ions [in carrying the current] takes place uniformly throughout the gas'. Neither is this true in general, nor is the other (and related) assumption, that was also made, true—that the electric field is uniform along a line of current flow. And, as we have already implied, strictly, the motions of the positive and negative ions should be treated separately—and a separate value of the mobility should be assigned to each.

Thomson was not long in making amends for the theoretical shortcomings of the 1896 paper. Early in 1899 he published the results of a rigorous mathematical investigation, 'On the theory of the conduction of electricity through gases by charged ions'. In this definitive treatment he took count of all the points to which we have just referred, and he went through the motions of including the effect of diffusion of ions in his formulation. But the differential equation to which he was led, even when diffusion was neglected, was not one for which he was able to obtain a general solution except in the case of ions of equal mobilities uniformly produced throughout the volume of the gas. In respect of other cases, he had to be content with qualitative conclusions, and with approximate results for the limiting situations of small values of i/i_s and $(i_s - i)/i_s$ as in the original paper. The matter was carried one stage farther by G. Mie, in 1904, when partial solutions for the case of unequal mobilities were obtained by a method of successive approximation. For our purposes it will be sufficient to illustrate, by way of a diagram, the extent to which the original treatment of Thomson and Rutherford was in error, according to the later calculations of Thomson and of Mie. In fig. 31 we show, schematically, how the electric field intensity, E, varies with x, the distance from the cathode in a parallel plate ionisation chamber containing air and uniformly irradiated with X-rays, according to the later calculations. Curve (a) refers to the limiting situation of small fields, when the current is proportional to the collecting voltage; curve (b) represents the situation of near saturation. It will be recalled that in the original treatment it was assumed that E was constant throughout the space between the electrodes (and that there was no excess of positive over negative ions anywhere in the gas). In fact, there must always be an excess of positive ions in the

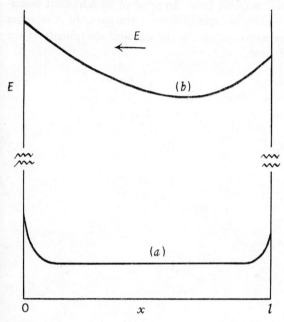

FIGURE 31

immediate region of the cathode, and an excess of negative ions near the anode, so that uniformity of E in these regions is impossible. The calculations of Thomson and of Mie showed that in the small field limit (curve (a)) the extent of these regions of varying field, and the magnitude of the variation within them, are related to the mobilities of the ions. In air the mobility of the negative ion is found to be greater than that of the positive ion in ordinary circumstances: in this gas the departure from field uniformity is correspondingly greater near the cathode than near the anode, as exhibited in the figure. But the essential fact for our purposes is that under the conditions represented by curve (a) the field intensity is indeed constant, within narrow limits, except very close to the two electrodes. The approximate treatment of Thomson and Rutherford, then, cannot have been greatly in error, under these conditions. Also, their estimate of the saturation current was clearly independent of any of the questionable assumptions that we have been discussing. In brief, therefore, we have, in the end, no apologies to make for having reproduced their arguments in their original form. In spite of its admitted inconsistencies (or, possibly, because of them!), the paper of November 1896 is rightly regarded as one of the classical documents of the modern era in physics.

CHAPTER 5

STEADY CURRENTS IN LIQUIDS

5.1. INTRODUCTORY

If our aim had been a purely chronological account, a good case could have been made for a discussion of the subject matter of this chapter before that of chapter 4, which we have just concluded. Indeed, in that chapter, we were compelled to refer ahead (see pp. 174, 183), in one case in some detail, to the electrolytic effects which we have reserved for consideration at this later stage. For it is a fact of history which cannot be gainsaid that familiarity with these effects contributed significantly to the understanding of the mechanism of electric conduction in gases. Thomson and Rutherford wrote 'the analogy between a dilute solution of an electrolyte and gas exposed to the Röntgen rays holds through a wide range of phenomena, and we have found it of great use in explaining many of the characteristic properties of conduction through gases'. However, we cannot be bound entirely by chronology, and we take the view that the simpler situation should be considered before one that is more complex—unless there are compelling reasons to the contrary. Without doubt, the physical situation in a gas is fundamentally simpler than that in a liquid: here, then, is the reason for our choice of order.

Having made one decision regarding order of presentation, we are at once confronted with another, at least as tiresome. The physical system consisting of a vessel containing an appropriate liquid, and furnished with two metal plates as electrodes, may be effective as a component of a complete current-carrying circuit in two quite distinct ways. It may act as the source of current in the circuit—as a voltaic cell—or it may be, to all appearances, a purely 'passive' component—an electrolytic cell in which chemical effects are produced by the passage of current generated in some other part of the circuit. The decision whether to treat of the voltaic cell before considering the phenomena of electrolysis, or *vice versa*, is not made any easier by the fact that the distinction between the two topics is not clear-cut. Many physical systems, of the general type that we have described, can act either actively or passively, according to the circumstances. It might appear to be a neat arrangement if we were to confine our attention to circuits in which the source of current for our electrolytic cells was in every case a battery of voltaic cells—then the consideration of the voltaic cell would appear to take logical priority over the other. Or we might attempt to justify the same decision historically, in that it needed Volta's invention of the pile before the electrolytic action of a steady current was discovered by Nicholson and Carlisle (see below). Yet we shall, in fact, take the other course. We shall treat first of electrolysis, as a 'passive' phenomenon, and then of the 'active' processes taking place in the voltaic cell. Obviously, from what we have already said, we cannot separate the two discussions completely. In each we are concerned with the passage of current through a volume of liquid. It was Ampère who followed up Oersted's discovery of the magnetic action of the current in a wire joining the terminals of a voltaic battery, by arranging his battery of cells in a linear array and showing that a compass needle placed above or below the line of cells was deflected in precisely the same way as it was when it was similarly placed with respect to the wires leading to and from the terminals of the battery.

5.2. THE PHENOMENA OF ELECTROLYSIS (I)

The discovery of electrolysis—which we may define as the production of chemical changes in a substance which are directly occasioned by the passage of an electric current through the substance (and are not to be ascribed to the heat generated by the current)—was a discovery made by accident and followed up with perspicacity. On 30 April 1800 William Nicholson and Anthony Carlisle (see p. 69) set up the first copy of Volta's pile in England, soon after news of its construction reached Sir Joseph Banks, then President of the Royal Society. It had long been the common practice of experimenters with 'static' electricity to use moistened threads as conductors (and we have already noted Henry Cavendish's (1775) estimates of the relative conductivities of rain water and sea water, to which we shall recur). On this occasion Nicholson and Carlisle used a drop of water to increase the effectiveness of the otherwise 'dry' contact between the upper plate of the pile and the wire leading from it. When the pile was in operation they noticed the formation of small bubbles of gas in the drop of water forming the contact. Thereupon, they immediately took a test-tube of water and placed in it the ends of two brass wires connected one to each pole of the pile. Again, gas was liberated at the one wire, and the surface of the other wire became dull. Because the liberated gas was inflammable, they judged it to be hydrogen; the other wire they described as having been oxidised over its surface. Two days later, using platinum (and, in another experiment, gold) wires in place of brass, they obtained a continuous evolution of gas from each wire—and they satisfied themselves by simple tests that the gas liberated at the one wire was hydrogen, that liberated at the other wire oxygen.

It would take us too far from our purpose to pursue the early history of the study of electrolysis through the first quarter of the nineteenth century. Indeed, if we were to do so we should, in the main, be following the investigations of chemists rather than of physicists; we should be recording spectacular advances in the field of practical inorganic chemistry, but little by way of an approach to a quantitative understanding of the physical phenomenon. In this period the art of the process of electrolytic decomposition was brought to a high state of effectiveness by Berzelius and Davy (see p. 69), thereby sodium and potassium were added to the list of the recognised elements, but the physicist's task remained for Faraday to accomplish—almost a generation later.

Michael Faraday, as we have seen (p. 122), was appointed assistant to Davy at the Royal Institution in 1812. In that capacity he must have been involved in many of Davy's researches in electrochemistry, but he did not take up the subject himself until some twenty years later. Towards the end of 1832 he was engaged in demonstrating, in a masterly series of experiments, the essential identity of the two electricities—'ordinary' electricity as obtained at high 'tension' and in small quantity from the 'electrostatic' machines of the eighteenth century, and 'voltaic' electricity as obtained at low tension and in large quantity from batteries of primary cells. Faraday's success in this endeavour was due to the consummate skill with which he contrived the appropriate arrangement of simple apparatus, in each case, in such a way that under these very diverse conditions the magnetic, thermal, physiological and electrolytic effects (and others) should be exhibited, in turn, whichever of the two kinds of electricity was employed. As we are here concerned solely with the electrolytic effects, we shall do no more than cite, as an example of his inventiveness in this series of researches, the type of electrolytic cell which Faraday used when working with electrostatic machines as a source of current. On a glass plate, providing suitable insulation, he would arrange two pieces of tinfoil, separated by a space of several inches. In between, there would be a small strip of litmus paper soaked with a neutral salt solution. Between each end of the paper strip and the piece of tinfoil opposite to it there would be a bridge of platinum wire—a short piece of wire so bent that it rested in stable equilibrium with one end on the tinfoil, the other end on the litmus paper, and an intermediate point touching the glass plate. Electricity from the insulated terminal of the machine would be 'led to' one piece of tinfoil by brush discharge from a sharp point and 'taken from' the other piece of tinfoil to the earth. In between, there would be the two platinum wire bridges and the 'electrolytic cell' of damp litmus paper traversed by the current. Evidence for electrolytic action would be seen in the change of colour of the litmus paper around its point of contact with one or other of the platinum bridge wires. Here was an arrangement of utter simplicity—and great delicacy.

It will be appreciated that these initial experiments in electrolysis, beautiful though they were, were only qualitative in nature. Faraday's main contributions to the subject were made in the following year, when he undertook a long series of quantitative experiments, using voltaic cells as a source of current—and glass vessels containing aqueous solutions of acids, alkalies and neutral salts, and furnished with metal electrodes, as electrolytic cells of more conventional design. He also carried out very many experiments, some of them semi-quantitative in nature, in less conventional arrangements, using fused salts as electrolytes.

Faraday embarked on his researches in the spring of 1833 with a strong conviction 'that the chemical power . . . is in direct proportion to the absolute quantity of electricity which passes'. This conviction he submitted to critical examination, testing and enlarging it step by step. First of all he arranged a series of electrolytic cells of different construction, and having platinum electrodes of different area (over a factor of 100), so that they contained

530 pHYSICS

530 ENcxdo

530 Hewit

530 Bio 815

21   QUATUM
            pHyicclles
            Lasers

509 Harre

Date: Tue, 24 Jan 1995 12:01:50 -0700
From: Francis Medaris <fmedaris@teal.c
To: Missy Bennett <mbennett@csn.org>
Subject: Forwarded mail....

Sending message.

\V/

Francis E. Medaris, Director
Monahan Library
fmedaris@csn.org

---------- Forwarded message ---------
Date: Tue, 24 Jan 95 03:30:55 EST
From: GPN BBS <gbbs@kraus.com>
To: fmedaris@csn.org
Subject:

Subject :GPN Now Has Mail Lists
Author : Admin
Topic number : 39
Topic name : News of our Network
 prepared May 31 15:55:38 1994

Entry # : 26294 Read by : Admin
          jimmyjoe   : at Thu Jun 2

samples of the same electrolyte (water acidulated with sulphuric acid) and were traversed by the same current. In some cells the hydrogen and oxygen evolved at the electrodes were collected separately, in others they were collected and measured together. From these experiments Faraday concluded 'that variation in the size of the electrodes causes no variation in the chemical action of a given quantity of electricity upon water'.

It is worth while, before proceeding, to say something regarding the absolute validity of this statement of physical law, in so far as it derives from Faraday's own experiments. Faraday did not claim that the total volume of gas evolved in each of the various cells in any single experiment was the same, within the limits of accuracy of his measuring equipment. Indeed, he admitted that there was a definite tendency for the measured volume to be slightly greater the smaller the area of the electrodes, and with electrodes of large area for the 'deficiency' to be somewhat larger in respect of the oxygen than the hydrogen set free. But he convinced himself that these were secondary effects, to be ascribed to the different solubilities of the product gases—and to differences in current density (inversely as electrode area) which were reflected in differences in bubble size (and so in speed of solution) at the electrode surfaces. Ever since the time of Galileo (see *M L & T*, p. 123), the investigator of genius has known intuitively how to separate the essential from the contingent in the results of his own researches!

One way of effectively increasing the area of the electrodes of one cell of a series sequence, without interrupting the circuit, is to join another cell in parallel with the cell in question. Faraday experimented with arrangements of this type, and found that the sum of the volumes of gas liberated in the two cells in parallel was not significantly different from the volume of gas liberated, in the same period, in any one of the single cells included in the same circuit. On the basis of his previous experiments this result was hardly unexpected, but Faraday pointed out that there was a difference (and it need not be trivial) between the situations produced by mere increase in electrode area in a given cell and the provision of the same additional area of electrode in a parallel cell of different geometrical form. What he called the intensity of the current—and what we should now refer to as the difference of potential across the cell traversed by the current—would not necessarily be the same in the two situations. From this simple variant of his earlier experiments (and from other evidence), Faraday therefore concluded that 'variation of intensity [potential difference] has no influence on the results if the quantity of electricity remain the same'.

Faraday next investigated the effect of varying the concentration of sulphuric acid in the different cells in his series arrangement. He found nothing to shake the conviction with which he had started his work. He wrote 'Slight differences occurred, as before, sometimes in one direction, sometimes in another; but the final result was, that exactly the same quantity of water was decomposed in all the solutions by the same quantity of electricity, though the sulphuric acid in some was seventy-fold what it was in others'.

These exhaustive tests having been concluded to his full satisfaction, Faraday provided himself with a set of acidulated-water cells of different construction which he subsequently used as current integrators (quantity-measuring devices) in his further investigations. Originally he gave the name 'volta-electrometer' to a cell of this type (in which the volume of evolved gas is proportional to the total quantity of electricity transmitted); later (1838) he contracted the name to 'voltameter', as it is now employed.

It would be unprofitable, in the present context, to describe the experiments which Faraday made with the help of his voltameter in as great detail as we have described those which he carried out in the course of its development. His own account of them is given tersely in more than a hundred numbered sections of *Experimental Researches in Electricity*. Suffice to say that, whilst he recognised 'that the final result of the action of the electric current upon substances placed between the electrodes, instead of being simple may be very complicated'—whilst he recognised, that is, that primary effects are often marked by secondary actions, Faraday still contrived to elicit a simple law from his observations. He nowhere stated that law in precise terms in which its limitations are admitted, but we may assimilate his various conclusions in summary as follows:

Whatever the electrolyte, if the result of electrolysis is the appearance of a single chemical substance at each electrode (or the simple dissolution of the material of one electrode and the appearance of a single chemical substance at the other), then the quantity of such substance appearing (or of the electrode material passing into the electrolyte) in a given time is represented by the product of the quantity of electricity transmitted by the electrolyte and the 'electrochemical equivalent' of the ion of the substance concerned.

The ratio of the electrochemical equivalents of two ions is the same as the ratio of the chemical combining weights of the substances to which they belong—or, if the (single) substances appearing at the two electrodes of any cell are identifiable as the sole constituents of a chemical compound present in the electrolyte, then the ratio of the amounts of these substances appearing in a given time is the same as the ratio in which they are combined in the compound concerned.

It will be clear that there are two separate assertions in our summary statement, one in each of the two paragraphs into which it is cast. In the first paragraph there is the implicit assertion that for all electrolytes (not only acidulated water), when the products are unique, the chemical action 'is in direct proportion to the absolute quantity of electricity which passes'. This was Faraday's original conjecture, as we have already recorded it (p. 198). In the second paragraph there is the assertion that the electrochemical equivalent of an ion is directly proportional to the chemical combining weight of the substance to which it belongs. This involves a new concept, which Faraday had developed during the course of his researches.

It will be noted that the term 'electrochemical equivalent' has already been used in the first paragraph of our statement. However, nothing is there asserted concerning its significance: it is introduced at that point, for the first time, in a form of words which merely serves to define the magnitude of the physical quantity to which the term refers. The measure of the electrochemical equivalent of an ion is that of the mass of the corresponding chemical substance transferred to or from an electrode when unit quantity of electricity passes through an electrolytic cell under the conditions specified.

Finally, we take note of the second part of the second paragraph of our summary statement. The notion of the chemical combining weight of a substance is not altogether without ambiguity (as the chemist's 'law of multiple proportions' unambiguously proclaims),

EM O

but brevity and precision are often incompatible requirements when generalities are to be expressed, and the situation in the first part of our second paragraph is no exception in this respect. The second part of that paragraph has therefore been added as a paraphrase of the first, unacceptable in isolation because it lacks the necessary generality, but, within its limitations, preferable to the first because of its greater precision.

We end this account of the early investigations of the phenomena of electrolysis, as these are manifest in chemical effects at the electrodes, by reference to two speculations which Faraday permitted himself in his published account of his work. The first speculation may be dealt with by direct quotation. Faraday wrote 'I think I cannot deceive myself in considering the doctrine of definite electro-chemical action as of the utmost importance. It touches . . . upon the beautiful idea, that ordinary chemical affinity is a mere consequence of the electrical attractions of the particles of different kinds of matter. . . .' The second 'speculation' was set out at greater length, in a separate dissertation, under the title 'On the absolute quantity of Electricity associated with the particles or atoms of Matter'. It consists of a wide-ranging discussion, the various strands of which can only be indicated here. Faraday took into consideration electrolytic effects at low and high tension (see p. 198), together with the functioning of the voltaic cell (which we are to consider later in this chapter, see §5.5)—and he cited, at some length, particular experiments which he had not otherwise found occasion to mention. That he was unable in the end to deduce a numerical value for the quantity of electricity associated with a single atom of matter (for which the title of his dissertation might have prepared his reader) need cause us no surprise, for the date was December 1833, but we are left in no doubt regarding his qualitative assessment of the situation. It may be represented by a composite quotation pieced together from various sections of the dissertation which we are discussing: 'It seems that, if the electrical power which makes a grain of oxygen and hydrogen in the right proportions unite into water could be thrown into the condition of a current, it would exactly equal the current required for the separation of that grain of water into its elements again. This necessary quantity of electricity is equal to a very powerful flash of lightning, yet when it has performed its full work of electrolyzation, it has only separated the elements of a single grain of water. What an enormous quantity of electricity, therefore, is required for the decomposition of a single grain of water! I have endeavoured to make a comparison, but the proportion is so high that I am almost afraid to mention it. It would appear that 800,000 such charges of the Leyden battery as I have referred to above would be necessary to supply electricity sufficient to decompose a single grain of water—or, if I am right, to equal the quantity of electricity which is associated with the elements of that grain of water, endowing them with their mutual chemical affinity.' Faraday employed the goldsmiths' grain, of Troy weight: its metric equivalent is approximately 65 milligrammes.

It may be said, by way of postscript, that neither in relation to his first speculation, nor in relation to his second, did Michael Faraday seriously deceive himself—or the scientists who followed him.

5.3. A MATTER OF NOMENCLATURE

In our description of Faraday's researches, in the last section, we made frequent use of the terms 'electrode' and 'ion', without formal definition (though 'electrolysis' was defined at the beginning of the section). We acted on the assumption that these terms are now so much part of the language of science that the reader would be in no doubt regarding their meaning. We did not have occasion to use 'anode' and 'cathode', or 'anion' and 'cation', but had we done so we should have made the same assumption regarding them. In fact, we made that assumption regarding 'anode' and 'cathode' in section 4.4.

In this section we digress to consider briefly the circumstances in which these various terms were introduced. They were introduced by Faraday, and the history of their coining and adoption* is as relevant today as it was at any time in the past century. In 1833, Faraday had found himself, not for the first time, investigating a phenomenon for which there was no obviously satisfying explanation within the framework of accepted theory. He had to communicate his discoveries to others, and he was scrupulously anxious to be able to communicate no more than the bare facts, so that his readers might assess their significance without bias. If

---

* Much of the information used in this section is taken from 'Faraday consults the scholars', by S. Ross, *Notes and Records of the Royal Society of London*, **16**, 187-220, 1961.

he wished to add his own tentative interpretation, it should be entirely evident that that was his aim. To borrow technical terms already in use in another context was to run the risk of borrowing the theory which supported them: he must, therefore, coin his own technical terms—and they must be of such a character as to be innocent of all theory, as far as may be. More than two years previously he had written, 'I cannot help thinking it a most unfortunate thing that men . . . should by the promulgation of their own theoretical views under the form of nomenclature . . . actually retard [the progress of science].' Faraday did not intend to be guilty of the same offence himself.

William Whewell (1794-1866) had been the recipient of the letter from which we have just quoted. He had submitted to Faraday, as editor of the *Journal of the Royal Institution*, an article 'On the employment of notation in Chemistry'. Whewell was at the time professor of mineralogy at Cambridge. In the previous year he had been consulted by the geologist Charles Lyell (1797-1875) with the request for names for the subdivisions of the Tertiary System (he provided Eocene, Miocene and Pliocene, which have since been universally accepted). In that year, also, he had added to the technical language of architecture. In his *Architectural Notes on German Churches* he wrote, 'I have ventured to employ a few new phrases . . . with a view to their being employed steadily and precisely for the future. . . . It is scarcely possible to describe new features without this much of innovation, or to describe anything distinctly without this much of technicality.' Already behind him was a career as a mathematician; ahead was his election as Master of Trinity College (1841) and his later excursions into the fields of history, philosophy, economics and international law.

Faraday did not consult Whewell on his own need for technical terms until he had 'deliberately considered the subject' with Whitlock Nicholl (1786-1838), his personal physician. Dr Nicholl was no ordinary general practitioner; he had been elected Fellow of the Royal Society in 1830 (Lyell and Whewell were already fellows) and he had already made his own contribution to anatomical terminology in the learned journals. He was able at once to provide Faraday with the terms 'electrolyte' (that which can be electrically loosened) and 'electrode' (the doorway by which the electricity passes in or out)—and with others which were adopted for a time and then later abandoned.

It was during this period of incomplete satisfaction with the terms which Nicholl had suggested that Faraday first put his problem to Whewell. We have already quoted the opinion of de la Rive (p. 94), 'nothing establishes . . . the true direction of the current, or even that the movement of electricity takes the form of a current'. That was written in 1854. Faraday, twenty years earlier, already held a similar view, with equal conviction. There was a directional effect, it was certain, in a complete voltaic circuit, as the associated magnetic phenomena indicated—and there was an asymmetry in the chemical effects at the two electrodes in an electrolytic cell. Faraday wished to give distinctive names to the electrodes to mark this asymmetry, but, as he wrote to Whewell, 'I want . . . names by which I can refer to [them] without involving any theory of electricity'. He suggested to Whewell that the best way to achieve this end would be to link the two phenomena associated with the so-called current, the electrolytic and the magnetic phenomena, so that the asymmetry of the one could be described in terms of the spatial relations characteristic of the other. In that way implied notions regarding the 'reality' of the electric current would be avoided. Faraday, therefore, imagined a voltaic circuit circling the earth 'in a line of latitude'. If the magnetic effect of that circuit was, on a global scale, such as to increase the magnetic field of the earth, then in an electrolytic cell included in the circuit hydrogen would be evolved at the western electrode, oxygen at the eastern. Conventionally, an electric current flowing in the circuit from east to west would be required (the axial magnetic field through the earth is from north to south). Possibly, Whewell might make something of this suggestion.

Faraday's letter had referred to other difficulties, also, besides the one we have mentioned. By return of post Whewell replied at length, dealing with all the matters put to him and making various sugestions regarding each. But in respect of the names for the electrodes, in particular, he expressed a strong preference—for 'anode' and 'cathode': anode, the eastern way, the way where the sun rises up; cathode, the western way, where the sun goes down.

Faraday did not accept Whewell's preferences immediately. He again consulted his friends in London. 'All to whom I have shown them have supposed at first that by *anode* I mean *no way*', he wrote. 'The notion of *anodos* meaning *no way* could only suggest itself to persons unfamiliar with Greek', retorted Whewell. The correspondence continued with great courtesy for about two weeks, then eventually Whewell had his own way. Besides 'anode' and 'cathode', Faraday accepted 'anion'—that thing which goes up, and 'cation'—that thing which goes down. He even accepted 'ion', under duress ('the word is not a substantive in Greek, but it may easily be so taken', Whewell confided)—'the last I shall have but little occasion for', he wrote, when he had finally accepted them all.

With later generations of scientists, 'ion', the word on which Faraday frowned, has found favour beyond that of all the others, but the history of his battle for integrity has its lesson, just the same.

5.4. THE PHENOMENA OF ELECTROLYSIS (II)

In section 5.2 we were concerned almost exclusively with Faraday's researches into the chemical phenomena taking place at the electrodes of an electrolytic cell. In this section we shall consider, more particularly, effects occurring throughout the volume of the electrolyte. The pioneers in this field of investigation were J.W. Hittorf (see p. 161) and F.W.G.Kohlrausch (1840-1910).

Over a period of six years, from 1853, Hittorf published a series of researches in which he established, for the first time by direct experiment, the way in which the electrolyte in an electrolytic cell is depleted by the passage of the current. It had become clear that, under ordinary conditions, the transport of chemical substance in electrolysis is considerably more rapid than the transport by diffusion. It was not difficult, therefore, by suitable design to arrange matters so that any preferential depletion of the electrolyte, around the electrodes or in any other region of the cell, should have time to attain measurable proportions before the effects of diffusion of the solute became appreciable. Hittorf's fundamental discovery may be expressed qualitatively as follows:

In an ideal electrolytic cell in which there is no diffusion, and in which there are no secondary processes involving the dissolution of the electrodes, the depletion of the electrolyte occurs initially in the regions in the immediate neighbourhood of the electrodes; only as electrolysis proceeds do these regions of depletion extend towards one another into the main body of the electrolyte. In general the initial rate of depletion is not the same at the two electrodes.

There had been earlier indications of this effect in work reported in 1844 by John Frederic Daniell (1790-1845), first professor of chemistry at King's College, London, and W. A. Miller, but the credit for its systematic investigation is due almost entirely to Hittorf. Hittorf made quantitative studies of the phenomenon in a number of electrolytes. His results may be most simply interpreted in terms of the hypothesis of spontaneous ionisation put forward by R. J. E. Clausius (see *M L & T*, p. 283) in 1857.

Clausius was the first seriously to suggest that in a solution which is an electrolyte, there is a continuous process of transient dissociation of solute molecules into ions, and recombination of ions into uncharged molecules. On this hypothesis the effect of the applied field is merely to cause a general drift of the oppositely charged ions to the electrodes. All previous hypotheses (and Faraday's tentatively expressed views on the matter must be included in this category) had started from the assumption that ionic dissociation is a direct result of the application of the field.

Let us consider the situation in an electrolytic cell with plane parallel electrodes, shortly after the current has been switched on, on the basis of Clausius' hypothesis. Across any plane normal to the direction of current flow, in the main body of the electrolyte, positively charged ions are drifting towards the cathode with velocity u^+ and negative ions are drifting towards the anode with velocity u^-. The original concentration of ions (say, n ions of each sign per unit volume) is unchanged over this plane. The current, per unit area of the plane is $n(u^+ + u^-)e$, e being the magnitude of the ionic charge. Provided that the process has not been so long continued that a significant fraction of the dissolved substance has been removed from the electrolyte, this statement accurately describes the situation over any plane normal to the direction of current flow—even across a plane fairly close to one of the electrodes. Suppose that B (fig. 32) is such a plane situated close to the plane surface of the cathode C. Current in amount $n(u^+ + u^-)e$ is carried to each unit area of C—by positive ions exclusively. Thus the rate of 'discharge' of positive ions at the cathode is $n(u^+ + u^-)$ per unit area. However, the rate of entry of positive ions into the region between B and C is only nu^+ per unit area of B. On balance, then, nu^- positive ions are lost to this region, per unit area of the electrode, per unit of time—and the same number of negative ions are lost through transport across B. Provided that there is no transport of solvent molecules along with the ions (provided, that is, that the ions have remained the simple entities formed by dissociation of the solute molecules, rather than become complexes by subsequent association of these entities with molecules of the solvent), effectively the region between B and C is being depleted of solute material at a rate of nu^- molecules per unit area of C. In the same way the region around the anode is being depleted of solute molecules at the rate of nu^+ per unit area of that electrode. Formally, in these statements, it will be seen, we have reproduced the essential results of Hittorf: solute depletion occurs initially in the immediate neighbourhood of the electrodes, and, in general, to a different extent at each.

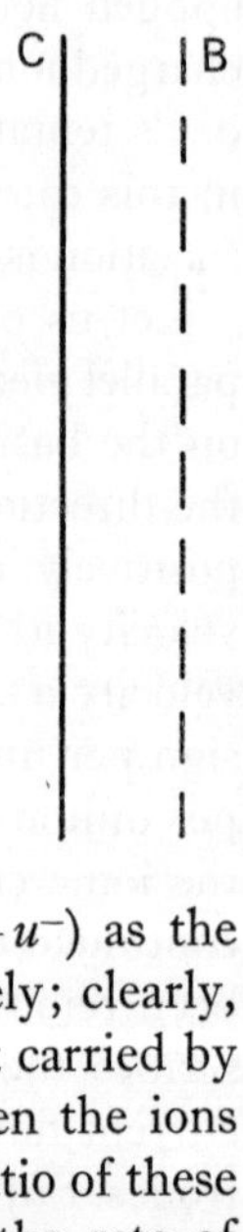

FIGURE 32

Hittorf defined the ratios $u^+/(u^+ + u^-)$ and $u^-/(u^+ + u^-)$ as the 'transport numbers' of the cation and anion respectively; clearly, these numbers denote the fractions of the total current carried by the oppositely charged ions, in the general case. When the ions are simple, so that there is no solvent association, the ratio of these transport numbers, as we have seen, is the ratio of the rate of solute depletion around the anode to the rate of solute depletion around the cathode, in the initial stages of electrolysis. (Obviously this result does not depend on the assumption of plane parallel electrodes of equal area which we effectively made in deriving it.)

Having stated Hittorf's main qualitative conclusion (in relation to an ideal electrolytic cell in which there are no secondary processes involving the dissolution of the electrodes—and in which the primary products of electrolysis are completely removed from the electrolyte, either as evolved gases or as solids deposited on the electrodes), we have given a formal account of the quantitative aspects of the phenomenon of electrolyte depletion in terms of Clausius' hypothesis. The reasons for this procedure are simple enough. Hittorf soon recognised, as Faraday had done, that in many cases 'the final result' of electrolysis 'may be very complicated' (see p. 200). There are very few substances, indeed, which when dissolved in aqueous solution and submitted to electrolysis, with whatever electrodes, are neatly separated into constituents both of which are quantitatively removed from solution at the electrodes without secondary action intervening. Again, complication of the phenomenon by the solvent association of ions is far from uncommon. More often than not, if complicating effects are absent at all, they are absent in respect of one electrode only (more often it is the cathode). If the primary cations discharge and are removed quantitatively at the cathode, whilst secondary processes occur at the anode, clearly, only the rate of solute depletion around the cathode is readily open to simple interpretation. It was under such limitations that Hittorf edged his way by experiment to an understanding of the phenomenon. If we measure the rate of solute depletion around the cathode in terms of w, the net rate of loss of cation substance in the region in question, and simultaneously determine W, the rate of deposition (or evolution) of cation substance at the electrode, in the ideal case, obviously, $w/W = u^-/(u^+ + u^-)$, in terms of our former analysis. Hittorf's primary determinations, then, were mostly of the transport numbers of the anions with which he was concerned. His estimates of the transport numbers of the corresponding cations (on the assumption that the sum of the two numbers should be unity, in every case) were in general more open to doubt.

In the upshot it may well appear that the phenomenon of solute depletion is too complicated for profitable discussion in an elementary treatment of electrolytic effects, but the notion of ion transport numbers and drift velocities is essentially independent of this particular effect (see below)—and it is a fact of history that these important ideas were introduced by Hittorf, precisely from the study of solute depletion, complicated though that effect undoubtedly is. Moreover, in spite of its complication, the experimental investigation of solute depletion remained as an active interest of electrochemists for more than two generations—and, fifty years after the publication of his first paper on the subject, Hittorf was still contributing to its literature in 1903.

The experimental work of Kohlrausch may be described more directly than that of Hittorf, with which we have just been concerned. It had to do essentially with the ohmic resistance of electrolytic cells, and with the way in which the resistivity of an electrolyte varies with the concentration of the solute. Indeed, Kohlrausch was the first to show convincingly that the concept of resistance is a valid concept in relation to electrolytic conduction generally. There had been earlier investigations directed towards this end, notably those of Gustav Heinrich Wiedemann (1826-1899) carried out (1856) when he was professor of physics at the university of Basle, but all had been vitiated, to some extent at least, by the effects of 'electrode polarisation'.

The phenomenon of electrode polarisation was well known to Faraday. If clean platinum electrodes are dipped into acidulated water, and if the electrolytic cell so formed is joined in circuit with a voltaic battery, it is found that the current through the cell decreases with the passage of time. If the electromotive force of the battery is below a critical value, the current soon falls effectively to zero; otherwise it falls to a steady value, which it retains until the battery begins to fail or the electrolytic cell to be significantly depleted of electrolyte. If, when the current has become steady in this way (or has sunk to zero), the circuit is broken and the platinum electrodes are connected by a wire, a 'reverse' current is found to flow in the wire (from anode to cathode), rapidly decreasing in value to zero (this last effect had been studied by J. W. Ritter as early as 1803, see *V & W*, p. 270). The general phenomenon is to be explained in terms of a modification of the surface of the electrodes by thin films of 'adsorbed' gas, or other material —and in the Ritter effect, in particular, the reverse current is attributable to the process of disappearance of these surface layers, and the return of the electrodes to their original unpolarised state (see p. 442).

In 1856 Wiedemann had been successful in avoiding the main complications of electrode polarisation by confining his investigations to cells in which the solute was a metallic salt, and the electrodes were made of the same metal as was present in ionic form in the electrolyte. Then, in 1869, Kohlrausch introduced the use of alternating current sources for resistivity measurements—and in so doing opened up the possibility of avoiding polarisation effects altogether. By working with suitably designed 'conductivity cells' he was able to show conclusively that Ohm's law is valid for electrolytic conductors generally.

Let us consider the implications of this general result, before proceeding farther. Let us imagine a cylindrical portion of electrolyte, of cross-sectional area A and length l, through which a current i is passing parallel to the axis of the cylinder. Kohlrausch's experimental result may be expressed conventionally, in the form of equation (67), $i = V/R$, V being the difference of potential effective over the length of the cylinder, and the constant parameter R being the empirically determined resistance of the portion of electrolyte concerned. It may equally well be expressed in either of the alternative forms (see p. 112)

$$i = VA/\rho l \text{ or } i = VA\sigma/l,$$

ρ being the resistivity and σ the conductivity of the solution. According to the formalism based on the hypothesis of Clausius, which we have already used in discussing the work of Hittorf (p. 207), for a simple binary solute,

$$i = n(u^+ + u^-)eA.$$

Kohlrausch's result effectively implies that the quantity σ is a characteristic quantity for a given solution. If the ionic concentration, n, is similarly characteristic (depending only on the nature of solute and solvent and on the strength of the solution), then the sum of the drift velocities of cation and anion, $(u^+ + u^-)$, must be proportional to V/l, the intensity of the electric field effective in the electrolyte. This is the primary implication that we were seeking. Accepting it, we define k^+ and k^-, the mobilities of the ions, writing $u^+ = k^+V/l$, $u^- = k^-V/l$, and we have, finally, for a binary solute,

$$\sigma = n(k^+ + k^-)e \qquad (126)$$

Kohlrausch defined the 'equivalent conductance' of an electrolytic solution in terms of the equation

$$\Lambda = \frac{\sigma}{c} \qquad (127)$$

Here Λ is the equivalent conductance, and c is the concentration of the solution in 'chemical equivalents' per unit volume. In this connection the chemical equivalent of any substance may be identified as the mass of the substance which would be decomposed and transported to the two electrodes as a result of the passage through a suitable electrolytic cell of a total quantity of electricity sufficient to liberate precisely 8 grammes of oxygen at the anode of a voltameter containing acidulated water, under ideal conditions.* Obviously, on the basis of this identification, the same quantity of electricity is required to decompose one chemical equivalent of whatever substance. This quantity is conventionally designated 1 faraday; it is approximately 96500 coulombs (see p. 174). If, in solution, one chemical equivalent of a substance were completely dissociated into ions, 1 faraday of positive charge would be carried by the cations and 1 faraday of negative charge by the anions so formed. This statement is true whether the solute is a binary solute (that is, one in which the molecule dissociates into two ions only, carrying equal charges of opposite sign) or whether the solute molecule dissociates into more than two ions (in any case its net charge is zero, initially). In respect of a binary solute—and in relation to equations (126) and (127)—ne represents the total charge in fact carried by the ions of one sign, per unit volume of the solution. On the other hand, if all the solute molecules were dissociated, the total charge which would be carried by the ions of one sign, in this case, would be cF, per unit volume, as we have just concluded. Here we have written F to represent the magnitude of 1 faraday in conventional units. Comparing the actual ionic charge density with the maximum possible charge density corresponding to complete dissociation, we may define the ratio α as the 'degree of dissociation' of the solute, at the given concentration, in terms of the equation

$$ne = \alpha cF \tag{128}$$

Then, combining equations (126), (127) and (128), we have

$$\Lambda = \alpha(k^+ + k^-)F \tag{129}$$

Although we have derived this last result through equation (126), valid for binary solutes exclusively, a little consideration will show that equation (129) is, in fact, valid generally. We proceed, then,

---

* Strictly, the isotopic composition of the oxygen in the water should be specified, if full precision is to be achieved.

to discuss Kohlrausch's detailed results in terms of equation (129) —merely pointing out in passing an underlying assumption which we have not as yet made explicit. Equation (129) has been based on the assumption that the solvent contributes nothing to the conductivity of the solution.

As we have stated, Kohlrausch's main investigation concerned the way in which the equivalent conductance of an electrolytic solution varies with the concentration of the solute. He first satisfied himself that the 'pure' water which he used as solvent in his experiments fulfilled the condition that it should contribute negligibly to the measured conductivity (indeed, it was fifty years before any other experimenter succeeded in purifying water so effectively in this respect). Then, by careful control of temperature he was able to obtain reproducible results, even with very dilute solutions. (In general the conductivity increases quite rapidly as the temperature rises—see below.) He found that for all electrolytes the equivalent conductance increases as the concentration decreases. Consistently with this general result, he recognised empirically two types of variation. For one group of electrolytes, notably those for which the equivalent conductance was large, he found that this quantity varied only slowly with increasing dilution, increasing steadily over the whole range. For the other group, even at the greatest dilutions at which he was able to measure the conductivity, it appeared that the corresponding rate of increase of the equivalent conductance was itself still increasing as the concentration decreased. For the former group of electrolytes (frequently referred to as 'strong' electrolytes) he succeeded in establishing a rough empirical law

$$\Lambda = \Lambda_\infty - bc^{\frac{1}{2}} \qquad (130)$$

(Λ_∞ being the 'equivalent conductance at infinite dilution', and the quantity b a constant for a given combination of solute and solvent at a given temperature), but for the latter group (the so-called 'weak' electrolytes) no correspondingly simple generalisation emerged from his researches.

The immediate result of the investigations which we have just summarised was that Λ_∞, the equivalent conductance at infinite dilution, became an experimentally determinable quantity for strong electrolytes. Λ, the equivalent conductance at concentration c, could be plotted against $c^{\frac{1}{2}}$, and the nearly straight-line graph extrapolated to $c = 0$. In reviewing the results obtained in this way for a large number of electrolytes (water being the solvent in each case, and the temperature being the same throughout), Kohlrausch, in 1876, recognised that, for binary solutes, Λ_∞ could significantly be regarded as the sum of two contributions, one representing the contribution of the anions the other the independent contribution of the cations to the total conductance. Evidence for this conclusion can be exemplified by formal expressions such as

$$\Lambda_\infty(\text{KCl}) - \Lambda_\infty(\text{NaCl}) = \Lambda_\infty(\text{KNO}_3) - \Lambda_\infty(\text{NaNO}_3),$$

which the experimental results were found to satisfy. Kohlrausch's generalisation receives a simple interpretation in terms of equation (129). We plausibly assume that, at infinite dilution, when the equivalent conductance has reached a 'limiting' (high) value, dissociation is complete for all electrolytes. In that case $\alpha = 1$, and equation (129) becomes

$$\Lambda_\infty = (k_\infty^+ + k_\infty^-)F \tag{131}$$

F, the magnitude of the faraday is a universal constant, and Λ_∞ is immediately exhibited as the sum of two terms relating to the oppositely charged ions concerned. Kohlrausch's generalisation, then, aptly became known as the 'law of independent ionic mobilities'. It implies that, at infinite dilution, the mobility of the anions is uninfluenced by the presence of the cations in solution—and *vice versa*. If we had been building up a speculative theory of electrolysis, rather than making cautious inferences from detailed experiments, we might almost have been forgiven for adopting this result as axiomatic from the beginning.

Equation (131) provides the basis of determining $(k_\infty^+ + k_\infty^-)$, the sum of the mobilities of the anion and cation of a binary solute in a strong electrolyte at infinite dilution. As we have seen, the ratio of the mobilities, when the concentration is finite, may be obtained from a knowledge of the transport numbers of the ions (see pp. 208, 209). Although these numbers are now known to vary significantly, for many electrolytes, with concentration, at constant temperature, extrapolation may be made 'to infinite dilution', on the basis of sufficiently accurate experiments. We then have, in an ideal case, $(k_\infty^+ + k_\infty^-)$ and, say, $k_\infty^-/(k_\infty^+ + k_\infty^-)$ as experimentally determined quantities, and we deduce the individual ionic mobilities, k_∞^+ and k_∞^-, at infinite dilution and at the relevant temperature. Nowadays, by direct or indirect means, well-established values of mobilities have been obtained for a large selection of ions in aqueous solution—and are to be found listed in the tables. At 25°C for example, the mobility of the hydrogen ion at infinite dilution, in aqueous solution, is $3 \cdot 63 \times 10^{-3}$ cm s^{-1}/V cm^{-1}, the mobility of the hydroxyl ion is $2 \cdot 06 \times 10^{-3}$ cm s^{-1}/V cm^{-1}, and the mobilities of most other simple singly-charged ions, under the same conditions, range between about 4×10^{-4} and 8×10^{-4} in the same units. Clearly, having regard to the definition of mobility (p. 211), the mobility of any ion is proportional to the charge carried by the ion, other things being equal. In general, therefore, the mobilities of the simpler doubly-charged ions are roughly twice as great as those of the singly-charged ions mentioned above.

We have now discussed the earlier work of Hittorf and Kohlrausch—and in each case we have used the hypothesis of Clausius (see p. 207) to give some measure of coherence to our account of their discoveries. Thereby we have deliberately 'simplified' the true history of the subject, in the interest of the reader (whose primary concern should be with physics rather than with physicists). However, if only briefly, we should pause to set the record straight. The hypothesis of spontaneous dissociation (ionisation) in electrolytes was put forward by Clausius in 1857. It was not generally accepted as providing a basis for the satisfactory understanding of the phenomena of electrolysis for more than a quarter of a century. By that time most of the pioneer experimental work of Hittorf and Kohlrausch had already been completed. As the followers of Newton had been responsible for delaying the acceptance of the wave theory of light, so Maxwell, the follower of Faraday, by his opposition to Clausius' views, fostered, at least for a time, the general notion of heterodoxy which became attached to them. Within the limits of his natural philosophy, he gave them fair treatment (*Treatise*, 1873, vol. 1, §§256-260), but he concluded 'It is extremely improbable that when we come to understand the true nature of electrolysis we shall retain in any form the theory of molecular charges, for then we shall have obtained a secure basis on which to form a true theory of electric currents, and so become independent of these provisional theories.'

The resurgence of the dissociation theory, and its final acceptance was due in the first instance to the work and writings of

Svante August Arrhenius (1859-1927). In 1883, whilst still a student at Stockholm, he presented to the Academy of Sciences of that city a paper, 'Recherches sur la conductibilité galvanique des électrolytes'. Four years later, before the Swedish Academy of Sciences, in a discourse 'On the dissociation of substances dissolved in water', he marshalled the evidence, other than that from electrolytic phenomena, for the hypothesis of molecular dissociation into ions. In particular, he drew attention to the then recent work of Pfeffer and van't Hoff on the phenomenon of osmosis. In 1877, Wilhelm F.P.Pfeffer (1845-1920), a German botanist, had succeeded in making the first really quantitative observations relative to this effect, which had been known, at least as a scientific curiosity, ever since it was described by Nollet (see p. 11) in 1748. Soon afterwards, on 14 October 1885, Jacobus Hendricus van't Hoff (1852-1911), a Dutch chemist, put forward the first theory of the effect in a paper presented to the Swedish Academy. Briefly, van't Hoff suggested that the osmotic pressure of a solution is the same pressure as would be exerted by the solute molecules if they were the sole occupants of a volume equal to the volume of the solution, behaving therein as the molecules of a perfect gas at the relevant temperature. According to the kinetic theory of gases, if this suggestion were correct, the osmotic pressure should be essentially independent of the nature of the solute, depending only on the molar concentration (or the number of solute molecules per unit volume of solution) and the temperature. Van't Hoff was able to show, from the experimental observations available to him at the time, that this simple result was valid 'for the majority of substances'.

At that time most of these observations related to organic materials—sugars and the like—in aqueous solution. Arrhenius pointed out that these solutions were electrically non-conducting, whereas the solutions for which van't Hoff's result was invalid (dilute solutions of inorganic acids, bases and salts) were indeed electrolytes. In every case, for solutions of this latter class, the osmotic pressure was greater than that predicted by the simple law: this could only imply, according to Arrhenius, that the number of independent 'molecules of equivalent gas' per unit volume of the solution was greater than the number of solute molecules introduced per unit volume. Van't Hoff's basic explanation of the phenomenon of osmosis, on this view, required no more than the acceptance of the hypothesis of molecular dissociation in electrolytes in order to bring both non-electrolytes and electrolytes within its purview.

Arrhenius's interpretation of the osmotic pressure 'anomalies', backed as it was by circumstantial evidence of a quantitative nature, had served, at last, to render the dissociation theory of Clausius scientifically respectable. In 1892, certain observations of Wilhelm Ostwald (1853-1932) opened up another field of enquiry in which the benefits of the theory were immediately obvious; thereafter only five years remained before the discovery of the electron (see §4.2), out of which all later views regarding the electrical structure of matter ultimately developed. In the context of these views the notion of ionic dissociation found a natural place.

Ostwald was professor of physical chemistry at Riga from 1882 to 1887, and at Leipzig from 1887 until he retired in 1906. His observations of 1892 related to the absorption spectra of dilute aqueous solutions of the alkali permanganates. They pointed the way to the realisation that the colours of dilute electrolytes generally are determined by the optical properties of ions rather than of neutral molecules (Ostwald obtained almost identical absorption spectra, in the visible region, for all permanganates, whatever the metallic constituent of the salt might be).

In resuscitating the dissociation theory of Clausius, Arrhenius introduced one important new element of precision, namely the assumption that dissociation in strong electrolytes at infinite dilution is complete. We have already adopted this, as a plausible assumption (p. 214), in discussing the experimental results of Kohlrausch. Clausius, on the other hand, not having the benefit of Kohlrausch's results on which to base a quantitative theory, had earlier supposed that in any practical situation the degree of dissociation would never be very great ($\alpha \ll 1$). On this matter all the evidence now available supports Arrhenius's assumption.

For many years scientists generally accepted, as a corollary to Arrhenius's assumption, the more detailed view that it is only at infinite dilution that the degree of dissociation is unity for strong electrolytes. It was on this basis that Arrhenius himself sought to interpret the variation of equivalent conductance with concentration in such cases. In terms of equation (129) he attributed the increase of Λ with decrease of c (equation (127)) solely to an increase in α (with $\alpha_\infty = 1$, as we have already assumed). There are many reasons why this simple interpretation cannot now be accepted. According to this point of view, when the temperature is constant the sum of the mobilities of anion and cation (($k^+ + k^-$) of equation (129)) should be independent of concentration. There is now an abundance of direct evidence for the variation of transport numbers (or ratios of mobilities) under these conditions (see p. 214). It is most unlikely that in all cases the sum of the mobilities should be concentration-independent when their ratio varies. Furthermore, there is the very considerable temperature variation of conductivity at constant concentration to be explained. At infinite dilution the temperature coefficient of increase of equivalent conductivity is of the order of 0·02 per degree C for strong electrolytes generally. On Arrhenius's hypothesis this, at least, must be interpreted in terms of a variation of ionic mobility (for α_∞ is assumed to be unity whatever the temperature). This conceded, it would appear to be altogether too naïve to insist that the mobility should be independent of concentration, it being necessary at the same time to assume that it varies so rapidly with temperature.

Already, by 1902, the speculative suggestion had been made by William Sutherland (1859-1911) that the matter ought more reasonably to be considered from an entirely different point of view. Sutherland postulated that dissociation is complete, for strong electrolytes, at all concentrations, and in so doing ascribed all the observed variations in equivalent conductance to variations in mobility. The rapid temperature variation, in particular, suggested to him the corresponding variation in liquid viscosity, and, although the concept of Newtonian viscosity cannot be applied directly to the motion through the solution of so small an entity as an ion, he noted the correlation between the rapid decrease of viscosity and the rapid increase in conductivity (or ionic mobility) as the temperature is raised. The notion of a type of 'effective viscosity' in which the predominant forces are of electrical origin (arising from the charges on the ions, and so dependent on the ionic concentration) can be traced back to this early suggestion of Sutherland. This notion was elaborated by S. R. Milner (1875-1958) during the period 1912-18 and, from a somewhat different basis by J. W. P. Debye (1884-1966) and E. Hückel from 1923. By the time Debye and Hückel were developing their theory the method of crystal structure analysis by X-ray diffraction, initiated in 1913 by W. H. Bragg (1862-1942) and W. L. Bragg (b. 1890), had already led to the unambiguous conclusion that for a large class of substances the structural unit in the crystalline solid is the atomic ion, rather than the molecule or the neutral atom (see p. 466). This is the case for most inorganic salts and highly basic hydroxides. All these substances yield strong electrolytes when dissolved in water. If it is indeed a fact that even in the solid state their molecules are uniformly dissociated into ions, it is no arbitrary assumption to suppose that dissociation remains complete when the inter-ionic forces, which are responsible for the stability of the crystal structure, are further loosened in the process of solution. Since 1923, then, the speculation of Sutherland and Milner that in strong electrolytes there is complete dissociation at all concentrations, has become a natural element in a general theory, rather than a somewhat heterodox opinion. In spite of this, the complication of the situation is such that no simple theoretical account of the phenomenon is able to describe the variation of equivalent conductance with concentration throughout the whole range. Moreover, it must be admitted that not all strong electrolytes are solutions of crystalline solids of the type that we have been discussing. Thus, a dilute aqueous solution of hydrochloric acid is a strong electrolyte, but pure hydrogen chloride is a non-conductor in the liquid state. Faraday made a considerable study of the electrolytic behaviour of fused salts (see p. 198) and pure liquids; generally the chemical compounds which are susceptible of easy electrolysis in the molten state are those which form ionic crystals when they solidify. In the light of present-day knowledge some writers make the distinction between 'true electrolytes' and 'potential electrolytes'. Substances which form ionic crystals are regarded as belonging to the first class; those which, though they may be completely dissociated in solution, are nonconductors as pure liquids (or solids) are regarded as belonging to the latter. According to this classification, dissociation of 'potential electrolytes' in solution is seen as involving some more specific participation of the molecules of the solvent than is necessary when a 'true electrolyte' is put in solution.

In respect of weak electrolytes, the variation of equivalent conductance with concentration is in general greater (over the range between saturation and infinite dilution) than it is for the strong electrolytes that we have been discussing hitherto. In this case this variation cannot by any means be ascribed wholly to a variation in ionic mobility, and it is generally assumed that Arrhenius's hypothesis, that the degree of dissociation increases, possibly from a very small value at saturation, to unity at infinite dilution, is broadly valid as a basis of explanation.

5.5. THE VOLTAIC CELL

The essential difference between a voltaic cell and an electrolytic cell, on open circuit, is that there is some physical asymmetry of the system in the former case which there need not be in the latter. If the electrolyte is a single homogeneous liquid, then the electrodes must be made of different (conducting) materials, if the system is to function as a source of current; conversely, if the electrodes are made of the same material, then the portions of electrolyte directly in contact with the two electrodes must have different characteristics—that is, contain different solutes, or the same solute in different concentrations.

On closed circuit, when current passes, the phenomena of transport of charge through the electrolyte of a voltaic cell are in every way identical with the transport phenomena which are exhibited in electrolysis, and which we have considered in detail in the last section. The questions that are new and have now to be considered are: what are the circumstances which determine the difference of potential which exists as between the electrodes ('poles') of a voltaic cell on open circuit, and what is the source of the energy which is dissipated as heat (or may otherwise be used) when the circuit is closed and current flows—not inexhaustibly, of course, but an effectively constant current which only ultimately falls away slowly to zero? The second of these questions has priority over the former in the perspective of history, and it is, perhaps, the simpler to answer: in any case we shall consider it first. Indeed, we have come near to presuming an answer to it, already, in previous discussions (see pp. 109, 140).

Faraday was compelled 'to take upon himself the labour of repeating and examining the facts' concerning 'the great question of the source of electricity in the voltaic pile' in the spring of 1834 because in this matter he found 'such contradictory evidence, such equilibrium of opinion, such variation and combination of theory, [as left him] in complete doubt respecting what he should accept as the true interpretation of nature'. He had already, in the previous autumn, carried out 'an experiment of great simplicity but extreme beauty' (as he himself described it) in which two plates of zinc (of which the surfaces had been amalgamated) and one plate of platinum were weighed and inserted into a trough of dilute sulphuric acid. One of the zinc plates being put into metallic connection with the platinum plate, bubbles of hydrogen immediately appeared on the platinum. After this action had proceeded for a convenient time, during which the evolved hydrogen had been collected, the various metal plates were removed from the solution and re-weighed. The platinum plate and the zinc plate which had remained isolated had retained their original weights, but the zinc plate which had been in contact with the platinum plate had lost weight. To be precise, the ratio of the loss of weight of this zinc plate to the weight of the hydrogen evolved at the platinum plate was, very closely, the ratio of the electrochemical equivalents (see p. 201) of these substances.

Faraday interpreted this result by regarding the two plates forming the zinc-platinum couple as acting at the same time both as the electrodes of a voltaic cell and as the electrodes of a simple electrolytic cell. The evolution of hydrogen he regarded as clear evidence of electrolysis: there must have been current passing through the dilute acid from the zinc to the platinum (and returning to the zinc through the region of metallic contact of the plates) to produce this result. Had both plates been of platinum they would have had to be separated and it would then have required an external source of current to produce the effect—but then there would have been evolution of oxygen at the other plate. When that plate was of zinc it was the 'chemical affinity' of the zinc for the oxygen which initiated the current. The attendant chemical change (dissolution of the electrode) must have involved the setting free of equal and opposite charges—and the quantity of electricity so set free in the initiation of the current, when one electrochemical equivalent of zinc was dissolved (or, oxidised and dissolved), was exactly that which was required for the electrolytic release of one electrochemical equivalent of hydrogen at the other electrode. Faraday wrote: 'What, then, follows as a necessary consequence of the whole experiment? Why, this: that the chemical action upon . . . one equivalent of zinc . . . was able to evolve such quantity of electricity in the form of a current, as passing through water, should decompose . . . one equivalent of that substance.'

In the spring of 1834 Faraday carried out a very great many qualitative experiments in order to test the view which he had already formed—and which we have just quoted. In the end he recorded his opinion quite clearly: 'The electricity of the voltaic pile . . . is entirely due to chemical action, and is proportionate . . . in its quantity to the quantity of matter which has been chemically active during its evolution.' It would be unprofitable in the present context to attempt to summarise all these experiments—but it is not, perhaps, superfluous to delineate by a single example the spirit of simple enquiry which informed them all. For Faraday's method was essentially his own; no one before or since, save possibly Rutherford in the early years of research in radioactivity (see p. 243), has similarly sought, with success, to elucidate the complexities of a new phenomenon merely by the exercise of an insatiable curiosity—by bombarding nature with a veritable barrage of direct questions framed with the insight of genius.

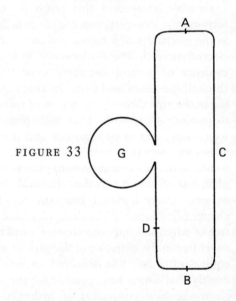

FIGURE 33

The example we choose for illustration may be given formal description in terms of fig. 33. As the figure is drawn, it represents a closed circuit of two metals. The portion ACB is of amalgamated zinc, the other portion AGDB is made of platinum. G is a galvanometer coil constructed of platinum wire. When the complete circuit is at a uniform temperature there is no current. If the circuit is broken at B, and the free ends of the platinum and zinc elements are inserted in dilute acid, current circulates through G in the direction from B to A. If the circuit is further broken at A, and the free ends of the metallic elements are there inserted in a solution of potassium iodide, the current through G is in the same direction as previously: the potassium iodide is electrolysed by current supplied by the voltaic cell at B, iodine being liberated on the platinum wire at A. The same general effect occurs if, the metallic junction having been restored at A, the circuit is next broken at D, a solution of potassium iodide being inserted there. In this case electrolysis takes place under conditions in which both anode and cathode are platinum wires. Now, if the metallic junction is restored at B, the dilute acid being removed, there is no current in the circuit: the potassium iodide 'cell' remaining at D is simply an inactive electrolytic cell in a closed circuit in which there is no 'external' current source. Finally, if the metallic junction at D is restored, and that at A broken again, the potassium iodide solution being re-introduced in its original position in the circuit, current once more flows through G. This time, however, the current through the galvanometer flows from A to B, iodine combining with the zinc, rather than being liberated at the platinum, at A. In this arrangement the potassium iodide cell is acting as a voltaic cell, being the only cell in the circuit. It is obvious that in these simple experiments there is a wealth of direct information on the relationship between the processes of voltaic current production and electrolysis. So it was, on the basis of many scores of experiments of this nature, that Faraday gradually acquired his profound understanding of the whole phenomenon.

Originally, we asked the question: what is the source of the energy of the voltaic cell? We should be unrealistic if we were to look for a precise answer from Faraday in these terms: the generalised concept of energy had not been formulated in 1834, when Faraday was working on the problem, and his conclusions, a we have seen, were expressed in terms of the 'chemical affinity' of elementary substances in the electrodes and the electrolyte. But at least Faraday pointed the way to an answer in modern terms. We should look for the energy in the chemical reactions taking place at the surfaces of the electrodes.

In the decade 1840-50 the energy-concept was slowly emerging in the work and writings of Joule and others. We have already (p. 108) based our definition of the unit of electrical resistance on the empirical law which Joule established (1840) in respect of the generation of heat in current-carrying conductors. According to this law, as Joule expressed it, the total rate of generation of heat in a complete circuit is proportional to 'the virtual intensity of the battery' (or, as we should say, to the e.m.f.)—then he was quick to add 'if a decomposing cell be in the circuit, the virtual intensity of the battery is reduced'. Here we have the echo of Faraday's experiment just described, but Joule was concentrating his attention on the evolution of heat: if a 'decomposing' (i.e. electrolytic) cell be inserted in a series circuit consisting of a primary battery and resistances, the total evolution of heat associated with the passage of a given quantity of electricity is thereby reduced. In 1843 Joule was able to produce some evidence that this 'missing' heat might, ideally, be recovered if the chemical substances separated in the electrolytic cell could be caused to revert to their original state through a process of normal chemical reaction.

Concurrently with Joule's investigations, and continuing over the next few years, the first systematic and precise experimental studies of the quantities of heat evolved in chemical reactions were made in Belfast and St Petersburg—in the latter place by Germain Henri Hess (1802-1850) professor of chemistry in the university, in the former by Thomas Andrews (1813-1885) at that time in private medical practice in the city. As a result of these studies, William Thomson (Kelvin) had at his disposal, in 1851, more accurate and more extensive information in this connection than had previously been available. With this, he set himself to extend Joule's considerations, and to calculate, in respect of the Daniell cell, the 'chemical heat' set free, and compare it with the 'ohmic heat' dissipated, when current is drawn from the cell through a resistive circuit. Corresponding to the passage of a total quantity of electricity equal to one faraday, the ohmic heat is $96500V$ joules (see p. 174), V being the e.m.f. of the cell in volts. In this case (see p. 212) one chemical equivalent of each of the reactants will have been involved in the cell reaction. In the Daniell cell the overall chemical change is the substitution of zinc for copper in a solution of sulphates; the 'chemical heat', then, is the difference between the heats of reaction of zinc and copper, respectively, with sulphuric acid of appropriate strength. If we adopt 25060 calories (that is 104850 joules) per chemical equivalent as an up-to-date value for this difference, and 1·097 volts as the value of V, we have to compare an 'ohmic heat' of 105860 joules with a 'chemical heat' of 104850 joules corresponding to 1 faraday of charge traversing the circuit. In 1851 Kelvin's comparison had produced values for these quantities which agreed with one another within almost equally narrow limits. It is not surprising, therefore, that he convinced himself that he had fully identified 'the source of the energy which is dissipated as heat' when the terminals of a voltaic cell are joined by an external resistance. In fact, time was to show that in this matter Kelvin had arrived at no more than a partial truth. However, it was more than thirty years before his conclusion was challenged: during the whole of that period it was generally believed that the electrical energy manifested in the operation of a voltaic cell is the precise equivalent of the chemical energy liberated in the cell reaction. We shall return to this point in a later chapter (p. 433), meanwhile we take up the other question which we formulated for consideration at the outset of our discussion. We asked (p. 220): what are the circumstances which determine the difference of potential which exists as between the electrodes of a voltaic cell on open circuit?

Let us reverse our normal procedure, and give first a dogmatic, formal answer to this question: afterwards, we will consider the evidence in support of it. We may justifiably take this course, largely because our discussion has already provided a sufficient basis on which to accept the answer as plausible. We assert that the circumstances which determine the difference of potential between the electrodes on open circuit are those which obtain at the various surfaces of discontinuity in the cell. There is a surface of discontinuity between electrode material and electrolyte at each electrode (and there may be additional such surfaces in between) —and one final surface of discontinuity which is not so immediately obvious, at first inspection. In order to see what it is, let us consider an 'ideal' experiment by which the open-circuit potential difference might be determined. For this purpose we imagine the electrodes of the cell to be connected by metallic wires to the plates of an attracted disk electrometer (see p. 42). For simplicity, we imagine the plates of the electrometer to be made of the same material as one of the electrodes (say, of copper, if the cell were a Daniell cell), and the connecting wires to be of that material, also.

Then the final surface of discontinuity is that between the other electrode and the connecting wire. According to this analysis this surface is in all cases a surface of discontinuity across a 'metallic' contact between the electrode materials. We assert, then, that the circumstances which determine the e.m.f. of a voltaic cell are those which obtain at at least three effective surfaces of discontinuity: that effective as between the electrode materials themselves, and the two surfaces of physical separation of the electrodes and the electrolyte (or electrolytes) which constitute the cell. We go further, and assert that the e.m.f. of the cell is, in fact, the algebraic sum of at least three independent components—the 'contact difference of potential' of the electrode materials, the two 'electrode potentials' (representing, respectively, the difference of potential between each electrode and the electrolyte in its immediate neighbourhood), and, if there is any other surface of discontinuity within the cell, a component corresponding to that interface, also.

It is a fact of history that the existence of contact differences of potential between pairs of 'dry' conductors was known before the principle of the voltaic cell was discovered. Volta proceeded to the latter discovery (see p. 69) as the result of a series of experiments extending from 1792 to 1799, and occasioned in the first instance by the publication of certain observations of Luigi Galvani (1737-1798). By about 1797 he had already elicited the main features of the phenomenon. In particular he had convinced himself that the contact difference of potential between two metals, say A and B, is equal to the algebraic sum of the contact differences of potential, from one metal to the next, in any series of which A is the first and B the last member in sequence:

$$_A V_B = {}_A V_C + {}_C V_D + \ldots + {}_R V_S + {}_S V_B \qquad (132)$$

This empirical result is entirely consonant with modern theory (see p. 409) and with the general laws of thermodynamics: it may be expressed, in slightly different form, in the statement that there is no resultant 'internal' e.m.f. in a closed circuit, at constant temperature, even though the circuit is made up of any number of different conductors in series. The only limiting condition is that none of the conductors shall be an electrolyte. In respect of our present problem we are, of course, considering just such an 'excluded' situation: in our case the electrode potentials characteristic of the electrolyte and the metallic conductors in contact with it, having their origin in a physical phenomenon quite different from that of the contact electrification of two metals, do not cancel to zero with the other potential differences effective in the circuit. However, from this analysis, we see the more clearly that in the voltaic circuit—whatever the nature of the conductors which join the electrodes of the cell 'externally'—there is one contact difference of potential remaining unbalanced, namely the contact difference of potential of the electrode materials, which would have been balanced if the electrodes had been connected 'internally' by a metallic conductor rather than by the electrolyte.

Full practical details concerning the evidence for that part of our assertion which states that individual 'electrode potentials' contribute to the e.m.f. of a voltaic cell (along with the contact difference of potential characteristic of the electrode materials) are beyond the scope of the present account. However, the nature of the ev dence may be indicated by a formal consideration of the characiteristics of the three voltaic cells which, in principle, may be constructed using a single electrolyte (E) and, for electrodes, pairs chosen from three metals (A, B and C). Let us denote by V_1 the e.m.f. of the cell having A and C as electrode materials, by V_2 that of the cell having B and C as electrode materials, and by V_{12} the e.m.f. of the third cell in which the electrode materials are A and B. We consider V_1 as positive when A is the positive terminal of the first cell, V_2 as positive when B is the positive terminal of the second cell, and V_{12} as positive when A is the positive terminal of the third cell. Then, on the basis of our primary assertion,

$$V_1 = {}_AV_E + {}_EV_C + {}_CV_A$$
$$V_2 = {}_BV_E + {}_EV_C + {}_CV_B \qquad (133)$$
$$V_{12} = {}_AV_E + {}_EV_B + {}_BV_A$$

Here, for example, ${}_AV_E$ is the decrease of potential across the surface of discontinuity between the electrode of metal A and the electrolyte E, and ${}_BV_A$ is the contact difference of potential between metals A and B (B being at a higher potential than A). From the first two of equations (133), we have

$$V_1 - V_2 = {}_AV_E - {}_BV_E + {}_CV_A - {}_CV_B,$$
or $$V_1 - V_2 = {}_AV_E + {}_EV_B + {}_BV_C + {}_CV_A.$$

From Volta's 'law of intermediate metals', equation (132), similarly,

$$_BV_C + _CV_A = _BV_A.$$

Thus, on the basis of the third of equations (133), we conclude

$$V_1 - V_2 = V_{12} \qquad (134)$$

Formally, it is sufficient to summarise the experimental evidence in favour of our assertion by the statement that such evidence is altogether consistent with the result given by equation (134), based directly upon the assertion in question.

A little consideration will reveal some of the implications, in respect of the practical situation, which are implicit in equations (133). It is evident, at once, that there is no basis, in these equations, for any method of direct evaluation of quantities such as $_AV_E$, which we have identified as the electrode potential of metal A in contact with electrolyte E. The best that can be done is to determine the e.m.f. of a cell in which this electrode (and its associated electrolyte) is combined with a standard comparison electrode (and the electrolyte associated with it).* If this is done for two electrodes (A and B of our analysis), then equation (134) shows how the e.m.f.s so determined may be regarded as contributing individually (one contribution associated with each electrode) to the e.m.f. of the cell B/E/A.

In respect of the practical situation, it is clearly impossible to apply equations (133), which have reference to one electrolyte only, directly to the case of cells which involve more than one electrolyte (as does the Daniell cell). Let us, therefore, generalise these equations, assuming that metal A is associated with an electrolyte E', metal B with an electrolyte E", and that the 'standard' electrode (metal C) is associated with electrolyte E. Then, by an obvious extension of our previous notation, we have

$$V_1 = {}_AV_{E'} + {}_{E'}V_E + {}_EV_C + {}_CV_A,$$

$$V_2 = {}_BV_{E''} + {}_{E''}V_E + {}_EV_C + {}_CV_B,$$

$$V_{12} = {}_AV_{E'} + {}_{E'}V_{E''} + {}_{E''}V_B + {}_BV_A.$$

---

* Modern writers on the energetics of voltaic cells frequently use the term 'electrode' to designate a system comprised of a single 'metallic' conductor in association with an electrolyte. In spite of the obvious economy of this usage, we have not thought it desirable in this chapter, treating of electric conduction in liquids generally, to invite possible confusion by changing the meaning of an important technical term in midstream.

From these equations we obtain, as before,

$$V_1 - V_2 = {}_A V_{E'} + {}_{E'} V_E + {}_E V_{E''} + {}_{E''} V_B + {}_B V_A,$$

and if $\quad {}_{E'} V_E + {}_E V_{E''} = {}_{E'} V_{E''},$

which, on general grounds, we have no reason to doubt, equation (134) remains valid as previously. This equation, thus generalised, provides the essential justification for the experimental determination and use of 'half-cell e.m.f.s' (such as V_1 and V_2) for the calculation of 'whole-cell e.m.f.s' (such as V_{12}) on a logically systematised basis.

The reason will be obvious why some other term, different from 'electrode potential', had to be found for the quantities V_1 and V_2 of equation (134). The term 'half-cell e.m.f.', generally adopted, would be more precisely descriptive of the quantity in question if the reference system (the electrode of metal C in association with the electrolyte E of our formal description) were such that ${}_C V_E = 0$. Attempts have indeed been made, not without some success, to develop such systems, but they are neither as convenient in use, nor as easily reproducible, as some other systems which are not limited by this requirement. In practice the 'standard half-cell e.m.f.s', which are to be found listed in the tables, are those which have been determined (either directly or indirectly) against an arbitrarily defined reference system constructed as follows. A clean strip of platinum is coated with platinum black (a deposit of finely divided metal) by making it the anode in an electrolytic cell containing a 2 per cent solution of chloroplatinic acid in normal* hydrochloric acid. The cathode of this cell is a similar strip of platinum, and the cell is operated at a current density of about 0·1 ampere per square centimetre of anode surface for about 30 minutes. The 'platinised' anode so produced is removed and thoroughly washed. Essentially, the reference system consists of this platinised electrode half immersed in hydrochloric acid (of appropriately specified strength) through which a stream of pure hydrogen is bubbled so as to impinge on the electrode and escape into the region above the electrolyte. When the system is in use, this region above the electrolyte (and surrounding the exposed portion of the electrode) should contain pure hydrogen at atmospheric pressure.

* A normal solution of an acid contains one chemical equivalent of the acid in 1 kg of aqueous solution.

In relation to the standard reference system just described, the half-cell e.m.f. corresponding to a zinc electrode in a solution in zinc sulphate is -0.763 volt at 25°C, that corresponding to a copper electrode in a solution of cupric sulphate is $+0.337$ volt at the same temperature. These are the half-elements of a Daniell cell, of which the e.m.f. at 25°C is measured as 1.097 volt. The values here quoted clearly substantiate equation (134), in this particular case, within narrow limits of experimental uncertainty.

It has already been stated that what is open to measurement in practice is not the electrode potential of our original definition (p. 228), but an arbitrarily defined half-cell e.m.f. which, at best, includes a contact potential difference in addition to the electrode potential appropriate to the half-cell concerned. In spite of this practical difficulty in direct evaluation, the potential difference across the boundary between an electrode and an electrolyte is of theoretical interest in its own right. We shall be returning to its consideration in a later chapter (p. 439).

CHAPTER 6

THE ELECTRICAL CONSTITUTION
OF ATOMS

6.1. INTRODUCTORY

In the Introduction to this book (p. 3) we noted the 'strong body
of opinion [which] has grown up in favour of a method of presenting the subject [of electricity] in which a knowledge of atomic
structure is assumed from the outset'. We decided, however, to
'proceed without systematic use of atomic concepts to begin with',
leaving these concepts 'to come into prominence, naturally, in
relation to the electrical phenomena' under discussion from time
to time. Eventually, a stage would be reached after which they
would be 'in constant use'. It is the object of this chapter to mark
the attainment of that stage, by summarising those concepts
which will be needed for the remainder of our discussion, indicating very briefly how they derive from experiment and what are
the limitations to their usefulness. In this connection we shall
assume that the primitive concept of atoms, as basic entities of
zero net electrical charge, is sufficiently established, by the success
of the kinetic theory of gases (see $M L \& T$, chap. 15) and the
gravimetric analyses of the chemists, to be accepted without
question. We shall be concerned only with the elaboration of this
concept, so as to bring into the interpretative scheme those elements which are necessary for the understanding of the electric
and magnetic properties of matter in bulk. We stated, dogmatic-
ally, in the Introduction, that all the properties of gross matter
(except, only, the property of gravitation) which had been investigated prior to 1920, are 'essentially electrical in nature'. Here, at
least, and in what follows, we shall be concentrating almost exclusively on those (non-gravitational) properties which are self-
evidently electrical in their primary manifestations.

6.2. THE NUMBER OF ELECTRONS IN AN ATOM

In chapter 4 we devoted two sections (§§4.2, 4.3) to the early investigations of the cathode rays and of the currents of negative electricity which may be obtained, in other ways, in gases at low pressure, or 'in vacuum'. In these investigations the negative electron was discovered as a common constituent of matter generally, a constituent of mass very small compared with the mass of the lightest atom, and carrying a perfectly definite charge of negative electricity. The natural consequence of this discovery was the conclusion that the negative electron must be a constituent particle in the structure of every atom—or perhaps we should rather say that, as a result of it, it became necessary to conclude, specifically, that atoms are not structureless entities, that at least they contain electrons as constituent particles. This conclusion accepted, it became pertinent to enquire further whether the atoms of the different chemical elements are to be distinguished one from another in terms of the number of electrons they contain —and, indeed, to enquire how many electrons are to be found in a particular atom.

Let us be clear what was the general background of ascertained fact out of which these speculations arose, and against which these questions first came to be asked. The negative electron had been identified as a free particle; its discovery had provided a plausible basis for 'understanding' the charges found to be associated with ions in electrolytes, or with the oppositely charged ions whose production 'gives conductivity' to a gas at ordinary pressures (p. 184). But the absolute value of the charge on a univalent electrolytic ion was not known with any precision, the identity of this charge with the charge on the gaseous ion was entirely a matter of speculation, and nothing at all was known, directly, concerning the charge on the electron itself. Only from one quarter, and that rather remote from the main centre of interest, was there any suggestion that the properties of neutral atoms could be the better understood on the basis of the assumption that negative electrons form part of their structure. It will be worth while to follow the implications of these various statements, in turn, before we attempt to deal with the two questions which we posed for answer.

The suggestion 'from a remote quarter' had already been made in a theoretical paper published early in 1897. The author was Hendrik Antoon Lorentz (1853-1928), professor, since 1878, at the university of Leyden. Lorentz had for some years been exploring the view that the optical properties of bodies are to be understood in terms of the motion, within the individual atoms or molecules, of discrete charges of electricity. In this respect he regarded himself as a disciple of Maxwell (though it is not clear whether the master would altogether have approved of the views of his pupil—see p. 215). Also in Leyden at the time was Pieter Zeeman (1865-1943) (see *V & W*, p. 221). On 31 October 1896 Zeeman submitted to the Academy of Sciences in Amsterdam an account of the first successful realisation of an experimental effect which had been looked for in vain by Faraday (in 1862), and by others in the intervening years (a report of a positive result by C.Fievez, in 1885, does not appear to have been accepted at its face value by scientists of the day).

In 1862, in his last recorded experiment, Faraday had sought to detect any effect on the frequency, or the state of polarisation, of the yellow light of a sodium flame, when a strong magnetic field was established in the region of the source. In 1896, Zeeman, having a more powerful electromagnet than Faraday, and—more importantly—a concave grating spectrograph (first devised by Rowland—see p. 169—in 1882) providing very considerably better resolution than Faraday was able to employ, satisfied himself and his potential critics that the yellow lines due to sodium (and the red line due to lithium) were significantly broader when the magnetic field was 'on' than when it was 'off'. 'The experiment could be repeated indefinitely', he wrote, in the elation of success. Zeeman showed that an exactly similar effect occurred in relation to the corresponding absorption lines (white light being passed through a heated porcelain tube containing sodium vapour and placed between the poles of the electromagnet); then, following a suggestion by Lorentz, he went on to look for certain polarisation effects which Lorentz had predicted. According to the hypothesis that he was developing, Lorentz expected a single spectral line to appear as a close doublet when light emitted along the magnetic field direction was analysed in the spectrograph, and he anticipated that the two lines of this doublet would exhibit circular polarisation in opposite senses. Zeeman verified that the light which formed the edges of his broadened lines was indeed polarised according to this prediction. Within a few months, by careful attention to detail, he was further able to confirm that his previously observed broadening obscured a real 'splitting' of the original line—into a doublet for light emitted along the field direction, and

EM Q

into a triplet for light emitted perpendicularly to this direction, as the hypothesis of Lorentz required.

By this time, his preliminary results having received wide publicity, Zeeman's findings had been independently confirmed in many other laboratories—and, in particular, by Marie Alfred Cornu (1841-1902), already in his thirtieth year as professor of experimental physics at l'École Polytechnique in Paris. By mid-1897, Lorentz could reasonably claim that his theoretical views provided an entirely satisfactory ground of explanation for these newly discovered experimental facts. He had calculated, on the basis of well-attested physical principles, the effect of a magnetic field on the periodic motion of an 'electron' bound by a central force within the structure of an atom, and his equations indicated a frequency-splitting in respect of the radiation emitted by an assemblage of such atoms. They indicated, moreover, a rotational effect having opposite sign for the two components of the modified radiation. The magnitude of the frequency-splitting was explicitly given in terms of the magnetic flux density in the field and the value of e/m for the moving particle—and the direction of the rotation associated with either component of the radiation was determined by the sign of the charge. Substituting the experimentally observed values for the frequency splitting (in magnetic fields of which the flux density was not very precisely known), Lorentz deduced values of e/m ranging from 10^{11} to $3 \cdot 4 \times 10^{11}$ coulomb/kg, and, noting that the sense of the circular polarisation of the doublet component of higher frequency was empirically found to be anti-clockwise for light travelling along the positive direction of the field (by an observer of necessity looking along the negative direction), he concluded that the charge of the emitting particle was negative. The identification of the hypothetical 'electron' of Lorentz (he had taken the name from Stoney, see p. 175) and the then only-just-discovered 'corpuscle' of Thomson could not have been more convincing on the basis of this numerical agreement alone.

We have made certain general statements regarding the results of Lorentz which we cannot substantiate in full in this account, but we can at least consider one simple case in detail, and in so doing take a long step towards an understanding of the physical situation to which they refer. We consider a source of radiation situated about the origin of a set of rectangular axes OX, OY, OZ, (fig. 34). We suppose that the radiation emitted in the direction OZ is circularly polarised in the 'positive' sense. We adopt, as a model of the source material, a large number of identical systems (atoms or molecules) within which 'electrons' of charge e and

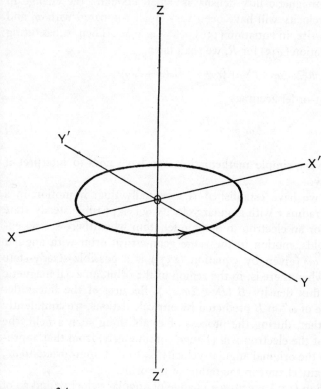

FIGURE 34

mass m revolve in circular orbits of radius r (in the positive direction about OZ as shown in the figure) under the action of central forces. If ω is the angular velocity of revolution of an electron in such an orbit, we have

$$m\omega^2 r = R \tag{135}$$

R being the magnitude of the central force. Suppose now that a magnetic field is established in the region of the source, in the direction OZ, and let B be the magnetic flux density. Then, if it is possible for the electron orbits to remain of the same radius, r, as before, the angular velocity of revolution must change to ω', where

$$m\omega'^2 r = R - Be\omega' r \qquad (136)$$

If the magnetic flux density is 'small enough', the change in angular velocity will have been very small compared with ω, and we may write, in equation (136), $\omega' = \omega + \Delta\omega$. Then, substituting from equation (135) for R, we shall have

$$m\{2\omega\Delta\omega + (\Delta\omega)^2\}r = -Be(\omega + \Delta\omega)r,$$

or, to first-order accuracy,

$$\omega' - \omega \equiv \Delta\omega = -\frac{Be}{2m} \qquad (137)$$

This is very simple mathematics. We have now to interpret it physically.

What we have established is essentially this: if motion in a circle of radius r with angular velocity ω is a possible steady-state motion for an electron in our model atom when there are no external fields, motion in the same geometrical orbit with angular velocity ω' (given by equation (137)) is a possible steady-state motion when there is, in the region of the orbit, an axial magnetic field of flux density B ($B \ll 2m\omega/e$). Because of the linear dependence of ω' on B predicted by our calculations, we confidently assume that, during the process of establishing such a field, the motion of the electron will change continuously, from that appropriate to the original angular velocity ω, to that appropriate to ω', without any change in the radius of the orbit.

Equation (137) specifies a change of angular velocity (and so of frequency) proportional to 'the magnetic flux density in the field and the value of e/m for the moving particle'—as we wrote in our general statement of the conclusions of Lorentz—and, derived, as it has been, in relation to a hypothetical source emitting 'positive' circularly polarised radiation only, it also contains a prediction concerning polarisation. We see that, if, when the magnetic field is established, 'positive' circularly polarised light is to be observed travelling along the field direction with a frequency greater than the frequency of the light emitted when the field is 'off', as Zeeman found, then the charge on the electron (e, in equation (137)) must be negative, according to conventional usage.

In our general statement we claimed that the equations of Lorentz indicated a frequency-splitting involving 'a rotational effect'. Equation (137), describing the simple case that we have considered in detail, can be interpreted in precisely this way. We may say that the effect of the magnetic field on the original motion is to superpose a rotation of the whole orbit with angular velocity $-Be/2m$ about the field direction. In this case, because we assumed that the original motion was circular motion in a plane at right angles to the field direction, this angular velocity is simply added to the angular velocity of the original motion. In a paper published in December 1897, Joseph Larmor (1857-1942) showed that, whatever the relative orientation of an electron orbit (under a central force) and an applied magnetic field, the (slightly) modified motion of the electron may be described as resulting from the precession of the original orbit about an axis through the centre of force and parallel to the field direction with angular velocity $-Be/2m$. We shall have occasion to refer to this so-called Larmor precession again, in a later chapter (p. 463).

Apart from the last remark, the account that has just been given of the successful investigations of Zeeman and Lorentz has been written, 'as of mid-1897'. The precision in respect of time is significant: within less than a year the whole situation had been overlaid with complexity, if not with doubt. Cornu, in Paris, and Thomas Preston (1860-1900), professor of natural philosophy in University College, Dublin, had shown that, examined under great resolution, the spectral lines which Zeeman had investigated exhibited more complex patterns of splitting than the original theory of Lorentz was able to explain. Thereafter, the Zeeman phenomenon continued as of professional interest to the experimental spectroscopist, but it did not again figure decisively in the discussions of the theorists until the classical picture of Lorentz had given way (1913) to the quantised atom model of Bohr—and until that model itself had so far exhausted its possibilities of explanation (1925) that it had to be supplemented by the concept of the intrinsic spin of the electron (see p. 459). Zeeman and Lorentz, then, had savoured the full satisfaction of success very briefly: but, if, indeed, there was something of anti-climax in what followed, neither they nor physicists generally were deceived. Complete understanding had been denied them, but no one doubted the authenticity of the insight that had been gained. The electron of Stoney and Lorentz was one with the cathode ray corpuscule of Thomson: the question 'how many electrons are to be found in a particular atom?' was not a meaningless question. In 1902, Lorentz and Zeeman were the joint recipients of the second Nobel prize for physics.

The model of an electron in orbit within an atom behaving as a light-source was in the tradition of Maxwell in that, according to the theory of Maxwell (and the experiments of Hertz—see *V & W*, §§9.1, 9.2) light is an electromagnetic radiation, and a moving charge which is accelerated is a source of such radiation. To be precise, if a charge e has acceleration a in free space, then, according to that theory, the instantaneous radiation power (rate of emission of energy) is given by the expression

$$P = \frac{\mu_0 a^2 e^2}{6\pi c} \tag{138}$$

Here c is the velocity of light, and μ_0 is the magnetic permeability 'of vacuum', $4\pi \times 10^{-7}$ henry/metre (p. 107). Although there was an obvious inconsistency in the model, which postulated stable orbits from which energy was required to be radiated, it was the best that could be done at the time. Within the same framework of classical theory, and with fewer reservations, the X-radiation of Röntgen was naturally regarded as a type of electromagnetic radiation, being produced by the sudden stopping (deceleration) of electrons in solid materials (*V & W*, p. 274). An answer to the question 'how many electrons are to be found in a particular atom?' was, indeed, first given, on the basis of direct experimental evidence, by considering the interaction of X-rays on matter from this point of view.

In 1904 C. G. Barkla (1877-1944) showed that when X-rays pass through matter, at least through matter of low atomic weight, the 'secondary' radiation, which is scattered out of the beam, is of the same 'quality' as the primary radiation. He found that the general penetrating power of the secondary radiation was the same as that of the primary radiation, in these circumstances, over the whole range of 'hardness' which he was able to cover with the modest equipment at his disposal. Under these conditions he found that the attenuation of the primary radiation was predominantly to be accounted for in terms of this process of scattering without change of quality, and he showed that the intensity of the effect was simply proportional to the density of the material traversed by the rays. With air as scattering material he obtained a numerical value for a 'linear scattering coefficient', σ, defined in terms of the exponential attenuation law

$$I = I_0 e^{-\sigma x} \tag{139}$$

In this expression x represents the distance in the material traversed by the rays over which the intensity of a (parallel) beam is reduced, from an initial value I_0, to I by the process of scattering alone.

The theoretical basis for the interpretation of Barkla's results was provided by J. J. Thomson. According to Maxwell's theory, if we regard I as a measure of the energy transported across unit area in unit time, we have, instantaneously,

$$I = \left(\frac{\epsilon_0}{\mu_0}\right)^{\frac{1}{2}} E^2 \tag{140}$$

where E is the magnitude of the electric field intensity in the radiation over the area concerned, and ϵ_0 is the permittivity of free space. (We have merely quoted this result, and that of equation (138); we cannot do more in the context of the present discussion.) Thomson regarded the electric field E as acting equally on all the electrons present in the atoms of the scattering material, as if they were in empty space, and he considered these electrons as radiating independently, and so producing the scattered radiation. He justified these assumptions, with some plausibility, on the basis of Barkla's result that scattering takes place without change of quality of the radiation.

Suppose, then, that there are, in total, n electrons per unit volume of the material. In a stratum of thickness Δx and unit area there are $n\Delta x$ electrons, each of them, instantaneously, having accleration Ee/m. On the basis of equation (138) the total rate of emission of energy from this stratum, in the form of scattered radiation, is

$$\frac{\mu_0 e^4 E^2}{6\pi m^2 c} \, n\Delta x,$$

instantaneously. The total rate of entry of energy as primary radiation is given directly by equation (140). The ratio of these two quantities, according to equation (139), is given by

$$-\frac{1}{I}\frac{dI}{dx}\Delta x.$$

Thus we have

$$\sigma = \frac{\mu_0 e^4 n}{6\pi m^2 c}\bigg/\left(\frac{\epsilon_0}{\mu_0}\right)^{\frac{1}{2}},$$

or, since $c = (1/\mu_0\epsilon_0)^{\frac{1}{2}}$ (p. 120),

$$\sigma = \frac{\mu_0{}^2 e^4 n}{6\pi m^2} \tag{141}$$

All the quantities in equation (141), except n, being known, Thomson naturally regarded the determination of the linear scattering coefficient σ as equivalent to a determination of the number of electrons per unit volume of the scattering material. The total number of atoms in unit volume being known, also, the number of electrons per atom could be calculated immediately.

In 1906 Thomson reviewed the information then available from this point of view. Taking Barkla's measured value of σ for scattering in atmospheric air (about 2×10^{-2} m^{-1}), he deduced that 'each molecule of air contains about 25 corpuscles'. On the basis of the 'qualitative' result that the scattering coefficient is proportional to the density, for 'light' elements, he further concluded that 'the number of corpuscles in each atom would be approximately equal to its atomic weight' (mean molecular weight of air = 28·8). From the standpoint of present-day knowledge it must be admitted that the accepted values of 1906 differed considerably from the true values of the 'fundamental constants' which should have been employed in deriving this result with the help of equation (141)—use of the true values would have reduced the calculated number of electrons per atom by some 25 per cent—and that the full complexity of the situation was not wholly appreciated at the time; however, the result was important for the development of the subject, and in the upshot Thomson's bold essay in interpretation was generally vindicated. In 1922, when much more had been learned regarding the various ways in which X-rays may interact with matter, C.W.Hewlett, of Iowa, was able to choose his experimental conditions in such a way that Thomson's formula would be expected to be valid. Using graphite as scattering material, and homogeneous X-rays of wavelength 0·71 Å ($7·1 \times 10^{-11}$ m) as primary radiation, he showed that the measured scattering coefficient agreed precisely with the predictions of the formula, on the assumption that an atom of carbon contains six electrons. However, by 1922, this conclusion had been firmly established by other means: it was already accepted that the number of electrons in the atom of any element is equal to the ordinal number of the element in the periodic table of the chemists (see p. 280). That statement must suffice for present purposes.

6.3. SPONTANEOUS ATOMIC CHANGE

The phenomenon of radioactivity was discovered by A. H. Becquerel (p. 176) in February 1896. He was looking for a possible (temporary) emission of X-rays by phosphorescent materials (Röntgen's X-rays appeared to originate in a patch of phosphorescence on the glass wall of his discharge tube, where the cathode rays fell). He found, instead, what seemed to be a persistent penetrating radiation, having nothing to do with phosphorescence, emitted by uranium metal and all chemical compounds containing that element. He detected the radiation by its 'blackening' effect on a photographic plate protected from the action of visible light by being wrapped in black paper. Four years later he showed, fairly convincingly, by a combination of electric and magnetic deflection experiments, that the radiation responsible for the blackening of his plates consisted of negative electrons—that is of particles identical with the cathode-ray particles, except that in general the velocities with which they were emitted were substantially greater than the velocities of the cathode-ray particles in the familiar discharge tube.

During the four years which elapsed between Becquerel's original discovery and the deflection experiments of 1900, most physicists were so occupied in following up Röntgen's prior discovery of the X-rays that the 'Becquerel phenomenon' received scant attention. However, in 1898, Marie Curie (1867-1934) and Gerhard Carl Nathanael Schmidt (1865-1949), independently, discovered that thorium and its compounds are similarly radioactive, and Marie and Pierre Curie (1859-1906) succeeded in separating, from a ton of residues from the uranium mines of Bohemia, small fractions (gramme amounts) that were immensely more active, weight for weight, than an equal quantity of uranium itself. Being convinced that radioactivity is an atomic property (M. Curie having shown that the intensity of the radiation from a uranium compound is proportional to the uranium content of the sample, and independent of the nature of the compound), the Curies interpreted their findings as evidence for the existence in the uranium ore of hitherto unknown chemical elements, which they had concentrated, rather than separated quantitatively, in their active fractions. On the strength of this conviction they named the yet-to-be-discovered new elements polonium and radium, respectively. Also in 1898, Rutherford, in continuation of the investigations, on the mobilities and coefficients of recombination of gaseous ions, which arose out of his pioneer work with Thomson (pp. 182-194), studied the ionising effect of the uranium radiation—and as a result of this study made a most important discovery. A full account of these investigations appeared in a long paper in the *Philosophical Magazine* in January 1899.

Rutherford's fundamental discovery was that the black paper in Becquerel's arrangement of 1896 had shielded his photographic plate from the action of a radioactive radiation which, estimated in terms of its ionising effect in air, was possibly one hundred times more intense (when a very thin layer of uranium compound was employed) than the radiation which actually penetrated the paper and affected the plate. Rutherford was so impressed by this discovery, of the very intense ionisation confined within the first few centimetres of air above his uranium preparation, that he wrote 'These experiments show that the uranium radiation is complex, and that there are present at least two distinct types of radiation—one that is very easily absorbed, which will be termed for convenience the α-radiation, and the other of a more penetrative character, which will be termed the β-radiation'. In the following year, as we have seen, Becquerel showed, in effect, that the β-radiation from uranium preparations consists of negative electrons; Rutherford's yet-to-be-identified α-radiation meanwhile was added to the Curies' yet-to-be-discovered new elements polonium and radium, as one of the experimenter's conceptual species awaiting further justification as a result of detailed investigation. Obviously, we should not be recounting this episode of history, in this brief survey, had not full justification of these concepts later emerged.

If one further quotation is to be made from the years 1896 to 1900, it should be from a paper by Elster and Geitel (p. 176) which was published in the same month as the paper by Rutherford to which we have just referred. Speculating on the nature of radioactivity, they wrote 'the atom of a radioactive element, after the manner of the molecule of an unstable chemical compound, passes over into a stable state as a result of the emission of energy ... this view would involve the assumption of a gradual transformation of the active substance into an inactive one, with alteration of its properties as a chemical element'. Physicists generally paid little attention to this suggestion. Possibly the first part of the statement appeared as no more than a truism—and the second part as too heterodox to warrant further consideration at the time. Certainly, its authors had no direct experimental evidence with which to support their opinion: that appeared only with the work of Rutherford and Soddy which we must now describe.

Frederick Soddy (1877-1956) had been appointed demonstrator in the department of chemistry at McGill university, Montreal, in the summer of 1900. Very early in 1901 he attached himself to the physics department for purposes of research. There Ernest Rutherford (1871-1937) was already in his third session as Macdonald professor of physics. He had arrived from Cambridge in October 1898, and in the intervening time he had made very considerable progress with the study of the Becquerel phenomenon which was to occupy him for the rest of his life. He had found it possible to separate from thorium compounds, in a stream of air, a gas-like 'emanation' which was itself radioactive, and he had found it to possess most remarkable properties. In the first place, when a volume of emanation-bearing air was examined in a closed vessel, the radioactivity in the gas decreased rapidly in intensity with the passage of time. In about one minute it had fallen to half value, in two minutes to about one quarter, and so on indefinitely. Eventually, after an appropriate interval (say, half an hour) if the gas was swept out of the vessel, it was found to be inactive. On the other hand, careful investigation showed that in the original vessel there remained a feeble activity originating on the inner wall of the vessel which had been in contact with the emanation-laden air. This 'excited' activity also decreased 'in a geometrical progression with the time', but more slowly than the other: the 'half-value period' was about 11 hours. To the challenge of these preliminary findings Rutherford and Soddy applied themselves with entire singleness of purpose for the next two years.

For twelve months the experiments of Rutherford and Soddy proceeded without publication, then between April 1902 and May 1903 there appeared, first in the *Transactions of the Chemical Society*, and then in the *Philosophical Magazine*, eight substantial papers, announcing their experimental results, and bringing closer to finality the hypothesis which they put forward in 'explanation' of the facts. These facts, as they had unravelled them, were indeed complex. With thorium, with radium, and with uranium, they had been able, by chemical or physical means, in each case to separate one or more short-lived activities, of characteristic half-value periods, and to show that, as any one of these activities decayed, so it appeared to be regenerated in the 'parent' material from which it had been separated.

Here we have written of the separation of 'activities'. There was never the appearance of any weighable amount of any new active substance being obtained in the pure state. The truly gaseous nature of the thorium emanation, for example, was attested by the fact that the activity by which it was recognised could be 'condensed out' on to a tube cooled in liquid air, and 'boiled off' the tube at a perfectly definite temperature (about $-135°C$) when the liquid air was removed. Similarly, of one of the non-gaseous 'activities' Rutherford and Soddy wrote, in their first published paper, '. . . the manner in which it makes its appearance . . . dragged down by precipitates when no question of insolubility is involved . . . suggests the view that [the substance responsible for the activity] is really present in minute quantity'. Indeed, the view was taken at the outset, and was never abandoned, that each distinctive 'activity' (distinguished by the half-value period of its decay, and the nature of the radiations involved) was to be ascribed to a distinct chemical species: 'radioactivity is at once an atomic phenomenon and the accompaniment of a chemical change in which new kinds of matter are produced', the investigators wrote in their second paper, in July 1902.

When their final paper of May 1903 came to be written, Rutherford and Soddy had, to their own satisfaction, so refined their original hypothesis that the whole body of ascertained fact came within its scope. Its final simplicity can best be conveyed by direct quotation:

... it is not possible to regard radioactivity as a consequence of changes that have already taken place. The rays emitted must be an accompaniment of the change.

The complexity of the phenomena of radioactivity is due to the existence as a general rule of several different types of matter changing at the same time ...

In all cases where one of the radioactive products has been separated and its activity examined independently of the active substance which gives rise to it, or which it in turn produces ... the law of radioactive change ... may be expressed in the one statement—the proportional amount of radioactive matter that changes in unit time is a constant ... the constant ... possesses for each type of active matter a fixed and characteristic value ...

Apparent constancy [of radioactivity] is merely the expression of the slow rate of change of the radioelement ...

The law of radioactive change ... is also the law of monomolecular chemical reaction. Radioactive change, therefore, must be of such a kind as to involve one system only ... in radioactive change the chemical atom must suffer disintegration.

Nothing that has since been discovered has thrown any doubt on the essential truth of these simple statements. Another simplifying statement (of April 1903), inessential to their main thesis, has not similarly stood the test of time—though we shall accept it in the formal discussions that follow. At that stage, Rutherford and Soddy had speculated 'that each type of radioactive matter when got by itself, free from the matter which produced it on the one hand and the products of its further change on the other, gives rise to homogeneous rays'. The implications of this statement are that the distintegration of each radioelement should be by a unique mode—should involve the emission of one type of radiation invariably (α-radiation or β-radiation), and result in the formation of product atoms of a single species. We now know that this is not the case, but our further discussion will lose little in generality if we ignore this complication.

Before we embark on a formal discussion, two further remarks are in order. We have already recorded Becquerel's identification of the β-radiation as composed of negative electrons of considerable kinetic energy. In February 1903 Rutherford (independently of Soddy) had published an account of a most remarkable experiment (having regard to the material and the equipment with which it was performed) in which he had observed the electric and magnetic deflection of the α-radiation for the first time, and thereby demonstrated, beyond any possible doubt, that this radiation, also, is composed of charged particles of great energy. He had estimated the specific charge on the partciles as 6×10^7 coulomb/kg—considerably less than that of the hydrogen ion in electrolysis—and he had shown that the sign of the charge was positive. The α-particles were, therefore, almost certainly positively charged entities of mass comparable with the mass of the lightest atoms (and thus very much heavier than electrons), but at least these two 'radiations' were of the same type—both were particulate in nature. Very obviously, this knowledge enormously strengthened conviction in respect of the disintegration hypothesis which was taking shape in Rutherford's mind.

Our second remark is more general in character. In 1903 the phenomena of radioactivity seemed, to many physicists, to be strange and mysterious. With uranium and thorium, in particular, there was the appearance of the persistent emission of energy, without limit in time. There was the obvious temptation to devise 'explanations' which, in respect of their premises, were as strange and mysterious as the phenomena themselves. Though Rutherford and Soddy startled the scientific world with their hypothesis of spontaneous distintegration of atoms, they maintained, and justly so, that they were the traditionalists among their contemporaries. They were not prepared to abandon the conservation laws—conservation of energy, or mass, or charge—in face of mere appearances. They had put forward an entirely conventional explanation of the facts, appreciating with full clarity the irrelevance of the human life-span as a significant unit of physical time—and the enormity of the number of atoms in the smallest bit of matter directly apprehended by the senses. They had merely postulated that certain atoms, complicated electrical systems as they appeared to be, must be energetically unstable in relation to spontaneous change involving the emission of particles. And they were, as we know, proved right in the end.

Let us now consider the experimental facts, and their interpretation, more formally. Let us imagine that we have a preparation containing 'radioactive atoms' of one kind only—and let us assume that the 'daughter' atoms, which are produced as a result of their disintegration, are devoid of activity. Let there be n radioactive atoms still unchanged at time t (we are dealing throughout with very large numbers). Let A be the activity of the preparation, at this time, as measured in terms of a (saturated) ionisation current, or by other convenient means. Then the empirical facts are summarised in the formal result

$$A = A_0 e^{-\lambda t} \tag{142}$$

Here A_0 is the initial value of the activity ($t = 0$), and λ is a constant (of dimension T^{-1}) characteristic of the particular radio-element concerned. On the general assumption that each atom of the radioelement contributes only once to the measured activity —when it emits a particle (α-particle or β-particle), and is transformed into an atom of the daughter product—the activity itself is a measure of the number of atoms which are so transformed in unit time. Instead of equation (142) we then have

$$-\frac{dn}{dt} = c e^{-\lambda t} \tag{143}$$

where c is a constant. If n_0 is the initial value of n, and if we plausibly assume that $n \to 0$ as $t \to \infty$ (to imagine otherwise would effectively be to deny that all our 'radioactive atoms' were radioactive), then

$$n = n_0 e^{-\lambda t} \tag{144}$$

and

$$c = \lambda n_0 \tag{145}$$

Finally, from equations (143), (144) and (145),

$$-\frac{dn}{dt} = \lambda n \tag{146}$$

Equation (146) will be recognised as 'the law of radioactive change' of our quotation from Rutherford and Soddy (p. 245). We have derived it formally from the experimental decay law (equation (142)), and in so doing we have given physical meaning to the empirical constant λ: λ is 'the proportional amount of radioactive matter that changes in unit time'. This characteristic constant is referred to as the 'disintegration constant' of the radioactive species in question; the 'half-value period' (p. 243) is $\log_e 2/\lambda$, or, numerically, $0 \cdot 693/\lambda$.

Suppose, now, that the daughter product is itself radioactive. Let λ_1 be the disintegration constant of the parent species, and λ_2 that of the daughter. Consider a freshly-prepared sample containing, initially, n_{10} atoms of the parent and none of the daughter species. If, at time t, there are present in the sample n_1 atoms of the first species and n_2 atoms of the second, then

$$\frac{dn_1}{dt} = -\lambda_1 n_1$$

$$\frac{dn_2}{dt} = \lambda_1 n_1 - \lambda_2 n_2 \qquad (147)$$

(each atom of the parent becomes an atom of the daughter species in the act of disintegration). The initial conditions being as stated, we have

$$n_1 = n_{10} e^{-\lambda_1 t}$$

$$n_2 = \lambda_1 n_{10} \left(\frac{1}{\lambda_2 - \lambda_1} e^{-\lambda_1 t} + \frac{1}{\lambda_1 - \lambda_2} e^{-\lambda_2 t} \right) \qquad (148)$$

If τ_1 and τ_2 are the half-value periods of the two species, and if $\tau_1 \gg \tau_2$ ($\lambda_2 \gg \lambda_1$), then when $t \gg \tau_2$, from equations (148), to a good approximation,

$$n_2 = \frac{\lambda_1}{\lambda_2} n_1 \qquad (149)$$

—from that time on the two species are in 'radioactive (secular) equilibrium', decaying together with the half-value period of the parent, and exhibiting equal activities ($\lambda_2 n_2 = \lambda_1 n_1$), provided these are defined in terms of the numbers of emitted particles, simply, without reference to energy or ionising power.

What we have just deduced in relation to two species, 'genetically related', may obviously be extended to any number of such species, each formed from its predecessor in a unique mode of radioactive change. When the initial parent is very long-lived compared with all the others, ultimately the whole 'disintegration series' attains a state of secular equilibrium, the number of atoms of any species present at a given epoch being directly proportional to the half-value period of the species.

Uranium and thorium are the 'initial parent' species of two independent disintegration series. Their half-value periods are now known to be 4.5×10^9 y and 1.4×10^{10} y, respectively. In an 'unchanged' uranium (or thorium) mineral the whole series is present in equilibrium. This is the formal explanation of the circumstances characterising the discovery of radium and polonium, by P. and M. Curie in 1898 (see p. 241): radium is the sixth member, and polonium the fourteenth member, of the uranium series. The half-value period of radium is 1622 y, that of polonium 138 d. Reckoned by atoms, therefore, the equilibrium concentration of radium is 1 in 2.8 million, that of polonium 1 in 1.2×10^{10} of the concentration of uranium in the primary ore. There is little wonder that pure samples of these products for so long eluded the most persistent efforts of those who sought to separate them by chemical means—even less, that by 1903 the full complexity of the genetic relationships of the series generally had not been resolved. But sufficient had been done, as we have seen, for Rutherford and Soddy to identify the underlying regularities, and to put forward an interpretative scheme which further investigation merely served to confirm in every essential particular.

6.4. THE LOCATION OF THE POSITIVE CHARGE

The naïve interpretation of the facts of radioactive disintegration as elucidated by Rutherford and Soddy was that negative electrons and positively-charged heavy particles (α-particles), to be available for emission, must exist as structural units in the atoms of the heavy elements. It was already recognised that negative electrons are to be found in all atoms. From that point of view, the facts of radioactivity added nothing new to the picture; more subtly, however, they introduced a distinction, which was not fully appreciated at the time—or for several years thereafter. The emission of a negative electron in radioactive disintegration is an irreversible process, as a result of it an atom of another chemical species is formed; on the other hand, the emission of a negative electron in the process of ionisation (whereby a positive ion is left behind) is reversible—ultimately recombination of oppositely charged ions takes place, and the original situation is restored. We merely note this distinction for later comment (p. 261); our present concern is with the positive charge in the atom.

Before it was discovered that the α-particles are positively charged (and of atomic, rather than electronic, mass), there was no direct evidence concerning the way in which the balancing positive charge in a neutral atom is disposed. There was, for example, no sign of spectral components in the Zeeman effect (p. 233) having polarisation appropriate to positive emitters. Already, in 1900, Larmor had drawn attention to this fact and pointed to the natural conclusion that the masses of the positive constituents must be large compared with those of the negative constituents of the atom (see equation (137)). More precisely, in 1906, Thomson also wrote 'we conclude that the mass of the carrier of unit positive charge is large compared with that of the carrier of unit negative charge. If we suppose the whole mass of an atom to be that of its charged parts, e/m for the positive unit charge would be of the order of $[10^8$ coulomb/kg]'. Thomson's conclusion was based on a theory of the optical dispersion of monatomic gases (concerning which there was very little experimental information at the time!) in which he assumed that the electrons in an atom are 'embedded in a sphere of positive electrification'. It was essentially the conclusion that, on the basis of this model, practically the whole mass of the atom must be attributed to the positive charge. It has no more than historical interest now: we quote it chiefly because it was expressed numerically—and because, by good fortune, the numerical estimate has proved to be very near to the truth.

Direct experimental evidence concerning the distribution of mass (and positive charge) in atoms generally came first from the experiments of Rutherford and his colleagues on the nature and properties of the α-particles. These experiments extended over the period 1906 to 1913, in Montreal and Manchester (where Rutherford went, as professor of physics, in 1907). In November 1902 Rutherford and Soddy had written 'the speculation naturally arises whether the presence of helium in minerals and its invariable association with uranium and thorium may not be connected with their radioactivity'. It will be recalled that the name 'helium' had been given in 1868 by Edward Frankland (1825-1899) and Joseph Norman Lockyer (1836-1920) to a hypothetical element postulated as the source of certain bright lines which they had observed in the spectrum of the chromosphere of the sun, but which had not at that time been obtained under laboratory conditions. In 1895 this element had been identified as an inert gas, present, in an occluded state, in certain terrestrial minerals, by William Ramsay (1852-1916) and Lockyer. Standard physico-chemical measurements had fixed the atomic weight as 3·96, on the conventional scale (H = 1).

In 1903 Soddy spent some time in Ramsay's laboratory in London, and, with him, established the fact that helium gas indeed accumulates in small quantities in sealed vessels containing radium salts, or radium emanation (they estimated the amount obtained, in 60 days, from their preparation of 50 mg of radium bromide, as one-tenth of a cubic millimetre at s.t.p.). About the same time Marie Curie and A. Laborde determined the rate of evolution of heat in a sealed radium preparation. They obtained a value of about 0·42 joule per hour per mg of radium (in equilibrium with its short-lived products). In an order-of-magnitude calculation, Rutherford immediately put these facts together with his own determination of the initial velocity of the α-particles (approximately 2×10^7 m/s), and, on the assumption that the heating effect was a measure of the kinetic energy of the emitted particles, concluded (15 August 1903) 'The determination of the mass of the α body, taken in conjunction with the experiments on the production of helium by the emanation, supports the view that the α particle is in reality helium.' From that day, this view became a firm conviction with him: some six years later, in collaboration with T. Royds, he succeeded in establishing its validity beyond suspicion of doubt.

The classic paper of Rutherford and Royds appeared in the *Philosophical Magazine* in February 1909. 'After some trials', Mr Baumbach, the departmental glassblower, had succeeded in blowing very thin-walled glass tubes which proved completely impervious to helium gas under the conditions of the experiment, but which were thin enough to allow the α-particles to pass through. In this way, with emanation-laden air in the tube, the α-particles were separated physically from the radium emanation in which they originated. So separated, they were shown to build up, over a period of days, a sample of helium in the surrounding vessel capable of identification spectroscopically when transferred to a capillary discharge. 'Dead' α-particles were ordinary atoms of helium, as Rutherford had long believed.

In the previous year Rutherford and Hans Geiger (1882-1945) had determined the positive charge on the α-particle as $3·1 \times 10^{-19}$ coulomb. Using a prototype geiger counter they had determined the rate of emission of α-particles by a weak source of one of the daughter products of radium—and, with a much stronger source, and a Faraday cylinder as collector, they had determined the rate of transport of charge by the particles. Correlating the two results, they deduced the charge on a single particle. By this time more accurate deflection experiments had established the value of e/m for the particles as almost exactly one-half of e/m of the hydrogen ion. If the α-particle was indeed a charged helium atom, of mass four times the mass of the atom of hydrogen, clearly the charge on the particle must be two fundamental units of charge. In this way Rutherford and Geiger concluded that the value of the fundamental (electronic) charge is, in fact, $1{\cdot}55 \times 10^{-19}$ coulomb. Up to that time no one else, by direct experiment, had obtained a result so close to what is now (see §6.7) the accepted value of this quantity ($1{\cdot}602 \times 10^{-19}$ coulomb).

We have stated that investigations on the nature and properties of the α-particles provided the first unambiguous evidence concerning the distribution of mass and positive charge in atoms generally. We have just reviewed, very briefly, the investigations which Rutherford and his colleagues made on the nature of these particles: we must now describe the other investigations to which we referred. They stem from an observation of Rutherford in 1906 that a beam of α-particles, travelling 'in vacuum' is very slightly diffused in passing through a thin sheet of mica. When the thickness of the mica is of the order of the equivalent of 1 cm of standard air, the angle between the directions of incidence and emergence of the α-particle is, in general, of the order of one or two degrees. For two years, following the experiment on the charge on the α-particle, Geiger examined this phenomenon of 'scattering', in thin foils of many different metals. The general approach to the problem of interpretation (and it was consistent with the atom model of Thomson, mentioned above) was that the (small) deflection actually observed should be regarded as the resultant of very many (much smaller) deflections, in 'random' azimuths, suffered by the α-particle as it traversed successive atoms in its path. On this basis the most probable angle of resultant deflection should be proportional to the square-root of the thickness of the foil (for a given material), and the precise form of the probability function, describing the overall pattern of resultant deflections, should be explicitly given once the most probable angle of resultant deflection was known. Within the range of scattering angles from zero to 10°, with several materials, and for many foil thicknesses, the careful observations of Geiger verified these predictions without serious exception.

In the meantime, however, under Geiger's own supervision, a most unexpected result had been obtained. Rutherford had assigned Ernest Marsden (b. 1889) to Geiger for training in research, and, ostensibly as a mere exercise, had suggested that Marsden should search for a possible 'diffuse reflection' of α-particles incident on metal foils. If the 'multiple' scattering theory, which Geiger was in the process of verifying, was securely based on the premiss that the maximum possible angle of deflection in a single encounter between an α-particle and an atom was of the order of a degree or less, then the probability of 'diffuse reflection' —that is, resultant deflection through an angle in excess of 90°— was minute to the point of derision. Yet Marsden had found α-particles, possibly one particle in 10^4 incident on a thin foil of gold, travelling back from the gold foil, under the conditions of his experiment. Geiger took full responsibility in attesting this wholly unforeseen result, a short account of which was published jointly by these authors in July 1909.

On 7 March 1911—nearly two years later—Rutherford made a preliminary announcement, at a meeting of the Manchester Literary and Philosophical Society, of the new atom model in terms of which he proposed to 'explain' the anomalous results of Geiger and Marsden. In May of that year he published his views in full in the *Philosophical Magazine*. Basically, these views are simple: the small-angle deflections which Geiger had studied in detail are the result of multiple scattering, as he supposed (almost any atom model involving charged constituents would predict such an effect); on the other hand the 'anomalous' effect at large angles is occasioned by 'single' scattering (one α-particle in 10^4, or thereabouts, suffering a single exceptional encounter in one of the many atoms which it traverses in its path into the foil)—and of this effect the Thomson model is certainly inadequate as a basis of explanation. Let us examine the implications of these simple views—and in so doing appreciate the considerations which led to their formulation and ultimate adoption.

We note, first, that if an α-particle is deflected through an angle greater than 90° in a single encounter with another particle effectively at rest, then the mass of the 'struck' particle must be greater than the mass of the α-particle (see *ML & T*, §12.2). As a first approximation, then, let us consider the struck particle to be infinitely massive, and let us suppose that it carries positive charge *Ze*. We know that the charge on the α-particle is 2*e*, *e* being the magnitude of the fundamental (electronic) charge. Let us consider the special case when the α-particle is deflected through 180°, being directly turned back in its path (its original direction of motion having been such as to pass through the centre of the massive particle). Let *M* be the mass of the α-particle, and *v* be its velocity at an 'infinite' distance from the point of 'collision'. In this case, if the α-particle is brought to rest instantaneously when the distance between the centres of the two particles is *b*, we may calculate *b* on the basis of the conservation of energy. Provided that the normal law of electrostatic repulsion is valid in this situation, we have

$$\frac{2Ze^2}{4\pi\epsilon_0 b} = \tfrac{1}{2}Mv^2 \qquad\qquad (150)$$

ϵ_0 being the permittivity of free space. Conventionally, in relation to situations in particle (and quantum) physics, we represent energies by the differences of potential through which unit (electronic) charge would have to 'fall' to acquire those energies. In the present case, if the kinetic energy of the α-particle before the 'collision' is *V* 'electron volts',

$$\tfrac{1}{2}Mv^2 = Ve$$

and $\qquad\qquad b = \dfrac{Ze}{2\pi\epsilon_0 V} \qquad\qquad (151)$

The experiments of Geiger and Marsden were carried out with α-particles for which the value of *V* was about 7×10^6 volts. Accepting the qualitative result that some of these α-particles were deflected through 180° in single collisions with massive 'scattering centres' in the gold foils employed (the difference between scattering through, say, 120° and 180° is trivial in relation to this argument), we conclude that these particles must have penetrated up to a distance *b*, as given by equation (151), from the postulated charge *Ze* responsible for the scattering. Otherwise expressed, our conclusion is that the scattering charge *Ze* is concentrated on a massive particle of radius less than *b*, as given by this equation.

Substituting for e the value which Rutherford and Geiger had obtained (p. 251), and for ϵ_0 its known value $8{\cdot}85 \times 10^{-12}$ farad/m (p. 118), we have, in respect of the experiment of Geiger and Marsden,

$$b = 4Z \times 10^{-16} \text{ (m)} \tag{152}$$

approximately.

When Rutherford carried through the simple calculation that we have made, it was already well known that the radius of a heavy atom, such as an atom of gold, is of the order of a few times 10^{-10} m. According to the result that we have obtained (equation (152)) it would require a positive charge Ze of a million electronic units distributed throughout the volume of such an atom (as in the Thomson model) to deflect an α-particle through $180°$ in a single encounter. Again, a solid material constituted of atoms so charged would be almost completely impervious to the passage of α-particles: large angle deflections would be the rule rather than the exception, even with the thinnest metal foils. As we have already stated, in this connection the failure of the Thomson model was complete. Instead, Rutherford interpreted equation (152) by supposing that the positive charge on the scattering centre was no larger than was necessary to neutralise the charge of the negative electrons known to be present in the atom. From this point of view, for the atom of gold, a value of Z of the order of 100 was appropriate. Then it had to be concluded that the radius of the scattering centre was less than about 4×10^{-14} m—about one ten-thousandth of the radius of the atom itself. This, very simply, was the argument on the basis of which the nuclear model of the atom was conceived. The whole of the positive charge in the atom—and the whole of the mass, except for the mass of the 'extranuclear' electrons— was assumed to be concentrated in a single 'nucleus' occupying no more than 10^{-12} of the volume of the whole atom.

The idea that the atom was 'mostly emptiness' was not new: it had been put forward by Lenard in 1903, as a result of the long series of investigations which followed from his original experiments on the passage of cathode rays through thin foils (p. 162). Lenard had concluded that not more than one part in 10^9 of the volume of solid matter is other than empty, 'as the heavens are empty': Rutherford gave precision to this estimate—and provided the first glimpses of a pattern in the emptiness of the microcosm.

It would be quite wrong to give an oversimplified view (as we may be held to have done) of the conclusions to which Rutherford gave expression in his paper of May 1911. In the discussion at the end of that paper he wrote '. . . it seems simplest to suppose that the atom contains a central charge distributed through a very small volume. . . . At the same time, the experimental evidence is not precise enough to negative the possibility that a small fraction of the positive charge may be carried by satellites extending some distance from the centre.' Again, 'The deductions of the theory . . . are independent of the sign of the central charge, and it has not so far been found possible to obtain definite evidence to determine whether it be positive or negative.' We have presented the nuclear atom model as involving a single positively-charged body (nucleus) at the centre of the atom: in 1911 Rutherford was prepared to admit that a model with several scattering centres might be as satisfactory as a single-centre model (except that the total charge on the centres would have to increase as their number increased)—or a model with a negatively-charged central mass be as satisfactory as one with a positively-charged centre. Rutherford had merely used the criterion of simplicity in favouring the single positively-charged nucleus—and he had no reason subsequently to renounce his choice. Within three years, from many quarters, experimental observations were reported which found immediate correlation in terms of this simple picture.

Let us consider the matter of α-particle scattering, again, now that we have the nuclear atom model as a basis for calculation. Let us suppose that a parallel beam of α-particles, of mass M and velocity v, is incident on a metal foil of thickness t containing n atoms per unit volume. Let the nuclear charge be Ze. The number of atom nuclei per unit surface area of this foil is nt, and the 'probability' that an α-particle traversing the foil shall pass within a distance p of a nucleus is $\pi p^2 nt$ (this expression gives the fraction of the total foil area 'obscured' by equal disks of radius p, one centred in each atom nucleus, having their planes parallel to the surface of the foil). We make the 'classical' assumption that there is a one-to-one (inverse) correspondence between ϕ, the angle of deflection of an α-particle in 'collision' with a nucleus, and p, the perpendicular distance between the centre of the nucleus and the 'initial' direction of motion of the α-particle (p is the so-called impact parameter). On this assumption, if $\pi p^2 nt \ll 1$, this quantity is the probability that an α-particle will be scattered, in a single nuclear encounter, through an angle greater than ϕ in passing through the foil. In respect of this statement we write, formally,

$$p = bf(\phi) \tag{153}$$

to represent the one-to-one correspondence that we have noted. Here, $f(\phi)$ is a hitherto unspecified function of the angle, and b (for dimensional homogeneity) is a characteristic length representative of the collision process in question. We note that, for a given foil, for sufficiently large values of p (and therefore small values of ϕ) the condition $\pi p^2 nt \ll 1$ will fail to be satisfied (that is why we wrote 'probability', with quotation marks, originally, until we had introduced the limiting condition). For every foil, therefore, over a range of small angles, resultant deflections will originate in 'multiple' rather than 'single' scattering of the transmitted particles: only beyond a certain angle (which is greater the greater the thickness of the foil) will the scattering be single.

In relation to equation (153) the quantity b was described merely as a characteristic length representative of the collision process. For that purpose there could be no more appropriate parameter than the length for which we have already used the same symbol in equation (150). The b of that equation involves the kinetic energy of the α-particle and the magnitude of the nuclear charge. No other 'variable' enters into a description of the process. Let us, therefore, identify the two lengths in question. We then have

$$p = \frac{Ze^2}{\pi\epsilon_0 Mv^2} f(\phi),$$

and, for the probability of single scattering through an angle greater than ϕ, under the conditions that we have specified,

$$\Pi(\phi) = nt \frac{Z^2 e^4}{\pi\epsilon_0^2 M^2 v^4} f^2(\phi).$$

Correspondingly, if the probability of scattering through an angle between ϕ and $\phi + d\phi$ is represented by $P(\phi)d\phi$, we have

$$-P(\phi) = 2nt \frac{Z^2 e^4}{\pi\epsilon_0^2 M^2 v^4} f(\phi) f'(\phi) \tag{154}$$

and, for the probability of scattering, per unit solid angle, in the direction ϕ, that is $P(\phi)/2\pi \sin \phi$,

$$-P_\omega(\phi) = nt \frac{Z^2 e^4}{\pi^2 \epsilon_0^2 M^2 v^4} \operatorname{cosec} \phi f(\phi) f'(\phi) \qquad (155)$$

According to equation (155), the assumptions underlying Rutherford's explanation of the occurrence of large-angle scattering, in the circumstances in which it was first observed, may be tested experimentally without knowledge of the form of the function $f(\phi)$. The assumption that single scattering is involved, at any angle ϕ, may be tested by determining the variation of scattered intensity with foil thickness, for a given scattering material. According to the equation, $P_\omega(\phi)$ should be directly proportional to t, for small thicknesses (v effectively constant throughout). The assumption that the coulomb law of electrostatic repulsion is valid for the scattering process may be tested by determining how the intensity of scattering, at a given angle, and for a thin foil, varies with the velocity of the α-particles incident on the foil. The variation, according to the equation, should be as the inverse fourth power of this velocity. Finally, it should be noted, the validity of the 'classical' impact-parameter method of treatment of the problem is itself an assumption which is under test concurrently with the others, in any comparison of equation (155) with the results of experiment.

These remarks having been made, it must now be admitted that the most sensitive test of Rutherford's detailed assumption (particularly the assumption regarding the validity of the impact parameter treatment) becomes possible only when the form of $f(\phi)$ is known. Hitherto, the form of this function has been left unspecified for purely pedagogic reasons: there is nothing recondite in the nature of the function concerned. The theory of 'central orbits' under inverse-square law forces has been given in almost every elementary text on applied mathematics since the days of Newton's *Principia* (it was from that treatise that Rutherford learned the theory when he came to Cambridge as a young research student from New Zealand in 1895). The result which we need is simply $f(\phi) = \frac{1}{2} \cot \phi/2$. Substituting this result in equation (155) we have the 'Rutherford scattering formula' in full, namely,

$$P_\omega(\phi) = \frac{nt}{16} \frac{Z^2 e^4}{\pi^2 \epsilon_0^2 M^2 v^4} \operatorname{cosec}^4 \frac{\phi}{2} \qquad (156)$$

During a period of two years, from 1911 to 1913, Geiger and Marsden submitted the predictions of equation (156) to rigorous test. Over a roughly tenfold range of t, over a similar range of v^4, and, in respect of $\operatorname{cosec}^4 \phi/2$, over a range of values covered by a factor of $2 \cdot 5 \times 10^5$, they were unable, using gold foils for the scattering, to establish any systematic discrepancy between prediction and fact. Examining the scattering from foils of other metals under comparable conditions, they concluded that the 'nuclear charge number' Z varies somewhat less rapidly than the atomic weight, for elements from aluminium to gold.

The observations of scattered intensity on the basis of which Geiger and Marsden 'verified' the Rutherford formula were essentially relative in character. No attempt was made to determine the probability of scattering absolutely. Equation (156), however, gives the absolute probability, per unit solid angle, explicitly, in terms of quantities all of which—except the nuclear charge number Z—are known, or are determinable in the context of a particular experiment. In 1920, James Chadwick (b. 1891) carried out the first absolute determination of the probability of large-angle scattering of α-particles in foils of copper, silver a nd platinum. By that time, on the basis of other evidence (see p. 280), the nuclear charge number had already been identified with the ordina l number of an element in the periodic table, as we have previously asserted (p. 241). For copper, silver and platinum the ordinal numbers are 29, 47 and 78, respectively. Chadwick's experimental values for Z, calculated on the basis of the Rutherford formula, were 29·3, 46·3 and 77·4, with an estimated accuracy of between 1 and 2 per cent. in each case. With these results, the nuclear atom model, and the classical description of α-particle scattering based on it, received their most direct justification.

One final point must be made, before we conclude this brief history of the discovery of the atom nucleus. We have already made the statement, on the authority of Rutherford's paper of 1911, 'The deductions of the theory [of scattering] are independent of the sign of the central charge.' In fact, the only difference between the (unclosed) orbits of particles in inverse-square law 'central' fields which are in the one case repulsive and the other attractive, is that in the first case these orbits are hyperbolas with the centre of force at the external focus, in the second they are hyperbolas with the centre of force at the internal focus. The relation between impact parameter and angle of deflection is essentially the same for each. Naturally, for sake of simplicity, Rutherford chose to assume that the charge on the nucleus is positive (p. 256), but we may reasonably enquire what was, in fact, the first direct evidence that this choice was the appropriate one.

The first clear evidence regarding the sign of the charge on the nucleus came from a study of the chemistry of the radioelements. Because the mass of the α-particle is so much greater than the electronic mass, it was inevitable, as soon as the nuclear atom model came to be accepted, that α-radioactivity should come to be regarded as a property of the atomic nucleus (just because there was no other constituent of the atom in which a particle as massive as the α-particle could be accommodated before disintegration). Over the period 1911 to 1913, Soddy and Alexander Fleck (b. 1889), in Glasgow, and others elsewhere, were studying the chemical properties of the various members of the radioactive disintegration series of uranium and thorium in an attempt to place these 'new' elements correctly in the periodic table. Out of these investigations the so-called 'radioactive displacement law' emerged. For our present purposes we may quote the law partially as follows: 'after α-disintegration the daughter product invariably belongs to an element two places lower in the periodic table than the parent element'. This correlation, itself, immediately suggests a close correlation between nuclear charge number and ordinal number in the table—but on closer inspection it makes sense only if the nuclear charge is positive. If the charge on the nucleus were negative, α-disintegration would result in a daughter nucleus of net negative charge two units greater than that of the parent. Again, the ordinal number of helium is 2; the α-particle carries two units of positive charge; it is a helium atom which has lost two electrons; it is emitted spontaneously from heavy nuclei; it can hardly be other than a helium atom nucleus itself. If that is the case, the charge on the helium nucleus, at least, is positive.

The clause in the displacement law which, previously, we did not quote states: 'after β-disintegration the daughter product invariably belongs to an element one place higher in the periodic table than the parent element'. Consistently with our previous interpretation, we now conclude (see p. 249) that the negative electron emitted from the atom in the act of β-disintegration comes from the atom nucleus invariably. Radioactivity, in general, then, is a property of the nucleus.

6.5. THE ARRANGEMENT OF THE ELECTRONS

According to the Rutherford model, the atom of an element of ordinal number Z consists of a massive nucleus of net positive charge Ze, and Z electrons, each of charge $-e$, in some way 'occupying' a volume approximately 10^{12} times as large as the volume of the nucleus. In this section we attempt to indicate the nature of the experimental evidence on the basis of which present views concerning the arrangement of these extranuclear electrons have been developed. We note, at the outset, two aspects of the problem of 'arrangement'. On the one hand, we may think naïvely in geometrical terms; on the other, we may concentrate attention on the energies concerned. If we think exclusively in geometrical terms, it must be obvious that we are, to a large extent, still essentially, model building; concentration on questions of energy brings us nearer to experiment—and leaves us relatively free from the artificialities of a particular model.

As a corrective to the models that we may later find it convenient to employ, even though we concentrate on the experimental results, let us consider first an experiment which relates not to energies but, in a fairly direct way, to the geometrical configuration of atoms. There are not many such experiments. In 1918, Lord Rayleigh (4th baron (1875-1947); see, also, V & W, p. 80) observed in the laboratory, for the first time, the effect which is responsible for the essential blue of the sky: he succeeded in detecting the scattering of light in dust-free gases. On any theory which regards light as a transverse wave motion, light scattered by spherically symmetrical molecules should be plane polarised when the angle of scattering is 90°. Lack of complete polarisation at that angle must indicate some departure from spherical symmetry. With diatomic and triatomic molecular gases, Rayleigh found (1920), as he anticipated, that polarisation was incomplete in the direction concerned (with nitrous oxide 26·7 per cent. of the scattered light was unpolarised); with the monatomic gases, helium and argon, on the other hand, he found it difficult to detect any unpolarised component (with argon only 0·46 per cent. unpolarised). Even the atom of helium, therefore, though it contains only three constituent particles (nucleus, and two electrons) appears as spherically symmetrical in its interaction with visible light. To assume that light is an electromagnetic wave motion (as, of course, Rayleigh assumed), is merely to emphasise the fundamental nature of this result: the three charged particles which constitute the helium atom appear as a spherically symmetrical system to the periodic electric and magnetic fields which constitute visible light.

Having anchored our discussion firmly to this inescapable fact, let us at once go to the extreme of artificiality, and, in order to fix our ideas quantitatively in relation to the energies involved in electronic configurations, consider a model consisting of an electron in a circular orbit with the nucleus at the centre. If the radius of the orbit is r, and the charge number of the nucleus is Z, the electrostatic potential energy of the circulating electron is constant during the motion, and of magnitude $-Ze^2/4\pi\epsilon_0 r$ (we take the potential energy to be zero when r is infinite). Assuming now that the electrostatic attraction is responsible for the centripetal acceleration of the electron, we have

$$\frac{Ze^2}{4\pi\epsilon_0 r^2} = \frac{mv^2}{r} \tag{157}$$

m being the mass of the electron and v the magnitude of its orbital velocity. If we write $\frac{1}{2}mv^2$ as the kinetic energy of the electron (assuming that its velocity is small compared with the velocity of light), then W, its total energy, is given by

$$W = -\frac{Ze^2}{4\pi\epsilon_0 r} + \frac{Ze^2}{8\pi\epsilon_0 r},$$

or
$$W = -\frac{Ze^2}{8\pi\epsilon_0 r} \tag{158}$$

If this energy is equivalent to $-V$ electron volts, then

$$V = \frac{Ze}{8\pi\epsilon_0 r} \tag{159}$$

The quantity represented by equation (159) is spoken of as the energy of binding of the electron to the nucleus in the orbit concerned. It would be necessary for the corresponding amount of work to be done to remove this electron in such a way that it was left 'at rest at infinity'. Substituting numerical values, as we did in equation (151), we have, for $r = 10^{-10}$ m,

$$V = 7 \cdot 2Z \text{ electron volts} \qquad (160)$$

Hitherto, we have considered a single electron in orbit around a nucleus of arbitrary charge number Z. Let us extend this crude model (as far as it may plausibly be extended) to the case of a neutral atom containing Z extranuclear electrons. If these are considered as occupying circular orbits of different radii, in that way filling out the whole volume of the atom, we may plausibly use equation (159) directly in relation to the innermost of these orbits (for, to a first approximation, the other electrons may be regarded as constituting a spherically symmetrical distribution exerting no resultant force on the enclosed charge—see p. 33). Conversely, we may justifiably employ the numerical relation given by equation (160), writing $Z = 1$, in order to obtain an order-of-magnitude value for the binding energy of the electron in the outermost orbit. (For such an electron, in whatever atom, as to order of magnitude, at least, $r = 10^{-10}$ m, as we have assumed— and we may consider the other $Z - 1$ electrons as effectively 'screening' the nuclear charge, so that the Zth electron moves in the field of a single positive charge only.) Taking the second case first, we conclude that the binding energy of the least-tightly-bound electron, in whatever atom, is likely to be of the order of some 10 electron volts, according to our model. In relation to the first case, the conclusion (from equation (159)) is not so clear-cut: it is obvious that the binding energy of the most-tightly-bound electron is more than Z times that of the least-tightly-bound, but whether, in the heaviest atom (Z of the order of 100), it is of the order of 10^4 or 10^5 electron volts would be hazardous to predict on the basis of these simple ideas alone. Let us, therefore, consider the experiments.

In 1914 James Franck (1882-1964) and Gustav Hertz (b. 1887) published the first of a series of papers describing the results of experiments on the collision of electrons of a few electron volts energy with the molecules in a gas. As early as 1902, Lenard had carried out similar experiments, not without significant results; but unaccountably, as it now appears, this line of investigation had not been actively pursued in the intervening years. The arrangement of Franck and Hertz is shown schematically in fig. 35. An electrically heated filament, constituting a source of low-energy electrons (see pp. 177, 180), was situated in the plane of electrode A, the potential of which was maintained the same as that of one end of the filament. The potential of the wire gauze C (positive with respect to A) could be varied, and throughout these variations the potential of the 'collecting electrode' B was maintained slightly negative (say, 1 or 2 volts negative) with respect to C. The gas under investigation was contained, at a convenient (low) pressure, in the glass vessel in which the electrode system was housed. It

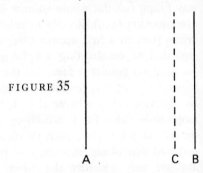

FIGURE 35

was found that the negative current passing to B increased steadily as the positive potential of C was increased, then at a perfectly definite value of this potential, which was different for different gases, the current decreased abruptly, to resume its previous up- wards trend when the potential of B (following that of C, as we have described) reached the 'critical' value which the potential of C had when the decrease of current set in. A further decrease of current was observed when the positive potential of C reached a value twice the 'critical' value, and so on. Fig. 36 shows the results obtained with mercury vapour. In this case the critical potential, as deduced from the curve, is 4·9 volts. As we have stated, the critical potential varied with the gas under investigation, but the initial increase of current, up to the first maximum of the curve of i_C against V_C, was very nearly the same in all cases, provided that the gas pressure was not too high.

On a crude classical picture, if the interaction between an elec- tron (of mass m) and a gas molecule (of mass M) is assumed to be 'elastic', then the maximum transfer of energy in a single collision (in which the molecule is effectively at rest initially) is $4m/M$ of the kinetic energy of the electron. This fraction, for collisions in hydrogen is very little greater than 10^{-3}; for a collision with the 'heavy' monatomic molecule of mercury it is less than 10^{-5}. It is not surprising, therefore, if the collisions are elastic—that is, if there is no specific interaction between the electrons and the particular atoms or molecules with which they collide—that the increase of current with accelerating potential should be practically independent of the gas which is present, at low pressure, in the experimental vessel, as Franck and Hertz observed.

Irving Langmuir (1881-1957) had given the theory of the variation of electron current with accelerating potential, for the ideal case in which there is no gas between the electrodes, at a meeting of the American Physical Society in October 1913. Provided that the temperature of the filament is high enough, so that the current is not limited by the supply of electrons liberated at the cathode, under these ideal conditions, the anode current is proportional to the three-halves power of the potential difference. In these circumstances, as Langmuir described the situation, the electron current is limited by the effect of 'space charge'. Very quickly, after the initial application of the external field, a steady state develops in which the field due to the concentration of negatively charged electrons in the neighbourhood of the cathode just more than annuls the applied field, with the result that some of the electrons emitted by the cathode are turned back in their paths and do not contribute to the current. The situation, in the experiments of Franck and Hertz, when the accelerating potential was less than the critical value for the gas in question, was not very different from the ideal situation discussed by Langmuir. Essentially, over this range, the variation of i_B with V_C (fig. 36), is space-charge limited, whatever the gas under investigation.

When the accelerating potential was slightly greater than the critical value, in the Franck-Hertz experiment, the situation was obviously quite different. Under these conditions many electrons, which would have been able to reach the collecting electrode if the accelerating potential had been only slightly smaller, were now unable to do so. Such electrons must have been those which, arriving close to the gauze C (fig. 35) with the full energy corresponding to motion through the field, had lost so much of that energy in a single encounter with an atom or molecule that they were turned back by the small adverse difference of potential

EM S

between C and B. This description of the situation is fully borne out by the subsequent increase in electron current when the potential difference between A and B reached and then exceeded the critical value. Clearly, 'inelastic' collisions, resulting in the transfer to gas atoms (or molecules) of energy corresponding to the critical potential were still taking place, in roughly the same numbers, in the space between A and C, but these collisions were occurring progressively nearer to A. After an electron had lost almost the whole

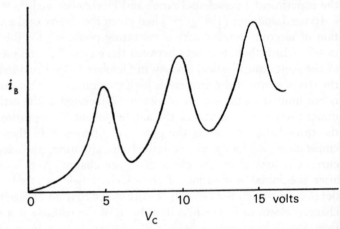

FIGURE 36

of its kinetic energy in such a collision it was still able, between the point of collision and C, to acquire more than enough energy to reach B against the retarding field. When the accelerating potential reached a value equal to twice the critical potential, on this view, the first batch of inelastic collisions would occur precisely midway between A and C, and the re-accelerated electrons which had been involved in them would be able to produce a second batch of such collisions in the immediate neighbourhood of C. In this way the second of the major features in the characteristic curve (fig. 36) would receive a natural explanation—and similar features, equally spaced along the voltage axis, as the accelerating potential was further increased.

The general conclusion of Franck and Hertz was that, in the gases which they investigated, the electron collisions were essentially elastic until the kinetic energy of the electron reached a critical value, characteristic of the gas, at which stage inelastic collisions took place with considerable efficiency, an electron transferring the whole of its available energy to the gas molecule. As we have stated, the molecules of mercury vapour are monatomic under the conditions of the Franck-Hertz experiments. In this case, therefore, these authors concluded that 4·9 electron volts is a characteristic 'critical energy' of the mercury atom.

As Lenard had done before them, Franck and Hertz assumed that the critical energy which they had identified for the mercury atom was indeed the energy necessary to ionise the atom—the binding energy of the least-tightly-bound electron in the atom,

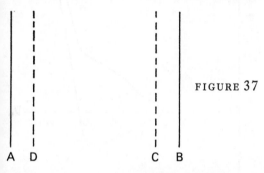

FIGURE 37

A   D   C   B

which we have estimated to be of the order of 10 electron volts generally. The first investigators to demonstrate by direct experiment that this is not the case, and at the same time to determine the ionisation energy, were Bergen Davis and F. S. Goucher, in New York (1917). These authors introduced a second gauze, D, between cathode A and collector B (fig. 37). The 'original' gauze, C, was maintained slightly negative with respect to the cathode throughout the experiment, the (variable) electron-accelerating potential was applied to D, and, for each value of this potential, the current to B was measured first with B slightly positive, then with B slightly negative with respect to C. In an experiment with mercury vapour in their apparatus, Davis and Goucher obtained the results shown in fig. 38. Curves I and II correspond to the two directions of the final collecting field above mentioned. It will be clear that, with the arrangement of potentials specified, all the 'primary' electrons emitted by the filament would be turned back before reaching C, also that any negative ions formed in the gas would be accelerated towards D. Only such positive ions as might be produced in the region between D and C would be accelerated through the latter gauze towards the collector B. With B slightly negative with respect to C all these ions would reach the collector (curve II); with B slightly positive only those possessing kinetic energy sufficient to overcome the small retarding field would be collected (curve I). In each case the current to B would be a positive current. With mercury vapour in their apparatus Davis and Goucher did not observe this situation of two positive currents (the greater current with B negative, the smaller with B positive

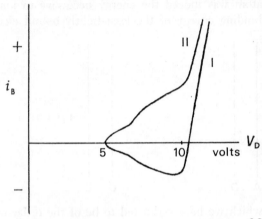

with respect to C) until the electron-accelerating potential of D had been raised somewhat above 10 volts, as shown in the figure. For accelerating potentials between 4·9 volts and 10 volts the net current to B was positive when B was negative, and negative when B was positive with respect to C. From what we have already said, it is clear that the carriers of these currents could only have been electrons liberated into the region between B and C by some secondary process.

Davis and Goucher supposed that under the conditions of their experiment, when the primary electrons had more than 4·9 electron volts energy, 'secondary' electrons were liberated from the surfaces of all the electrodes. Indeed, Franck and Hertz had shown that mercury vapour, when traversed by electrons of just more than the critical energy (4·9 eV), emits ultraviolet light (monochromatic light of wavelength 2537 Å): this radiation would be expected to liberate electrons from metal surfaces, as Davis and Goucher had supposed. When B was negative with respect to C (curve II) the 'photoelectrons' liberated from the surface of B would be accelerated towards C, the net current to the collector being positive; when B was positive with respect to C (curve 1) the photoelectrons liberated from B would not escape, but those liberated from C would be collected—as a negative current. On the basis of this wholly reasonable and self-consistent interpretation, all the main features of fig. 38 were satisfactorily explained, and the ionisation energy of the mercury atom was fixed at 10·4 electron volts, rather than 4·9 electron volts as previously supposed. Nowadays, either from direct determination in experiments such as those of Davis and Goucher, or otherwise, ionisation energies are known with considerable accuracy for almost all atoms in the normal state; they range from 24·6 electron volts for helium to 3·9 electron volts for caesium. It appears, then, that our original rough estimate of this quantity (p. 263) must have had some justification!

Having identified the ionisation energy, we are not in this section specifically concerned with the detailed interpretation of the various other 'critical' energies which are brought to light, in experiments of the type of the Franck-Hertz experiment, with all gases (fig. 38 provides clear evidence of a second critical energy of the mercury atom at 6·7 eV). It should be said, however, very briefly, that these experiments demonstrate conclusively that neutral atoms are capable of existing, for a short time at least, with an energy content greater than the normal by perfectly definite amounts (for each type of atom there is a discrete series of 'allowed' values of this additional energy). In general such an 'excited' atom reverts to the normal state by the emission of quasi-homogeneous radiation (belonging to the visible or ultra-violet region of the spectrum). It is traditional to suppose that in the excited atom the least-tightly-bound electron is the recipient of the additional energy. The critical energies, therefore, on this view, are the well defined energies, characteristic of the atom concerned, which may be given to the 'outermost' electron in the atom without removing it completely from the system. The 'first' ionisation energy, as we have supposed all along, is the minimum energy necessary to remove that electron 'to infinity'.

The idea that the possible energies of atomic electrons are 'quantised'—that is, are restricted, through the operation of some basic law of nature, to certain 'discrete' values—was first incorporated in a formal 'theory' by Niels Henrik David Bohr (1885-1962) in 1913. Bohr's theory was based on the nuclear atom model of Rutherford, and for our present purposes its most important assertion has to do with those electrons which move in the 'unscreened' field of the nucleus. Bohr postulated that in every atom the orbit of the 'innermost' electron (or electrons) is circular, and that the angular momentum of this electron about the axis of its orbit is the same for all atoms. We have already pointed out (p. 238) the essential instability of electron orbits on classical electromagnetic theory. Bohr's hypothesis of 1913 was grounded in the postulate of 'stationary' (non-radiating) orbits: it did not resolve the classical dilemma—it merely dismissed it openly as an irrelevance. If, for the moment, we write H for the universal value of the orbital angular momentum of the most-tightly-bound electron in an atom of nuclear charge number Z, according to Bohr, equation (157) is supplemented by the angular momentum condition

$$mvr = H \tag{161}$$

and the orbit is no longer arbitrary, but specified in detail. We then have

$$r = \frac{4\pi\epsilon_0 H^2}{Ze^2 m} \tag{162}$$

and, from equation (158),

$$W = -\frac{Z^2 e^4 m}{32\pi^2 \epsilon_0^2 H^2} \tag{163}$$

or (see equation (159)),

$$V = \frac{Z^2 e^3 m}{32\pi^2 \epsilon_0^2 H^2} \tag{164}$$

Our interest in the energy of binding of the most-tightly-bound electron in an atom, at this stage, has to do with its relevance to the phenomenon of the emission of 'characteristic' X-radiation. We shall have to consider this phenomenon in some detail; first of all, however, it is useful that we should amplify what has already been written regarding the basic postulates of Bohr's theory. Let us consider the particular case of the hydrogen atom. In this case there is only one extranuclear electron, and equation (163), with $Z = 1$, gives the energy of this electron in the neutral atom in its 'ground-state' orbit. Bohr began his attempt to 'explain' the optical spectrum of atomic hydrogen by assuming that other circular orbits were possible for the electron, defining the 'excited' states of this atom. He postulated that the angular momentum should be an integral multiple of H for every such orbit, and that the process of radiation involves the 'quantum jump' of the electron from one orbit to the orbit of next lower energy (or 'quantum number'). In this connection he made use of a postulate of Planck. In 1900 Max Karl Ernst Ludwig Planck (1858-1947) had put forward a new theory of 'black-body' radiation, based on the restrictive hypothesis that transfer of energy between matter and the radiation field is not continuous but takes place discretely, in amounts proportionate to the frequency of the radiation concerned. Thereby Planck's constant, h, was introduced into physics through the equation

$$\Delta W = h\nu \tag{165}$$

ΔW is the measure of the energy transferred when one quantum ('photon') of radiation of frequency ν is emitted or absorbed. In Bohr's use of this postulate, ν_n, the frequency of the (emitted) radiation corresponding to the electron 'jump' from the circular orbit of quantum number n, to the orbit of next lower energy, is given, in the case of the hydrogen atom, by

$$\nu_n = (W_n - W_{n-1})/h \tag{166}$$

Here, in conformity with equation (163), and the extended angular momentum condition described above,

$$W_n = -\frac{e^4 m}{32\pi^2 \epsilon_0^2 n^2 H^2}.$$

To be precise, therefore,

$$\nu_n = \frac{e^4 m}{32\pi^2 \epsilon_0^2 h H^2} \cdot \frac{2n-1}{n^2(n-1)^2} \tag{167}$$

It will be realised—and we have already drawn attention to the fact—that Bohr openly dismissed the classical theory of electromagnetic radiation as irrelevant to the atomic situation in framing the assumptions from which equation (167) derives. He did not, however, dismiss the classical description entirely. In the limiting situation of very large quantum numbers, he said, the atomic system becomes macroscopic in size (r varies as n^2, see equation (162)), and in that case the two descriptions must merge into one. If f_n is the frequency of orbital revolution of the electron with quantum number n (fractionally, insignificantly different from f_{n-1}, when n is very large), then, according to Bohr's so-called 'principle of correspondence',

$$\text{Lt}_{n \to \infty}(\nu_n/f_n) = 1 \tag{168}$$

Now $\quad f_n = \dfrac{v_n}{2\pi r_n},$

$$= \frac{1}{2\pi} \frac{v_n r_n}{r_n^{\,2}}.$$

Thus, replacing H by nH, and writing $Z = 1$, in equations (161) and (162), as is appropriate to our present consideration, we have, substituting,

$$f_n = \frac{1}{2\pi} \frac{nH}{m} \left(\frac{e^2 m}{4\pi\epsilon_0 n^2 H^2} \right)^2,$$

or $\qquad f_n = \dfrac{e^4 m}{32\pi^3 \epsilon_0^{\,2} n^3 H^3} \tag{169}$

Finally, combining equations (167), (168) and (169), we obtain

$$\text{Lt}_{n \to \infty}\left\{ \frac{2n-1}{n^2(n-1)^2 h} \middle/ \frac{1}{\pi n^3 H} \right\} = 1,$$

that is $\quad H = h/2\pi \tag{170}$

In terms of equation (170), Bohr's principle of correspondence is seen to have related his own otherwise arbitrary postulate of the quantisation of orbital angular momentum to Planck's postulate of energy quantisation of an earlier decade. The relation is independent of the particular case of the hydrogen atom here used for purposes of illustration: henceforth, therefore, in so far as we need to refer to any of equations (161) to (164), or to equation (167), we shall treat them as modified by substitution from equation (170) as required.

We are now in a position to return to the consideration of the

phenomenon of the characteristic X-radiation—and the relevance
to that phenomenon of the modified equation (163), namely,

$$W = -\frac{Z^2 e^4 m}{8 \epsilon_0^2 h^2} \qquad (171)$$

We have already (p. 238) given consideration to Barkla's conclusion (of 1904) that the interaction of X-rays with matter of low
atomic weight is to be broadly understood as taking place predominantly by a process of scattering without change of quality.
Extending his investigations to materials of higher atomic weight,
Barkla found (1906) the situation to be considerably more complex. Examining the 'secondary' radiation from these 'heavier'
materials in respect of its absorption in aluminium (as a standard
'absorber' of low atomic weight), Barkla showed that it consisted
in general of a component (or components) characteristic of the
material irradiated by the primary beam, together with a component of scattered radiation of roughly the same quality as the
primary. When a 'characteristic' radiation was present in this way,
Barkla found that it was always less penetrating (in aluminium)
than the primary radiation. Having satisfied himself that the
characteristic radiations which he identified were indeed characteristic of the chemical elements (when non-elementary materials
were irradiated, secondary radiations characteristic of the constituent elements were observed), Barkla was able to trace the way
in which the penetrating power of the radiation varied with the
atomic weight of the radiator. With a series of elements from
calcium (atomic weight 40) to molybdenum (atomic weight 96) he
observed a single radiation in each case. For these radiations the
linear absorption coefficient in aluminium varied smoothly from
1170 cm^{-1} to 12·7 cm^{-1}. This sequence continued through the
elements up to cerium (atomic weight 140), by which stage the
linear absorption coefficient had further decreased to 1·6 cm^{-1}.
Throughout the series silver (atomic weight 108) to barium (atomic weight 137), Barkla observed a second component of characteristic radiation, also, less penetrating than the first (linear
absorption coefficient 1900 cm^{-1} for the silver radiation, 600 cm^{-1}
for that of barium), and he followed this second sequence through
to bismuth (atomic weight 209) in respect of which element
a linear absorption coefficient of 51 cm^{-1} in aluminium was obtained. Barkla convinced himself that only the contingencies of the

experiment prevented him from observing two components of characteristic radiation for each element examined (for the heavier elements the more penetrating component would not be excited if the primary radiation from his X-ray tube were not itself sufficiently penetrating; for the lighter elements the less penetrating component would be so strongly absorbed in the air that it would not enter his detector in measurable intensity). He therefore concluded that, under excitation by primary radiation of sufficiently great penetrating power, the atoms of any element may be caused to emit characteristic X-radiation of two widely different qualities: a 'harder' component (the 'K X-radiation'), and a 'softer' (the 'L X-radiation'). For each component the penetrating power increased smoothly—and very notably—with increasing atomic weight of the radiator.

In 1909 G. W. C. Kaye (1880-1941) showed that these characteristic X-radiations are present in the general X-radiation emitted from the anti-cathode (target) of an X-ray tube, provided that the energy of the cathode rays incident on the target is sufficient for their excitation. In this case, of course, the characteristic radiations are those appropriate to the chemical element (or elements) of which the target is made. Reviewing the experiments of Barkla and Kaye, and some later observations of R. Whiddington (b. 1885), Thomson suggested (1912) that the phenomenon of characteristic X-ray emission must involve the most-tightly-bound electrons in the atom. Indeed, it appeared from Whiddington's experiments (1911), and more directly from the investigations of R. T. Beatty of the following year, that the critical energy for the excitation of the K X-radiation of copper by the cathode-rays was of the order of 11000 electron volts, and that over the range of elements from aluminium to selenium (that is from atomic weight 27 to 79) this critical energy was fairly closely proportional to the square of the atomic weight of the element concerned. At that time Bohr's theory had not been developed, even the concept of nuclear charge number had still to be formulated, but clearly in these results there was material in waiting for an equation such as our equation (171) to take shape as a basis of their interpretation. Let us recall: equation (171) predicts, on the basis of Bohr's theory, that the energy required to remove the most-tightly-bound electron from an atom, of which the nuclear charge number is Z, is proportional to Z^2.

By the time that the first of Bohr's papers, setting out the details of his new theory, had been published, a new experimental effect had been discovered which added another dimension of precision to the study of the characteristic X-radiations of the elements. At the meeting of the Bavarian Academy of Sciences on 8 June 1912, Arnold Johannes Wilhelm Sommerfeld (1868-1951), professor of theoretical physics in Munich, presented an account of an experiment which had been carried out in his department at the suggestion of Max Felix Theodor von Laue (1879-1960), one of his lecturers. Von Laue had been given the task of writing the chapter on wave optics in an encyclopaedia volume of which Sommerfeld was editor, and in the course of this work had entertained the idea of a crystal as potentially a three-dimensional diffraction grating, requiring only a radiation of sufficiently short wavelength for its exploitation. If X-rays were indeed such a radiation (see V & W, p. 274), then possibly diffraction effects might be observed with them which would give an indication of their wavelengths. Walter Friedrich (b. 1883), then recently appointed as experimental assistant to Sommerfeld was invited to help. At first Sommerfeld was sceptical, taking the view that the thermal motion of the atoms in the crystal would mask any positive effect, but eventually, in collaboration with C.M.Paul Knipping (1883-1935), a graduate from Röntgen's department, Friedrich carried out the test. Originally with a crystal of copper sulphate, and then even more convincingly with each of two plates of zincblende, one cut perpendicular to the fourfold axis of symmetry of the crystal and the other perpendicular to the threefold axis, they obtained a two-dimensional array of 'diffraction maxima' on a photographic plate exposed to the X-rays which had traversed the crystal. The gross morphological symmetry of the crystal (in relation to the direction of the X-ray beam, in each case) was clearly evident in these two-dimensional patterns. So it was that, in a single unsophisticated experiment, von Laue, Friedrich and Knipping provided the first entirely unambiguous evidence for wave-like properties with X-rays generally, and at the same time confirmed the long-standing (1850) view of the French mathematician Auguste Bravais (1811-1863) that the macroscopic symmetry of crystalline solids is the consequence of an ordered arrangement of 'atoms', in a 'space lattice' of conformable microscopic symmetry in each case.

In relation to the characteristic X-rays of the elements, the credit for the successful application of von Laue's discovery belongs jointly to William Lawrence Bragg (p. 219) and Henry Gwyn Jeffrey Moseley (1884-1915). Bragg had just taken his degree at Cambridge when news of the Munich experiments became known. Within a few months, during which time he had had the benefit of long discussions with his teacher, C.T.R.Wilson (see p. 311), Bragg had reduced the three-dimensional phenomenon, conceptually, to a one-dimensional one—and had thereby laid the foundations of X-ray spectrometry. He had pointed out that in a regular crystal lattice an 'almost infinite' number of sets of parallel planes may be drawn through the lattice points ('atoms') of the crystal. In any one set the planes would be equidistant, and in general the spacing of the planes would be inversely as the superficial density of lattice points in them. In respect of any axis of symmetry of the crystal, the totality of sets of planes would exhibit the essential symmetry of the axis. On this view, in the formation of any particular 'Laue spot', one set of planes, only, was to be considered —and only X-rays of certain particular wavelengths. The set of planes involved was that for which, if 'specular' reflection were a possibility, the incident X-rays would be reflected from those planes in the direction of the spot—and the wavelengths in question were those for which 'reflections' from successive planes of the specified set would be in phase. 'Specular reflection' imposes the condition that the wavelets scattered from each lattice point in a single plane shall necessarily be in phase in the direction of reflection; the additional condition (satisfied only for particular wavelengths when the angle of 'reflection' is specified), that reflections from successive planes shall be in phase, ensures coincidence of phase for the wavelets scattered from every lattice point lying in all these planes. Bragg concluded that a major factor determining the intensity of a diffraction maximum ('Laue spot') was the superficial density of the lattice points in the corresponding 'reflecting planes'. Because, for any crystal, the number of sets of planes having a large superficial density of lattice points is relatively small, the diffraction maxima which appeared on the original photographs of Friedrich and Knipping were not in fact very numerous.

Having outlined Bragg's general approach to the problem, let us formalise his main conclusion with the help of a diagram. In fig. 39 AB, A'B', A"B" represent the traces in the plane of the

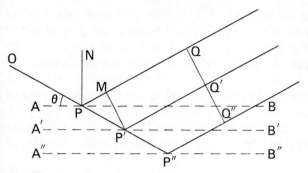

FIGURE 39

paper of three neighbouring planes of a set of which PN is a common normal. OP is the direction of incidence of a parallel beam of X-rays, and $\angle OPA = \theta$. According to Bragg, there will be a diffraction maximum in the direction PQ ($\angle QPB = \angle OPA$) if there is present in the primary X-ray beam a component of wavelength λ such that

$$PP' + P'Q' - PQ\ (\ = P'P'' + P''Q'' - P'Q') = n\lambda,$$

where n is an integer. Here P', P'' are the intersections of A'B' and A''B'', respectively, with OP produced, as shown in the figure, and QQ'Q'' is perpendicular, in turn, to PQ, P'Q' and P''Q''. If P'M is drawn perpendicular to PQ, Bragg's condition may be written

$$PP' - PM = n\lambda,$$

or, if d is the common spacing of the planes in question, as

$$d\ \mathrm{cosec}\ \theta\ (1 - \cos 2\theta) = n\lambda,$$

that is $\quad 2d \sin \theta = n\lambda \qquad\qquad\qquad (172)$

Equation (172), appropriately interpreted (and we have given the essential details of that interpretation above), provides a full description of the relative positions of the diffraction maxima recorded on a photographic plate in an arrangement similar to that of von Laue, Friedrich and Knipping. More importantly, it provides the basis of a new experimental method, that of 'X-ray crystal spectrometry', as we have already asserted.

Suppose that A (fig. 40) represents a crystal mounted so as to be capable of rotation about an axis through P perpendicular to the plane of the diagram. The mounting is such that a set of atom-rich 'reflecting planes' is parallel to the axis of rotation. OP is the direction of incidence of a narrow beam of X-rays, and PQ is the direction of specular reflection from these planes under the conditions as illustrated. B is a suitable recording instrument (ionisation chamber, or other device) mounted on an arm pivoted at P, and arranged so as to accept radiation travelling along PQ. The experimental procedure is to record the intensity of the radiation reaching B as a function of θ, the 'grazing angle of incidence'

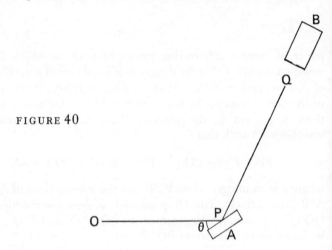

FIGURE 40

relative to the set of reflecting planes employed. In order to achieve this end, B must be rotated about the axis through P in angular steps twice as great as those applied to the rotation of A. (An alternative procedure is to replace B by a strip of photographic film lining the inside of a cylindrical surface coaxial with the crystal turn-table, and to rotate the crystal at a small constant rate during an exposure.) Using an ionisation chamber in an arrangement of the former kind, William Henry Bragg (p. 219), then professor of physics at Leeds, obtained the first X-ray spectrum early in 1913. It should be re-emphasised, at once, that the X-ray spectrum is a diffraction spectrum, as is that obtained with a ruled grating and visible light; thus the complication of successive spectral 'orders' (successive values of n in equation (172)) is inherent in its interpretation. Moreover, in general, the sensitivity of the detector is not limited to a single octave or thereabouts, as the human eye is limited; thus the problem of 'overlapping orders' is a serious one, even for the smallest values of n. W. H. Bragg obtained his first spectrum using the radiation from a low-voltage X-ray tube with a platinum anticathode: with this arrangement he observed a series of sharp 'lines' on a continuous background. By performing absorption measurements on that part of the radiation which was responsible for the lines in his spectrum, he was led to identify it with the characteristic L X-radiation of Barkla.

H. G. J. Moseley's work on the characteristic X-ray spectra of the elements was carried out in two short periods of a few months: during the late summer of 1913, whilst he still held a junior post in Rutherford's laboratory in Manchester, and in the spring of 1914, after he had returned to Oxford. He left Oxford in June of that year, travelling through Canada to attend the meeting of the British Association in Sydney, Australia, enlisted in the army as soon as he was back in England, and was killed on active service in Gallipoli on 10 August 1915. Before he left Manchester, Moseley had photographed the K X-ray spectra of ten of the eleven elements 'occupying consecutive positions' in the periodic table from calcium to zinc inclusive (scandium being the eleventh element, a sample of which he was unable to obtain for use as anticathode in his X-ray tube). His results were published in the *Philosophical Magazine* in December 1913. In the same journal, four months later, he recorded his observations on thirty-eight more elements. He had been able to follow the K series of radiations 'through the periodic table' as far as silver; for elements of greater atomic weight he observed the L series only (compare p. 274). At Sydney he reported still further observations, mostly on the L X-rays of the rare-earth elements, which, as events proved, were never published.

Empirically, the most obvious feature of the spectra that Moseley obtained was that they were essentially of the same structure for all elements. He observed two lines for each element in the K series, and five lines in the L series of radiations. Employing crystals of the same material (potassium ferrocyanide) throughout his investigations, he was able to assign relative values of wavelength (or frequency) to the individual radiations (using equation (172)), thereby achieving a more fundamental method of ordering these radiations than that of Barkla (p. 273). The regular increase of penetrating power (in aluminium), which Barkla had shown to characterise the radiations of either series, as the atomic weight of the radiating element was increased, was shown by Moseley to be paralleled by a correspondingly regular increase in frequency. For the stronger of the two K-series radiations it appeared that the frequency, ν_K, could, with considerable accuracy, be represented by the simple formula

$$\nu_K = k(Z_0 - 1)^2 \tag{173}$$

For the most intense of the L-series radiations, though with somewhat less accuracy,

$$\nu_L = \frac{5k}{27}(Z_0 - 7\cdot4)^2 \tag{174}$$

provided a formal description of the results. In either expression, Z_0 is the ordinal number of the element in the periodic classification and k is a constant.

According to Bohr's theory, as we have seen (equation (167)), the ratio of the frequencies of the radiations corresponding to the transitions $n = 3$ to $n = 2$, and $n = 2$ to $n = 1$, in the neutral hydrogen atom, is precisely 5/27. If the charge number of the nucleus were Z, rather than 1, and there were only a single electron, these two frequencies would stand in the same ratio, but each would be greater than the corresponding frequency in the spectrum of atomic hydrogen by a factor Z^2 (equation (171)). These conclusions from theory begin to resemble the experimental facts as observed by Moseley (equations (173) and (174)). However, Moseley's results referred to the radiation from near-neutral atoms (possibly once or twice ionised, as a result of the cathode-ray bombardment): it was natural, therefore, from the outset, to expect a 'screening correction' to apply. Such a correction would be necessary to represent the effect of the other electrons in the atom (see p. 263). On the basis of this view, then, Moseley's equations (173) and (174) were convincingly interpreted: Z_0, the 'atomic number' of the element in the periodic classification, was identified with Z, the charge number of the nucleus, the two numbers 1 and 7·4 were identified as charge-screening constants in respect of the electron transitions involved in the K series and the L series X-ray emissions, respectively, and these transitions themselves (in respect of the most intense 'line' in each series) were identified as taking place between electron orbits of 2 and 1, and 3 and 2 units of angular momentum, as the case may be.

It has already been necessary more than once in our discussion (pp. 241, 259), to accept the identification of Z_0 and Z without full experimental justification—though we have noted the evidence in favour of this identification which the 'radioactive displacement law' (p. 260) provided. The results of Moseley carried conviction of another order: in the nature of the case, the radioactive displacement law had reference only to the heaviest elements; Moseley's results concerned the entire range, from aluminium ($Z_0 = 13$) to gold ($Z_0 = 79$). Even though the displacement law antedated Moseley's conclusion by a twelvemonth, it must be regarded as confirmatory of that conclusion, rather than independently decisive, in this particular context.

We cannot, in this section, afford the space to continue our historical account of the experiments through which detailed knowledge has been gained of the arrangement of the Z (extranuclear) electrons in an atom of nuclear charge number Z, for all values of Z. Enough has been said, however, to give credibility to the statement that these Z electrons are in some measure distinguishable in terms of the minimum energy which must be supplied to remove any one of them, and so produce a singly-charged positive ion from an originally neutral atom. The experiments of Davis and Goucher (p. 267), and similar experiments of later date, give directly the energy of binding of the least-tightly-bound electron (of the order of 10 electron volts for all atoms); those of Whiddington and Beatty (p. 274), and the investigators who followed them, the energy of binding of the most-tightly-bound electron (of the order of 10^5 electron volts for the heaviest atoms). In principle, values of intermediate ionisation energies might be determined in the same way (by a study of the inelastic collisions of electrons and atoms); in fact, our knowledge concerning them has been built up gradually from a detailed study of the emission and absorption of electromagnetic (quantum) radiations, rather than from investigations with accelerated electrons.

In this connection the most direct overall picture is provided by the absorption experiments. Fig. 41 indicates, schematically, results published in 1955 by B. Lindström of Stockholm. In this figure the variation of μ, the linear absorption coefficient of monochromatic X-rays in platinum ($Z = 78$), is shown as a function of wavelength λ, in a (double) logarithmic plot. With the heavy elements, over the range of wavelength appropriate to the phenomenon under discussion, 'true absorption', rather than scattering (see p. 273), is chiefly responsible for the attenuation of the radiation, and in these circumstances, in general, absorption increases rapidly as the wavelength of the radiation increases (or the

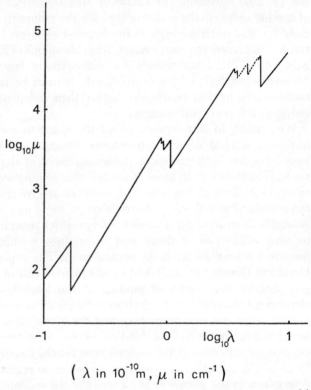

$(\lambda \text{ in } 10^{-10}\text{m}, \mu \text{ in } \text{cm}^{-1})$

FIGURE 41

frequency decreases)—roughly as the third power of the wavelength. At certain critical frequencies, however, there is a discontinuity in the process—an abrupt decrease in absorption, before the general trend is resumed. Empirically, the pattern of this effect is the same for all elements: in order of increasing wavelength the first gross discontinuity is single, the next is a group of three individual discontinuities, the third is a group of five, and so on. ('And so on', here, represents the voice of the theorist: the experimental study of the five-fold discontinuity already calls for technical virtuosity of a high order!)

Physically, the absorption process that we are discussing is a 'photoelectric' process (p. 390); it involves the transfer of the whole energy E from a quantum of incident radiation to an atomic electron according to Planck's equation, $E = h\nu$ (p. 271). For this reason, discontinuous decreases in absorption occur at those frequencies at which the quantum energy E becomes infinitesimally smaller than one or other of the characteristic binding energies of the electrons in the atom of the elementary absorber. In respect of fig. 41, for example, the characteristic energies of binding of individual electrons in the neutral atom of platinum are given by the quantity hc/λ_e, c being the velocity of light, and λ_e taking on the various 'critical' values corresponding to the 'absorption edges' which are evident in the figure. In an absorption experiment, when the wavelength of the incident radiation is smaller than the smallest value of λ_e characteristic of the absorber, secondary ('fluorescent') X-rays are emitted comprising the complete spectrum of characteristic radiations; when the wavelength of the incident radiation is just larger than this value of λ_e, the fluorescent radiation contains all except the K series X-rays, according to Barkla's classification (see p. 274). Similarly, Barkla's L radiations disappear when the incident wavelength becomes larger than the largest of the next group of three critical absorption wavelengths, and the M radiations when the incident wavelength is larger than the largest of the group of five critical wavelengths which is next in order. For this reason the absorption edges, and the corresponding binding energies, have come to be referred to as the K, L, M, . . . edges and binding energies, respectively. To be precise, we use the nomenclature L_I, L_{II}, L_{III}, M_I, . . ., M_V, . . . when we wish to represent the full complexity of the phenomenon.

Conventionally, information concerning X-ray absorption edges and electron binding energies is summarised in the form of an energy-level diagram. A realistic diagram would be one in which energies are exhibited on a linear scale, but the general pattern of energies is such that this is well-nigh impracticable. Table 2 gives the complete list of electron binding energies in respect of the neutral atom of platinum (which we have already taken as example in the present discussion). Quoted values are in electron volts. Clearly, a diagram employing a linear scale of energies is entirely inappropriate in the context of the table. More often than not, in the light of these considerations, a purely schematic representation is resorted to; here we give a systematic representation, though we base it on an arbitrary transformation. In fig. 42 vertical distances (measured downwards) represent the angle θ, linearly, and $\tan \theta = B/B(M_I)$. In this connection B denotes any one of the binding energies listed in the table, and $B(M_I)$ the binding energy corresponding to the M_I absorption discontinuity. It will be noted that fig. 41, having reference only to a restricted range of energies (reciprocal wavelengths), employed a logarithmic scale: such a

TABLE 2

K	78395	N_{II}	609
L_I	13880	N_{III}	519
L_{II}	13273	N_{IV}	331
L_{III}	11564	N_V	313
M_I	3296	O_I	102
M_{II}	3027	N_{VI}	74
M_{III}	2645	N_{VII}	71
M_{IV}	2202	O_{II}	65
M_V	2122	O_{III}	52
N_I	722	P_I	9

scale would have been unsuited to the complete diagram of fig. 42, for which the zero of the energy scale is an essential feature.

According to Chadwick's experiment (p. 259), the number of extranuclear electrons in the neutral atom of platinum is 78: according to the experimental results which we have summarised in table 2, only 20 discrete values of electron binding energy characterise this neutral atom. To reconcile these two numbers it is necessary to assume that some at least of the 'energy levels' are 'populated' by more than one electron—and it would not be unreasonable to conjecture that almost all are of this type. To follow through the experimental evidence bearing on this question would delay us unduly at this stage; here it must suffice to state the conclusions. The first general conclusion is that the number of electrons in any energy level tends to be an even number; the second, for our purposes, relates to the total numbers of electrons in the K, L, M, ... levels when these are 'full'. These numbers are: K, 2; L, 8; M, 18; N, 32, ... In the neutral atom of platinum, the K, L, M and N levels are indeed complete; there are also 17 electrons in O levels, and one electron in a P level.

Taking these facts in relation to the data of table 2, we make the pertinent comment: with 800 eV of energy in the form of a quantum of 'soft' X-rays (or as kinetic energy of a 'bombarding' electron) we can 'reach' and dislodge any one of 50 less-tightly-bound electrons in an atom of platinum; to dislodge either of the two most-tightly-bound electrons (out of the total of 78) we need

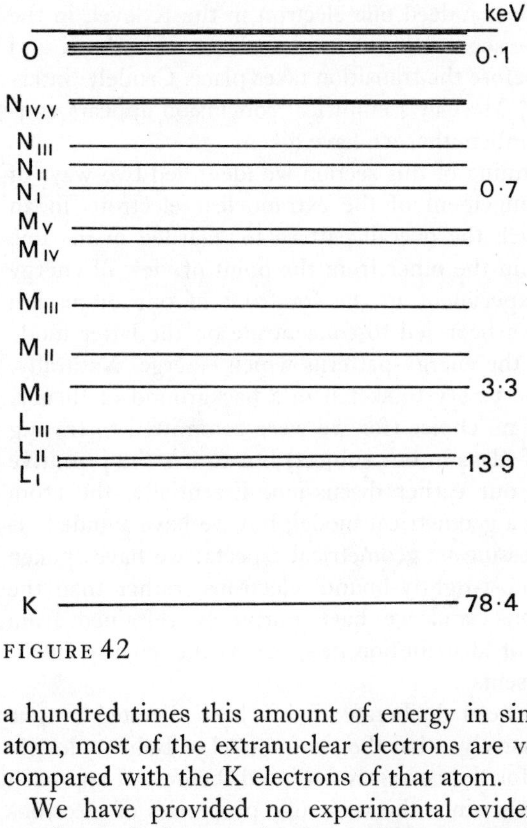

	keV
O	0·1
N$_{IV,V}$	
N$_{III}$	
N$_{II}$	
N$_I$	0·7
M$_V$	
M$_{IV}$	
M$_{III}$	
M$_{II}$	
M$_I$	3·3
L$_{III}$	
L$_{II}$	13·9
L$_I$	
K	78·4

FIGURE 42

a hundred times this amount of energy in similar form. In any atom, most of the extranuclear electrons are very loosely bound, compared with the K electrons of that atom.

We have provided no experimental evidence justifying the numbers of electrons in the various energy levels, as we have quoted them in the last paragraph, but we may, in conclusion, refer back to the 'screening constants' of Moseley which we have already discussed (p. 280). From his empirical results, Moseley concluded that the electron transition responsible for the emission of the 'most abundant' of the characteristic K X-rays takes place, in any atom, in a central field in which the nuclear charge number is effectively diminished by 1; correspondingly, that, for the transition responsible for the emission of the most abundant of the characteristic L X-rays, the nuclear charge number appears less than its actual value by 7·4. In the first case the transition is that of an electron from an L level passing over to occupy a vacancy in the K level, in the second case that of an M electron filling a vacancy in an L level which has previously been ionised. According to our figures, there is indeed one electron in the K level, in the first case, and in the second there are nine electrons in the K and L levels together, before the transition takes place. Crudely 'interpreted' in this way, Moseley's empirical conclusion appears consonant with the numbers that we have given.

At the very beginning of this section we identified two ways of describing the arrangement of the extranuclear electrons in an atom—ways in which the overall pattern is regarded in the one case geometrically, in the other from the point of view of energy values. Keeping experiment in the forefront of our discussion throughout, we have been led to concentrate on the latter mode of description, and the energy-patterns which emerge. Naturally, we have found it necessary to sketch in a background of theory, and in this we had no choice (for we were committed to tracing the development of ideas in our subject) but to use the primitive theory of Bohr in our earlier discussion. Essentially, the atom model of Bohr was a geometrical model, but we have avoided, as far as possible, stressing its geometrical aspects: we have spoken generally of 'the most-tightly-bound' electrons, rather than the 'innermost' electrons—and we have purposely refrained from attaching any idea of 'distribution in space' to the 'energy levels' which fig. 42 represents.

Our caution has been deliberate: it has been dictated by one consideration exclusively—that the atom model of Bohr no longer provides the basis for the currently accepted theoretical approach to our problem. Ever since the wave-like properties of electrons in motion were directly demonstrated by experiment (see $V \& W$, §9.4), theorists have sought to replace the classical mechanics of particles by a mechanics of waves, in so far as small-scale phenomena are concerned. In respect of low-energy processes, at least, wave mechanics is now a fully articulated, and highly successful, formal system. The electron orbits of the old theory no longer feature in the descriptions which the wave-theorist gives of the 'architecture' of atoms: to the extent that this architecture is still described in geometrical terms, these orbits are replaced by volume distributions relative to probability functions. Naïvely, the probability functions may be thought of as specifying volume distributions of charge and current in the extranuclear domain. According to the old view, the simplest structural feature was the electron rotating in a circular orbit around the nucleus; according to present ideas the simplest feature is a spherically symmetrical distribution of electron charge density having the nucleus at its centre. We may note this basic change, which has overtaken the concept of 'simplicity' in this context, with some satisfaction. As a prelude to the discussions of this section we drew attention (p. 261) to the requirement of near-spherical symmetry which the experiments of Rayleigh imposed on any atom model which was to represent satisfactorily the optical behaviour of so simple an atom as the atom of helium.

Here, finally, we must draw the line, and leave the reader to pursue the matter of the arrangement of the extranuclear electrons elsewhere: it is not, after all, our main concern.

6.6. THE STRUCTURE OF THE NUCLEUS

Rutherford's hypothesis—that all but a very small fraction of the total mass of an atom is concentrated in a positively-charged nucleus occupying some 10^{-12} of the whole volume of the atom—is accepted without question today. In this section we wish to refer very briefly to present views regarding the structure of the nucleus. So far, we have merely adduced certain experimental evidence regarding its size, and quite definite information regarding the magnitude of its positive charge; we have also attributed the phenomena of radioactivity to the spontaneous disintegration of nuclei. We wish to attempt to see these facts in some sort of theoretical perspective.

First, in relation to size and positive charge alone: let us accept that the nucleus of an atom of platinum has a radius of, say, 10^{-14} m (p. 255), and a charge of 78 electron charges (pp. 259, 281), say, 1.25×10^{-17} coulomb. Let us imagine a (continuous, as distinct from discrete) charge of this magnitude resident on an ideal spherical conductor of the size of the nucleus. According to equation (22), with $\gamma_0 = 1/4\pi\epsilon_0$ (p. 118), the outwards pressure over the surface of the conductor, resulting from the mutual repulsion of the elements of the distributed charge is $\sigma^2/2\epsilon_0$, σ being the surface density of charge. Substituting the values that we have agreed upon, the magnitude of this pressure is

$$\left(\frac{1 \cdot 25 \times 10^{-17}}{4\pi \times 10^{-28}}\right)^2 / 1 \cdot 77 \times 10^{-11} \text{ newton/m}^2,$$

or, approximately,

$$5 \cdot 6 \times 10^{25} \text{ atmospheres,}$$

for the platinum nucleus.

We were led to the concept of the nucleus by accepting the view (and the detailed experiments of Geiger and Marsden justify this acceptance) that the ordinary law of electrostatic repulsion of charges is valid at distances of separation not many times greater than 'the radius of the nucleus'. Our present calculation involves a trivial extrapolation beyond that limit; it cannot be greatly in error, even though it is based on the crudest of models. Yet the result of it is altogether astonishing—and, numerically, entirely beyond our direct comprehension. Similarly, from the simple fact that, in general, the volume of the nucleus is of the order of 10^{-12} of the volume of the whole atom, we conclude, with even less possibility of error, that the density of 'nuclear matter' is some 10^{12} times the density of the gross matter of common experience, in the solid state. Clearly, we can have no intuitive 'feeling' for the nature and properties of matter which is so highly 'condensed'—and which is able, through the action of 'cohesive' forces that we have yet to understand, to sustain the disruptive forces of electrostatic repulsion of the magnitude that we have indicated.

We have used the term 'nuclear matter', but, so far, only in a loosely descriptive sense. However, the term itself is capable of carrying greater significance than that. In recent years the most systematic information concerning the sizes of nuclei has come from a detailed study of the scattering of high-energy electrons (rather than α-particles). This information indicates that the nuclear volume is fairly accurately proportional to the mass of the nucleus, for all elements—so that there is, indeed, to a good approximation, a unique density, the density of nuclear matter. This is not a precise statement, by any absolute standard, but at least we can say that, whereas the densities of the elementary solid substances of common experience range over a factor of 10, the effective densities of the nuclei of the atoms of these same elements do not differ by more than 10 per cent. from the mean. The densities of solid substances, generally, reflect, in fact, the different degrees of spatial extension which characterise the extranuclear structures of the isolated atoms (which structures we have discussed in the last section): the densities of atom nuclei, differing so little from one nucleus to another, bespeak a cohesive force of a type of which we have not hitherto had evidence in any other context.

That the cohesive force responsible for the condensation of nuclear matter is of an unfamiliar type is evident from the outset. In the macroscopic world we are familiar with only one force which is uniformly attractive in all situations, namely, the force of gravitation. However, simple calculation will show that as between particles having the charge-and-mass characteristics of atomic nuclei (see p. 246) the ratio between electrostatic repulsion and gravitational attraction is of the order of 10^{36}. Atomic nuclei, clearly, are not held together by gravitational attraction. Moreover, we must postulate a force which effectively operates only within the nucleus; it cannot be thought of as acting on the extranuclear electrons. An eminently successful theory of the behaviour of these electrons, giving remarkably exact numerical agreement with the results of experiment, has been built up without any consideration of such a force. Obviously, the first question to ask is: what are the structural units whose nature it is that they should attract one another in this way, at separations of 10^{-14} m or less?

Let us look at the experimental facts, without prejudice. Our main lead comes from the relative values of the specific charge (e/m) of the (singly-charged) positive ions of the various elements as determined by electric and magnetic deflection experiments. J. J. Thomson had been the pioneer in this field of investigation, over the years 1906 to 1914; thereafter the first systematic results of adequate precision were due to Francis William Aston (1877-1945). Aston, who had followed G. W. C. Kaye (see p. 274) as Thomson's assistant, in 1910, had served his apprenticeship with the original 'parabola method' of 'positive-ray analysis' until the outbreak of war in 1914. Returning to Cambridge in 1919, he built himself a new 'mass spectrograph' of different design,* and

---

* In Thomson's parabola method (first used by Kaufmann with electrons in 1901) the positive ions passed through superposed electric and magnetic

from that date, for twenty years, he worked alone, without assistant or pupil, extending his analyses to cover the whole range of known elements and gradually refining the accuracy of his determinations.

Aston's first 'qualitative' discovery was the discovery of 'isotopes'. With very many elements, more than one species of singly-charged positive ion was found to be recorded on his photographs. In explanation of these findings it was necessary to suppose that, for these elements, all the atoms of a given element have not the same mass—or, more precisely, that different values of nuclear mass may be found associated with the same value of nuclear charge. Already, in 1913, on the basis of quite different evidence, Soddy had identified the same phenomenon with the radioactive disintegration products of uranium and thorium—and had introduced the term 'isotopes' (in the plural) to describe it. In the radioactive disintegration series of which uranium and thorium are the parent members, there are various sequences of three transformations in which, overall, one α-particle and two β-particles are emitted (in whatever order is of no consequence). According to the radioactive displacement laws (p. 260) the combined result of three such transformations is that the product which undergoes the first transformation and that which remains after the third belong to 'the same place' in the periodic table of the elements. These two products are 'isotopes' according to Soddy's terminology: manifestly the atoms of the two products differ in mass— moreover, as the displacement laws imply, the two products are chemically indistinguishable.

By 1927 the main results of Aston's investigations were already clearly established. He had succeeded in obtaining the positive ions of more than fifty elements, and in recording their mass spectra—in favourable cases deducing relative mass values with an accuracy of 1 part in 10^4. (When this accuracy is attained, it becomes significant, with the very lightest elements, to correct the

fields applied in the same direction at right angles to the direction of motion of the ions; in Aston's mass spectrograph the ions passed first through a transverse electric field, then through a transverse magnetic field, the two field directions being mutually perpendicular in this case. In Thomson's arrangement, on a photographic plate placed perpendicular to the original direction of motion of the ions, the locus of the points of arrival of ions of different velocities but the same specific charge was a portion of a parabola; in Aston's arrangement, with the fields suitably adjusted, and the photographic plate positioned appropriately, ions of the same specific charge, having velocities distributed over a considerable range, were focused so as to produce a line image of the entrance slit, for any value of e/m.

ratio of the masses of the singly-charged ions for the mass of the 'missing' electrons in order to deduce the mass ratio for the corresponding neutral atoms.)

Originally, in 'atomic weight' determinations, gravimetric chemists expressed their results on the hydrogen scale, setting the atomic weight of elementary hydrogen as unity. For the very practical reason that many more elements enter into direct combination with oxygen (yielding 'well-behaved' compounds) than give rise to manageable hydrides, Jean Servais Stas (1813-1891), professor of chemistry at the Royal Military Academy in Brussels, introduced the oxygen standard in his own extensive work in this field over the years 1860 to 1865. In order that previously accepted values should need the minimum of adjustment, Stas fixed the atomic weight of oxygen as precisely 16. Aston reduced his observations adopting each of these standards in turn. (In 1927 there was no evidence to indicate that hydrogen and oxygen were other than simple elements.) According to the first method of reduction, he assigned the value 1 atomic mass unit, precisely, to the mass of the neutral atom corresponding to the singly-charged hydrogen ion recorded on his mass-spectra; according to the second method, the value 16 a.m.u. to the mass of the neutral atom of oxygen correspondingly represented. On the basis of the hydrogen standard no self-evident numerical regularity emerged from his calculations; on the basis of the oxygen standard, on the other hand, it was immediately evident that the measures of the masses of the neutral atoms of all the various atomic species were very nearly integral. The mass of the hydrogen atom on this scale was 1·008, or thereabouts, and even for the heaviest atom studied (that of bismuth) the deviation from the 'whole number rule' was barely outside the limits of experimental uncertainty at the time. Nowadays, we generally employ the symbol M to represent the mass of a neutral atom in atomic mass units (either on the basis of the oxygen standard, or by assigning the precise value 12 a.m.u. to the mass of the neutral atom of the most abundant isotope of carbon), and we denote by A the integer nearest to M. A, uniquely defined in this way, we refer to as the mass number of the atom (or nucleus) concerned.

Even before this degree of formalism came to be adopted, Aston's 'whole number rule' was widely interpreted as indicating that atomic nuclei generally are composite structures based, at the most, on a very small number of different types of structural unit. In this connection it was natural that attention should first be focused on the hydrogen nucleus itself as a possible common constituent of more complex nuclei. To this extent there was a return to Prout's hypothesis (1815)—transferred from Dalton's atom to Rutherford's nucleus, and rendered more credible in the process.* In 1920, echoing this discarded hypothesis of the chem-ists, the early nuclear physicists had adopted the name 'proton' to designate the hydrogen nucleus in isolation. In so doing they were espousing the view that protons are common constituents of nuclei generally. Only a year previously Rutherford had published the first account of an observation indicating that atomic nuclei may suffer transformation other than spontaneously in radioactive dis-integration. The nuclei of helium (of mass number 4) and nitrogen (of mass number 14) are perfectly stable under ordinary conditions, but Rutherford found evidence that when these two nuclei collide, in circumstances in which their energy of relative motion is of the order of several million electron volts, a hydrogen nucleus (proton) may be released as a result of the collision.

Briefly, Rutherford's experiment consisted in allowing the α-particles from a radioactive source to pass through various gases and in searching for the possible projection of particles of range greater than the range of the α-particles themselves. Only with nitrogen, among the simple gases which he used (oxygen, carbon dioxide and helium) did Rutherford find any such particles whose presence could not be explained away as due to 'trivial' causes. Over the period 1920 to 1925, Rutherford and Chadwick found similar positive effects with most of the elements from boron to potassium, and in 1925 P.M.S. Blackett (b. 1897) succeeded in recording individual transformation events in nitrogen by C.T.R. Wilson's method of cloud-track photography (see p. 311). As a result of these many investigations it had become clear, by 1927, that artificially produced nuclear transformation was no mere

---

* William Prout (1785-1850), a London physician, suggested that the atoms of all substances might be regarded as condensations of atoms of hydrogen, being led to this view by the fact that atomic weights, as then imperfectly known, were in many cases very nearly integral on the hydrogen scale. Among the later gravimetric chemists, Stas, in particular, was predisposed to Prout's opinion, but eventually he denounced it as pure illusion, unable as he was to reconcile his own most careful determinations (see above) with the predictions which appeared to issue from it. However, some twenty years later, long after he had resigned from his professorship, he returned to the subject: 'One cannot escape the belief', he wrote, 'that there is something at the bottom of it all'.

alchemist's dream, and, in particular, that in all cases which had then been investigated a single statement adequately described the phenomena which had been observed. In all these cases it appeared that momentarily, as a result of the nuclear collision, the α-particle and the 'target' nucleus had coalesced in a single system which almost immediately had disintegrated, emitting a proton in the process. In the case of nitrogen, in the standard formalism of the present day, the overall process is represented:

$$^{14}_{7}\text{N} + ^{4}_{2}\text{He} \rightarrow ^{17}_{8}\text{O} + ^{1}_{1}\text{H}.$$

In this representation the ordinary chemical symbols are given subscripts (strictly superfluous in the context) specifying the charge numbers (Z) of the nuclei concerned—and superscripts specifying the mass numbers (A) as already defined (p. 291).

In summary, then, in 1927, there was direct experimental evidence for the emission of protons, from some nuclei, in processes of artificial transformation, and for the emission of negative electrons and α-particles (helium nuclei) from others in spontaneous processes of radioactive change. To make the simplest hypothesis, on the basis of this evidence, was to suppose that protons and negative electrons are the fundamental constituent particles of nuclei generally, the α-particle comprising four protons and two electrons—and any nucleus, indeed, A protons and $A - Z$ electrons. On this assumption, certainly, the correct value of the nuclear charge would be ensured, and it could be accepted as a fact of experience (calling for 'explanation') that the actual mass of a complex nucleus is in general less than the sum of the masses of its constituent particles (by something less than 1 per cent.—a fraction varying very little from one nucleus to another).

Let us dispose, first of all, of this question of 'mass defect', for it is of more general significance than the particular hypothesis which has brought it to our attention. As we have already stated (footnote, p. 289), Kaufmann was the first to use the method of crossed deflections ('parabola method')—in order to determine the specific charge of the electron. Using a radioactive preparation as a source of β-particles (electrons) characterised by a wide spectrum of (high) velocities, he found (1901) that the specific charge was smaller at high velocities than at low (the continuous trace on his photographic plate was not simply parabolic). This effect was not unexpected, indeed it had been foreseen as a possibility by Thomson as early as 1881. Developing the classical view (see p. 141) that the establishment of an electric current—or the setting of a charge in steady motion—involves the storage of electromagnetic energy in the surrounding medium, Thomson had shown that the amount of energy so stored (in the case of the moving charge) is proportional to the square of the velocity, when the velocity is negligible compared with the velocity at which electromagnetic disturbances are propagated, but that the stored energy increases more rapidly than the square of the velocity when the velocity of the moving charge becomes comparable with the propagation velocity. The stored energy which Thomson evaluated represented an amount of work (proportional to the square of the charge and inversely proportional to its linear dimension) which had been performed— in the thought experiment—when the charge was set in motion. In Newtonian mechanics, in order that a particle shall be set in steady motion, an amount of work given by one half the product of the mass and the square of the velocity must be performed. Thomson concluded, therefore, that a charged particle must behave as if it has 'electromagnetic mass' proportional to the square of its charge—and as if this mass increases as the velocity of the particle approaches the velocity of light. Once the negative electron had been discovered, it was speculated that the whole of its inertial mass might be electromagnetic in origin—and it was pointed out that this could well be the case if the radius of the electron was of the order of 10^{-15} m. Kaufmann's (not very precise) observations were not inconsistent with this point of view.

Classical electromagnetic theory predicts that, in so far as the inertial mass of a charged particle (or, for that matter, a neutral particle possessing an electric dipole moment) is electromagnetic in origin, the effective mass will increase as the kinetic energy of the particle increases. According to the special theory of relativity of Einstein (see $ML \, \& \, T$, p. 134), inertial mass in general is velocity-dependent; further than this, according to Einstein's theory (1905), when the energy of any system is increased (be the increase in the form of kinetic or potential energy) the inertial mass of the system increases proportionately. Einstein's result is simply expressed:

$$\Delta E = c^2 \Delta m \qquad\qquad (175)$$

Here ΔE is the increment of energy, c is the velocity of light, and

Δm is the amount by which the inertial mass increases. Briefly, the basis from which this result issues is the belief (or conviction) that the conservation laws of dynamics express a fundamental truth regarding the real world—and that this truth should be equally discernible by any competent observer, whatever be his state of uniform motion with respect to the physical systems on which his observations are made.

The first to draw attention to Einstein's result in relation to the problem of nuclear structure was R. Swinne (1913). In respect of any composite system in an equilibrium configuration, it is a truism to say that energy must be supplied to the system in order to separate its component parts and bring them 'to rest at infinity'. On the basis of Einstein's result this statement implies that the total mass of the infinitely dispersed system is greater than the mass of the system in its previously condensed form, or, simply, that the mass of any such composite system is less than the sum of the masses of its constituent particles in the free state. Swinne pointed out that for the first time there was a possibility of testing equation (175) in relation to radioactive phenomena. Translated into conventional units, equation (175) reads:

1 atomic mass unit is equivalent to
931 million electron volts of energy.

Radioactive disintegration energies (in α-particle disintegration) may approach 9 MeV; thus in single disintegration processes 'disappearances of mass' of the order of 0·01 a.m.u. are to be expected.

These predictions were fully confirmed by A. J. Dempster in 1936. Dempster was the first to obtain the mass spectra of uranium, thorium and lead under conditions of high resolution. In this way he was able to deduce the difference in mass between the neutral atoms of $^{238}_{92}$U and $^{206}_{82}$Pb—the parent species and ultimate stable end-product of the uranium disintegration series—and correspondingly for $^{232}_{90}$Th and $^{208}_{82}$Pb, the first and last products of the thorium series. In the one case the difference was greater than the mass of eight neutral helium atoms by 0·056 a.m.u., in the other it was greater than the mass of six neutral helium atoms by 0·046 a.m.u. These were precisely the differences expected from a knowledge of the total amount of kinetic energy associated with the α-particles and β-particles emitted in the various disintegrations (these α-particles and β-particles, together with the extranuclear electrons 'lost' during the transformation processes, effectively make up the eight or six neutral helium atoms, as the case may be). Nowadays, there is an abundance of evidence, from all manner of spontaneous and artificially-contrived nuclear processes, for the validity of Einstein's relation in the nuclear context. Without more ado, therefore, we shall use it to interpret the 'mass defects' of nuclei in terms of the total energy of binding of all the particles out of which these nuclei are constituted.

With this point established, let us return to the problem of the identification of the nuclear constituent particles themselves. We have already canvassed the suggestion that complex nuclei are constituted of protons and electrons—A protons and $A - Z$ electrons in a nucleus of mass number A and charge number Z. In 1917, W. D. Harkins (1873-1951), of the university of Chicago, pointed out that nearly 90 per cent. of the material of the earth's crust is composed of elements of which the charge number is even. Ten years later, when Aston's first mass-survey was complete, it became clear that among these even-charge-numbered elements stable isotopes of even mass number greatly outnumber those of odd mass number. We now know that this preponderance is in the ratio of $3:1$, or slightly greater. More importantly, perhaps, we know, also, that among elements of odd charge number (at least for $Z > 7$) in no case is there certainly a stable isotope of even mass number. These are particular regularities—and there are others of similar import: overall we conclude that the distinction between odd and even (and it can only be in relation to the numbers of constituent particles of the various kinds) is an important distinction in relation to the problem of nuclear stability.

Regarded from the point of view of the proton-electron model, this matter of odd-even discrimination appears somewhat perplexing. The most stable species, it seems, are those for which A and Z are both even, and, consequently, those for which the numbers of protons and electrons are likewise even numbers. On the other hand, the least stable species (with Z odd and A even) are those containing an even number of protons and an odd number of electrons. If we were to accept this analysis at its face value, we should conclude that the matter of stability is decided primarily by the parity or imparity of the number of electrons in the nucleus. However, to set against this conclusion, we should have to record the fact that the distribution of species of odd mass number follows precisely the same pattern, whether Z is odd or even (no element, save only tin, has more than two stable isotopes of odd A—and, except in four cases, every element up to bismuth has at least one). In so far as concerns the species of odd A, therefore, we should be led to suppose that the parity or imparity of the electron number is of no significance (in this case the electron number is odd when Z is even and even when Z is odd). In summary, then, no consistent interpretative pattern emerges: the distinction between odd and even numbers of nuclear particles permits of no satisfactory rationalisation of the empirical data on the basis of the proton-electron model of nuclear structure.

In 1932 the proton-electron model was abandoned as a result of a new experimental discovery—that an uncharged particle of mass number 1 (rather than a proton) is sometimes set free in transformation collisions of α-particles with other nuclei. The idea of such a 'neutron' had been entertained speculatively for some time previously. In February 1920, Harkins, in continuation of a series of publications, to one of which we have already referred (see above), took note of Aston's first published results in a long paper in the *Physical Review*. He suggested that a neutral particle, a combination of two hydrogen nuclei and two electrons, might be an important constituent of heavier nuclei. Later in the same year, he envisaged the possibility of neutral particles having 'masses 4, 3, 2 and 1, and possibly other values'. On 3 June 1920, for the second time in his career (the first had been in 1904), Rutherford gave a Bakerian lecture at the invitation of the Royal Society of London. His title was 'Nuclear constitution of atoms'. In the published version, which appeared in print in the following month, we can read of his cautious speculations in the same direction: 'it seems very likely that one electron can also bind two H nuclei and possibly also one H nucleus. . . . In the [latter] case, [this] involves the idea of the possible existence of an atom of mass 1 which has zero nucleus charge. . . . The existence of such atoms seems almost necessary to explain the building up of the nuclei of heavy elements'. Again, in the same year, and independently, David Orme Masson (1858-1937), professor of chemistry in the university of Melbourne, Australia, wrote of the possibility of a singly-charged particle of mass number 2 'as a secondary unit of positive charge'—and of an electrically neutral 'couplet' of unit mass. Masson's paper was published in the *Philosophical Magazine* in February 1921.

During the years 1921 and 1922 experiments were carried out in Rutherford's laboratory in an attempt to test the idea that neutrons might be produced, by the close combination of protons and electrons, in the hydrogen discharge. No evidence was found of any penetrating radiation of unusual properties, or any un-identifiable escape of energy. Then, ten years later, when it must have seemed even to Rutherford himself that his hypothetical neutron was still-born, again in Rutherford's own laboratory, Chadwick identified the highly penetrating radiation emitted by beryllium under α-particle bombardment as a neutron radiation:

$$\ce{_4^9Be} + \ce{_2^4He} \rightarrow \ce{_6^{12}C} + \ce{_0^1n}.$$

Until 1930 no evidence had been obtained of any nuclear trans-mutation resulting from the α-particle bombardment of beryllium. Then Walter W. G. F. Bothe (1891-1957) and H. Becker in Berlin reported that a radiation at least as penetrating as any known photon radiation (γ-rays) could be observed, even when the energy of the incident α-particles was quite small. Following up an observation made by Irène Curie (1897-1956) and Frédéric Joliot (1900-1958) in Paris, Chadwick showed that the penetrating radia-tion from beryllium was capable of transferring energy, in simple collision processes, to the nuclei of atoms of whatever substance was placed in its path. On this basis he devised a simple experi-mental method of deciding whether the whole of the radiation was a photon radiation, as Curie and Joliot supposed, or whether the effect which they had observed was due to a 'heavy' neutral particle component of previously unrecognised character. He determined the maximum amount of energy transferred, in collisions with the nuclei of various atoms, from hydrogen to argon. Assuming only the validity of the laws of conservation of momentum and energy, he was able, in relation to each assumption in turn, to obtain a value for the energy which the photon (or particle) had to possess in order to explain the observations in each case. It became clear, immediately, that no self-consistent explanation was possible on the photon hypothesis—the requisite photon energy was widely different when it was calculated in relation to collisions in hydrogen from what it was when calculated, for example, in relation to collisions in nitrogen. On the other hand, a perfectly satisfactory explanation was possible on the neutral particle hypothesis—

provided that the mass of the particle were assumed to be very closely the same as the proton mass. Chadwick had, indeed, discovered the neutron (of mass number 1) by direct experiment, and the circumstances of his discovery invited the conclusion that this neutral particle was one of the common constituent particles of nuclei generally (almost immediately many other examples of neutron emission under α-particle bombardment were incontrovertibly established).

On the basis of the proton-neutron model of nuclear structure, a nucleus of mass number A and charge number Z contains Z protons and $A - Z$ neutrons. When both A and Z are even, therefore, both the proton number and the neutron number are even numbers; when A is even and Z odd, both the proton number and the neutron number are odd numbers. One of these numbers is odd and the other even when A is odd, whether Z is even or odd. On this basis, the regularities regarding isotopic abundance (p. 296) which the proton-electron model was unable to illuminate, fall into intelligible order: for either nuclear constituent, independently of the other, an even total number of particles tends to confer greater stability, an odd total number less stability, on any nuclear species whatever. It would take us too far from our course to follow up the various other points of comparison of the two models; suffice to repeat that, since 1932, the proton-electron model has ceased to be of more than historical interest.

For our purposes, then, the intense cohesive forces effective within the nuclei of atoms are to be regarded as operating in highly condensed systems of protons and neutrons. The simplest such system, consisting of one proton and one neutron, is the nucleus of the atom of deuterium, the hydrogen isotope of mass number 2. This isotope (present in ordinary hydrogen to the extent of 1·5 atoms per 10^4 atoms of ^1_1H) was discovered by Harold Clayton Urey (b. 1893) and collaborators in 1932. In 1934, Chadwick and M. Goldhaber showed that neutrons are liberated when γ-rays of sufficient quantum energy are used to irradiate deuterium gas. Subsequent study of this first example of a 'nuclear photoelectric effect' has given an accurate value of the minimum amount of energy which is necessary to effect this disintegration—and, therefore, an accurate value of the mass defect of the deuterium nucleus ('deuteron'). Taking this determination together with the mass-spectrographic determinations of the masses of the singly-charged ions of the two hydrogen isotopes, we eventually deduce the individual masses of the neutral atom of 'light' hydrogen and the neutron, separately. Currently accepted values, in atomic mass units on the oxygen scale, are

$$^{1}_{1}\text{H}, \ 1.008145; \ ^{1}_{0}\text{n}, \ 1.008985.$$

Once the masses of the constituent particles are accurately known, values of the mass defects of all other nuclei can be calculated from their measured masses (negligible error, for our present purposes, is introduced if neutral-atom masses are used throughout, and the neutral atom $^{1}_{1}\text{H}$, rather than the proton, is regarded as the constituent particle responsible for the whole of the positive and negative charge in any complex atom). Broadly speaking, when these calculations are carried out, the empirical fact that atomic masses in general are almost exactly integral on the oxygen scale (pp. 291, 293) leads to the result that the mass defect (and so the total binding energy of any nucleus) is fairly closely proportional to A, the total number of particles in the nucleus. This is a very important conclusion. It suggests, straight away, that in respect of the cohesive forces (to which the energy-loss in nuclear synthesis must be attributed) protons and neutrons are equivalent particles—and it has a more specific implication which we must briefly consider.

In order to clarify our ideas, let us refer again to the case of gravitational attraction which we have mentioned already (p. 289). Let us imagine a uniform sphere of material of density ρ to be assembled, atom by atom, out of an infinitely dispersed cloud of 'vapour'. When a stage has been reached at which the radius of the sphere is r, the gravitational potential (p. 27) at the surface of the sphere is $-\frac{4}{3} \pi r^2 G \rho$, G being the measure of the constant of gravitation. During the process of 'condensation' of the next layer of material, of thickness dr, gravitational potential energy is therefore 'lost' in amount

$$\tfrac{4}{3} \pi r^2 G \rho . 4\pi r^2 \rho \ dr,$$

and the total loss ($-W$, compare p. 262), when the radius of the sphere has reached its final value a, is given by

$$-W = \int_0^a \tfrac{16}{3} \pi^2 G \rho^2 r^4 \ dr,$$

$$= \tfrac{16}{15} \pi^2 G \rho^2 a^5.$$

If M is the total mass of the material condensed, we have

$$- W = \tfrac{3}{5} \frac{GM^2}{a} \tag{176}$$

Equation (176) gives the measure of the energy of binding, which is derived from the operation of the attractive force of gravitation, of a uniform spherical body of mass M and radius a. We note that this binding energy is proportional to M^2—that is, to the square of the number of gravitating particles ('atoms') in the body. Clearly, the same result would be obtained in relation to the operation of any other 'universal' force, if by this adjective we imply that the force is such that 'every particle in the universe acts on every other particle', without discrimination. By and large, as we have seen, the total binding energy of an atomic nucleus is directly proportional to the first power of the number of inter-acting particles in the nucleus; obviously, then, the nuclear co-hesive force is not a 'universal' force in the sense that we have defined.

In attempting to understand—that is, to become more familiar with—the characteristics of this 'unconventional' force, we may note one striking fact of experience. Stable species are known having all values of the mass number A from 1 to 209, except that no such species exists for which $A = 5$, or $A = 8$. In respect of the first exception, we may comment, in colloquial terms, that it appears that neither an additional proton, nor an additional neutron, will 'stick' if presented to a helium nucleus of mass number 4; in respect of the second, we may say, similarly, that two such nuclei (α-particles), brought into intimate contact, will not cohere, either. In these simple empirical results there is very clear evidence that the residual nuclear cohesive force effective outside a group of two neutrons and two protons organised as an α-particle is very small by appropriate standards. Having established this conclusion, we need only add that if the range of action of the cohesive force is of the order of magnitude of the radius of the α-particle—so that it is small compared with the radius of a fairly complex nucleus, it is not altogether surprising that the total energy of binding of such a nucleus, arising through the operation of this force, is proportional to the total number of particles involved. It would be out of place to say more than this, in this context.

The general success of the proton-neutron model of nuclear

structure, sketched and exemplified in the brief account which has just been given, must not be allowed to obscure one aspect of difficulty which should not be overlooked. In accepting a model based upon 'heavy' particles exclusively, we have still to provide a rational description of the process of radioactive β-disintegration within the conceptual framework of our model. An electron is emitted from the radioactive nucleus in this process; according to our model, there are no electrons in the nucleus. Again, we appeal to direct experiment, in order to find a way out of this verbal paradox. The experimental fact is that the neutron, itself, is β-active in the free state. In 1951, J. S. Robson found negative electrons (and protons) appearing along the path of a beam of neutrons travelling 'in vacuum' from a nuclear reactor. Dealing quantitatively with his observations, he showed that the characteristic half-value period for neutron disintegration is 12·5 minutes —and that the energy released in the process is 0·782 MeV, as the values of the 'exact' masses of neutron and hydrogen atom (proton plus negative electron) that we have already quoted (p. 300) would lead us to predict.* We conclude, simply, that the problem of β-disintegration is more subtle than we supposed: the underlying similitude of neutron and proton is basic for its further consideration, the condition that electrons shall exist as structural units in nuclei is altogether irrelevant. To this gloss, only one further comment is appropriate here. For most nuclei—even for most β-active nuclei—the average deficit of energy, for each neutron bound in the nuclear structure, is some ten times greater than the β-disintegration energy of the free neutron. From that point of view there is no mystery in the fact that such nuclei are permanent (or quasi-permanent) structures. A complex nucleus of mass number A and charge number Z is β-active not because, in that context, the neutron is itself an unstable particle (which it is in the free state) but because the 'neighbouring' nucleus of mass number A and charge number $Z+1$, together with a negative electron, represents a system of less mass than the other. Internal energy is available for the transformation—and there is always the chance that that energy will 'become concentrated on a single neutron', and that disintegration will occur. In that event, one

---

* In this connection it should be pointed out that the neutron of Chadwick's discovery is different from the neutron of Rutherford's speculation, which was assumed to be stable against electron emission.

neutron in the original nucleus will have so changed its character as to become a proton, a negative electron having been 'created' in the process. Self-evidently, this is not a complete—or completely satisfying—description, but it takes us as far as we need to go within the limits of our present survey.

Our general topic is electricity and matter. In terms of mass, all but a minute fraction of the matter of the universe is nuclear matter, constituted, according to our naïve categories of description, of protons and neutrons. The essential forces of cohesion binding these particles together are non-electrical—that is, neither electrostatic nor electromagnetic forces as we understand these terms. On the other hand, when electric charges appear, as they do in the β-disintegration of the neutron, we cannot pretend that the phenomenon is irrelevant to our subject. Even neutron-behaviour cannot be subsumed in terms of non-electrical categories entirely. 'Tell me what electricity is', wrote Kelvin, more than a hundred years ago (p. 158), 'and I'll tell you everything else.' Quite clearly Kelvin's viewpoint was mistaken, but his question still stands unanswered after a century's endeavour.

6.7. THE FUNDAMENTAL UNIT OF CHARGE

The fundamental natural unit of electric charge is the charge of the electron. Apart from the question of sign, it is also the charge of the proton, half the charge of the α-particle, or the whole—or, alternatively, some integral sub-multiple—of the charge associated with any ion in an ionised gas or a volume of electrolyte. This is a comprehensive statement: on analysis it may be held to have more of the character of a statement of belief than of a summary of ascertained fact. Matter in the ordinary state is devoid of charge; it is constituted of atoms themselves devoid of net charge when free from extraneous influence; each atom is constituted of a positively-charged nucleus and negative electrons; an ion is an atom (or group of atoms) which has temporarily lost one or more of its extra-nuclear electrons—if all these propositions are accepted, then our 'comprehensive statement' takes on the character of a truism.

Possibly these comments on our original statement appear to the reader as merely confusing—or, at the least, as unnecessarily pedantic. They have, however, been introduced, deliberately, as a caution against misunderstanding. For the fact is that it is very difficult to determine the charge of the electron, with any high

degree of precision, by a direct experiment. Values of the fundamental unit of charge have been deduced by a variety of more or
less indirect methods (relying on one or other of the assertions
made in our statement of equivalence), and the mutual agreement of
these values leads us to suppose that what has been determined is
indeed the same quantity as the charge of the electron. The brief
summary of experimental investigations, to which this section is
devoted, will be developed from this particular point of view.

We have already described (p. 251) the first direct determination
of the charge of the α-particle by Rutherford and Geiger in 1908,
and have quoted the value of the electron charge $(1\cdot55 \times 10^{-19}$
coulomb) which these authors deduced from their experiments.
This determination, it will be recalled, involved three sets of
measurements: estimation of the mean rate of emission of α-par-
ticles by a weak source, measurement of the rate of transfer of
charge by the α-particles from a much stronger source, and a
comparison of the 'strengths' of the two sources (in terms of their
γ-ray activities). Because no more direct method of charge determination is possible (given the orders of magnitude involved), we
give pride of place to this method in our survey. The introduction
of 'modern' electronic devices as an aid to particle detection and
counting can be dated fairly precisely in 1927. It is not surprising
that shortly thereafter attempts should have been made, in more
than one laboratory, to increase the accuracy of the determination
of the α-particle charge by adapting this classical method to their
use. In Rutherford's laboratory this re-determination was completed in 1929. The value of the electron charge to which it led
was $(1\cdot60 \pm 0\cdot01) \times 10^{-19}$ coulomb.

In the last paragraph we were careful to refer to the 'mean rate
of emission of α-particles'—and to use the term 'estimation',
rather than 'measurement', in the same context. Radioactive disintegration, by nature a spontaneous process, is intrinsically un-
predictable in the ultimate analysis; the fundamental law of
radioactive change (equation (146)) gives merely the most probable
number of disintegrations in a given source in a specified interval
of time. In any actual situation, and in respect of any single period
of observation, the observed number of disintegrations is unlikely
to be precisely this most probable number; in any series of equivalent observations the observed numbers will exhibit 'statistical
fluctuations', which will be relatively the more serious the weaker

the source (and so the smaller the most probable number of dis-integrations in a single period of observation of standard length). The classical method of determining the charge of the α-particle necessarily involves the use of weak sources for the counting experiment, as we have seen; its overall accuracy is limited by the statistical fluctuations which are inevitable in such situations.

If a steady, but 'strictly random', sequence of events is counted over a very large number, N, of consecutive observation periods of constant duration, if n is the number of events recorded in any such period and n_0 is the mean value of n over the whole series of observations, then, more precisely as N is increased, will it be found that

$$\sum_N (n - n_0)^2 \to N n_0.$$

If an 'event' is the arrival, on a collecting electrode, of a charged particle carrying a charge e, and if q is the total charge so collected in a single observation period, as above described, correspondingly, we may predict that, in the limit of large N,

$$\sum_N (q - q_0)^2 = N e q_0 \tag{177}$$

Obviously, equation (177) points the way to a possible method of charge determination in which the intrinsic fluctuations of a random process are made use of—rather than regarded as a nuisance. Equally obviously, it is not a method which in practice can easily be applied with high precision. In fact, in the case of the negative electron, it is the most direct method which has been applied with any measure of success. The temperature-dependent emission of electrons from the surface of an incandescent metal (p. 396) is believed to be a random process: if such a source of electrons is mounted in an evacuated vessel, and if the potential difference between this source and a collecting electrode is suffi-ciently great that the rate of collection is not 'space-charge limited' (see p. 265), the individual values of the charge collected in con-secutive equal periods will be so distributed about the mean that equation (177) will apply. In that case all that is needed for an evaluation of the charge of the electron is that the mean-square deviation of the charge collected shall be divided by the mean value of the collected charge (in respect of the time interval chosen for the analysis of the experimental results). By an experimental method which in principle was precisely as we have indicated—but in fact very much more complicated—N. H. Williams and H. B. Vincent, of the university of Michigan, determined the charge on the electron as $1 \cdot 59 \times 10^{-19}$ coulomb, to an estimated 1 per cent. accuracy, in 1926.

By comparison with the direct methods that we have just described, indirect methods of determining the magnitude of the fundamental unit of charge have an accuracy greater by two or three orders of magnitude. As we shall see, the most accurate method essentially determines the charge on that conceptually generalised entity 'the univalent ion in electrolysis'; the next most accurate the charge on a gaseous ion of arbitrary provenance. This being the case, it is instructive to refer to an early experiment of John Sealey Edward Townsend (1868-1957), professor of experimental physics in the university of Oxford from 1900 to 1941. In 1899, as a pupil of Thomson at Cambridge, Townsend had made the first systematic study, experimental and theoretical, of the diffusion of ions in gases. He showed, then, that there exists a formal connection between the coefficient of diffusion and the mobility (p. 185) of ions generally; nine years later he published an account of a very elegant experiment in which this relationship was made the basis of a direct demonstration (given one particular assumption) of the identity, or near identity, of the charge on a gaseous ion with that on the univalent ion in electrolysis. It cannot be claimed that Townsend's numerical precision was better than a few per cent., but his experimental method was basically so simple (though complicated in the incidental mathematical analysis in terms of which the results were evaluated) that his investigation remains important in its own right.

Gaseous diffusion is the process by which local variations of concentration of any component of a gas mixture (or, indeed of the molecules of a pure gas) become obliterated with the passage of time. If, for example, the concentration of ions of a particular type, in an ionised gas, is, at any instant, a function of one spatial co-ordinate only, there will be, at that instant, a drift of ions in the corresponding direction, tending to equalise the ionic concentration everywhere. In this simple case, u, the effective drift velocity of the ions, is given by

$$nu = -D \frac{dn}{dx} \qquad (178)$$

In equation (178) n is the number of ions (of the specified type) per unit volume (the ionic concentration), assumed to be, instantaneously, a function of x only, and D is defined, in terms of the equation, as the coefficient of diffusion of the ions through the gas in question.

The concept and the measure of 'mobility' have already been adequately discussed (p. 186). Numerically, the mobility of an ion in a given gas is the measure of the drift velocity acquired per unit applied electric field. If the charge on the ion is e, and the measure of the applied field is denoted by E, the definition of the mobility, k, can be given dynamical significance by writing

$$u = \left(\frac{k}{e}\right) Ee \qquad (179)$$

Equation (179) expresses the fact that the ion acquires a steady drift velocity u when it is accelerated by a constant force Ee (and retarded by collision with the molecules of the gas through which it moves). In this form of words the nature of the 'accelerating force' is not explicitly stated—and we cannot but believe that it is of no consequence what the precise nature of the force may be. Conversely, in any situation in which ions are drifting through a gas with a velocity small compared with the 'thermal' velocities of the gas molecules, we may justifiably seek to identify a force, which in relation to the individual ion has a magnitude given by equation (179).

Now, in relation to the diffusion phenomenon, equation (178) may be written

$$u = -\frac{D}{n}\frac{dn}{dx},$$

or, if p is the partial pressure of the ions, when the concentration is n,

$$u = -\left(\frac{Dn}{p}\right)\left(\frac{1}{n}\frac{dp}{dx}\right) \qquad (180)$$

We regard the drift velocity, in this case, as arising from the distributed force due to the gradient of partial pressure which equation (180) identifies, and we note that $-(dp/dx)$ is the measure of this distributed force over a unit volume of the gas which contains

n ions of the type with which we are concerned. On the basis of this analysis,

$$-\frac{1}{n}\frac{dp}{dx}$$

is the measure of the distributed force effective on a single ion. This conclusion accepted, comparison of equations (179) and (180) leads to the result

$$\frac{k}{e} = \frac{Dn}{p}.$$

We now introduce the particular assumption to which we have already referred: we suppose that the ions are in thermal equilibrium with the gas through which they are moving. On this assumption, if P is the pressure, T the absolute temperature, and V the molar volume of the gas under these conditions, if N is Avogadro's constant and R the universal gas constant, then

$$\frac{k}{e} = \frac{DN}{PV},$$

or $$Ne = \frac{k}{D} RT \qquad (181)$$

According to equation (181), measurement of k and D, for ions of a given type, in the same gas and under the same conditions of temperature and pressure—or, better still, the determination of k/D in a single experiment—enables the total charge carried by one mole of the ions to be evaluated. The total charge carried by one mole of any univalent ion in electrolysis is the measure of the faraday (p. 212). Clearly, then, equation (181) provides the theoretical basis for the (indirect) comparison of the charges on gaseous and electrolytic ions, respectively.

Townsend's experiment was devised as a determination of k/D directly. By the application of an appropriate small difference of potential between the plate A and the gauze B (fig. 43) ions of one sign, produced in the intervening gas, were directed towards a circular aperture in the parallel metal plate C. Beyond this aperture the apparatus was axially symmetrical, the axis of the aperture being the symmetry axis. An electric field, the strength of which could be varied over a considerable range, was established between

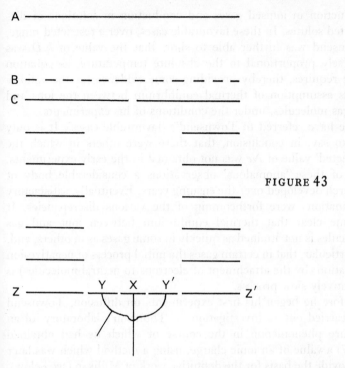

FIGURE 43

C and the composite electrode ZYXY'Z' -and suitably spaced intermediate ring electrodes, appropriately connected, ensured that the field was uniform over the experimental region. The composite electrode consisted of a central disk X, a surrounding annulus YY' and an external 'guard ring' ZZ'. The experiment consisted in measuring the ion currents received by X and YY', respectively, for different values of the electric field effective between C and ZYXY'Z'. Qualitatively, it is clear that the ratio of the first of these currents to the second will be greater, the greater is the value of kE/D, E being the measure of the electric field employed. In detail, this ratio is a complicated function of the linear dimensions of the essential components of the apparatus, but evaluation of the results was straightforward, and, as already stated, Townsend was able to obtain good agreement, in a sufficient number of cases, between his experimental value of Ne (equation (181)) and the faraday, to establish the identity of the ionic charges effective in the two types of conduction concerned—

conduction in ionised gases and conduction in solutions of dissociated solutes. In these favourable cases, over a restricted range, Townsend was further able to show that the value of k/D was inversely proportional to the absolute temperature, as equation (181) requires, thereby providing some evidence for the validity of his assumption of thermal equilibrium between the ions and the gas molecules, under the conditions of his experiments.

We have referred to Townsend's 'favourable cases'. It is only fair to say, in conclusion, that there were others in which the 'expected' value of Ne was not obtained in the early experiments. Out of these 'anomalous' observations a considerable body of research developed over the ensuing years. Eventually, satisfactory explanations were forthcoming of the various discrepancies. It became clear that thermal equilibrium between ions and gas molecules is not attained as quickly in some gases as in others, and, in particular, that in certain gases the initial process of negative-ion formation (by the attachment of electrons to neutral molecules) is a relatively slow process.

Before he began his first experiments on diffusion, Townsend had carried out an investigation, in Thomson's laboratory, of an obscure phenomenon in the course of which he had obtained (1897) a value of an ionic charge, using a method which was later to provide the basis for the definitive work of Millikan (see below). It had been known for more than a century that the rapid evolution of a gas, as a result of chemical action taking place in solution, frequently results in the gas being 'electrified'. Townsend found that similar effects could be obtained with gases liberated in electrolysis. The 'electrification' was not removed when the gas was passed through a tube tightly packed with glass-wool;-and this result and determinations of mobility showed that the carriers were certainly very much more sluggish (and, therefore, presumably much larger) than ordinary gaseous ions. It was found that when a stream of gas electrified in this way was passed into a damp atmosphere a cloud was formed, the total amount of precipitation being proportional to the charge conveyed by the electrified gas. Townsend naturally concluded that each drop in such a cloud was formed around one of the 'large ions' introduced by the electrolytic gas, and he proceeded to estimate the charge carried by such an ion by observations on the cloud. By observing the velocity of fall of the cloud under gravity, he deduced the effective radius of the droplets, and so the mass of liquid condensed on each ion. By measuring the total mass of the cloud (or, rather, of the liquid brought down when the cloud had settled) he calculated the number of droplets, and dividing the total charge carried down by this number he deduced the charge on the individual ion. For the first of these determinations he made use of Stokes's law, giving the terminal velocity v of a sphere of radius r falling through a gas of coefficient of viscosity η (see *M L & T*, p. 262):

$$v = \tfrac{2}{9} \frac{r^2 \rho g}{\eta} \tag{182}$$

Here ρ is the density of the liquid forming the spherical drop, and g is the acceleration due to gravity. Townsend concluded that the charge on the large ions in his electrolytic oxygen was 1.7×10^{-19} coulomb.

During the next few years very similar methods were developed in Cambridge by Thomson and Harold Albert Wilson (1874-1964), later professor of physics at the Rice Institute, Houston, Texas. Thomson used the method of adiabatic expansion of a damp gas in order to obtain condensation on the ions produced in air and certain other gases by X-rays, by ultra-violet light, and by the radiations from radioactive substances. Working in the same laboratory, Charles Thomson Rees Wilson (1869-1959) had just published (1897) the results of his pioneer experiments on this phenomenon—and his professor made immediate use of his findings. Starting from an investigation of condensation on dust particles, C. T. R. Wilson had shown that, in air saturated with water vapour, a sudden expansion of volume-ratio 1·38:1 produces a dense cloud of very small drops, however carefully the air is freed from dust. Under these conditions, at expansion ratios between 1·25:1 and 1·38:1, a few large drops were always obtained at each expansion—and removed, because of their rapid fall to the floor of the vessel. At expansion ratios less that 1·25:1, no drops at all were observed. Wilson was inclined to believe that the 'rain-like condensation' was in some way related to the feeble natural conductivity of the air (see p. 190). He therefore repeated his experiments placing his expansion vessel in a beam of X-rays. He still found it possible to make sudden expansions of volume-ratio less than 1·25:1 without droplets being formed, but between this limit and the dense-fog limit of 1·38:1 he obtained clouds more or less dense according to the intensity of the X-rays employed. In this way—and by more detailed experiments—he demonstrated conclusively that simple gaseous ions act as condensation nuclei in respect of water vapour in air under conditions of fourfold supersaturation or more.

Thomson's first experiments using C.T.R.Wilson's condensation method gave a value of $2 \cdot 2 \times 10^{-19}$ coulomb for the ionic charge (1898). In 1899, carrying his condensation experiments further, Wilson showed that, in air saturated with water vapour, only the negative ions act as nuclei for condensation when the expansion ratio is less than $1 \cdot 30$, the positive ions remaining ineffective until a ratio of $1 \cdot 31$ is attained. Thomson's further experiments were made in the light of this new knowledge—and with the aid of an improved apparatus—and yielded a value for the charge almost exactly one-half of the previous value (1903).

H.A.Wilson's experimental survey was less extensive than Thomson's, but he introduced a refinement of method which proved basic for all later work on the problem. Essentially, Wilson set out to compare the force which a charged cloud-drop experienced in a known electric field with the (calculable) force of gravity acting on the drop. As before, observations were made, not on individual drops, but on the upper boundary of a well-defined cloud—and the velocities of fall were determined, under gravity alone (v_1), and when a vertical electric field E was applied so as to increase the rate of fall (v_2). Under these conditions, if w is the weight of a drop (of radius r) carrying a charge e, and if Stokes's law is valid,

$$\frac{w + Ee}{w} = \frac{v_2}{v_1}.$$

Also $w = \frac{4}{3}\pi r^3 \rho g$,

and (see equation (182)),

$$r^2 = \frac{9}{2}\frac{\eta v_1}{\rho g}.$$

Therefore

$$e = 9\pi \frac{v_2 - v_1}{E}\left(\frac{2\eta^3 v_1}{\rho g}\right)^{\frac{1}{2}} \tag{183}$$

—the charge on the drop is given in terms of the increase in the velocity of fall, the intensity of the applied electric field, the values of the acceleration due to gravity, the coefficient of viscosity of the air, the density of water, and the observed velocity of fall under gravity alone.

Wilson used condensation expansions of volume-ratio less than 1·30:1, thereby concerning himself with negative ions exclusively, and obtained a final value of the ionic charge of $1·0 \times 10^{-19}$ coulomb (1903). In the course of his experiments, Wilson noticed a very remarkable phenomenon. In fall under gravity alone, the upper boundary of his cloud remained relatively well-defined and the cloud itself remained uniform in texture. When the rate of fall was increased by the application of an electric field, it appeared as if subsidiary boundaries were advancing through the cloud, all the time gaining distance from the primary boundary which marked the cloud top. From the estimated rates of fall of these subsidiary boundaries, Wilson satisfied himself that the effect was due to the fact that some drops had acquired a second, and some even a third, charge between the time of condensation and the time of observation.

The 1903 values of the ionic charge as determined by Thomson and Wilson agreed with one another to within 10 per cent. It may be held that, in giving prominence to the experiments in which they were obtained, we have been writing under false pretences, for it has to be admitted that these mutually concordant values were eventually shown to be in error by some 50 per cent. of the mean. No apology is offered: running through the experiments of Townsend and Thomson and H. A. Wilson there is the slow process of the forging of experimental method in a new field of enquiry. It is important, from time to time, to expose such a process, so that the rising generation of physicists may see their own problems in sharper perspective. In any case, the definitive work of Millikan was, in principle, no more than a repetition of the experiment of Wilson—using a vastly refined technique; moreover, in the upshot, Millikan's final result, in its turn, carried an unsuspected systematic error of more than 0·6 per cent. for well-nigh twenty years.

Robert Andrews Millikan (1868-1953) started his investigations at the university of Chicago in 1908. His 'final' value for the ionic charge was published in 1917 as $(1·592 \pm 0·002) \times 10^{-19}$ coulomb.

In reaching this result, Millikan had made all the obvious refinements which the form of equation (183) suggests. The circular metal plates by which the electric field was established were 'optically flat' and were separated by glass spacers whose thickness had been determined to 1 part in 10^5 interferometrically; the viscosity of air at the temperature of the experiment was re-determined with great care (by a research student). In addition, and more importantly, Millikan had dispensed with the condensed cloud of the earlier experimenters, making his observations, instead, on single drops. He had replaced water, which introduces grave problems of evaporation, by a low-vapour-pressure oil, as drop material. He had applied his electric field so as generally to oppose, rather than to assist, the force of gravity—thereby enabling him, by alternate application and suppression of this field, to make observations on a single drop over a great many back-and-forth transits of his telescopic field of view. Finally, he had brought to light, and had satisfactorily accounted for, a not unexpected failure of Stokes's law for the smallest drops (when the radius of the drop is not large compared with the mean free path of the gas molecules).

Millikan produced his oil drops by spraying through a fine nozzle. Very frequently the drops emerged charged ('by friction'), but the experiments were chiefly concerned with the magnitude of the changes of charge of individual drops brought about by collisions with ions produced in the surrounding air by X-rays or other suitable agents. It was these changes of charge which Millikan showed to take place always in integral multiples of a 'natural' unit (and usually in single units, rather than multiples). Almost certainly, from the point of view of fundamental physics, the demonstration in these experiments that several thousand changes of charge on single oil drops followed this rule without exception represents a contribution of greater significance for our subject than the definitive value of the ionic charge (0·6 per cent. in error) to which the investigation finally led. It will be noted (equation (183)) that nothing more than accurate determinations of velocity of fall, using the same value of field strength throughout, were necessary to establish this integral relation (strict 'quantisation' of charge): this result, therefore, is not only to be regarded as the most significant of the results of Millikan's experiment—it is also its most direct revelation.

In the three years from 1935 to 1937 three independent redeterminations of the viscosity of air, corrected to the temperature of Millikan's experiment, were carried out—at Uppsala in Sweden, at Reading in England, and at Pasadena in the United States. These showed conclusively that the value on which Millikan had relied was some 0·5 per cent. too low—and his 'final' value of e, therefore, too low by 0·75 per cent., or thereabouts (see equation (183)). Already, with hindsight, we have attributed an error of 0·6 per cent. to this value (in the same sense). In the end, then, Millikan was vindicated as an experimenter (if not as an infallible judge of the reliability of the work of his research students): in relation to the oil-drop observations, in particular, he had attained an overall accuracy of measurement of the order of 1 part in 1000, as his stated limits of error implied. No one has since done better with this particular method—though the attempt has been made.*

The revival of interest in Millikan's experiment in the 1930s was a direct consequence of the publication during the preceding few years of the earliest results obtained by the method which we have already identified (p. 306) as the most accurate of all—the method whereby the value of Avogadro's constant is first determined, and, through substitution of this result in the expression for the faraday ($F = Ne$), the value of the charge on the univalent ion in electrolysis. This method, which is generally referred to as 'the X-ray method' of determining the fundamental unit of charge, originated with Arthur Holly Compton (1892-1962) of the university of Chicago. The method was taken up in many laboratories, and, during 1935 alone, detailed accounts were published of three determinations which agreed with one another to within 1 part in 2000. The '1935 mean value', based on these three determinations was $1·603 \times 10^{-19}$ coulomb.

The 'X-ray method' is basically very simple—though in practical realisation it is not more immune from the need for careful application, and no less subject to the necessity of small corrections for adventitious effects, than any other experimental method from which the ultimate in accuracy is required. The practicability of the method depends on Compton's success, in 1925, in operating

---

* In 1939, J. A. Bearden (b. 1903), of the Johns Hopkins university, Baltimore, published an account of a determination of the viscosity of air which set an entirely new standard of precision in relation to this measurement. Bearden's estimated probable error was 1 part in 30,000. He had planned to repeat the oil-drop experiment, aiming at a similar order of accuracy, but the project was never brought to a conclusion.

an X-ray spectrometer with a ruled grating used 'in reflection' at very small angles of grazing incidence. When a plane grating, of line-spacing D, is used in this way, a parallel beam of monochromatic X-rays of wavelength λ being incident at a small grazing angle θ, diffraction maxima are observed at grazing angles of 'reflection' ϕ, given by

$$D (\cos \theta - \cos \phi) = n\lambda,$$

n being an integer. The angles in question being very small compared with 1 (in radian measure), we may write, as a reasonably accurate approximation,

$$(\phi - \theta)(\phi + \theta) = \frac{2n\lambda}{D}.$$

Here we note that $(\phi + \theta)$ is the angle between the incident and diffracted beams, and $(\phi - \theta)$ the angle between the diffracted beam (of the nth order) and the zero-order central reflection. In the experiments of Compton and his successors the wavelengths of the characteristic X-rays used were some 10^{-10} m; with $D = 10^{-6}$ m, or somewhat less, and $\theta = 2 \times 10^{-2}$ (say $1°$), the angular separation of the first-order diffraction maximum from the central reflection was 30 minutes of arc, or thereabouts. Evidently, the first practical problem attending the development of the X-ray method was the measurement of small angles such as this with an accuracy considerably better than 1 part in 1000.

Once that accuracy had been attained, the much simpler measurement of the angles of 'Bragg reflection' of the same characteristic X-radiation using a suitably chosen crystal could be undertaken with profit. We may summarise the ruled-grating observations in the formal expression

$$\lambda = k_1 D \tag{184}$$

Here, D (see above) is a macroscopically-known length, and k_1 is a pure number representing the overall result of these observations. Similarly, the observations on Bragg reflections may be formalised (see equation (172)):

$$d = k_2 \lambda \tag{185}$$

In this equation d is the spacing constant for the particular set of crystal planes employed, and, again, k_2 is a pure number determined from the observations. The 'suitably chosen crystal' used for these observations will have been chosen because of its chemical purity and because its macroscopic symmetry is high. We may assume, therefore, that the material of the crystal is a simple chemical compound of known composition and accurately known 'molecular weight' M. If N is the measure of Avogadro's constant, the mass of a single molecule of the compound is M/N, and ρ, the density of the crystal, is given by

$$\rho = \frac{M}{N} \frac{1}{k_3 d^3} \qquad\qquad (186)$$

where k_3 is a pure number.

Clearly, there is no need to justify equation (186) dimensionally —the mass of a single molecule is divided by a quantity having the dimensions of a volume (and it is a submicroscopic volume, if k_3 is of the order of magnitude of 1)—but its detailed physical interpretation is a different matter, and the method of determining the pure number k_3, at least, requires further elucidation. Briefly, it should be stated that k_3 is determined from an analysis of the Laue diffraction patterns obtained by the use of X-rays having a continuous spectrum of wavelengths (see pp. 275, 276) with the same crystal. As already explained, one set of symmetrically repeated 'spots' in these patterns can be identified as attributable to the Bragg reflections from the 'atomic' planes, of grating spacing d, used in the 'reflection' experiment. The positions of the other sets of spots enable the grating spacings of other sets of 'reflecting' planes to be determined—in terms of d as an arbitrary unit of length. For a 'suitably chosen crystal', having characteristics as set out above, it should not be difficult, from this information alone, to work out the 'architecture' of the crystal in detail, and so to determine in full the geometrical constants of the 'unit cell'— all in terms of d as unit of length. By 'unit cell' in this connection we refer to that volume which effectively contains the atomic constituents of a single molecule of the crystal substance, and which, repeated in a three-dimensional array, determines the sub-microscopic symmetry of the crystal. The volume of the unit cell is represented in equation (186) by the quantity $k_3 d^3$: this is in accordance with the procedural description that we have just given —d^3 represents unit volume in terms of the arbitrary unit of length employed in the analysis, and k_3 is a purely numerical 'shape factor', the value of which becomes known when the analysis is complete.

From equations (184), (185) and (186), we have

$$N = \frac{1}{k_1^3 k_2^3 k_3} \frac{M}{\rho D^3},$$

then, if F is the measure of the faraday (p. 212), finally,

$$e = k_1^3 k_2^3 k_3 \frac{F \rho D^3}{M} \tag{187}$$

Equation (187) summarises the measurements that have to be made in order to evaluate the charge on the univalent ion in electrolysis by the X-ray method. Briefly recapitulated, they are as follows: the value of the total charge carried by 8 grammes of oxygen ions in electrolysis (F), the density (ρ) of a crystal of a pure chemical compound, the molecular weight (M) of this compound on the oxygen scale (p. 291), the line spacing (D) of a ruled grating, the pure numbers k_1, k_2 and k_3 determined, respectively, in experiments with the ruled grating and the crystal, using the same characteristic X-radiation, and with the crystal using 'white' X-rays. By 1945 the overall accuracy attained in these several measurements was estimated at 1·25 parts in 10^4—and the value quoted for e at that time, as a result of a survey of similar determinations made in various laboratories, was $(1·6018 \pm 0·0002) \times 10^{-19}$ coulomb.

Here we must leave the problem of the magnitude of the fundamental unit of charge, having already taken it farther, perhaps, than was strictly necessary for the purposes of this book—abandoning it precisely where the professional compiler of tables of fundamental constants takes over. The table-compiler sets himself the goal of providing a self-consistent set of values of all the virtually independent 'constants' revealed by the investigations of the experimenter. In working towards that goal he generally finds that he can narrow the limits of error attaching even to the 'best' series of 'direct' measurements of the individual constants. However, his methods are not for discussion here: we have no real concern for 'the last decimal place' in the chapters which follow.

CHAPTER 7

STEADY CURRENTS IN SOLIDS

7.1. INTRODUCTORY

When the poles of a voltaic cell are connected by a metallic conductor, current flows in the completed circuit, and the total rate
of transport of charge is the same across every plane section of the
circuit (p. 196). Within the voltaic cell this transport is effected
by the migration of ions to the two electrodes: after the cell has
been in use for some time the distribution of chemical material in
the cell is measurably different from the initial distribution (§5.5).
On the other hand, apart from adventitious effects, such as
might, for example, result from excessive heating, the metallic
conductor is in no way permanently changed. It may have been
the vehicle of current for an indefinite time; afterwards no physical
examination will reveal this fact. Even while the current is flowing,
the only physical change in the conductor itself is an increase in
temperature—and such changes in density and mechanical properties as are a regular consequence of the application of heat, by
whatever means this is effected. Within the framework of presently
accepted views on the constitution of matter, as we have sketched
them in the last chapter, this behaviour can be understood only
on the basis of the hypothesis that metallic conduction is conduction by electrons: in the simple voltaic circuit that we have
discussed it must be supposed that negative electrons, released at
the negative electrode, as a result of electrolytic effects occurring
at its surface, enter the external conductor through the negative
pole of the cell, while at the same time negative electrons in equal
number pass from the conductor to the positive pole of the cell
and at the surface of the positive electrode 'neutralise' positive
ions arriving there. In the next chapter we shall be concerned in
more detail with effects occurring at surfaces of discontinuity (such
as the electrode surfaces in this example); here we confine our
attention strictly to the conduction process within homogeneous
solid materials. In general terms, our basic hypothesis applies to

all such materials: we shall suppose that we are dealing with electronic conduction throughout. However, there are broad divisions to be recognised, once this general viewpoint has been accepted. These we shall consider separately in what follows.

First of all we shall deal with conduction in metals. There are many reasons for this choice, not the least of which, pedagogically, derives from the fact that we have already become familiar with situations in which negative electrons are emitted from metal surfaces under the action of heat (p. 176) or radiation (p. 177). We can be confident, therefore, that our concept of 'mobile electrons in metals' is of wider significance than its present use implies. In later sections, and in less detail, we shall discuss the properties of 'semiconductors' and 'insulators'. Technologically, these substances are of great importance in the modern world; in this book, however, given its aims and its standard of presentation, they cannot be treated as fully as might otherwise be appropriate.

7.2. METALLIC CONDUCTORS

The concept 'metal' is not a precise concept. For our restricted purposes a metal might be defined as an elementary substance in a state in which its electrical resistivity (p. 112) is less than 10^{-7} ohm m (electrical conductivity greater than 10^7 ohm^{-1} m^{-1}). Such a definition limits the class 'metals' to the 'best' conductors. Generally, however, this class is less precisely delimited—and no single physical property is employed in defining it. Metals are conventionally recognised as being good conductors of heat as well as of electricity; they are opaque substances, capable of taking a high polish in the solid state. Substances which are not elementary, which are, rather, homogeneous mixtures (or compounds), may exhibit similar properties overall: such substances are referred to as metallic alloys, or simply as 'alloys'. In this section, unless it is otherwise stated explicitly, we shall be dealing with solid metals which, chemically considered, are pure elements.

We introduced the notion of 'the electrical conductivity of a material', formally, in section 3.4, pointing out that this notion had been used qualitatively for almost a century before it was given precision by Ohm in 1827. Ohm's formulation had reference more particularly to the conductivities of metals: consideration of its relevance in the case of electrolytic conduction in liquids has already occupied our attention, for a large part of section 5.4.

Here, as a preliminary to the discussion of the physical phenomenon of metallic conduction, we must return to a more critical
examination of the validity of 'Ohm's law' in its original context—
for the experimental results by which it was supported in the first
instance were not of a high order of accuracy. We are not doubting
the significance of the concept of the electrical resistance of a
(metallic) conductor as defined by equations (66) and (67); we are
merely raising the question how far, and under what conditions,
the electrical conductivity of a pure metal is a physical quantity
having a definite value. In respect of an electrolytic solution, once
the chemical composition and the temperature have been specified,
the physical properties of the system are uniquely defined; on the
other hand, we know that the mechanical properties of metals may
be modified by 'cold working', or by 'heat treatment' of one kind
or another. We are led to suspect that no unique value can be
assigned to 'the electrical conductivity of metal M at temperature
T'—and we may wish to enquire specifically, whether, under
extreme conditions such as very high current densities, or at very
low temperatures, some new feature of the phenomenon appears.

In 1837, in the year in which he developed the tangent galvanometer, Claude S. M. Pouillet discovered that in general the resistivities of 'hard-drawn' metals decrease when the metals are
annealed: thereafter, when precise measurements of resistivities
were undertaken, it became standard practice to use specimens
which had been treated in this way. The original discovery of the
temperature-variation of resistivity has already been mentioned
(p. 111): it was made by Davy in 1821, six years before Ohm's law
was formulated. The effect was further investigated by A. E. Becquerel (see p. 176), H. F. E. Lenz (p. 127), and A. Arndtsen. On
the basis of the results obtained by these investigators, it was
pointed out, in 1858, by Clausius (p. 207), that for pure metals
generally the resistivity appears to be directly proportional to the
absolute temperature over a considerable range. Even Clausius
was prepared to admit exceptions to this rule, and it is now recognised as, at the best, a rough approximation of limited applicability; in spite of this, if we were to use Clausius's statement as a
definition of what we mean by a metal, we should be defining
almost the same class of 'best' conductors as we defined at the
beginning of this section on a different basis.

Most measurements of resistivity are made by 'null' methods

and naturally depend for their accuracy on the sensitivity of the galvanometer employed. With a given galvanometer, precision in fixing the null-point, in a given arrangement, is obviously the greater, the larger is the current through the specimen. In spite of this, measurements are normally made using currents which are as small as practicable: in this way extraneous effects due to heating of the specimen (and the comparison resistors) are automatically avoided. On the other hand, as Maxwell was the first to emphasise, the question is important in its own right, whether the resistivity of a metal is the same at very high current densities as it is when the current density is small. In this connection, if a uniform conductor of length l and cross-sectional area A is traversed by a current i, and if the potential difference between the ends of the conductor increases by ΔV when the current is increased from i to $i + \Delta i$, the (differential) resistivity of the material of the conductor at current density i/A is defined by the relation

$$\rho' = \frac{A}{l} \cdot \frac{\Delta V}{\Delta i}.$$

Maxwell was concerned to enquire whether ρ' is, in fact, independent of i/A over the whole range of conditions accessible to experiment. George Chrystal (1851-1911), who four years later was to become professor of mathematics in the university of Edinburgh, and who had just taken his degree at Cambridge, as second wrangler, in 1875, was given the task of investigating the matter experimentally. On 4 March 1876, Maxwell reported the results of this investigation to Lewis Campbell, professor of Greek at St Andrews—a school friend of his early years: '[Chrystal] has worked steadily at the testing of Ohm's Law since October, and Ohm has come out triumphant, though in some experiments the wire was kept bright red-hot by the current.'

It was not until 1922 that any significant 'failure of Ohm's law' was observed in the laboratory. In that year, Percy Williams Bridgman (1882-1961) of the university of Harvard published an account of experiments that he had made with gold and silver foils at current densities of several million amperes per cm². He had found that the differential resistivities of these metals were some 1 per cent. greater at a current density of $5 \times 10^6 \, \text{A cm}^{-2}$ than under normal experimental conditions. We shall have occasion to refer to this result at a later stage in our discussion (p. 327).

Earlier in this section we identified two types of extreme condition under which it might be profitable to examine the resistivities of metals: conditions of very high current density and very low temperature. The possibility of investigations at very low temperatures arose first with the liquefaction of helium in 1908. Even before the discovery of the inert gases (see p. 250), Heike Kamerlingh Onnes (1853-1926) had been making plans for the development of a 'cryogenic laboratory' at the university of Leyden (where he was professor of physics from 1882 until his death). Once the lightest of these monatomic gases became available in sufficient quantity, Onnes's plans bore fruit beyond all rational expectation. Almost immediately the range of temperature from $4 \cdot 2° K$ (the normal boiling point of helium) to $1° K$ became accessible to controlled experiment—and almost at once Onnes embarked on a detailed study of the resistivities of pure metals under these 'extreme' conditions. Choosing mercury as the metal most easily purified, Onnes discovered the phenomenon of 'superconductivity' in 1911. He found that as the temperature of his specimen was reduced through $4 \cdot 15° K$, the electrical resistance fell abruptly to a negligible value. (In 1914 he showed that this 'discontinuous' change was by a factor of at least 10^{12}.) In 1913 he found that the resistance was restored to its normal value when a sufficiently strong current was passing through the specimen; in the following year he demonstrated that the resistance (to small currents) was similarly restored when a magnetic field of sufficient strength was established in its neighbourhood. Subsequent research has shown that the former of these effects is no more than a special case of the latter: restoration of normal resistance, at temperatures below the critical temperature for the onset of superconductivity, depends upon the establishment of a magnetic field of sufficient intensity at the surface of the specimen. This critical field can be produced externally, or by the current through the specimen itself: in either case its effect is essentially the same.

Since 1914 superconductivity has been established as a property of many metals (a review article listed 24 such, in 1963, with transition temperatures ranging from $9 \cdot 5° K$ to $0 \cdot 13° K$)—and of intermetallic compounds (alloys) of many types and having a wide range of composition. Here, however, we cannot continue the discussion of this interesting phenomenon; the theory of it is beyond the scope of this book. To have failed to refer to it would have been to have given an incomplete account of the temperature dependence of the electrical conductivity of metals which is essential to our present enquiry; to spend more time on it now would be unprofitable.

In the introduction to this chapter we have already accepted the hypothesis that the passage of electricity through metallic conductors involves the transport of electrons—and nothing more. This view of the matter was developed independently by several writers, soon after the electron itself was discovered, and, in the first decade of the new century, more particularly by Paul Karl Ludwig Drude (1863-1906), J.J.Thomson and H.A.Lorentz. In general, what was developed was a 'free-electron theory' of conduction: 'A piece of metal . . . contains a large number of free corpuscules. . . . These corpuscules can move freely between the atoms of the metal just as the molecules of air move freely about in the interstices of a porous body' (Thomson, 1907). We need not here accept the crudity of this early analogy, but it will be worth while exploring the formal consequences of the theory, nevertheless.

We consider a pure metal at temperature T and we assume that there are n free electrons per unit volume. We suppose that under these conditions there is a characteristic distribution function representing the steady-state velocity-spectrum of the electrons, and a characteristic mean free path λ, relative to the collision processes by which changes in individual electron velocities occur. On this basis we calculate the rate of evolution of heat in a conductor of length l and cross-sectional area A which is traversed by a current i. V is the difference of potential between the ends of the conductor. We have already given a qualitative account of this process of heat generation in section 3.4; here we give, much simplified, a quantitative version.

In this connection there is one simplification that we can make at the outset which is not an approximation in the general sense of the term, for it is acceptable at any level of treatment of our problem. We shall discuss its justification at a later stage of the argument; for the present we merely formulate it without comment. It involves the assumption that the maximum amount of energy that a 'conduction electron' can acquire, through the operation of the electric field in the conductor, in a single free path, is very small compared with the average steady-state kinetic energy of the electron. If we accept this assumption, we shall conclude that the collision frequency is essentially the same whether the electric field is 'on' or 'off'—and we shall likewise be at liberty to assume that the probability function describing the velocity of an individual electron following its next-ensuing collision when the field is 'on' is essentially the same as the characteristic distribution function representing the steady-state velocities when the field is zero.

This having been said, for our 'much simplified' treatment we accept the extreme approximation that all electrons have the same steady-state speed v, and we assume that all free paths are of the same length λ.

Suppose, then, that an electron, of charge e and mass m, is travelling between successive collisions at an angle θ to the axis of the conductor. Such an electron will be subject to a force Ve/l for a time λ/v, according to our simplifying assumptions. In that time it will have acquired a component of velocity of magnitude $Ve\lambda/mvl$ parallel to the axis, and, having left the point of 'first' collision with speed v (or, so we have assumed), it will arrive at the point of 'second' collision with speed v' given by

$$v'^2 = v^2 + u^2 + 2uv \cos \theta \qquad (188)$$

where $\quad u = Ve\lambda/mvl \qquad (189)$

According to our assumptions, it will transfer an amount of energy equal to

$$\tfrac{1}{2}m(v'^2 - v^2)$$

to the 'substance' of the conductor at the 'second' collision. This transference of energy, according to equation (188), may be written

$$\tfrac{1}{2}m(u^2 + 2uv \cos \theta) \qquad (190)$$

—and since $v \cos \theta$ is the component, along the axis of the conductor, of the velocity of the electron in the zero-field, steady-state, distribution, and since there is no current through the conductor in the absence of an applied field, when the collisions of all the conduction electrons are considered the contribution from the second term in (190) will be zero. We consider all these collisions by summation over the whole conductor. Then, since the overall collision frequency is $Alnv/\lambda$, P, the net rate of energy transfer (or the measure of the electric power dissipated in the conductor) is given by

$$P = \frac{Alnv}{\lambda} \cdot \tfrac{1}{2}mu^2,$$

or, on substitution from equation (189), by

$$P = V^2 \frac{A}{l} \frac{ne^2\lambda}{2mv} \tag{191}$$

We note, with satisfaction, that equation (191) is of precisely the same form as the equation

$$P = \frac{V^2}{R}$$

by which R, the resistance of our conductor is defined (compare equations (66) and (67))—and that the length of the conductor, and its cross-sectional area, enter into the expression for the power dissipation as experiment requires that they should. Obviously, such an end-result is mandatory for any acceptable theory of metallic conduction: we merely note that the free-electron theory has passed its first crucial test satisfactorily (whatever its later failings may prove to be)—and we proceed to extract from equation (191) an explicit expression for the resistivity. Having regard to our original definition of this quantity (p. 112), we obtain

$$\rho = \frac{2mv}{ne^2\lambda} \tag{192}$$

Evaluation of the success or failure of the theory must begin with an order-of-magnitude calculation based on equation (192). If we re-write this equation in the form

$$\frac{v}{n\lambda} = \frac{\rho}{2}\left(\frac{e}{m}\right)e \tag{193}$$

and substitute numerical values for (e/m) and e, using M.K.S.A. units, we have

$$\frac{v}{n\lambda} = 1\cdot41 \times 10^{-8}\ \rho\ (\mathrm{m^3\ sec^{-1}}).$$

Let us now consider a moderately good conductor, for which, at room temperature $\rho = 7 \times 10^{-8}$ ohm m (see p. 320), then, in this case, $(v/n\lambda) = 10^{-15}$ m³ sec⁻¹. In such a conductor, being a pure metal, the number of atoms per unit volume (1 m³) is of the order of 6×10^{28}. Let us suppose that there are, on the average, α free electrons per atom in the metal. On this basis, $v/\alpha\lambda$ is of the order of 6×10^{13} sec⁻¹. If we make the 'obvious' assumption that the mean free path is of the order of the interatomic distance, say 2.5×10^{-10} m, or thereabouts, v/α is some 1.5×10^4 m sec⁻¹. The 'next most obvious' assumption is that the mean speed of the electrons is the 'gas kinetic' speed: at room temperature this is about 1.1×10^5 m sec⁻¹. On this basis we conclude that α must be of the order of 7—perhaps within a factor of two either way. This is not an easy conclusion to accept for any metal. If we had made our calculation for calcium, a metal of very low density, and a good conductor, we should have obtained the value $\alpha = 28$, at room temperature. Now the atom of calcium has only 20 extra-nuclear electrons, all told. Clearly, we are not making good sense, numerically, out of equation (192)—but it may well be that the assumptions that we have made in its evaluation are at fault rather than the equation itself. The experiments of Bridgman (p. 322) are relevant in this connection.

Bridgman's experiments, it will be recalled, showed that a significant increase in the differential resistivity of a good conductor takes place when the current density in the conductor reaches a value of some 5×10^{10} A m⁻². On the basis of the free-electron theory, we assume that this effect arises from the fact that under these extreme conditions (of high field) it is no longer true (see p. 324) that the maximum amount of energy which a conduction electron gains in a single free path is negligibly small compared with the steady-state kinetic energy of the electron. (That the effect is inappreciable at current densities less than 10^{10} A m⁻² is similarly taken as evidence for the validity of this approximation in more normal circumstances.)

In the arrangement of the uniform linear conductor that we have considered in the formal development of the theory, the current density, j, is given by

$$j = \frac{V}{AR},$$
$$= \frac{V}{l\rho}.$$

We may use this last result, in conjunction with equation (189), to obtain the relation

$$\frac{u}{v} = j\left(\frac{e}{m}\right)\frac{\rho\lambda}{v^2} \tag{194}$$

This is an explicit relation showing that, when Ohm's law is valid, the ratio of u, the velocity acquired by an electron in a single free path, to v, its randomly-directed steady-state velocity, is directly proportional to the current density, j. If our interpretation of Bridgman's experiment is correct, we should expect that the value of u/v calculated from equation (194), when 5×10^{10} A m^{-2} is substituted for j, is not negligibly small compared with unity. Taking, as before, $\rho = 7 \times 10^{-8}$ ohm m, as representative of a moderately good conductor, and, on the basis of the assumptions previously made, writing $\lambda = 2\cdot5 \times 10^{-10}$ m, $v = 1\cdot1 \times 10^5$ m sec^{-1}, we have, in fact, under the conditions specified,

$$\frac{u}{v} = 1\cdot3 \times 10^{-5}.$$

Clearly, at face value, this is not an acceptable result. Arguing along these lines, Bridgman concluded (1922) that if the free-electron theory were to be retained it must necessarily be modified by the proviso that the mean free path, λ, involved in the theory, is many orders of magnitude greater than the distance between neighbouring atoms in the solid. It will be noted that the acceptance of this proviso goes far towards removing previous doubts concerning the number of free electrons per atom required by the theory as originally interpreted. In relation to equation (193), if λ is increased, then n is correspondingly decreased, provided that v remains the same.

So far, we have not considered the temperature dependence of resistivity, in relation to the free-electron theory. Accepting Clausius's generalisation (p. 321) as providing an approximate account of the normal variation, for pure metals, we have to conclude that the quantity $v/n\lambda$ is roughly proportional to the absolute temperature, for a given material. Making the simplest assumption, that the number of free electrons per atom is independent of the temperature, we attribute the whole of this variation to variation of the single electron collision frequency, v/λ. We cannot go farther than this, without making further assumptions.

If our previous assumption were revived, that the mean speed of the electrons is the 'gas kinetic' speed (p. 327), then v would be proportional to $T^{\frac{1}{2}}$, and, of necessity, λ would be inversely proportional to v. However, a little reflection will show that the assumption of the gas kinetic value for v was not a critical assumption in our earlier arguments. We can hardly imagine that the mean electron speed is less than the gas kinetic value; if it is indeed greater than this, the arguments proceed as before, only even larger values of λ (or n) are required to match the experimental results. We maintain an open mind, therefore, on this particular issue. As early as 1917, Bridgman wrote 'a successful theory of metallic conduction must discard the old viewpoint, which explained resistance in terms of the properties of an assemblage of electrons little affected by the inert framework of atoms, and substitute an explanation in terms of the properties of the atomic framework'. He was at that time canvassing the idea that a main contribution to the temperature variation of resistivity is provided by the variation in amplitude of the thermal vibrations of the atoms of the 'inert framework' (crystal lattice) of the metal, whereby the effective mean free path of the conduction electrons is the smaller the higher the temperature of the metal.

Early writers on the free-electron theory laid particular stress on its apparent success in giving a precise quantitative account of the relation between the thermal and electrical conductivities of metals. We remarked, at the beginning of this section, that metals are conventionally recognised as being good conductors of heat as well as of electricity. In 1853 G. H. Wiedemann (see p. 210) and R. Franz, having made an extensive series of determinations of the thermal conductivities of pure metals, put forward the empirical generalisation that the ratio of the measures of the thermal and electrical conductivities is the same, for all such materials, at the same temperature. Later, in 1872, Ludwig Valentin Lorenz (1829-1891) was able to assert that the value of the Wiedemann-Franz ratio is directly proportional to the absolute temperature. Nowadays, it is usual to refer to the quantity $\kappa/\sigma T$ as the Lorenz constant (L): the full statement of the empirical law is, therefore, that the Lorenz constant is the same for all metals. (In the expression $L = \kappa/\sigma T$, κ and σ are the measures of the thermal and electrical conductivities, respectively, and T denotes the absolute temperature.) Modern research has exposed the limitations of the law, particularly at low temperatures (the Lorenz constant generally decreases rapidly, with decreasing temperature, below $50°$ K), but its approximate validity at temperatures above $250°$ K is sufficiently striking to warrant serious discussion. For purposes of such discussion we may take the 'normal' experimental value of the constant to be $2·4 \times 10^{-8}$ volt^2 deg^{-2} K.

On the free-electron theory, it is supposed that the conduction of heat through a metal takes place as a net transport of kinetic energy, in the direction of heat flow—or of (falling) temperature gradient, by the same electrons as are involved in electrical conduction when a potential gradient obtains. In the electrical case there is, as we have seen, an overall drift of electrons across any plane perpendicular to the direction of current flow; in the thermal case, across any plane perpendicular to the direction of heat flow, there is no net drift of electrons, only the kinetic energy carried by the electrons which cross the plane in one direction is slightly greater than that carried by those which cross in the other. In either case, in our simple version of the theory, we suppose that, at the end of each free path λ, each electron comes into dynamic equilibrium with the lattice, taking up a randomly-directed velocity v (or a kinetic energy E) appropriate to the temperature of the material of the conductor at the point of collision. In the electrical case, we assume that the temperature is constant throughout the conductor; in the thermal case it is of the essence of the matter that the temperature varies from point to point. Essentially, then, the formal difference between the two situations is that in the one case the conduction electron has its energy modified by the 'external constraint', continuously, between collisions; in the other case the external constraint determines the sudden changes of energy which take place in the collisions themselves.

Let us now consider the thermal case in more detail on this basis. We may imagine a uniform cylindrical conductor, as before, and assume that the temperature, T, increases uniformly with distance, x, measured along the axis of the conductor. The kinetic energy, E, of an electron which has just made collision at any point in the conductor is uniquely determined (or so we suppose) by the temperature of the material of the conductor at that point —but we make no assumption, at this stage, regarding the functional relation between E and T. We wish to calculate the net rate of transport of kinetic energy across an arbitrary right-section of the conductor. Because the average distance travelled by an electron parallel to the axis of the conductor, from its point of last collision until it crosses the plane section concerned, must be proportional to λ, the mean free path, we conclude that the average amount of kinetic energy transported across the section, by an electron which crosses the section in the direction of the heat flow (x decreasing), may be written

$$E + f_1 \lambda \frac{dE}{dT} \frac{dT}{dx},$$

where f_1 is a numerical constant. Correspondingly, for electrons crossing the section in the opposite direction, the average transfer of energy is

$$E - f_1 \lambda \frac{dE}{dT} \frac{dT}{dx},$$

per electron crossing. If v is the characteristic speed of the conduction electrons in dynamic equilibrium with the lattice at temperature T, $f_2 n v$ electrons cross unit area of the section in unit time, in each direction. Again, f_2 is a numerical constant, and n is the number of conduction electrons per unit volume, as before. Thus, across the right section of area A, the net rate of transport of energy is given by

$$\frac{dQ}{dt} = 2A f_1 f_2 n v \lambda \frac{dE}{dT} \frac{dT}{dx}.$$

Now, according to the definition of κ, the thermal conductivity of the material of the conductor, in this case,

$$\frac{dQ}{dt} = A \kappa \frac{dT}{dx}.$$

We have, therefore,

$$\kappa = 2 f_1 f_2 n v \lambda \frac{dE}{dT}.$$

The value of the numerical factor $2f_1 f_2$ is deduced (with various degrees of elaboration) in the standard books on the kinetic theory of gases. Here we merely quote the result, $2f_1 f_2 = 1/3$, and so obtain, explicitly, on the basis of our simplified version of the free-electron theory,

$$\kappa = \tfrac{1}{3} nv\lambda \frac{dE}{dT} \tag{195}$$

In the electrical case, $\sigma = 1/\rho$, thus, from equations (192) and (195), we have

$$L = \frac{2}{3} \frac{mv^2}{e^2 T} \frac{dE}{dT},$$

or, since $mv^2 = 2E$,

$$L = \frac{4E}{3e^2 T} \frac{dE}{dT} \tag{196}$$

According to the empirical law of Lorenz, L is a universal constant for all metals. We write, therefore,

$$\frac{E}{T} \frac{dE}{dT} = a,$$

and obtain, generally,

$$E^2 = E_0{}^2 + aT^2 \tag{197}$$

In this general solution, E_0 represents a characteristic energy which may be different for different metals; only a must be the same for all, if the empirical law is valid.

The early writers who made great play with the success of the free-electron theory in providing a quantitative 'explanation' of the Lorenz rule consistently assumed that the characteristic energy E_0 of equation (197) is zero for all metals. They assumed, in fact, that the conduction electrons could be likened to the molecules of a monatomic gas for which, according to straightforward kinetic theory considerations (see *M L & T*, p. 286), we have

$$E = \tfrac{3}{2} kT,$$

k being Boltzmann's constant. On that assumption, $a = 9k^2/4$, and

$$L = 3 \frac{k^2}{e^2} \tag{198}$$

If we substitute $k = 1 \cdot 38 \times 10^{-23}$ joule deg^{-1} K, $e = 1 \cdot 60 \times 10^{-19}$ coulomb, in equation (198), we obtain $L = 2 \cdot 23 \times 10^{-8}$ volt^2 deg^{-2}

K. Comparing this value with the experimental value $2\cdot4 \times 10^{-8}$ volt^2 deg^{-2} K, already quoted (p. 330), we need not be surprised that the quantitative agreement was regarded as highly significant.

Although it was generally held that the numerical agreement that we have just exposed is indeed significant, it soon came to be realised (Thomson, 1907) that the simple theory faced a major difficulty. According to the empirical law of P. L. Dulong and A. T. Petit (1819) the thermal capacity per mole is the same for all metals. This generalisation is at least as uniformly valid as that of Lorenz (it fails at low temperatures, as the other does). The value of the Dulong-Petit constant ($2\cdot5 \times 10^4$ joule deg^{-1} K, per kg mole) had been convincingly explained on the assumption that the thermal energy of a metal is simply the vibrational energy of the individual atoms, in amount $3kT$ per atom, on the average, as the general law of equipartition of energy would require (see *M L & T*, p. 297). On this basis it was obviously an acute embarrassment to have to consider the possibility that the 'free-electron gas' might have a significant contribution to make to the specific heats of metals at ordinary temperatures: empirically, there was essentially no 'unexplained' heat capacity under such conditions. The difficulty, like so many others, was not fully resolved until a wave-mechanical theory of electrons in metals was finally developed (see p. 336): that is no reason, however, why we should not discuss it further within the context of the classical theory with which we are now familiar.

According to the classical theory, if there are effectively α conduction electrons per atom in the metal (p. 327), and if we do not specify the precise dependence of the electron energy, E, upon temperature (T), the ratio of the electronic and the atomic contributions to the specific heat of the metal may be written

$$\frac{c_e}{c_a} = \frac{\alpha}{3k} \frac{dE}{dT} \tag{199}$$

(the atomic contribution, per lattice atom, is $3k$, as, in effect, we have just asserted). According to equation (196)—we assume that this equation gives a formally correct expression for the Lorenz constant whatever the functional dependence of E on T—we have

$$\frac{dE}{dT} = \frac{3Le^2}{4} \frac{T}{E} \tag{200}$$

Empirically, equation (198) gives a numerically acceptable value for L, whatever the theoretical justification, or lack of justification, may be for our method of deriving it. We combine equations (199), (200) and (198), therefore, on this basis, and we obtain

$$\frac{c_e}{c_a} = \frac{\alpha}{2} \cdot \frac{3kT}{2E}.$$

Writing $3kT/2$ as E_g, the gas-kinetic value of the average energy of a conduction electron, we have, finally,

$$\frac{c_e}{c_a} = \frac{\alpha}{2} \frac{E_g}{E}$$

—and the condition to be satisfied, if the free-electron theory is to survive the challenge of the empirical law of Dulong and Petit, is simply expressed in the inequality

$$E \gg \frac{\alpha}{2} E_g.$$

Obviously, unless $\alpha \ll 1$, the original assumption of the theorists of the early years of the century ($E = E_g$) cannot be accepted. If we do not wish to accept this restriction on the value of α, we have to return to the general solution represented by equation (197), and to enquire whether the 'normal' law of equipartition of energy is possibly inapplicable to the interactions between the conduction electrons and the lattice. It may be that E_0 is not zero: indeed, if we make the assumptions that we have already made (that equation (196) is fundamentally correct, and equation (198) numerically accurate), the constant a in equation (197) becomes $9k^2/4$, and the equation itself takes the form

$$E^2 = E_0{}^2 + E_g{}^2.$$

We see that we need not necessarily accept the restriction $\alpha \ll 1$, provided that $E_0 \gg E_g$. We conclude, in the end, that the free-electron theory might still be salvaged, if we were to suppose that the conduction electrons possess kinetic energy greatly in excess of the thermal energy corresponding to the temperature of the conductor—and if we were to accept the fact that a large fraction of this energy (E_0/E) is not interchangeable with the vibrational energy of the lattice in the collision processes that occur.

At this stage we should summarise our various conclusions. We started out with a naïve view of conduction by free electrons, present to the extent of α per atom of the metal. We considered the speed, v, and the kinetic energy, E, of these electrons, in the steady state, to be characterised by mean values assumed to be temperature-dependent. In respect of the energy-modifying collisions with atoms of the lattice, we introduced an electron mean free path, λ. Then, as we followed through a detailed comparison of the results of experiment with the natural theoretical consequences of our original viewpoint, we were compelled to admit one 'unexpected' conclusion after another. Failure to have done so would have been to have abandoned our viewpoint altogether. We had first to admit that the mean free path of our theory must be very much greater than the mean distance between atoms in the lattice; we had then to envisage the serious possibility that the mean kinetic energy of the conduction electrons might be very much greater than that of the lattice atoms at the same temperature, the major fraction of this energy being temperature-independent; finally, we have a lingering suspicion (against our natural prejudices) that values of α considerably less than 1 may be necessary, if our theory is to survive. This last possibility (which we have not hitherto discussed in detail) is hardly less unexpected than the other two. In a pure metal, ideally there should be no valid basis of discrimination between one atom and another, whereby, in the steady state, an electron from the one atom is 'free', whereas the corresponding electron from the other is 'bound'. Alternatively, if a small fractional value of α were to be interpreted in terms of a process of dynamic equilibrium, then we should expect α to increase rapidly with increasing temperature. On this basis it would be difficult to understand why the conductivity of a pure metal should decrease as the temperature rises (see p. 356).

When a physical theory has to be buttressed by particular assumptions which do not derive directly from the premises on which the theory is founded—or at least fit naturally into the general conceptual framework within which the theory has been developed—then the theory is failing in a most important respect. It may be of some use as providing a formally acceptable model, descriptive of an isolated phenomenon, but it fails to correlate this phenomenon with others on the basis of general principles of wide validity. The classical free-electron theory of metallic conduction of heat and electricity must be adjudged to be in this category: it provides a pictorial representation of these phenomena which even now is not seriously misleading, but in a wider context it is sterile and unprofitable. Before these two phenomena could be understood in detail in their relation to other phenomena in physics, classical notions of energy transfer had to be superseded by 'quantum' notions, and classical mechanics be replaced by wave mechanics as descriptive of the motions of the conduction electrons. We shall find it necessary to make use of these non-classical ideas somewhat more systematically in the next section of this chapter; here we sketch very briefly their relevance to our present problem.

The 'general principle of wide validity' which is basic for the correlation of the phenomena of conduction in metals with other physical phenomena is the 'exclusion principle' of Wolfgang Pauli (1900-1958). At the time of its enunciation in 1925, this principle was put forward in an attempt to formulate a rule descriptive of the experimentally known facts concerning the arrangement of the extranuclear electrons in atoms (see §6.5). It referred to the assignment of quantum numbers to such electrons—four quantum numbers to each electron—and it can be most simply expressed in the statement that no two electrons in the same atom can have the same set of four quantum numbers. In this form it is an empirically based statement pointing to a fundamental (and possibly inscrutable) property of electrons as elementary particles.

In 1928 Sommerfeld (p. 275) examined the consequences of applying the Pauli principle to the free electrons in a lump of metal. Using wave mechanics to calculate the wavelengths of the standing de Broglie waves—and so the momenta and energies of the electrons—Sommerfeld concluded that the electron energy levels would form a quasi-continuous distribution in which the number of levels per unit energy interval was proportional to $E^{\frac{1}{2}}$, E being the kinetic energy of the electron. In the absence of any kind of 'perturbation', the N electrons present in the lump of metal concerned would occupy completely the allowed states of lowest energy (as in an atom)—two electrons per level, taking count of the two values which the electron 'spin' quantum number can take (see p. 467). It is of the essence of the quantum description that no perturbation of this particular energy distribution can be effective unless it results in an electron acquiring sufficient energy from the source of the perturbation so that it is raised from its initial state to one of the 'unoccupied' states of higher energy (again, as is the case for the extranuclear electrons in an atom). On this basis, for 'small' perturbations, only the electrons possessing the largest energies in the unperturbed distribution are available as energy receptors when the perturbation is applied.

In 1926 Enrico Fermi (1901-1954) and Paul Adrian Maurice Dirac (b. 1902) had developed, independently, the appropriate method of treating, statistically, on the basis of the Pauli principle, the thermal equilibrium of a large number of electrons in relation to their environment. The process by which the free electrons in a metal attain thermal equilibrium with the lattice may be regarded as imposing an ever-present perturbation on the ideal (zero temperature) energy distribution that we have discussed above. When Sommerfeld applied 'Fermi-Dirac statistics' to this problem, he obtained an expression for the energy distribution of the free electrons at temperature T of the form

$$N(E) = \frac{3n}{2E_0^{\frac{3}{2}}} \frac{E^{\frac{1}{2}}}{e^{(E-E_T)/kT} + 1} \tag{201}$$

In terms of this formula, $N(E)dE$ represents the number of free electrons per unit volume having energies between E and $E + dE$, E_0 is the maximum energy possessed by any electron when the temperature is zero (at the absolute zero, all allowed energy states from 0 to E_0 are completely occupied), and in respect of E_T, when $E_0 \gg kT$, as in all practical situations, to a good approximation

$$E_T = E_0 - \frac{\pi^2 k^2 T^2}{12E_0} \tag{202}$$

More precisely, in respect of equation (201), according to Sommerfeld's calculations,

$$\frac{3n}{2E_0^{\frac{3}{2}}} = 4\pi \left(\frac{2m}{h^2}\right)^{\frac{3}{2}},$$

or $$E_0 = \frac{h^2}{8m}\left(\frac{3n}{\pi}\right)^{\frac{2}{3}} \tag{203}$$

h being Planck's constant (p. 271), n the total number of free electrons per unit volume and m representing the mass of the electron, as before.

Obviously, in the present account, we can do no more than quote

Sommerfeld's results without proof. Let us, then, accept them as quoted, and examine their implications—and let us, first of all, justify our claim that, in the context of the theory, $E_0 \gg kT$ in all practical situations. We have already (p. 327) taken 6×10^{28} as a rough order-of-magnitude estimate of the number of atoms per unit volume (m³) of a representative metal such as silver or copper. Assuming one free electron per atom, and writing $h = 6 \cdot 6 \times 10^{-34}$ joule sec, $m = 9 \times 10^{-31}$ kg, in equation (203), we have $E_0 = 9 \times 10^{-19}$ joule. Since $k = 1 \cdot 38 \times 10^{-23}$ joule deg^{-1} K (p. 332), for all ordinary temperatures ($T < 1000°$ K, say) $E_0 \gg kT$, as we have claimed. Clearly, this result would not be valid if the number of free electrons per atom were very much less than one, but, abandoning the classical picture, we have in effect already concluded (p. 335) that any acceptable theory must postulate an integral number for this ratio, so we continue our discussion on this basis.

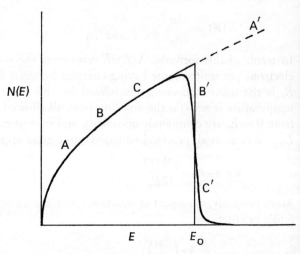

FIGURE 44

If $E_0 \gg kT$ in all practical situations, then the energy distribution described by equations (201) and (202) is of the form shown in fig. 44. Here the dotted curve AA' represents the distribution of allowed states, the full curve BB' represents the occupied states at the absolute zero of temperature, and the full curve CC' the occupied states at some 'ordinary' temperature T. Curve BB' is sharply terminated at energy E_0 (on the assumption of one free electron per atom of the lattice); curve CC′ has no abrupt discontinuity, but is indistinguishable from BB′ except within an energy range of some $3kT$ on either side of E_0. On the scale of the figure the difference between E_T and E_0 (equation (202)) is insignificant.

The immediate conclusion to be drawn from a comparison of curves BB′ and CC′ is that in exchanges of 'thermal' energy, as between free electrons and lattice atoms, only those electrons take part whose energies are close to E_0 (say, within $3kT$ either way). In respect of thermal conductivity, therefore, only a very small fraction of the free electrons are effective carriers. In respect of electrical conductivity, when Ohm's law is valid, we have already assumed (p. 325) that the amount of energy derivable from the field in the space of an electron free path must be such as to be exchangeable with a lattice atom at the 'next' collision. Again, therefore, within the range of validity of Ohm's law, only a very small fraction of the free electrons are involved in the dissipation of 'Joule heat' in the conductor. In each case, though we have postulated that there is one free electron per lattice atom, in relation to our previous 'classical' viewpoint it is indeed as if $\alpha \ll 1$. Finally, in respect of specific heat, (see p. 334) the same statement is true. In order to calculate the contribution, per free electron, to the thermal capacity of the conductor at temperature T, we have to evaluate

$$\frac{d}{dT} \int_0^\infty EN(E)dE.$$

According to equations (201) and (202), when $E_0 \gg kT$,

$$\int_0^\infty EN(E)dE = \tfrac{3}{5}E_0 + \frac{\pi^2}{4}\frac{(kT)^2}{E_0} \qquad (204)$$

Thus, the contribution to the thermal capacity, per free electron, according to the Sommerfeld theory, is

$$\frac{\pi^2}{2}\left(\frac{kT}{E_0}\right)k,$$

and the ratio of the electronic and atomic contributions (see p. 333) becomes

$$\frac{c_e}{c_a} = \frac{\pi^2}{6}\frac{kT}{E_0}.$$

We have already shown that for a representative good conductor kT/E_0 is of the order of 10^{-2} when $T = 650°\,\text{K}$, thus at normal temperatures the electronic contribution to the heat capacity is well-nigh negligible according to the Sommerfeld theory.

Equation (204) gives the mean kinetic energy per free electron at temperature T. Using an obvious notation we may write, instead,

$$\bar{E} = \bar{E}_0 + \frac{3\pi^2}{20}\frac{(kT)^2}{\bar{E}_0} \tag{205}$$

According to the much simplified version of the classical free-electron theory which we employed in our earlier discussion, we obtained equation (197) as the most general expression for the same quantity, using the Wiedemann-Franz-Lorenz law as the criterion of generality. We naïvely identified the constant a with $9k^2/4$ on the basis of simple numerical agreement—and, with that substitution, and using our new notation, we can now re-write the equation, accurately to the second order in $kT/\bar{E}_0$, in the form

$$\bar{E} = \bar{E}_0 + \frac{9(kT)^2}{8\bar{E}_0} \tag{206}$$

We note the precise similarity of equations (205) and (206)—and we see that, for all the simplicities of our earlier classical approach to the problem, even the magnitudes of the multiplying constants, $3\pi^2/20$ and $9/8$ are the same within a $4:3$ ratio.

In relation to the three 'unexpected conclusions' which we had to admit as particular assumptions in order to buttress the classical free-electron theory of metallic conduction (p. 335), we have now seen that all except the assumption of unexpectedly long free paths follow naturally from the Fermi-Dirac-Sommerfeld theory as we have so far developed its implications. Our remaining task, therefore, is to explain how this last feature, also, arises directly in the development of the theory.

Sommerfeld described the motion of the conduction electrons through the metal using the formalism of wave mechanics rather than classical mechanics. For his purpose, therefore, the de Broglie wavelength Λ (see V & W, §9.4), rather than the particle speed v, was the significant parameter. Now, the product of the measures of these two quantities is constant, for particles of a given kind, provided that all speeds are small compared with the speed of light. We have, in fact,

$$\Lambda v = \frac{h}{m} \qquad (207)$$

h being Planck's constant, and m the mass of the particle concerned. In this case, if Λ_0 is the de Broglie wavelength of electrons of speed v_0 and energy E_0 (effectively the maximum energy possessed by a conduction electron in the metal at ordinary temperatures), equation (207) becomes

$$\Lambda_0 = \frac{h}{mv_0} = \left(\frac{h^2}{2mE_0}\right)^{\frac{1}{2}};$$

then, on substitution from equation (203), we obtain

$$\Lambda_0 = \left(\frac{8\pi}{3}\right)^{\frac{1}{3}} \left(\frac{1}{n}\right)^{\frac{1}{3}} \qquad (208)$$

Equation (208) is very simply interpreted. It implies that, for any metal, the de Broglie wavelengths of those free electrons which are effective in conduction are very closely twice the value of $(1/n)^{\frac{1}{3}}$ for the metal in question. Now, we have been assuming, latterly, that n, the concentration of free electrons, is the same as the concentration of lattice atoms, in a representative good conductor—and we have been supposing, all along, that our materials are isotropic. If we take a simple cubic lattice as fulfilling the last requirement, then $(1/n)^{\frac{1}{3}}$ represents the fundamental lattice constant: no set of 'reflecting planes' (p. 276) in the metal can, on these assumptions, have a characteristic separation greater than this quantity. We conclude, then, on the basis of equation (208), that, for the materials with which we are concerned, the de Broglie wavelengths of the conduction electrons are always greater than the spacings of the reflecting planes—and almost always greater than twice the spacing. The wave groups (see $V \,\&\, W$, p. 285), or 'wave packets', by which we may seek to represent individual electrons according to this mode of description, obviously extend over distances very considerably greater than the fundamental lattice spacing of the metal crystal.

It is a general result, valid for all types of wave propagation—the limitation implicit in the Bragg reflection law for X-rays (p. 277) is a particular exemplification of it—that a monochromatic radiation is propagated, through a perfectly regular periodic structure of characteristic spacing less than one-half the wavelength of the radiation, without coherent scattering. In relation to the de Broglie waves of the conduction electrons in metals this result implies (on the classical picture) an infinite particle mean free path in a perfect crystal of infinite extent. The wave-mechanical interpretation of non-zero resistivity, therefore, ascribes the scattering of the waves (and so the resistance of the metal) to the 'imperfections' of the lattice.* Within the limits of our treatment, which hitherto has been restricted to the altogether elusive ideal of the 'perfectly pure' specimen, the only intrinsic imperfection that we can allow is the thermal vibration of the lattice atoms. Because of this effect, the instantaneous aspect of the actual lattice, at an arbitrary time, is not a perfectly regular array of lattice atoms, but rather an array which is disordered to an extent which is greater as the temperature is greater. The effective mean free path for scattering is determined by the scale of this thermal disorder†: obviously, it is many times greater than the interatomic distance in all practical situations; obviously, also, the effective mean free path decreases (and so the resistivity increases) as the temperature rises.

We set ourselves the task of showing how the unexpectedly long free paths of the conduction electrons, according to classical theory, arise naturally in the wave-mechanical treatment of the problem. This we have done—at least as far as simple qualitative arguments can take us. For the first time, since we originally imposed the condition (p. 320) that we should be confining attention to perfectly pure metals, we have, in the course of this discussion, admitted the impossibility of ever attaining that ideal in practice. Here we may usefully interpose, very briefly, a reference to the effects of such residual impurities as must inevitably be present in any piece of metal actually available for experiment. Basically, the impurity atoms represent 'imperfections' in the lattice, according to the terminology that we have just been using. Even if there were no thermal vibration of the lattice atoms, these impurity imperfections would define a mean free path for scattering (very long indeed compared with the interatomic distance in a very pure specimen) —and there would be a small component of resistivity associated

* This view derives from the work of Felix Bloch (b. 1905) in 1928, when he was a young research student in the university of Leipzig.

† The most striking example of this effect, on the macroscopic scale, is the optical opalescence of fluids under near-critical-state conditions—an effect examined in detail by W.H.Keesom (1911), R.Fürth (1920) and others.

with that scattering. It is generally found, with actual specimens, that the resistivity does not decrease monotonically as the temperature is reduced, but rather reaches a constant small value beyond which it does not fall significantly at still lower temperatures. From what we have said, this is just the behaviour that we should expect if this residual resistivity were due to impurity imperfections, the mean free path associated with which would be very nearly independent of the temperature of the specimen.

At this point it is useful to interpose another consideration of a more general character. In our recent discussions we have been attempting to make the transition from a classical to a wave-mechanical description of the basic electron-transport phenomena in metals. In so doing we have naïvely carried forward the classical concept of mean free path, as if it had a natural place in the new formalism. It has, in fact, no such place, being essentially a statistical concept valid only within the domain of particle physics. It will be worth while, therefore, to show how the phenomenon of electrical conduction can be described, formally, without use of this concept. In this way, whilst still employing classical terms, we shall approximate more closely to the point of view which is fundamental to the wave-mechanical treatment. At first sight, in abandoning the concept of particle free paths, we shall appear to have sacrificed unnecessarily the crispness of detail of the old description—but the more carefully the small-scale phenomena of physics are studied, the more certain it becomes that the old classical crispness is illusory in this context. The simple empirical fact that beams of electrons exhibit wave-like properties provides irrefutable evidence that in the realm of the very small Nature is not crisply organised according to the pattern of the model-makers of the nineteenth century. In the twentieth century we have to live with this conclusion.

Let us return, then, to the electron energy distribution of Sommerfeld represented by equations (201)-(203). This distribution, we suppose, represents the state of affairs in respect of the free electrons in a good conductor in the absence of an applied field. It can equally well be represented by a velocity distribution function (in respect of the 'resultant' velocities—or speeds—of the electrons)—or, in greater detail, by three (formally identical) distribution functions relating to the components, with respect to any arbitrary set of rectangular axes, of the resultant velocities.

These last three distributions are mutually indistinguishable because, in the absence of a field, there is no streaming of electrons in any 'preferred' direction in the specimen. In the limiting case when the temperature is zero, so that the energy distribution function (equation (201)) takes the simple form

$$N(E) = \frac{3n}{2E_0^{\frac{3}{2}}} E^{\frac{1}{2}} \qquad (0 \leqslant E \leqslant E_0),$$

the resultant velocities (speeds) of the electrons are represented by the function

$$F(v) = \frac{3n}{v_0^3} v^2 \qquad (0 \leqslant v \leqslant v_0) \qquad (209)$$

and the velocity components, in any arbitrary direction i, by the function

$$f(v_i) = \frac{3n}{4v_0} \left(1 - \frac{v_i^2}{v_0^2}\right) \qquad (-v_0 \leqslant v_i \leqslant v_0) \qquad (210)$$

In each case $v_0^2 = 2E_0/m$, E_0 is given by equation (203), as before, n is the number of free electrons per unit volume of the conductor, and $F(v)dv/n$ and $f(v_i)dv_i/n$ represent, respectively, the fraction of the electrons having speeds between v and $v+dv$, or velocity components (in the direction i) between v_i and $v_i + dv_i$, as the case may be.

We have already introduced the notion that, at temperatures other than the absolute zero, the equilibrium state of the conduction electrons (in the absence of an applied field) is a 'slightly perturbed' variant of the zero-temperature state that we have just described in greater detail than before. It is our present object to extend the use of this concept of a 'steady, but slightly perturbed, state' to take count of the applied field situation as well.

We revert, then, to the case of the long cylindrical metallic conductor (length l, cross-sectional area A) between the ends of which a difference of potential V is maintained (p. 324). We take the axis of the conductor as the axis of x. In this situation, the effect of the applied field may be specified in terms of the constant acceleration a ($= Ve/ml$) effective in augmenting the x-component of velocity of each of the conduction electrons. The y- and z-components of velocity are unaffected by the field. We specify the action of the lattice in terms of a characteristic 'relaxation time', τ. It is through interactions with the lattice atoms, in the absence of the field, that the conduction electrons preserve the velocity (or energy) distribution appropriate to the temperature of the conductor. If these distributions were to become significantly different from the equilibrium forms, for any cause (which then ceased to act), the process of restoration of the equilibrium state would not be instantaneous. In the present case, the applied field tends continuously to 'distort' the distribution of x-component velocities: in respect of this type of 'distortion' it is assumed that the tendency towards restoration of the equilibrium distribution, for small distortions, is expressible in terms of an exponential decay law (compare §6.3). If the applied field were suddenly removed, at a time when each conduction electron had acquired, through the previous action of the field, an additional velocity u_0 in the x-direction, then, after a time t, the (average) additional x-component velocity remaining, per conduction electron, would, on this assumption, be given by

$$u = u_0 e^{-t/\tau} \qquad (211)$$

τ being the relaxation time for this particular type of perturbation. According to equation (211), the 'normalising' effect of the electron-lattice interactions is expressed by a deceleration term

$$\frac{du}{dt} = -\frac{u}{\tau} \qquad (212)$$

Contrariwise, the 'distorting' action of the field is given by

$$\frac{du}{dt} = a = \frac{Ve}{ml},$$

as we have already agreed. On the assumption that a steady state is reached when the field is steadily applied, these two effects must balance; on this basis there will be a permanent small distortion of the distribution of the x-components of velocity of the conduction electrons, to the extent of a superposed drift velocity u_0 given by

$$\frac{u_0}{\tau} = \frac{Ve}{ml} \qquad (213)$$

under the conditions specified. Under these conditions the lattice atoms are absorbing momentum (in the x-direction) from the conduction electrons at an effectively steady rate of mu_0/τ per electron (see equation (212))—and they are absorbing kinetic energy at a rate that we must now proceed to calculate.

We have already deduced (p. 325) the average increase in kinetic energy resulting from the superposition of a small drift velocity u on the randomly-directed velocities v of a large number of electrons all of which originally have the same kinetic energy ($\frac{1}{2}mv^2$). We concluded that the average energy increase per electron is $\frac{1}{2}mu^2$, in these circumstances, whatever the value of v. In general, then, if p_x is the additional momentum, per electron, in the x-direction, and W is the average energy increase, under these conditions, we have, simply,

$$W = \frac{p_x^2}{2m}$$

and, hence, formally

$$\frac{dW}{dt} = u\,\frac{dp_x}{dt} \tag{214}$$

For the conduction electrons in our cylindrical conductor, in the steady state, when the applied field is V/l, $u = u_0$ and, as we have already concluded, the effect of the electron-lattice interaction is represented by

$$\frac{dp_x}{dt} = -\frac{mu_0}{\tau}.$$

Thus, for the conduction electrons, on the average, the rate of absorption of kinetic energy into the lattice is given by

$$\frac{dW}{dt} = -\frac{mu_0^2}{\tau},$$

or, substituting from equation (213), by

$$\frac{dW}{dt} = -\frac{V^2 e^2 \tau}{ml^2}$$

per conduction electron. For the entire conductor, the net rate of energy transfer to the lattice is then

$$P = V^2 \frac{A}{l}\frac{ne^2\tau}{m} \tag{215}$$

This is the rate of 'Joule heating', for which, on the basis of the classical free-electron theory we previously obtained the result given in equation (191). Continuing the argument as before, we now obtain for the resistivity

$$\rho = \frac{m}{ne^2\tau} \tag{216}$$

in place of the result given in equation (192). Comparing equation (216) with that equation, we see that the relaxation time τ has taken the place of $\lambda/2v$.* With the disappearance of the purely classical quantity mean free path, the steady-state 'thermal' velocity of the electrons is no longer specifically represented in the expression for ρ. In respect of the temperature variation of resistivity, we are not now invited to speculate whether it is the mean free path or the thermal velocity of the electrons which is temperature-sensitive: on the basis of equation (216) we conclude, simply, that the relaxation time is inversely proportional to the absolute temperature, for good conductors. On the same basis, and making use of our previous calculations (p. 327), we estimate that, at ordinary temperatures, when there is one free electron per lattice atom, the relaxation time is of the order of 10^{-14} sec in a representative metal.

There is one further order-of-magnitude calculation which will help to give reality to our formal descriptions. The central notion that we have been exploring is that of the very slightly distorted, steady-state, velocity (or energy) distribution which characterises the conduction electrons when current is flowing through a conductor. We have agreed that when the applied field is V/l, so that the conduction electrons acquire and preserve a steady drift velocity u_0 proportional to the field (equation (213)), the total kinetic energy of the conduction electrons is raised by an amount which corresponds to $\frac{1}{2}mu_0$ per electron. Let us calculate by how much the temperature of the specimen must be raised (the electric field being 'switched off') in order that the total kinetic energy of the conduction electrons shall be increased by the same amount. We already have an expression (p. 339) for the thermal capacity per electron on the basis of Sommerfeld's calculation (and we have

---

* The factor 2 in this expression arises from the approximations introduced into our classical-theory calculations; it does not represent a specifically quantum-theory effect.

discussed the smallness of this quantity in relation to the gas-kinetic value—so that a large increase of temperature is necessary to produce a significant increase of energy). Using this expression, and the expression for u_0, if an increase of temperature ΔT is equivalent in respect of energy increase to an applied field V/l, we have

$$\frac{\pi^2}{2}\frac{kT}{E_0}k\Delta T = \frac{e^2\tau^2}{2m}\left(\frac{V}{l}\right)^2,$$

or

$$\Delta T = \frac{1}{\pi^2}\frac{E_0}{kT}\frac{e^2\tau^2}{km}\left(\frac{V}{l}\right)^2.$$

Taking the values for the representative good conductor that we used in previous calculations (p. 326), E_0/kT is of the order of 220 when $T = 300°$K, and $\tau = 10^{-14}$ sec (see above); thus, numerically, V/l being expressed in volts per metre and T in degrees Kelvin, under these conditions,

$$\Delta T = 4\cdot4 \times 10^{-12}\left(\frac{V}{l}\right)^2.$$

We conclude that, even in extreme conditions (say, when the applied field is as great as 10^5 volts per metre), ΔT is very much less than $1°$C. The steady distortion of the energy distribution of the conduction electrons on account of the field, in any practical situation, is insignificant to a high degree.

Let us summarise our discussion very briefly. We have provided a description of the conduction process in which the classical concept of particle free path does not enter. This description is less clear-cut than the classical description, but formally it is equally comprehensive—and it is less at variance with the basic principles of wave mechanics than was the earlier version. It focuses attention on the essential problem which the theorist has to tackle in order to calculate the resistivity in any case: he has to calculate the relaxation time τ, given the energy distribution of the conduction electrons and a full specification of the lattice. There is no doubt, in one sense, what fraction of the free electrons take part in the conduction process: under conditions of steady current flow effectively all these electrons drift in the field with velocity u_0; n, in equation (216), is the total number of free electrons per unit volume of the conductor. But in another sense, the description, as we have given it, does not answer the question from which electrons the 'Joule heat' is transferred to the atoms of the lattice. The details of that transfer remain undisclosed, only the time-scale of the process is represented by the parameter τ. But we must accept the answer which we gave previously: if it is a question of gaining a small amount of energy in a 'sudden' process, 'only the electrons possessing the largest energies in the unperturbed distribution are available as energy receptors' (p. 337) —similarly, if it is a matter of giving up energy to the lattice atoms, only the selfsame electrons are possible donors.

In this brief account of the application of quantum notions, and the use of wave mechanics, in relation to the behaviour of the conduction electrons in a metal, it has been necessary to make many statements which the reader will have no option but to accept on trust. It is satisfactory, therefore, that, theoretical considerations apart, there is evidence of a fairly direct character to show that, in the simplest cases, the energy spectrum of these electrons is indeed very closely as given in terms of equations (201)-(203) and represented graphically in fig. 41. Basically, the difference between the classical and quantum theoretical viewpoints centres on the form of this energy spectrum, and, because the difference in this respect is very considerable, it is the more important that there should be independent support for the 'new' point of view. The evidence in question is provided by a study, under high resolution, of the softer characteristic X-rays of the metallic elements. The first significant results were obtained by T.H. Osgood in 1933 and H.M. O'Bryan and H.W.B. Skinner in 1934; later, refinements in technique enabled R.H. Kingston (1951) to make a detailed and successful study of the spectra of the very soft X-rays of sixteen metals, ranging from lithium ($Z = 3$) to zinc ($Z = 30$). Since then, these studies have been very considerably extended, and qualitatively similar results have been obtained with non-metals also.

We have already given a general account, in terms of the Bohr atom model, of the process of characteristic X-ray emission (p. 280). One of the more-tightly-bound electrons having been removed from the atom, a less-tightly-bound electron 'falls' to take its place. In this way a quantum of energy is liberated as an X-ray photon. In Table 2 (p. 284) we gave the binding energies of the extranuclear electrons in an atom of platinum. Strictly, the tabulated values refer to an isolated atom: in that case all the energy values are well defined. If an isolated atom of platinum were ionised in (say) the O_{II} shell, the vacancy would eventually be filled by the P_I electron, and the quantum energy of the very soft X-ray ('extreme ultra-violet') photon would be 56 eV (effective wavelength 220 Å, or $2·2 \times 10^{-8}$ m). In platinum metal, on the other hand, we imagine that all the P_I electrons are 'free'—each in a state of permanent disassociation from the residual ion (lattice 'atom'). According to the wave-mechanical theory, the energies of these P_I (conduction) electrons are no longer unique, but are distributed over a relatively wide range (a few eV). If atoms of platinum in a lump of metal were ionised in the O_{II} shell (the energies of all the 'bound' electrons remain essentially well defined in the metal), the spectral 'line' corresponding to the filling of these vacancies by electrons from the conduction 'band' would, on this basis, have a breadth (on the energy scale) equal to the energy breadth of the conduction band. In more detail, the line shape of the emission line would be directly related to the shape of the energy spectrum of the conduction electrons. The experiments of Kingston (and, less completely, those of his predecessors) showed, beyond possible doubt, for the 'simplest' metallic elements that we have referred to, that the spectral lines of the corresponding radiations have the predicted shapes—and the expected breadths. For lithium metal, for example, Kingston's experimental value of E_0 was $4·2 \pm 0·3$ eV, for aluminium it was $11·8 \pm 0·5$ eV, and for copper $7·0 \pm 0·5$ eV: according to equation (203), on the basis of one free electron per lattice atom in each case, these values should be 4·7 eV, 11·7 eV and 7·1 eV, respectively.* The agreement is certainly as good as could be expected, having regard to the difficulties of the experiments, and possible uncertainties regarding the strict applicability of the theory (of necessity, the radiation analysed in the spectrometer originated in atoms not many layers deep below the surface of the metal target).

The notion of a fundamental (sub-atomic) unit of charge did not, as we know, commend itself to Maxwell (p. 215). For that reason he did not permit himself to speculate on the physical mechanism involved in the conduction of electricity through metallic conductors. On the other hand he wrote (1873) 'the mechanical

---

* The corresponding values in joules are $7·5 \times 10^{-19}$, $18·7 \times 10^{-19}$ and $11·4 \times 10^{-19}$ (see p. 254).

force which urges a conductor carrying a current across the lines of magnetic force acts, not on the electric current, but on the conductor which carries it'. In 1879, Edwin Herbert Hall (1855-1938), at that time a pupil of Rowland in Baltimore, carried out an experiment which went a long way to refute the view of Maxwell, and substantiate the contrary view (see p. 169) to which Rowland himself was more favourably disposed.

Hall's experiment consisted in applying a magnetic field at right angles to the surface of a thin rectangular strip of gold through which a current was passing in the direction of its longest dimension. He found that, across the strip, in a direction at right angles to the directions of both the current flow and the magnetic field, a difference of potential was established which was proportional to the product of the current and the field. If the (conventional positive) current were regarded as flowing in the positive direction of x, and the magnetic field direction were regarded as the positive direction of y, then the difference of potential could be described in terms of a separation of positive and negative charge parallel to the axis of z such that (the rectangular axes being a right-handed set) negative charge accumulated along that edge of the strip which was towards the positive side of the z-axis and positive charge along the edge which was towards the negative side of that axis.

According to equation (59), the mechanical ('ponderomotive') force on the strip, under the conditions that we have specified, is along the positive direction of z. This being the case, Hall's observations may be understood, on the assumption that the force acts in the first instance on the charged carriers of the current (see equation (105)), provided that the carriers (in gold) carry a negative charge. The 'Hall e.m.f.' is then the measure of the transverse difference of potential which must be maintained across the strip if the drift of carriers across the direction of current flow (for which drift the magnetic field is responsible) is to be effectively annulled. Before the magnetic field is applied there is no excess of charge, of one sign or the other, anywhere throughout the strip, although the current is flowing. As soon as the field is established, the carriers drift in the direction of the resulting transverse force until the overall separation of charge in that direction is sufficient to generate the nullifying electrostatic field required.

Let us formulate the statements that we have just made, more precisely. If u_0 is the mean drift velocity of the carriers in the direction of current flow, and e is the charge, the current density, j, is given by

$$j = neu_0,$$

n being the number of carriers per unit volume of the conductor. When a magnetic field of flux density B is applied, the time-average of the effective transverse force on a single carrier is eu_0B. Here we write 'effective force', relying on the fact that there is no 'transverse' e.m.f. when there is no current flow, however large the magnetic field.* We suppose that, in the steady state, the separation of charge parallel to the direction of this force is such as to produce a transverse electrostatic field of intensity E. Then the necessary steady-state condition is

$$Ee = eu_0B,$$

or $$E = \frac{jB}{ne} \qquad (217)$$

Nowadays, it is general to refer to the quantity E/jB as the 'Hall coefficient' for the material under consideration. If we denote the measure of this quantity by R, we have

$$R = \frac{1}{ne} \qquad (218)$$

(In relation to equations (217) and (218), it should be noted that for a given specimen, when the measured Hall e.m.f. is V, the value of E is given by $E = V/b$, b being the breadth of the rectangular strip employed.)

Hall's first experiments (carried out nearly twenty years before

---

* All along we are assuming that u_0 is very small compared with the thermal velocities of the conduction electrons. When there is no current ($u_0 = 0$) the overall effect of an applied magnetic field is to cause a circulation of charge around the field direction (in the classical picture all the paths are slightly curved in the same sense, but there is no change in the speed of the electrons). There is a tendency towards a transverse drift of charge only when there is a longitudinal current and an applied magnetic field. If all electrons always had the same free path, and thus acquired the same velocity u_0 from the longitudinal field, the Hall field would cancel this tendency completely and the circulation would be effectively the same as in the absence of current. In fact, because the free paths of individual electrons at any (finite) 'instant' are not all the same, there is a second-order back-and-forth transport of electrons across the conductor, deriving energy from the Hall field, effectively increasing the Joule heat (for constant current), and so the resistivity of the specimen. This effect was first studied in detail by P.L.Kapitza (b. 1894) in 1929.

the discovery of the negative electron) were made, as we have already stated, with gold as conductor. Over the next five years he extended his investigations to other materials, and found that the magnitude of the effect varied very greatly from one substance to another—and that even the sign of the effect was not always the same (it appeared, on a simple interpretation, that the current carriers were positively charged in some materials and negatively charged in others). Many other investigators joined in this general field of research, so that when the classical free-electron theory of metallic conduction came to be formulated at the turn of the century much detailed information concerning the Hall effect (and other related effects which we have not the space to enumerate here) had been accumulated—but on a crude interpretation almost half the materials investigated appeared to owe their conductivity to the motion of positive carriers.

In recent years considerably more order has become apparent in the empirical results. The 'simplest' metals, from our point of view—and the best conductors—are the elements of group I of the periodic table of Mendeleeff. These monovalent chemical elements are, one would surmise on any basis of estimation, the most likely to have one free electron per atom in the solid state. For all these metals—the alkali metals and copper, silver and gold*—the Hall coefficient is negative (that is, the sign of the Hall e.m.f. is what would be predicted on the assumption of negative carriers), also the absolute values 'make sense' when interpreted in terms of equation (218). On the basis of this equation, values of α (the number of free electrons per lattice atom) may be calculated from measured values of the Hall coefficient at ordinary temperatures as follows:

Li, 0·80; Na, 0·99; K, 1·12; Cu, 1·34; Ag, 1·27; Au, 1·47.

It will be realised that our discussion of the Hall effect, up to this stage, has been carried out entirely on a classical theory basis. For the metals of group I, at least, such a procedure reveals no gross inadequacy in the theory, provided always that the finer details of the phenomenon are not in question. Equally clearly, the classical theory is demonstrably inadequate as a basis for the

---

* According to more modern classifications it is customary to sub-divide Mendeleeff's groups, placing the alkali metals in group IA and copper, silver and gold in group IB.

description of the effect in those cases in which the Hall coefficient is positive. Amongst metallic conductors this is the situation with beryllium, iron, zinc, molybdenum, cadmium and tungsten. Unless we are to assume that in these metals conduction is indeed effected by positive carriers, we are forced to conclude that the interpretation of the empirical results is more complicated than we had supposed. We shall return, briefly, to this problem in the next section (p. 362); here, to bring our discussion of metallic conduction to an end, we shall describe an experiment which indicates clearly that, not only for metals of group I, but for all others, the carriers of current are, in fact, negative electrons.

The experiment was first carried out, with adequate precision, using the metals copper (group I) and aluminium (group III), for both of which the Hall coefficient is negative, in the research laboratories of the General Motors Corporation at Detroit, by C. T. Kettering and G. G. Scott, in 1944. The metal under investigation was used in the form of a circular coil of wire suspended in a horizontal plane by a torsion fibre. Essentially the object was to determine the magnitude and sign of the impulsive angular momentum communicated to the coil when a steady current was reversed in it. Necessarily, the experiment involved many difficulties which we cannot here discuss (or the methods used to surmount them). It must suffice if we indicate the underlying principle and quote the results.

Suppose, then, that a (conventionally positive) current is flowing in a known direction in a wire of cross-sectional area A forming a closed circular loop of radius r ($r^2 \gg A$). Let n be the number of charge carriers per unit volume of the wire, e and m be the charge and mass of a carrier, and u_0 be the mean drift velocity in the conditions of the experiment. Then the 'total drift momentum' of all the carriers in motion in the wire is $2\pi r A n m u_0$, and when the current is reversed there is an impulsive change in the angular momentum of the carriers, and an equal and oppositely directed change in the angular momentum of the suspended system, of amount $4\pi r^2 A n m u_0$ about the axis of suspension. The first qualitative decision which the experiment can make is whether this latter change is in the same sense as the change in the direction of the conventional current (as it would be for negatively-charged carriers)—then, if the observations permit the quantitative estimation of the impulsive change, the specific charge of the carrier can be deduced, as we shall proceed to demonstrate. If i is the current which is reversed in the wire, we have

$$i = Aneu_0;$$

thus the impulsive change in angular momentum, ΔH, is given by

$$\Delta H = 4\pi r^2 i \frac{m}{e}.$$

Obviously, a measurement of $\Delta H/i$ determines e/m when r is known.

In the 1944 experiments of Kettering and Scott, the impulsive change in the angular momentum of the suspended coil was found to be proportional to the strength of the current reversed, for wires of copper and aluminium, the direction of this change was found to be that appropriate to a sudden change in drift momentum of negatively-charged carriers, and the mean value of the specific charge of these carriers, as deduced from the observations, was $1\cdot76 \times 10^{11}$ coulomb/kg—almost exactly the value of the specific charge of the negative electron (see p. 181). In 1951, Scott, still in the employment of the General Motors Corporation, repeated the experiment with a suspended coil of cadmium wire, obtaining essentially the same result. The 'true' carriers in this metal, for which the Hall coefficient is positive, are certainly negatively charged, and the measured value of their specific charge ($1\cdot8 \times 10^{11}$ coulomb/kg) proves beyond question that they are negative electrons also. In the same year similar results were obtained by S. Brown and S. J. Barnett, in California, with zinc and molybdenum. Clearly, an explanation of the positive Hall coefficients is to be sought elsewhere than in the sign of charge of the actual carriers (see p. 367).

7.3. SEMICONDUCTORS

Of the various criteria that we proposed (p. 320) for the purpose of distinguishing metallic conductors, possibly the most fundamental is that which requires that the resistivity should be fairly closely proportional to the absolute temperature over a considerable range. There are some two dozen elementary substances which, in the solid state, have resistivities less than 10^{-7} ohm m at $0°C$; almost twice as many are characterised by temperature coefficients of resistivity which are positive over the range 0° C to 100° C and of the appropriate order of magnitude. In regarding this criterion as more fundamental than any other, we are emphasising the fact that in metallic conductors the temperature dependence of the resistivity is determined by the behaviour of the lattice atoms, rather than by any feature of the energy distribution of the conduction electrons which may be temperature-dependent. We have already hinted (p. 335) that if α, the number of free electrons per lattice atom, were to vary with temperature, we should expect α to increase, and the resistivity of the specimen to decrease, as the temperature increased.

There is a fairly small class of elementary substances of moderately high resistivity (greater than 10^{-4} ohm m at 0° C) for which the resistivity decreases rapidly as the temperature is raised. Carbon (graphite), silicon and germanium (of group IV) and selenium and tellurium (of group VI) are the best known examples of this class. We refer to them as 'intrinsic semiconductors'. Fairly closely, over a considerable range of temperature, the reciprocal of the resistivity (conductivity) varies exponentially, as $e^{-b/T}$, T being the absolute temperature and the constant b being characteristic of the particular substance concerned. On the basis of classical statistical theory there is good reason to suppose that a temperature variation of this type reflects the fact that the number of electrons available for conduction increases rapidly as the temperature increases. Indeed, it is a general result, due to Boltzmann, that if there are two possible energy states for the individual 'particles' of an assembly of similar particles, then in thermal equilibrium at temperature T the ratio of the numbers of particles in the higher and lower energy states, respectively, is $e^{-W/kT}$, where W is the difference in energy of the states and k is Boltzmann's constant. Following the work of Bloch (footnote, p. 342), we have now come to recognise that the energy states of the least-tightly-bound atomic electrons in an elementary solid are grouped in quasi-continuous 'allowed bands' (see below). It is natural to explore the possibility that in intrinsic semiconductors two of these bands are separated by a not-too-large 'energy gap', and that it is only when an electron is 'thermally excited' from the lower to the upper band that it becomes effective for the purpose of conduction. The experimentally observed temperature variation of conductivity would appear to admit of a natural interpretation on this basis. As long ago as

1914, basically the same suggestion had been made by J. Königsberger.

We have stated the Pauli exclusion principle in the form: no two electrons in the same atom can have the same set of four quantum numbers. This is not the same assertion as that no two electrons in an isolated atom can 'occupy the same energy level', or have the same binding energy. The point was clearly made when we listed the complete set of single-electron binding energies for the platinum atom (p. 284): there are 78 extranuclear electrons in that atom and only 20 different binding energies. We stated, then, that the number of electrons in any atomic level tends to be even: we might say more precisely that there is no atomic energy level which could not be occupied by an even number of electrons, given suitable conditions. In neutral atoms of odd atomic number, of necessity at least one level must have an odd number of electrons: in fact, in such atoms, never more than one level is so occupied. In atoms of even atomic number, usually every level carries an even number of electrons: in this connection platinum (which we took as example throughout much of our discussion in the last chapter) is one of a small minority of exceptions. As we stated earlier, two of the 'outermost' levels in platinum carry odd numbers of electrons.

It is a result of Bloch's 'band theory' that, corresponding to each atomic energy level which is capable of accommodating a (maximum, even) number β of electrons, there are precisely $N\beta$ distinguishable electronic energy states in a lump of metal consisting of N similar atoms. In Sommerfeld's theory, which we used exclusively in the last section, the notion of discrete bands, each containing a finite number of possible energy states, did not arise. Sommerfeld's basic assumption had been that the free electrons within a metal move in an essentially field-free space (when no external fields are applied). This was, admittedly, a 'zero-order' approximation to the truth. When, instead, Bloch took a three-dimensionally periodic function to represent the potential field of the lattice atoms (ions) as 'seen' by the electrons, the band structure of the permitted energy states appeared naturally in the solution of his problem. We have used the Sommerfeld theory—it has seemed with some success—but only for the very best metallic conductors. That for these substances (elements of group I of the periodic classification) there is only a single electron in the outermost atomic level is the key to such success as we have had. In respect of N atoms only N electrons are available to fill the $2N$ allowed states of the 'conduction band', and it turns out that Sommerfeld's approximation does not seriously distort the resulting description: equation (201) is a sufficiently good representation of the distribution of states in the lower half of that band (though not of the whole band)—and that is all that is necessary for our purposes. We now have to consider the general situation—and we must abandon Sommerfeld's approximation in favour of the more realistic theory of Bloch.

When there are two electrons in the least-tightly-bound atomic level, these electrons occupy completely the $2N$ states constituting the allowed band in the elementary solid—and, if that were the end of the matter, the solid material would be a perfect insulator. We have accepted the principle that no changes of energy (or momentum) are possible within the band unless there are 'vacant states' to which 'transitions' may occur. These simple considerations, however, do not encompass the whole story. As the experiments of Franck and Hertz showed (p. 263), there are discrete energy levels in every atom to which an outer electron may be raised, when energy is absorbed by the system, transitions from which levels are responsible for 'optical' spectra generally. These energy levels, characterised by smaller binding energies than the ground-state level of the outermost electron in the neutral atom, are certainly possible levels for 'free' electrons in the solid. And, just as the ground-state level from which these electrons originate becomes broadened into a band of states, when the atoms are brought together in the solid, so these excited states also generate bands of finite extension. It may be that the band corresponding to the first excited state overlaps the ground-state band on the energy scale, or it may be that there is a gap in energy between the lower limit of the one and the upper limit of the other. From what we have said regarding the magnitude of first ionisation energies (p. 269), we shall not be greatly in error if we estimate the range of possible values of the energy gap as 0 to 5 eV.

When the two bands that we have considered overlap, then obviously the resultant continuum of states is capable of accommodating more than two free electrons per atom. In such cases the solid may indeed be a moderately good conductor, rather than an insulator, when in the isolated atom there are two electrons in the least-tightly-bound state. On this basis, or on the basis of the overlapping of other states, the conductivity of beryllium, magnesium, calcium, cobalt, nickel, zinc and cadmium may be generally understood.

If the two allowed energy bands do not overlap, then the magnitude of the energy gap determines the degree of conductivity of the solid material at any temperature. Ideally, at the absolute zero all such solids would be perfect insulators, provided only that the gap is of finite width. Otherwise, under equilibrium conditions, there will be some electrons in the lower energy states of the upper band—the more the higher the temperature and the smaller the width of the gap. If, in energy units, the gap width is W, we might naïvely expect that an order-of-magnitude estimate of the fraction of the valency electrons excited to the upper band at temperature T would be given by the Boltzmann factor $e^{-W/kT}$, but, in fact, detailed calculation shows that this is not the case. Taking a simple model in which the distribution of states in the lower range of the upper band is given by the Sommerfeld formula (equation (201)), and assuming that the distribution in the upper range of the lower (valency) band is the mirror-image of that distribution, we find that the fraction of valency electrons excited to the upper band is of the order of $e^{-W/2kT}$. Since $k = 8 \cdot 6 \times 10^{-5}$ eV deg^{-1} K, numerically this is a small fraction ($< 1/400$), for $T(°\text{K}) < 10^3 W (\text{eV})$). A material of gap width 1 eV, therefore, at ordinary temperatures, is at the best a very poor conductor— but its conductivity increases rapidly as the temperature rises.

Let us consider this model* of a semiconducting material a little more closely. Hitherto we have implied that the conductivity is completely described in terms of those electrons which, under equilibrium conditions, through 'thermal excitation', occupy a very small proportion of the (lower lying) energy states in the allowed band which corresponds to the first excited state of a 'valency electron' in the isolated atom. This is not, in fact, the full story. In the conditions of thermal equilibrium that we are considering, the allowed band corresponding to the atomic ground state is depleted of electrons in exact measure as the upper band is populated. There are as many vacant levels (or 'holes') among the uppermost states in the former as there are occupied levels in the latter. Let us consider these vacancies in relation to the velocity

* Originally developed by A.H.Wilson (b. 1906) in 1931.

distribution functions that we have already introduced in our earlier discussion (p. 343). If there were no vacancies in the ground-state band, then the velocity distribution of the electrons in the band would be 'spherically symmetrical', whatever the value of the applied field (the material being an insulator—see above). If there were no applied field, and a relatively small number of vacancies of the type that we are discussing, the velocity distribution of the electrons in the not-quite-full band would still be spherically symmetrical (that is, the vacancies, themselves, if they were filled, would relate to a sub-population of electrons carrying no net current in any direction in the specimen). In these conditions, when a field is applied, distortion of the distribution takes place (distortion is possible just because there are vacancies), there is a slight balance of velocities in the direction in which negatively-charged carriers would move in the field (the magnitude of this effective drift velocity being determined by the relaxation time appropriate to the case—see p. 345) and, as a consequence, there is a current due to the electrons in the slightly depleted band, over and above that carried by the electrons whose thermal excitation to the upper band is responsible for the depletion of the lower band.

It is in many ways convenient to describe this 'depletion current' in terms appropriate to the vacant energy states in the nearly-full ground-state band, the so-called 'holes' in the velocity (or energy) distribution. On this basis, the departure from spherical symmetry which the application of a steady field imposes on the velocity distribution of the ground-state electrons may be seen as an excess of 'holes' having components of velocity in the direction in which positive carriers would move in the field. That is, the vacant states in the distorted velocity distribution are states which collectively describe motion in this direction. If these states were filled (with negative electrons), so completing the whole band, this motion would exactly counterbalance the motion of the electrons actually populating the band (an applied field can have no effect on a completely full band). Obviously, therefore, we may describe the actual situation, either as we have already done, in terms of the 'real' motion of the negative electrons which nearly fill the allowed band in the energy spectrum, or in terms of fictitious carriers the motion of which is the 'virtual' motion appropriate to the un-occupied states. If we adopt the latter course (as it is now suggested that we should), clearly we must assign positive charges to these carriers. We are suggesting that we replace the description in terms of a nearly-full band, populated by negative electrons, with one in which the band of negative-electron states is completely full (or completely empty) and there is superimposed a distribution of positive carriers corresponding to the velocity (or energy) states which in fact are vacant. In terms of this description we come to realise that there must at least be some aspects in which the 'depletion current' which we set out to describe appears to behave as if it were due to the motion of positive carriers.

In respect of a pure intrinsic semiconductor the description that we have just outlined may be formalised quite simply. If, when the temperature is T, there are n electrons per unit volume thermally excited into the upper band, then there are also n fictitious positive carriers per unit volume (each carrying unit charge) in the depleted ground-state band. Under the influence of the applied field, E, the mean drift velocity of the electrons in the upper band is k_-E and that of the fictitious carriers in the ground-state band is k_+E, in the opposite direction. The current density, i, is then given by

$$j = ne(k_- + k_+)E \qquad (219)$$

We are assuming that, for all practicable values of the field, the drift velocities are directly proportional to the field, but the corresponding mobilities, k_- and k_+, are not in general the same—the appropriate relaxation times for the two distributions are unrelated to one another (see equation (213)*), and we have not raised the question (and it is too complex to enter into here) whether the effective mass of the fictitious carriers is the same as the electronic mass. These two parameters, together with the charge, determine the mobility of the carriers according to our previous treatment; here, taking the matter no farther than is indicated by equation (219), we do not propose to enter more deeply into a problem which we should not, in any case, be able to resolve completely within the framework of theory that we have erected hitherto.

We have stated (in effect) that there will be some aspects of the electrical properties of semiconductors, and possibly of other materials, which are to be understood, most directly, in terms of

---

* In equation (213), if we write $V/l = E$, $u_0 = kE$, we have, simply, $k = \tau e/m$.

the hypothesis of fictitious positive carriers of charge ('holes'). Detailed theoretical treatment shows that the Hall effect belongs in this category. Let us repeat the simple classical theory calculation of the Hall coefficient (p. 351), for the case of an intrinsic semiconductor, on this basis. We distinguish between E_l, the value of the applied field giving rise to the longitudinal current, of current density j_l, and E_t, the equilibrium value of the Hall field when the applied magnetic field is of flux density B. Then we re-write equation (219) in the form

$$j_l = ne(k_- + k_+)E_l \qquad (220)$$

and we note that a transverse electric field of magnitude E_t, if it were acting alone, would similarly give rise to a component of transverse current, of current density $_1j_t$ given by

$$_1j_t = ne(k_- + k_+)E_t \qquad (221)$$

In fact, transverse motion of the carriers is not due to this electric field acting alone: through the action of the magnetic field each negative carrier which is effective in conveying the main current experiences an effective transverse force ek_-E_lB (see p. 352) and each 'hole' an effective force ek_+E_lB. Because the negative carriers and the 'holes' have oppositely directed (longitudinal) drift velocities, these forces act in the same sense, and as a result there is a further net component of transverse current, of current density $_2j_t$ given by

$$_2j_t = ne(k_-^2 - k_+^2)E_lB \qquad (222)$$

(Equation (222) has been derived, by analogy with equation (221), by noting that in the former equation the (steady) force on an individual carrier is given by eE_t—and taking count of the fact that in relation to the new situation the negative carriers and 'holes' contribute components of 'Hall current' of opposite sign.) In the equilibrium situation that we are discussing, the components of transverse (negative) current represented by equations (221) and (222) must be oppositely directed—and they must, indeed, cancel completely. We have, therefore.

$$(k_- + k_+)E_t = (k_-^2 - k_+^2)E_lB,$$

and, for the Hall coefficient, $R(\equiv E_t/j_lB)$,

$$R = \frac{1}{ne} \frac{k_-^2 - k_+^2}{(k_- + k_+)^2} \qquad (223)$$

According to equation (223), the sign of the Hall coefficient for a pure intrinsic semiconductor will be different, depending on whether the mobility of the thermally excited electrons in the upper energy band is greater or less than the mobility of the corresponding 'holes' in the ground-state band. In fact, for all intrinsic semiconductors which have been studied under conditions of high purity, the Hall coefficient has been found to be negative (see p. 353). For such materials the absolute value of the coefficient decreases very rapidly as the temperature increases. This effect is the counterpart of the rapid decrease in resistivity, which we have already noted, and which we have related to the rapid increase of n, the concentration of thermally excited electrons, with increasing temperature, according to the Boltzmann equation (p. 356).

It should be clear from what has now been said that the distinction between a pure solid substance which behaves essentially as a perfect insulator at ordinary temperatures, and one which exhibits the characteristic behaviour of an intrinsic semiconductor, is one of degree rather than kind. It depends solely on the magnitude of the energy gap between the 'top' of the ground-state band and the 'bottom' of the first energy band to which electrons may be excited in the solid: ideally, at the absolute zero, all such substances would be perfect insulators (p. 359). The 'fairly small class of elementary substances' which we have identified as intrinsic semiconductors (p. 356) is just the class of elements for which this energy gap is not too large (p. 365). To these should be added certain metallic compounds which, when studied in the pure state, show the same behaviour. Lead sulphide (PbS), indium antimonide (InSb) and indium arsenide (InAs) are examples of these.

In the last section we referred briefly (p. 342) to the effect of 'residual impurities' on the electrical conductivities of metals. Generally, there is no significant effect except at low temperatures: when this effect is appreciable it is in the direction of an increase in resistivity (decrease in conductivity) due to the impurity present in small concentration. In relation to substances of low conductivity, on the other hand, the effect of impurities is enormously greater, in general, than this: it is very considerable over a large temperature range, and it is in the direction of an increase in conductivity with increasing (small) concentration of impurity. Indeed, semiconducting materials are so impurity-sensitive in respect of their electrical properties* that the notion of a 'pure intrinsic semiconductor' represents an almost unrealisable ideal. There must be many substances which would show the characteristic behaviour of intrinsic conductivity at ordinary temperatures, if only they could be prepared in a sufficiently pure state.

Applied physicists have not been slow to exploit the wide range of properties which may be achieved by the controlled addition of suitable impurities to materials which in the pure state would behave as intrinsic semiconductors. Semiconductors of technological importance are, nowadays, 'impurity (extrinsic) semiconductors', in large measure. In the trade, these materials are described as 'doped' with the impurities concerned. In the present account, following through the programme which we set ourselves at the beginning of this chapter, we can do no more than indicate in outline the theoretical ideas involved, merely making credible the broad distinction between the two types of impurity semiconductor generally recognised, the so-called n- and p-types, respectively.

Empirically, the distinction between these two types of semiconductor is in terms of the sign of the Hall coefficient. For n-type semiconductors the sign of the coefficient is that appropriate to conduction by negative carriers, for p-type materials it corresponds to conduction by positive carriers ('holes'). Apart from this difference, the properties of the two types are, qualitatively, very much the same. Usually, the conductivity is not highly temperature-dependent, at least over ordinary temperature ranges, frequently passing through a broad maximum and falling again, before rising rapidly at the highest temperatures (when the intrinsic conductivity of the base material becomes significant in comparison with the impurity effect).

Let us particularise by considering germanium as base material. This element, as we have remarked, belongs to group IV of the periodic classification. Its atomic number is 32; 28 of the extra-nuclear electrons go to complete the K, L and M shells of the atom (compare p. 284), the remaining 4 electrons (valency elec-

---

* As a numerical example we may quote the case of antimony added as an impurity to germanium. When the atomic concentration of this impurity is increased from 10^{-8} to 10^{-5}, the conductivity of the material increases a thousand-fold, at ordinary temperatures.

trons) belong to N_I and N_{II}. In respect of the solid material there is an energy gap (of some 0.746 eV) between the 'top' of the ground state band, 'completely' filled by the N_{II} electrons, and the 'bottom' of the 'empty' allowed band corresponding to the first excited state of the neutral atom. Let us take, in imagination, two samples of pure germanium and add a very small amount of arsenic to the one and a very small amount of gallium to the other. The resulting materials, made homogeneous by suitable treatment, prove to be, in the first case an n-type semiconductor, in the second a p-type semiconductor. Arsenic and gallium were chosen for this 'thought experiment' as being the group v and group III elements, respectively, belonging to the same period of the periodic classification as germanium itself. They are of atomic numbers 33 and 31, and the extranuclear electron configurations of their atoms are the same as that of the atom of germanium up to and including the two valency electrons in the N_I sub-shell. The only difference is that in the atom of gallium there is only one N_{II} electron (rather than two, as in germanium)—and in the atom of arsenic there is an additional electron in N_{III} (as well as the two in N_{II}). In the pure (solid) state, the atomic volumes of arsenic and gallium are each slightly less than the atomic volume of germanium—some 4 per cent. less in the first case, and 15 per cent. less in the second.

We erect our 'demonstration of credibility' on the basis of the factual information of the last paragraph. In the first place, it is plainly credible, on the evidence of the atomic volumes of the three solid elements, that when 'trace' amounts of arsenic or gallium are introduced homogeneously into a lump of germanium the impurity atoms should occupy regular lattice sites in the crystalline material (rather than that they should disturb the regularity of the lattice by occupying supernumerary or 'interstitial' sites). If this is accepted, then, from the point of view of electrical conductivity, the arsenic impurity in germanium is essentially an impurity of excess electrons (one N_{III} electron per atom of arsenic) —and the gallium impurity is essentially a defect impurity (the lack of one N_{II} electron per gallium atom). At the absolute zero of temperature, each excess electron would remain bound to a particular atom of arsenic, in the one case; in the other, each gallium atom in the lattice would remain the permanent site of an electron vacancy in the crystal as a whole. It is not easy, in an elementary account, to give a convincing numerical estimate of the energy of binding of the excess electron to the arsenic atom, in the first case, or of the amount of energy necessary to bring about the transfer of one of the N_{II} electrons from an atom of germanium to a gallium atom in the second. We are compelled, therefore, merely to state the facts: experiments on the temperature dependence of the conductivity of arsenic- and gallium-doped germanium lead to the conclusion that at ordinary temperatures a large fraction of the excess ('impurity') electrons are in a state of freedom from attachment to arsenic atoms in fixed sites in the lattice—and, correspondingly in the other case, that an electron vacancy is no more likely to be associated with any particular gallium atom than with one of the neighbouring atoms of germanium. If we accept this conclusion as evidence, we are led, in retrospect, to the view that the electron attachment (or separation) energies that we did not calculate must be of the order of 0·01 eV, or thereabouts. For other impurities (in the same base material) the characteristic electron attachment energies have different values, generally larger than this: it is no coincidence that we chose for purposes of example, impurities having all the 'desirable' features.

We have come to the conclusion that in arsenic-doped germanium at ordinary temperatures there are 'free electrons' in concentration of the same order as the concentration of impurity atoms in the lattice—and that in gallium-doped germanium, similarly, there are electron vacancies which are mobile in the crystal and of concentration comparable with that of the impurity atoms. Having set our sights no higher than to demonstrate the credibility of a simple theoretical account of the phenomenon, we offer no further comment than this: that for the n-type conductivity of the former material the free impurity electrons are the effective carriers; for the p-type conductivity of the latter material the mobile impurity electron vacancies are effective. Naturally, we may generalise and say that other group IV base materials (such as silicon) doped with any group V impurity (antimony, perhaps, or phosphorus) are likely to prove to be n-type semiconductors—or, conversely, to be p-type semiconductors if doped with a group III impurity (such as boron, or indium). Beyond that we have not sufficient basis in theory on which to predict with confidence.

Before we conclude this section on semiconductors it is appropriate that we should revert to the problem of the 'positive' Hall effect with certain metallic conductors, which we left without explanation at an earlier stage (p. 355). Only since we have been dealing with semiconductor properties have we introduced the notion of fictitious positive carriers of charge ('holes')—and have accepted the point of view that there are some aspects of the electrical behaviour of solids (the Hall effect being one of them) that can 'be understood, most directly, in terms of the hypothesis of . . . holes' (p. 361). It appears, empirically, that the metallic elements for which the Hall coefficient is positive are those which would be insulators (or intrinsic semiconductors) in the solid state if it were not for the fact of overlapping of allowed energy bands (p. 358). The elements in question are elements of even atomic number. Such a situation offers many possibilities in relation to 'mixed' conduction by electrons and 'holes'. In the simplest case, equation (223), suitably interpreted, should provide a satisfactory basis of interpretation of the experimental results; in other cases the theoretical expression for the Hall coefficient will be more complicated. It is not our purpose to explore these complications here: suffice to say that the occurrence of positive Hall coefficients for some elementary solids of even atomic number should cause no surprise, if we accept the background of theory which we have developed in this section.

7.4. INSULATORS

In terms of the band theory of Bloch, which we introduced in the last section, we have already indicated (p. 359) the essential characteristics of a solid material which is an insulator. It must be a pure substance—element or chemical compound—for which the energy gap between the top of the ground-state band and the bottom of the first excited-state band is very large compared with the 'Boltzmann energy' (kT) at the temperature in question. Fundamentally, then, the 'theoretical' definition of an insulator is temperature-relative—and the distinction between an insulator and an intrinsic semiconductor is a matter of degree rather than kind (p. 363). We have seen something of the reasons why impure substances are, at best, imperfect insulators (p. 364): reflecting this fact we have imposed the (unattainable) requirement of absolute purity in the formal definition.

In this section we shall not pursue the band theory description of solid insulators farther (except to quote values for the energy gap for a few such substances: carbon (diamond), 5·3 eV;

magnesium oxide, 7·4 eV; zinc oxide, 3·2 eV; zinc sulphide 3·8 eV); we shall rather revert to a completely classical model in which the atoms (or molecules) of the pure material are assumed to develop a dipole moment under the action of an applied field. On the basis of this model, if the effective value of the field acting on an atom or molecule is E', it is assumed that the induced dipole moment is $\alpha E'$ in the direction of the field. We refer to α as the polarisability of the atom or molecule concerned.* In an earlier chapter we calculated the dipole moment induced in an uncharged conducting sphere situated in a uniform electric field (p. 53). If we wish to particularise our classical model of a dielectric by representing the atoms (or molecules) of the material as conducting spheres of radius a situated in otherwise empty space, and making no contact with one another, we may interpret equation (39), writing $\gamma = 1/4\pi\epsilon_0$ (p. 118), to give

$$\alpha = 4\pi\epsilon_0 a^3 = 3\epsilon_0 \Gamma \qquad (224)$$

Γ being the volume of the model atom (or molecule) concerned.

Faraday, at an early stage (1838), put forward ideas on dielectric action which were very much as we have just outlined; later, these ideas were extended and given mathematical formulation by Ottaviano Fabrizio Mossotti (1847), Clausius (see p. 207) (1867) and Lorentz (see p. 232) (1878). It is our present purpose to follow these ideas through merely to the extent of showing how, on certain assumptions, they lead to expressions relating the macroscopically determined dielectric constant of a material, ϵ/ϵ_0 (p. 117), to the atomic (or molecular) polarisability, α, by which the ultimate constituent particles of the material are supposed to be completely described in our model.

Suppose that we consider an infinite parallel-plate condenser of which the plates A and B (fig. 45) are separated by a distance d. Let us assume that the condenser plates are isolated, and that they carry equal and opposite charges giving rise to a uniform electric field E, in the region between the plates, when the system is 'in vacuum'. In this arrangement the difference of potential between a point P, at a distance x from the negatively-charged plate, and that plate, is Ex. Suppose now that the space between

---

* Because we are here dealing with insulators (non-conductors) we can use α for polarisability without risk of confusion with the same symbol previously used to denote the mean number of 'free' conduction electrons per lattice atom (p. 327).

the plates is 'completely filled' with a dielectric material. Let there be n exactly similar atoms (molecules) per unit volume of this material, and let the atomic (molecular) polarisability be α. In this situation each atom (molecule) will develop a dipole moment $\alpha E'$ in the direction of the 'local field' E'. The essence of our problem is in the evaluation of E'.

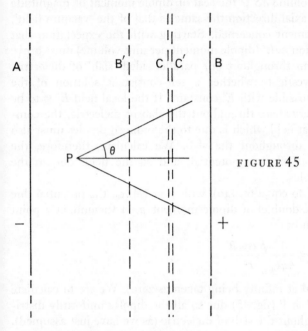

FIGURE 45

Realistically, having adopted a molecular model for our dielectric, we are bound to admit that the actual field (as 'experienced' by a hypothetical 'test charge') must vary from point to point through the material. There will be the constant component E, due to the charges on the condenser plates, and another component, due to the induced dipoles, the magnitude and direction of which will vary with the precise location of the test charge within the (regular or irregular) array of atoms (molecules) which constitute the material dielectric. The course—and outcome—of our calculation of E' will depend on the assumptions that we make in relation to this second component.

As an approximation of 'zero order', we shall assume, in relation to any atom (molecule), that the component of the local field E'

due to the induced dipoles may be calculated without explicit consideration of the contribution arising from the 'near neighbour' atoms (molecules), which, realistically, must be held to be important for our problem. For this first crude approximation we shall assume, in fact, that the structure of the dielectric material is quasi-continuous (rather than discrete), supposing that any small element of volume dS is the seat of dipole moment of magnitude $n\alpha E' dS$ and axial direction the same as that of the 'vacuum field', E, at the element concerned. Starting with the expectation that the polarisation $n\alpha E'$ (dipole moment per unit volume) must prove to be uniform throughout our parallel-sided 'slab' of dielectric, we shall investigate whether a self-consistent solution of the problem is possible with E' constant. If the local field E' is to be the same everywhere throughout the slab of dielectric, the component of that field which is due to the induced dipoles must also be constant throughout the slab. We calculate, therefore, the distribution of electric potential, and so the field, due to the induced dipoles.

According to equation (40), with $\gamma = 1/4\pi\epsilon_0$, the potential due to an electric doublet of dipole moment p, in vacuum, at a point (r, θ) is given by

$$V = \frac{1}{4\pi\epsilon_0} \frac{p \cos \theta}{r^2}$$

(the potential at infinity being taken as zero). We are to calculate the potential at P (fig. 45) due to all the dipoles uniformly distributed throughout the slab of dielectric (as we have just assumed). Let B' represent the plane in the dielectric which is parallel to the condenser plate A and distant $2x$ from that plate. Then P is centrally situated in the portion of dielectric included between A and B' and the potential at P due to the dipoles contained in this portion of the dielectric is obviously zero. (Any elementary volume of dielectric between A and B' can be matched by an exactly equal volume, such that P is midway between these two elements of volume, and because the polarisation is uniform throughout, and $\cos (\pi - \theta) = -\cos \theta$, the potential at P due to the dipoles in these two representative volume elements is zero uniquely.) At P, therefore, the potential due to all the dipoles is the same as the potential due to those dipoles contained in the portion of the dielectric between B' and B. We evaluate this potential by considering first the dipoles in an elementary stratum of dielectric lying between the planes C and C', parallel to B' and B and distant y and $y + dy$, respectively, from P.

Consider a cone, of semi-vertical angle θ having the perpendicular drawn from P to C as axis. This cone intersects C in a circle of radius $y \tan \theta$, and the corresponding cone of semi-vertical angle $\theta + d\theta$ intersects C in a circle of radius $y \tan \theta + y \sec^2 \theta \, d\theta$. These two cones intercept an elementary portion of dielectric of volume $2\pi y \tan \theta \cdot y \sec^2 \theta \, d\theta \cdot dy$, between C and C'. The dipoles in this element of volume are all similarly situated with respect to P (their axes are directed perpendicularly towards A), and their total dipole moment is $n\alpha E' 2\pi y^2 \tan \theta \sec^2 \theta \, d\theta \, dy$; they contribute to the potential at P an amount

$$\frac{1}{4\pi\epsilon_0} \frac{2\pi n\alpha E' y^2 \tan \theta \sec^2 \theta \, d\theta \, dy \cdot \cos \theta}{y^2 \sec^2 \theta}.$$

For the whole stratum CC', therefore, the contribution to the potential at P is

$$\frac{n\alpha E' dy}{2\epsilon_0} \int_0^{\pi/2} \sin \theta \, d\theta,$$

or

$$\frac{n\alpha E'}{2\epsilon_0} \, dy.*$$

We note, as we should expect when an infinite plane stratum is concerned, that the contribution to the potential at P (a 'near' point) is independent of y, the distance of P from the stratum (and that it is proportional to the thickness of the stratum). Thus the potential at P due to the dipoles contained in the portion of dielectric between B' and B (and so the potential due to all the dipoles in the whole slab of dielectric between A and B) is given by

$$V = \frac{n\alpha E'}{2\epsilon_0} (d - 2x),$$

$d - 2x$ being the distance between B' and B. By symmetry, the direction of the electric field at P, due to all the dipoles, is along the common perpendicular through P to A and B; its magnitude,

---

* We could have obtained this result directly, had we so wished, by appropriate re-interpretation of the symbols of equation (96), derived (p. 148) in relation to a uniform magnetic shell of arbitrary form.

in the sense from A towards B, is given by $-dV/dx$. This component of field, then, is of magnitude $n\alpha E'/\epsilon_0$—and it is oppositely directed to the vacuum field E. Finally, the local field, E', at P, being the resultant of these two fields (according to our present assumptions), is given by

$$E' = E - n\alpha E'/\epsilon_0 \qquad (225)$$

We see, at once, that the expectation of uniform polarisation, on which we based our calculation, has been justified in the outcome: equation (225) leads to a unique value of E', independent of x, and so to a unique value of the polarisation, $n\alpha E'$ when the vacuum field is given. Explicitly, from this equation,

$$\frac{E}{E'} = 1 + \frac{n\alpha}{\epsilon_0} \qquad (226)$$

It is from equation (226) that we obtain an expression for the macroscopically-determined dielectric constant—which is our ultimate aim. This constant, being given by the inverse ratio of the capacitances of a condenser 'in vacuum' and 'filled' with the material in question (p. 117), or by the direct ratio of the corresponding differences of potential between the condenser plates, for constant charge on the plates, in our case is equally given by the ratio of the vacuum field to the local field in the dielectric (assumed constant throughout), again for constant charge on the condenser. Writing K for the magnitude of Faraday's dielectric constant, we have, therefore, from equation (226),

$$K - 1 = \frac{n\alpha}{\epsilon_0} \qquad (227)$$

—then, substituting for α/ϵ_0 from equation (224), as would be appropriate if we were to adopt the conducting-sphere model of the atoms (molecules) of our dielectric material, we have, finally,

$$K - 1 = 3n\Gamma \qquad (228)$$

Referring to equation (228), we note that the product $n\Gamma$ represents the fraction of the total volume of the dielectric occupied by the atoms (molecules), idealised as conducting spheres. Now, the fraction of the total volume occupied by the actual atoms (molecules) must always be less than 1, even for a solid material; the effective fraction $n\Gamma$ is likely to be considerably less, just because the polarisability of the real atom (molecule) is very unlikely to be as great as that of a conducting sphere of the same radius. On the basis of an argument such as this, we might conclude, taking equation (228) at its face value, that the dielectric constant K should be significantly less than 4, for all materials. The facts are otherwise: even for so simple a material as pure carbon (in the form of diamond) $K = 5.7$.

It is perhaps not surprising that our zero-order approximation should have run into difficulties when applied to solid dielectrics. After all, we took no account of the 'graininess' of the material, and we paid no particular attention to the contribution of 'near neighbours' to the local field responsible for the polarisation of individual atoms (molecules): we considered this local field as the same everywhere, and we effectively identified it with the field which a test charge would experience in traversing the dielectric from one condenser plate to the other. Faced with the facts, we have to admit that equations (227) and (228) give a reasonable description of the dielectric properties of certain simple gases (for which $K - 1$ is proportional to the density over a significant range, and is independent of temperature)—but nothing more: in relation to more 'condensed' materials we must start again and develop our calculation from other assumptions. To a large extent we shall still retain the assumption of a quasi-continuous dielectric medium, but we shall consider separately that portion of the dielectric in the immediate neighbourhood of a representative point—and the rest of the dielectric—and we shall attempt to formulate our main problem in terms of a distribution of ('induced') charges rather than a distribution of dipoles.

For this new calculation, fig. 46 represents the arrangement of dielectric-filled, infinite parallel-plate condenser, as before. For convenience, the plane boundaries of the dielectric, A′ and B′, are shown as separated from the condenser plates, A and B, though these surfaces are macroscopically in contact in pairs. X is a representative point between A′ and B′, at which an atom (molecule) of the dielectric material is centred, the local ('polarising') field, E', in the vicinity of which we have to evaluate. Charge on the condenser plates, of surface density $-\sigma$ (on A) and $+\sigma$ (on B), is responsible for the vacuum field E, in terms of our previous nomenclature. Again, we assume that the polarisation, $n\alpha E'$, is essentially uniform throughout the material. For purposes of our present calculation we resolve the atomic (molecular) polaris-ability, α, into two factors q and λ; q represents the magnitude of a characteristic charge, and λ is the constant of proportionality relating the charge separation to the polarising field. In effect, we represent the elementary induced dipole $\alpha E'$ as a charge-doublet, q and $-q$, of separation $\lambda E'$: according to this representation there

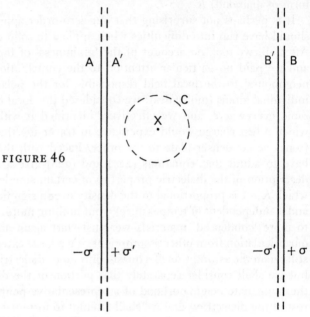

FIGURE 46

is a small physical movement of charge, across the dielectric, in the development of polarisation. The quantity of charge involved is nq, of each sign, per unit volume of the dielectric, and the net result is the appearance of charges on the boundary surfaces of the dielectric of amount $nq\lambda E'$ per unit area. To be precise, the surface charge on A' is positive and that on B' negative, in the arrangement illustrated in fig. 46. Throughout the volume of the dielectric there is no excess of charge of either sign in any elementary region large compared with the volume occupied by a single atom (molecule).

In the last three sentences we have made two positive assertions which, it may be held, we have not justified beyond possible question. It is appropriate, therefore, that we should enquire whether, if we accept these assertions as a basis of calculation, neglecting any contribution of 'near neighbours' to the local field,

E', as we did before, we are in fact led to the same expression for E' as we previously obtained. If this is indeed the case, we can proceed with our new calculation with the greater confidence. For this enquiry we denote by $\pm \sigma'$ the surface density of charge developed on A' and B', the bounding surfaces of the dielectric, and we have

$$\sigma' = nq\lambda E' = n\alpha E'.$$

Again, obviously,

$$\frac{E'}{E} = \frac{\sigma - \sigma'}{\sigma}.$$

From general principles (see equations (5) and (14), with $\gamma = 1/4\pi\epsilon_0$),

$$\sigma = \epsilon_0 E.$$

We combine these three results, and we obtain

$$\frac{E'}{E} = 1 - \frac{n\alpha E'}{\epsilon_0 E}.$$

This is equation (225) of our previous calculation: we proceed, therefore, with our new approximation, having disposed of our doubts.

It is convenient, at this stage, that we should distinguish between the values of the local (polarising) field (which we have hitherto denoted by E') as deduced on the basis of our successive approximations. Let us represent our zero-order approximate value by E'_0, and the first-order approximate value, which we are now to determine, by E'_1. E'_1 is related to the polarisation P_1, deduced on the basis of our new approximation, by the equation $P_1 = n\alpha E'_1$, and E'_0 is given (see equation (225)) by

$$E'_0 = E - P_1/\epsilon_0 \tag{229}$$

Around X (fig. 46), the centre of our representative atom (molecule), let us describe a sphere, 'large compared with the volume occupied by a single atom (molecule)' of the dielectric material, but of radius small compared with the distance between the condenser plates. This sphere is represented, considerably exaggerated in size, by C in the figure. In order to evaluate the difference between our zero-order and first-order estimates of the local field effective for the atom (molecule) at X, we admit (at last) that the structure of the dielectric material within C is indeed discrete, but we retain the fiction of a quasi-continuous medium for that portion of the dielectric which is external to C. On this basis we write, formally,

$$E'_1 - E'_0 = E_1 + E_2 \qquad (230)$$

(and we should, strictly, imply vector addition here, though we disregard this complication in what follows)—and thereby identify the two new contributions that we have to consider. E_1 represents the contribution to the local field at X due to the discrete dipoles situated within C, E_2 the contribution from any surface charge developed over the inner spherical boundary of the quasi-continuous medium which represents that portion of the dielectric external to C. We deal first with E_2.

According to our zero-order approximation the whole volume of the dielectric was regarded as quasi-continuous and uniformly polarised. This being the case, the distribution of surface charge over the boundary C of our new model must be everywhere equal and opposite to that on the surface of the uniformly polarised sphere of quasi-continuous dielectric material, which placed within C, to the exclusion of the 'actual' dipoles, and suitably orientated, would reconvert this new model into the zero-order model which we previously employed. E_2, then, is the local field at the centre of such an (isolated) sphere of dielectric, with 'reversed' polarisation P_1 ($=n\alpha E'_1$). For that calculation (see above) we take account only of the surface charges. In relation to the field directions indicated by fig. 46, and in accordance with our current notation, we have, therefore, to consider the case of an isolated sphere of dielectric of polarisation P_1 directed from left to right across the page.

As previously (p. 374), we represent the unpolarised material by the superposition of two essentially uniform volume distributions of charge, of amount nq, of each sign, per unit volume, these distributions being displaced, relatively, by a small distance $\lambda E'$ when the effective polarising field is E'. In this situation the polarisation is given by $P_1 = nq\lambda E'_1$, and our problem reduces to the calculation of the field on the line of centres of two nearly-superimposed 'equal and opposite' uniform spherical distributions of charge of volume density and relative displacement as specified

$$X_1 \qquad X_2 \qquad\qquad F \qquad\qquad \text{FIGURE } 47$$

bove. Let X_1 (fig. 47) be the centre of the uniform sphere of negative charge, and X_2 that of the precisely similar sphere of positive charge, and let F be any point in the straight line through $X_1 X_2$ and within both spheres. Generally, according to Gauss's theorem (§2.4), the field at any point distant r from the centre of a uniform spherical distribution of charge arises only from the charge situated within a distance r of the centre of the sphere—and would be unaltered if the whole of that charge were concentrated at the centre. We have then, generally, for a uniform spherical distribution of charge of volume density ρ, at a distance from the centre,

$$E = \tfrac{4}{3}\pi r^3 \rho \, \frac{1}{4\pi\epsilon_0 r^2} = \frac{r\rho}{3\epsilon_0}.$$

In relation to the present case, for the sphere centred at X_1 $\rho = -nq$ and, for the sphere centred at X_2, $\rho = +nq$. In this case, the field at F, directed towards the left in fig. 47, is given by

$$\frac{nq}{3\epsilon_0}\,(X_1 F - X_2 F),$$

or by $\qquad \dfrac{nq\lambda E'_1}{3\epsilon_0},$

since $X_1 X_2 = \lambda E'_1$ in our notation.

The result that we have just obtained shows that the field in the uniformly polarised dielectric sphere is independent of position along the diameter parallel to the direction of polarisation (it is, in fact, independent of position generally). We have, therefore, for E_2, directed from right to left in relation to fig. 46,

$$E_2 = \frac{nq\lambda E'_1}{3\epsilon_0} = \frac{P_1}{3\epsilon_0} \tag{231}$$

since the positive direction of E'_1 and E'_0 is also from right to left in the figure, equation (230) becomes

$$E'_1 - E'_0 = E_1 + \frac{P_1}{3\epsilon_0}.$$

EM 2B

It is satisfactory that the magnitude of E_2 proves to be independent of the volume of C. For our present model to be a reasonable one, however, E_1 must also be independent of this volume—given the initial assumption that C is sufficiently large to contain a large number of atoms (molecules) of the dielectric material concerned. In relation to E_1, Lorentz showed that, for a crystalline solid dielectric having cubic symmetry, E_1 would indeed be zero—as it would be for a gas in which, instantaneously, the structure is a random one. Each result depends, of course, on our primary assumption that a single parameter α describes the relevant behaviour of the atom (molecule) involved. We accept Lorentz's result, and examine the consequences of writing simply

$$E'_1 - E'_0 = \frac{P_1}{3\epsilon_0} \tag{232}$$

In our zero-order calculation we deduced the difference of potential between the condenser plates, in the presence of the dielectric, by 'identifying the field which a test charge would experience in traversing the dielectric from one condenser plate to the other' with the local field effective in polarising the atoms (molecules) of the dielectric material (compare equations (226) and (227)). Later, in our critical estimate of this calculation (p 373), we raised the question of the validity of this identification. In relation to the new model, which we have used for our first-order approximation, obviously the corresponding identification is no longer legitimate. We have explicitly referred our calculation of the polarising field to the location of a 'real' atom (molecule). Clearly, this is not a representative point for the purpose of calculating the average field acting on a test charge traversing the dielectric. A much better case can be made for the assumption that E'_0, the local field of our zero-order calculation, is the appropriate average field in this connection. This is, in fact, the assumption that we make. We then have

$$K = E/E'_0,$$

and, by substitution in equation (229),

$$P_1 = \epsilon_0(K-1)E'_0 \tag{233}$$

Explicitly, $P_1 = n\alpha E'_1$: substituting for E'_1 in equation (232) in these terms, we obtain

$$P_1\left(\frac{3\epsilon_0}{n\alpha} - 1\right) = 3\epsilon_0 E'_0 \tag{234}$$

From equations (233) and (234), finally

$$\frac{3\epsilon_0}{n\alpha} - 1 = \frac{3}{K-1}$$

or
$$\frac{K-1}{K+2} = \frac{n\alpha}{3\epsilon_0} \tag{235}$$

Equation (235), which is generally known as the Clausius-Mossotti equation, reduces directly to equation (227) of our zero-order approximation when $(K-1) \ll 1$. This being so, for those simple gases, at ordinary pressures, for which equation (227) is satisfactory in practice, equation (235) is equally satisfactory. Moreover, it does not suffer from the disadvantage of the earlier equation in imposing an upper limit on the value of K (p. 372). Our previous argument that the ratio $n\alpha/3\epsilon_0$ must be less than 1 for any real material remains unexceptionable: according to equation (235) this quantity cannot be greater than 1, whatever the value of K.

Direct experiment has shown that for certain simple gases, over a range of pressure up to 1000 atmospheres, equation (235) gives a good account of the variation of dielectric constant with density. It is difficult to know how far the equation is applicable to solids (we have already noted the restriction to solids of cubic symmetry). In order to test it in practice it is necessary to have an independent method of estimation of α. All that we can say is that when it has been possible to investigate a simple substance in more than one state of aggregation—say as gas and liquid, or as liquid and solid—it has not infrequently proved to be the case that the Clausius-Mossotti equation, with a constant value of α, has provided a satisfactory representation of the experimental results.

In this chapter our chosen topic has been the electrical behaviour of solids; so far as the dielectric behaviour of such materials is concerned, in this section, to date, our discussion has led no farther than to a formal understanding of such behaviour for a very small class of substances in the solid state. Our zero-order approximation was found not to be applicable to solids of any type; even our first-order approximation applies only to a restricted few—the solidified rare gases and halogens, some elementary intrinsic semiconductors (if their feeble conductivity be disregarded), some organic compounds, in crystalline form.

There is more to our failure to formulate an all-embracing theory than our previous decision not to go beyond the Lorentz result that the near-neighbour contribution to the local field is zero in cubic crystals and random structures (p. 378). A little reflection will show that we built into our theory at the outset a degree of inflexibility which is unlikely to be matched in the real situation. In describing the atoms (molecules) by a single parameter only, the polarisability, α, we set up a theory which is inherently incapable of explaining any possible temperature-dependence of dielectric constant at constant density, and any variation of dielectric constant with frequency, in alternating fields, at least at frequencies less than the characteristic 'optical' frequencies of the isolated atom or molecule. It is a matter of experience that with many (polyatomic) molecular gases the dielectric constant decreases as the temperature is increased, at constant density—and for many liquid and solid substances there is not only a variation with temperature (in the same sense) but also a variation with frequency, at frequencies much smaller than the optical frequencies that we have mentioned. In order to explain these results we have to suppose that the molecules of the dielectric materials concerned possess permanent electric dipole moments—and we have to superimpose a contribution due to 'orientation polarisation' on the 'intrinsic polarisation' which, alone, we have discussed hitherto. In relation to frequency dependence, once we have postulated an orientation process involving permanent molecular dipoles, we are naturally led to the notion of a 'relaxation time' (see p. 345) characteristic of the process and the material in question. These ideas, entirely necessary for the development of a thorough-going theory of dielectric behaviour in condensed systems, we shall not pursue farther in this section. We shall meet them again, unhindered by the necessity to consider intrinsic polarisation in the same context, when we come to deal with the magnetic properties of bodies (p. 466). The treatment that we shall there develop may be taken over, under suitable limitations, and applied to the electrical case by the interested reader. Here we would merely add that whereas it is difficult to imagine a single atom, constituted of a central positive nucleus and surrounding electrons, to have a permanent electric dipole moment in the normal state, it is only natural to suppose that, in those polyatomic molecules in which the inter-atomic binding involves the transfer, partial or complete, of an electron, or electrons, from one atom to another, the molecule should possess such a dipole moment. There is nothing unexpected or inexplicable in the notion of permanent electric dipole moments of molecules.

CHAPTER 8

CURRENTS ACROSS SURFACES OF DISCONTINUITY

8.1. INTRODUCTORY

In chapters 4 and 5 we discussed in detail the processes of electric conduction in gases (at normal and negligible pressures) and in liquids. All the time it was implicit—and, frequently, in chapter 5 it was explicitly stated—that the experimental arrangements employed in the study of these conduction processes involved the use of metallic electrodes to convey current to and from the sample of gas or liquid concerned. In all these situations, therefore, there were surfaces of discontinuity across which current passed. In the situation discussed in section 5.5, in particular (we were there concerned with the processes occurring in voltaic cells), we recognised that these surfaces of discontinuity must themselves be the seat of non-trivial interactions. We wrote (p. 225) 'the circumstances which determine the difference of potential between the electrodes on open circuit are those which obtain at the various surfaces of discontinuity in the cell'. In the simplest such cell, we said (p. 226), there are 'three effective surfaces of discontinuity: that effective as between the electrode materials themselves, and the two surfaces of physical separation of the electrodes and the electrolyte which constitute the cell'.

In the course of chapters 6 and 7 we laid the foundation for a more detailed discussion of these surface effects generally: in chapter 6 the necessary notions concerning the electrical structure of atoms were elaborated, in chapter 7 consequent notions concerning the mechanism of electronic conduction in metals. Since our following considerations will be confined almost exclusively to cases in which the material on one side of a surface of discontinuity is a metallic conductor, obviously these ideas will be all-important. Indeed, a qualitative description of the passage of current across the surface of separation between a metallic electrode and a liquid electrolyte has already been given in the introductory section of chapter 7 (p. 319); in this chapter we have to attempt a quantitative account of this and similar phenomena.

8.2. METALS 'IN VACUUM'

In an earlier chapter we considered at some length the currents of negative electricity which may be obtained from the surfaces of incandescent metals, or, at ordinary temperatures, from clean metal surfaces irradiated by ultra-violet light, 'in vacuum' (see §4.3). At that stage, however, we were concerned almost exclusively in establishing the result that the carriers of these currents are identical with the cathode-ray particles (negative electrons). Apart from brief reference to the fact that the initial energy of emission of the electrons is generally small under normal laboratory conditions (no more than about 1 eV—see p. 180), we did not enquire further into the details of the two processes of emission. Here we attempt to remedy that deficiency—and we shall attempt to remedy another, also. In section 7.3 we discussed two approximations to a description of the potential energy of a 'test' electron as a function of position within a lump of metal. According to the first crude approximation of Sommerfeld, the electron was supposed to move in a field-free space, its potential energy independent of position. According to the more realistic description of Bloch, the potential energy was three-dimensionally periodic, reflecting the lattice structure of the crystalline metal, the lattice sites being the positions of the minima of the potential energy pattern. But we did not in section 7.3, or elsewhere, relate this description to the outside world; we did not discuss the way in which the potential energy of the test electron varies across the bounding surface of a piece of metal isolated in vacuum. That we shall proceed to do now—and having taken the discussion as far as we can, and then considered the experimental facts relating to the two emission processes (photoelectric and thermionic emission), we shall see how the two matters which we previously neglected are intimately related. That, indeed, is why they were neglected in the first place.

Let S (fig. 48) represent a portion of the surface of separation of a lump of metal (situated to the left of S in the figure) from 'vacuum'. Because we shall be dealing, generally, with distances from the surface, in vacuum, not many orders of magnitude greater than the interatomic distance, d, characteristic of the solid metal, we may regard S as an infinite plane. Similarly, being concerned with matters of detail, we may imagine S to be a regular crystal face (even though lumps of metal, in general, are not 'single crystals', but aggregates of minute crystals, randomly orientated).

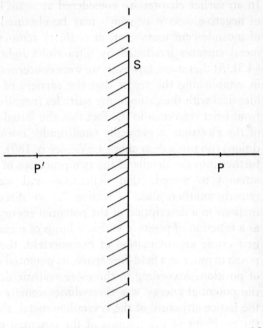

FIGURE 48

On this basis we consider a test electron, of charge e, situated at P, at a distance x from S. Our real problem is to take account of the fact that the bounding surface of the metal is not abruptly discontinuous: over a distance of the order of magnitude of d (and different, perhaps, for different crystal faces), at right angles to the surface, the essential physical parameters vary from those of vacuum to those of the metal in bulk. For precision, therefore, we regard S as the median plane of this region of variable parameters. Considering geometrical strata, of thickness small compared with d, parallel to S, we shall anticipate that the net charge in any such stratum is not necessarily zero—and we may envisage the possibility that, though the lump of metal as a whole is uncharged, different portions of its surface (different crystal faces) may be the seat of resultant charge, positive in some regions and negative in others. In any case, under the influence of the test electron at P, there will be a minute separation of positive and negative charge ('by induction'—see p. 10) resulting in the appearance of effective positive charge over that portion of the surface nearer to P (of total quantity very slightly less than one electron charge), and corresponding negative charge over the more distant portions of the surface. Our problem is to consider the potential energy of the test electron in its dependence on the distance x (and on the crystal face involved): for the solution of this problem we need to know the spatial distribution of all the surface charges to which we have drawn attention in this detailed statement.

Obviously, we have not the factual information, or the basis of theory, on which to solve the problem that we have set ourselves. We shall, therefore, in the end, be driven back on general arguments and a direct appeal to experiment. However, there is one calculation that we can make, which is independent of atomic theory, and which provides a valid starting point and an order-of-magnitude scale for the overall effect—and justifies, incidentally, the claim that we made that we shall not be concerned with distances, x, on the vacuum side of S, 'many orders of magnitude greater than the interatomic distance, d'. It is a calculation that applies equally whichever crystal face is in question.

For $x \gg d$ we can calculate the potential energy of the test electron in the field of the induced charges, quite simply, by the method of images (§2.7). We replace the actual distribution of induced charge on S by a charge $-e$ at P', the image point of P as shown in the figure, and we have, directly,

$$U_i = -\frac{e^2}{16\pi\epsilon_0 x} \tag{236}$$

If we express U_i (joules) as V_i (electron volts), then, numerically,

$$V_i = -\frac{e}{16\pi\epsilon_0 x}.$$

Let us accept equation (236) as giving a sufficiently accurate value of the image-field contribution to the potential energy of the test electron for $x \geqslant 5 \times 10^{-10}$ m. On this basis, when $x = 5 \times 10^{-10}$ m, $V_i = 0.72\,\text{eV}$; when $x = 3.5 \times 10^{-7}$ m, $V_i = 10^{-3}\,\text{eV}$. Clearly, for our present purposes, we have no need to consider distances outside the bounding surface of a metal greater than the wavelength of visible light: for distances greater than this, provided there is no externally applied field (and no residual charge over macroscopic areas of the surface), the potential energy of the test electron is insignificantly different from its potential energy 'at infinity'.

For the time being let us carry forward our general argument in terms of the Sommerfeld model to which reference has already been made (p. 383). We may give it some measure of respectability by defining the constant 'internal' potential energy, U_0, characteristic of that model, as the space average of the realistic (Bloch) energy taken over the whole volume of the lump of metal concerned. The corresponding potential V_0 (volts) is often referred to as the 'inner potential' of the metal in question. We are imagining a test electron, originally at rest at a small distance from the surface of the metal, to approach the bounding surface and pass through, without restraint, into the interior. Ultimately, the kinetic energy of the electron will be $-U_0$ (a positive quantity), and to this quantity $-U_i$ (equation (236)) will have made a small contribution. As already stated, we have not the means to evaluate the major contributions which go to make up the difference, $-(U_0 - U_i)$. These contributions become effective over the range of distances, x, from 5×10^{-10} m to -5×10^{-10} m in an actual case. It would be intellectually satisfying if we could follow them in detail, but our main concern, once we have discussed their origin (which we have already done) is with the value of U_0. We rest content, therefore, with fig. 49, showing the image-field contribution (assumed to be the only contribution effective over that range) in terms of the full curve AB, the constant internal potential energy, U_0, by the straight line CD, and filling in the intervening range schematically using the dotted curve BC. U, of course, is the potential energy of the test electron at any distance x from S, the median plane of the physical surface of the metal (fig. 48).

Consider now an actual experiment (as distinct from the ideal experiment with a test electron with which we have so far been concerned) in which a 'parallel beam' of electrons of kinetic energy V (electron volts) falls normally on a foil of polycrystalline metal, so thin that most of the electrons pass through the foil without significant loss of energy. These are conditions under which, as G. P. Thomson and A. Reid first found, diffraction effects may be observed. On a photographic plate placed at right angles to the beam, in vacuum, on the side of emergence, circular fringes may be obtained, providing irrefutable evidence of wave-like properties belonging to the electron beam (see *V & W*, §9.4). The diffraction effects observed in this way are entirely analogous to those which may be obtained with a beam of X-rays homogeneous in respect of wavelength (see p. 341). As with X-rays, the three-dimensional diffraction grating which is effective in the process

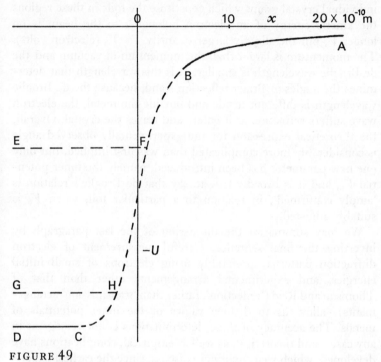

FIGURE 49

is the regular array of atoms constituting the crystal lattice of the metal—and, in respect of the wavelength to be ascribed to the electron beam, the statement may be made that experiment has amply confirmed the correctness of de Broglie's relation $\Lambda = h/P$ (*P* denoting the momentum of an electron in the beam and *h* Planck's constant).

The last statement, regarding wavelength, though disarmingly simple, merits further attention. Suppose that the kinetic energy of the electrons is varied in the experiment under consideration. As the kinetic energy is increased, the particle momentum increases and, according to de Broglie's relation, the wavelength decreases in inverse ratio. The (grazing) angles of reflection (diffraction) decrease correspondingly according to Bragg's law (p. 277). Qualitatively, this is just the effect which is observed, but careful experiment shows that numerical agreement is not complete if the electron momentum is calculated in terms of the incident energy V. This is not surprising: diffraction takes place within the individual crystal grains which constitute the foil; in these regions the kinetic energy of an electron belonging to the beam is no longer V, but the slightly larger quantity $V - V_0$ (electron volts). The momentum is larger than the momentum in vacuum and the de Broglie wavelength is smaller. It is this wavelength that determines the angles of Bragg reflection—and, because the de Broglie wavelength is different inside and outside the metal, the electron wave suffers refraction as it enters and leaves the crystal. Overall, the theoretical expression for the experimentally observed angle is considerably more complicated than was first implied, but only one new parameter has been introduced, namely the inner potential V_0, and it is broadly true to say that de Broglie's relation is 'amply confirmed', in relation to a particular foil, when V_0 is suitably adjusted.

We may summarise the discussion of the last paragraph by inverting the final sentence. Careful measurement of electron diffraction patterns—preferably using electrons of small initial energies, and experimental arrangements other than that of Thomson and Reid ('reflection', rather than 'transmission' arrangements)—allow us to deduce values of the inner potentials of metals. The accuracy of these determinations is not very great in any case—and theoretical, as well as empirical, complications have developed, which we cannot here discuss, since the earliest experiments were made; but the order of magnitude of the results is at least significant. Values of V_0 appear, in general, to lie in the range from -10 V to -25 V.

Realistically considered, our discussion of the value of the inner potential has no very direct relevance to the main phenomena with which we are concerned in this section. It was important that we should derive the general form of the potential energy curve illustrated in fig. 49 (recognising, moreover, that the portion CD is merely a zero-order approximation to a periodically varying internal potential energy); now, however, our real interest lies in locating the energy band of the conduction electrons on this figure.

For this purpose we re-interpret the scale of ordinates (labelled U) as giving the total energy of the electrons (kinetic plus potential energy); then the potential curve ABCD gives the total energy of an electron at rest at an arbitrary distance x from the median plane of the physical boundary of the lump of metal concerned.

Suppose that we consider a metal of group I of the periodic classification, as providing the simplest example. The conduction electrons, in this case, 'fill the lower half' of the allowed (valency) band, according to the Bloch theory. To a sufficiently good approximation, as we have already agreed (p. 358), the energy distribution function of the Sommerfeld model (fig. 44) may be taken as representing the distribution of occupied states in this half-filled band, provided that the energy of the lowest state in the band is arbitrarily set at zero. On this basis we might be tempted to suppose that the lower limit of the band should be located, on the total energy diagram of fig. 49, along the line CD. However, this would be altogether too naïve a supposition. According to the Sommerfeld model, it is true, the kinetic energies of the conduction electrons have 'all' values from zero to E_0 (p. 337), at the absolute zero of temperature, but the allowed band of Bloch is developed out of the discrete bound state of the valency electron in an isolated atom—and in that state the total energy is part potential and part kinetic energy. In principle, the upper and lower limits of the band may be precisely located with respect to the periodic potential energy surface which represents the field of the lattice atoms on the Bloch theory, but U_0 is merely the space average of the potential energy of that surface (p. 386); clearly, therefore, there is no justification for identifying the lower limit of the valency band with the line CD of fig. 49. This point decided, we have drawn in, arbitrarily, in fig. 49, the line GH to represent the lower energy limit of the conduction band, and the line EF to represent the 'Fermi level' (the uppermost occupied energy level at the absolute zero of temperature). We have previously described (p. 349) how the difference of energy represented by the 'vertical' distance GE in the figure can be deduced from line breadths in the spectrum of the low-energy characteristic X-rays of the metal in question; here our last concern with the numerical values of the inner potential, V_0, as deduced from experiment, is to note that for every metal investigated the corresponding energy U_0 is, numerically, greater than the energy-width of the partially occupied band, as deduced from the X-ray observations. If the relative positions of the various levels are as indicated in fig. 49 this result is to be anticipated. This final comment made, we look again to experiment for information concerning the precise position of the Fermi level EF with respect to the arbitrary energy zero of fig. 49, the potential energy of an electron at a small distance (of the order of a wavelength of visible light) outside the metal surface in vacuum. The most direct evidence comes from a consideration of the photoelectric effect with ultra-violet light.

The history of the discovery and early investigation of the photoelectric effect, from 1887 onwards, has been given elsewhere (V & W, §9.3). Neglecting history at this stage, let us summarise some of the essential facts in terms of the hypothetical results of an ideal experiment. Let us imagine a clean metal plate, in an evacuated enclosure, almost completely surrounded by a collecting electrode cut from the same sheet of metal. By means of suitable windows and apertures, a steady beam of ultra-violet light can be directed on the first plate ('emitter'). External connections allow a difference of potential to be established between emitter and collector, and any current which flows through the external circuit to be measured. It is assumed that the temperature of the electrodes is maintained at or near the absolute zero, that the ultra-violet light which is employed is monochromatic and that its wavelength (or frequency, v) can be determined by standard techniques. Then, if the frequency of the ultra-violet light is greater than a certain critical value, a current (of negative electrons passing from the emitter to the collector) will be recorded, provided the difference of potential of the electrodes is suitably adjusted. If the magnitude of the electron current, i_e, is studied as a function of this potential difference, results of the type illustrated in fig. 50 will be obtained. As the potential of the collector is made less negative with respect to the emitter, the electron current will start 'abruptly' (the potential of the collector then being $-V_m$ with respect to the emitter), and it will reach a 'saturation' value, i_s, when the potential difference has been reversed in sign and the collector is very slightly positive with respect to the emitter.

Suppose, now, that this investigation is repeated using ultra-violet light of different frequencies. A series of values of V_m will be obtained, each value corresponding to a particular frequency v. It will be found, empirically, that these two quantities are linearly related, in the sense indicated by fig. 51. Because V_m is the measure of the maximum 'retarding' potential required completely to prevent collection of the emitted electrons, it is also the measure (in electron volts) of the maximum kinetic energy of emission. We have, therefore, the empirical result, in non-relativistic terms as is here appropriate,

$$\tfrac{1}{2}mv_m^{2}/(v - v_0) = \text{constant.}$$

m is the mass of the electron, v_m the maximum velocity of emission when the light frequency is v, and v_0 is the critical (or 'threshold') value of the frequency below which there is no effect with the metal concerned (i_s is zero when $V_m = 0$).

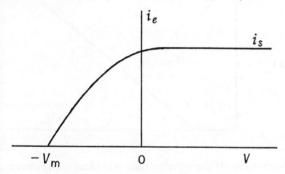

FIGURE 50

We may interpret the hypothetical results of our ideal experiment in terms of fig. 49, and the hypothesis which Einstein put forward in 1905—when there was little on which to base an explanation of the photoelectric effect except the original work of Lenard (*V & W*, p. 277). First, according to fig. 49, if the metal is at the absolute zero of temperature, the least energy that must be given to a conduction electron, situated just below the surface of the metal, if it is to escape from the surface (with negligible kinetic energy), is the energy difference between the Fermi level, which we have represented by EF, and the arbitrary zero approximated by A in the figure. We shall denote this quantity by ϕ in what follows. Secondly, according to Einstein's hypothesis (which we have already invoked in relation to the photoelectric absorption of X-rays—see p. 283), energy is conveyed by the incident light in quanta of magnitude hv, h being the universal constant of Planck, and is communicated to the electrons in entire quanta.

The interpretation then is simple: the empirical constant deduced on the basis of the hypothetical results exhibited in fig. 51 (and a knowledge of the electronic charge, e) is essentially Planck's constant, and the quantity $h\nu_0$ is the required energy ϕ. On this basis, the final result of our ideal experiment may be given formal expression as follows:

$$\tfrac{1}{2}mv_m^2 = h\nu - \phi \tag{237}$$

—when the incident quantum has more than enough energy to lift the conduction electron out of the metal, the excess appears as

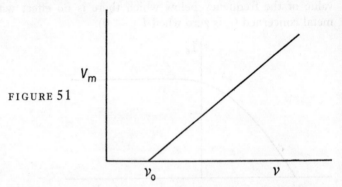

FIGURE 51

kinetic energy of emission. If we were to take our ideal experiment at its face value, we might expect, on the basis of equation (237), to be able to determine ϕ values for the various metals, without undue difficulty or ambiguity, by following through the recipe as indicated. In practice, needless to say, the situation is not as clear-cut as we have imagined it to be.

R. A. Millikan, in 1916, was the first to publish the results of a 'real' experiment of high accuracy carried out according to the pattern that we have just described. It is worth while listing the features that were 'non-ideal' in his experimental arrangement, and which were the source of the complications that we have hinted at, at the end of the last paragraph. In the first place, the collector and emitter were in general made of different materials. For the most part Millikan used the alkali metals, lithium, sodium and potassium, as emitters, and oxidised copper for his collector. His aim was to test the linear relation of equation (237) over the greatest possible range of frequency—and for the alkali metals, exceptionally, the photoelectric threshold frequency is in the visible, rather than the ultra-violet, region of the spectrum. He used oxidised copper for his collector, having established the fact that there was no photoelectric emission from this material, even at the highest frequencies employed in the experiment (it was difficult to prevent some radiation being reflected on to the collector from the emitter and the walls of the enclosure). Wisely, then, Millikan chose different materials for his electrodes, but this led to the complication that contact differences of potential were introduced: ultimately the complication proved to be the source of further information; however, it made it necessary that these contact potentials should be separately determined before ϕ values could be deduced (see p. 405).

The second feature that was non-ideal in Millikan's arrangement was that the electrodes were at room temperature, rather than at the absolute zero. In fig. 52 we have reproduced the essentials of fig. 49, superimposing, to the left of the figure, the energy distribution curve of the Sommerfeld model taken from fig. 44 (this figure being rotated through 90° to bring the energy axes of the two figures into conformity one with the other). The abrupt onset of photoelectron current under slowly decreasing retarding potential, which fig. 50 predicates as characteristic of the ideal conditions of our 'thought experiment', derives from the electron energy distribution at absolute zero, represented (for an alkali metal) by the full curve LMN. At room temperature, however, the distribution of conduction electron energies is as represented by the full curve LM'N' (or, more correctly, by a similar curve less easily distinguishable from LMN). Obviously, under these conditions, the onset of photoelectric emission is not abrupt, and there is some difficulty in determining V_m, other than intuitively, from the $i_e - V$ curves. In 1916 Millikan had not the benefit of the prediction of the Sommerfeld model on which to base an objective procedure of extrapolation: this was first introduced in 1933, by L. A. Du Bridge.

The third feature of the ideal arrangement which calls for discussion is the 'cleanliness' of the electrodes. We specified 'a clean metal plate' as emitter—and we implied that the collecting electrode should be equally clean, being 'cut from the same sheet of metal'. The concept of cleanliness, in this context, will be understood by reference to our earlier discussion (p. 384) of the factors determining the form of the potential energy curve ABCD of fig. 49. The form of this curve is determined predominantly by the distribution of charge in the atoms occupying the first few layers on either side of the median plane S (fig. 48), which we have taken to represent the geometrical boundary between metal and vacuum. This being the case, even a single layer of 'foreign' atoms

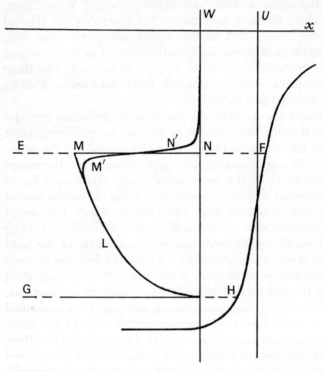

FIGURE 52

on the emitting surface will modify the photoelectric properties of a specimen significantly—and if the ϕ values of the pure metals are to be obtained from experiment, surface contamination must be avoided 'completely'. Equally important, the surface of the collector must be uncontaminated, or, at the least, it must remain absolutely constant in character throughout its use, for the contact difference of potential to which we referred (p. 393) is a function of the surface states of emitter and collector, jointly.

It would be unfair to say that Millikan's arrangement was demonstrably non-ideal in the matter of cleanliness of surface, but the achievement of this cleanliness involved an experimental complication of a major kind (having regard to the general state of the laboratory arts of the day). Millikan found it necessary to arrange that the surfaces of his specimens of the alkali metals were freshly cut, and re-cut from time to time, in vacuum. For this purpose the rotor of a small electric motor, carrying a cutting tool on its axle, was mounted within the evacuated vessel, the field coils of the motor being outside the vessel. The specimens were mounted on a rotatable stage, so as to be capable of presentation, in turn as required, for the cutting of a new surface. Millikan referred to the arrangement, colourfully, as 'a machine-shop *in vacuo*'.

In the upshot, Millikan convincingly verified the linear relation between the energy represented by $V_m e$ and the frequency v which, in the results of our 'thought experiment', is exhibited in fig. 51—and which is predicted by Einstein's hypothesis in equation (237). On the basis of this equation, and using the value of the electronic charge which he was concurrently engaged in determining (see p. 313), Millikan finally obtained, for Planck's constant, the value $(6.56 \pm 0.03) \times 10^{-34}$ joule sec. If, instead, he had used the 'correct' value for e (see p. 318), his value for h would have been $(6.60 \pm 0.03) \times 10^{-34}$ joule sec. The currently accepted value of this universal constant is 6.625×10^{-34} joule sec. It is one of the marks of the experimenter of genius that his intuition be unerring when it comes to the matter of disregarding contingent circumstance, and 'extrapolating to ideal conditions', aided only by his own feeling for the essence of the situation.

From the analysis that we have given of the various practical difficulties attending Millikan's investigation, it will have become obvious that the determination of ϕ values characteristic of the pure metals was one stage more difficult than the verification of Einstein's hypothesis and the evaluation of Planck's constant. So far as the emitting and collecting surfaces are concerned, it is necessary only that these remain entirely stable in constitution, and constant in behaviour throughout the experiment, for the evaluation of h to be possible; for the determination of the characteristic ϕ values of the pure metals, it is necessary that the emitting surfaces be 'perfectly' clean (and that contact potential differences be known). It is little wonder, then, that Millikan's results in this last respect have been 'improved' by later workers. Presently accepted values of ϕ for lithium, sodium and potassium are 2·28, 2·29 and 2·26 eV, respectively; Millikan's values ranged from 1·9 eV to 2·4 eV.

Our final consideration in this section is with thermionic emission: as we shall see, detailed investigation of this phenomenon also permits the evaluation of ϕ, in relation to the material (and surface state) of the emitter. In some sense the experimental difficulties of this approach are less serious than those characterising determinations of the photoelectric thresholds of the pure metals by the method of Millikan, for the emitters, being incandescent, can be taken to be free of contamination by volatile materials. Theoretically, however, the method is less direct. Originally, thermionic emission was seen to involve a characteristic energy which could be evaluated experimentally, and the term 'work function' was applied to its empirically determined value. For some time it was regarded as an open question whether this work function was the same as the quantum energy $h\nu_0$ characteristic of the photoelectric threshold of the metal. Here we have assumed this identity from the outset: we have defined $-\phi$ as the energy of a conduction electron occupying the Fermi level in the metal (with reference to the state of rest just beyond the effective influence of the image field), and we have asserted that ϕ may be determined from experiment by investigations of thermionic emission, as also by investigations of the photoelectric emission of electrons. Our task, then, is to describe the basis of the experimental method and to justify our assertion.

The classical experiments on thermionic emission were carried out by O. W. Richardson (see p. 180) and his co-workers in the years between 1901 and 1916. Using a simple 'diode' arrangement, consisting of an electrically heated filament and a surrounding cylindrical collecting electrode, in an evacuated tube, Richardson was the first to show that, though the electron current to the collector increases initially as the potential of the collector becomes increasingly positive with respect to the filament potential, it reaches a saturation value (provided that the temperature of the filament remains constant) under easily attainable laboratory conditions. In an earlier discussion of the experiments of Franck and Hertz (§6.5), we have already referred to the factors which limit the electron current in the pre-saturation phase. Here, we shall not be further concerned with that aspect of the matter,* but

* We may, however, compare, in passing, the electron-current *versus* anode-

rather with the way in which the saturation current itself depends on the temperature of the filament, and on its physical constitution.

Richardson published his first results on this subject in 1902. Using a platinum filament, he found that the electron current increased some two thousand times as the temperature of the filament was raised from 1000° C to 1300° C. Very similar results were reported with other metals during the next few years. From the outset, three general assumptions were made the basis of the theoretical discussion of these experimental results. Essentially similar assumptions underlie all modern treatments of the problem. In the first place it was assumed that the electrons involved in the process are the 'free' conduction electrons of the metal. Secondly, it was supposed that a conduction electron, in its passage through the surface layers of the metal, comes under the action of electro-static forces against which it has to do work, at the expense of its kinetic energy, in escaping from the surface. (These are the forces that we have already discussed in relation to fig. 49.) Finally, the view was taken that in the ideal situation in which a lump of metal is assumed to be isolated in a perfectly evacuated vessel at constant temperature (the walls of the vessel being perfect reflectors of electrons) there would be established an equilibrium state, the electrons in the metal coming into equilibrium with the 'electron gas' in the surrounding space. A temperature-dependent 'vapour pressure of electrons' would characterise such a situation, the equilibrium would be maintained by the opposing processes of thermionic emission from the metal and return of electrons from the gas, and the problem of calculating the saturation value of the thermionic current would resolve itself into the more manageable problem of calculating the rate of return of electrons from the 'vapour phase'.

The first attempt at a theory of thermionic emission along these lines effectively regarded the problem of the equilibrium state as that of a constant-temperature atmosphere in which the pressure gradient is at right angles to the surface of the metal and the force-field is limited to the surface region, a few atoms thick, in which

voltage curves for a photoelectric cell and a thermionic diode of similar geometrical form. Under normal operating conditions, 'space-charge limitation' as described by Langmuir (p. 265) determines the resultant current over a considerable range of voltage in the latter case, but over an altogether negligible range in the former (see fig. 50). The fact is that, generally, the saturation current in a photoelectric cell is several orders of magnitude smaller than that in a thermionic diode of similar size.

the escaping (and returning) electrons come under the action of the electrostatic forces to which we have referred. On this basis, the ratio of the equilibrium concentrations of electrons, in the surrounding space and within the metal, respectively, is given by the Boltzmann factor (see p. 356) $e^{U_0/kT}$. Here U_0 is the (negative-valued) 'internal' potential energy of a conduction electron (effectively as we have defined it on the basis of the Sommerfeld model of a quarter of a century later—see p. 386), and T is the absolute temperature. Starting from this point of view, Richardson derived his first equation giving the value of the saturation current per unit area of thermionic cathode surface in the form

$$j = AT^{\frac{1}{2}}e^{-b/T} \tag{238}$$

During the ten years which followed, many careful experiments demonstrated the success of this equation in representing the empirical results over a wide range of temperature and for a large variety of cathode materials.

In assessing the significance of this success, it is important to recognise that the two temperature-dependent terms in equation (238) are of a very different character, the one representing a very slow, the other a very rapid, variation of j with T over the relevant range. The empirical results were certainly sufficiently accurate to establish the dominance of a term of the form $e^{-b/T}$ in the expression for j, but, equally certainly, they were not accurate enough to determine whether the multiplying term in T should be $T^{\frac{1}{2}}$, or T, or T^2. In an investigation reported in 1915, K. K. Smith showed that, even when the temperature range was such that the saturation current varied by a factor of 10^{12}, it was equally possible to represent the results by equation (238), or by a similar equation (with slightly different values for A and b) in which $T^{\frac{1}{2}}$ was replaced by T^2. Doubts concerning the theoretical justification of the $T^{\frac{1}{2}}$ term had been growing for some time—indeed, ever since H. A. Wilson first applied thermodynamical reasoning to the problem in 1903.

That thermodynamical reasoning should be able to establish general results against which particular theories of thermionic emission might be tested is rendered likely by the form of words that we used in describing the third of the basic assumptions listed at the beginning of this discussion. The notion of an equilibrium state characterised by a vapour pressure exerted by the electrons in a confined space surrounding a lump of metal at a specified temperature bears a clear analogy to that of the more familiar equilibrium state which involves a pure liquid and its vapour, isolated in an isothermal enclosure. The standard thermodynamical result which applies to this general situation may be written

$$\frac{dp}{dT} = \frac{1}{V_2 - V_1} \frac{L}{T} \tag{239}$$

In this form, the equation gives the rate of change of saturation vapour pressure, p, with temperature, T, in terms of L, the molar heat of vaporisation at that temperature, and V_1 and V_2, the molar volumes of the substance in the liquid and vapour phases, respectively, under the conditions of equilibrium specified. In general $V_2 \gg V_1$; to a good approximation, therefore,

$$\frac{dp}{dT} = \frac{L}{V_2 T}$$

—and the more nearly this approximate result is valid, the more closely the vapour obeys the ideal gas laws, so that

$$\frac{dp}{dT} = \frac{pL}{RT^2},$$

R being the universal gas constant. Under these conditions, then,

$$\frac{d(\log p)}{dT} = \frac{L}{RT^2},$$

and $\qquad \log\left(\frac{p}{P}\right) = \int_{\infty}^{T} \frac{L}{RT^2}\, dT \tag{240}*$

It was not supposed, some fifty years ago (1916), when the discussion of the relevance of thermodynamical arguments to the problem of thermionic emission was becoming seriously engaged, that the approximations underlying equation (240) could be other than valid in relation to the saturation vapour pressure of electrons in the equilibrium state that we are now considering. As we have

---

* We have written 'infinity' as the 'lower' limit of integration to signify a temperature which is sufficiently high that the value of L/RT is very small indeed compared with 1. This would no doubt be a temperature unattainable in practice—and, in any case, the metal would melt at a considerably lower temperature—but we are considering an ideal experiment, and, as we shall see, this very high temperature never enters into our practical considerations.

already seen, Richardson's simple-minded calculation in terms of the isothermal-atmosphere model effectively gave

$$p = Pe^{U_0/kT} \tag{241}$$

The critics of this calculation, basing their criticism on equation (240) or its equivalent, pointed out that Richardson's result could be justified, formally, only if the 'latent heat of vaporisation of electrons' were assumed to be independent of temperature. In that case, equations (240) and (241) would be equivalent, with $L/R = -U_0/k$. On the other hand, the critics said, Richardson's calculation could in no case be justified physically, for to identify $-NU_0$ with the molar heat of vaporisation ($N \equiv R/k$ being Avogadro's constant) in terms of Richardson's model would be to imply that this heat is wholly used in doing 'internal' work. In relation to the 'reference' process of evaporation of liquids, it had been accepted for more than half a century that 'external' work, in amount RT per mole, is necessarily performed at the expense of the latent heat (provided the vapour obeys the ideal gas laws). The situation must be similar in respect of the emitted electrons, so the critics said. If that were so, the external latent heat being clearly temperature-dependent, the sum of the external and internal latent heats was most unlikely to be temperature-independent —and Richardson's equations (241) and (238) would lack the necessary basis of formal justification, anyway. By this time Richardson was himself numbered among the critics of his earlier theorising, and when he came to write the definitive account of his work in *The Emission of Electricity from Hot Bodies* (1916) he had given detailed reasons for supposing that equation (238) should be replaced by

$$j = A'T^2 e^{-b'/T} \tag{242}$$

This we may call Richardson's second thermionic equation. Because it is founded on thermodynamical reasoning, we shall assume, at least provisionally, that any calculation of the saturation value of the thermionic current density, j, which is based on a particular model is acceptable only if it gives a result of the same form as equation (242).

It is very satisfactory that a direct calculation for the metals of group I, based on the Sommerfeld model, leads to precisely this result with the minimum of assumption. If we accept equation

(201) as giving the distribution of kinetic energy among the conduction electrons in a monovalent metal at temperature T, and, on the basis of the corresponding distribution function for the component momenta, calculate the rate of arrival, at the inner boundary of the surface-layer field, of electrons capable of traversing this field and escaping from the surface, we arrive at an expression for the electron current issuing from unit surface area as follows:

$$j = \frac{4\pi m e k^2}{h^3} T^2 e^{(U_0 + E_T)/kT} \tag{243}$$

In this connection, the axis of x being taken at right angles to the emitting surface, and the kinetic energy of a conduction electron being expressed, in a self-evident notation, in the form $E = \frac{1}{2}m(\dot{x}^2 + \dot{y}^2 + \dot{z}^2)$, the condition that the electron shall be capable of traversing the surface-layer field may be written

$$U_0 + \tfrac{1}{2}m\dot{x}^2 \geqslant 0.$$

As before, U_0 is the negative-valued 'internal' potential energy, and E_T is the kinetic energy of the conduction electron occupying the centre of the slightly diffuse 'band' which corresponds to the Fermi level at temperature T (see fig. 44).

There are three points to be made concerning the significance of equation (243). First, it has been derived specifically on the basis of the Sommerfeld model, and cannot therefore be expected to be more generally applicable than to the metals of group I. Secondly, it contains no arbitrary constants: the absolute value of the current density is given, not merely its temperature dependence. Finally, if it is taken in conjunction with equation (242), then the empirically determined work function ϕ ($\equiv kb'$) is seen to represent the minimum energy which has to be communicated to an electron at the centre of the diffuse Fermi band to enable it to escape from the metal.

Merely noting the first of these three points, let us consider the other two in more detail. We start with point number three. It has already been emphasised that it has proved impossible, empirically, to distinguish between the first and second of Richardson's thermionic equations, equations (238) and (242). This is equivalent to the statement that the empirically determined quantities b and b' are so nearly independent of temperature, over the experimentally accessible range, that any actual temperature dependence cannot be established with certainty from the observations concerned. (Formally, equation (238) may be obtained from equation (242) by writing $b' = b + \frac{3}{2}T \log T/T_0$.) When we wrote, in stating point number three, of 'the empirically determined work function ϕ ($\equiv kb'$)', we were naïvely assuming that b' is indeed independent of temperature: what we have just said should make it clear that we have no justification for this assumption. On the basis of the Sommerfeld model, in fact, E_T is known to decrease, if only very slowly, as the temperature increases (see equation (202)); thus ϕ increases, according to the model, with increase of temperature. In spite of this, it is no contradiction that the predicted temperature dependence of ϕ is beyond the range of detection when experimental results are analysed in terms of equation (242) (by plotting $\log (j/T^2)$ against $1/T$): according to equation (202),

$$\frac{d\phi}{dT} = \frac{\pi^2 k^2 T}{6E_0}$$

—which is one-third of the contribution per conduction electron to the thermal capacity of the metal at temperature T (see p. 339). As to order of magnitude, then,

$$\frac{T}{\phi}\frac{d\phi}{dT} \sim \left(\frac{kT}{E_0}\right)^2,$$

for ϕ and E_0 do not in general differ by more than a factor of 2, and numerically, for a representative group I metal (*ibid.*),

$$\frac{T}{\phi}\frac{d\phi}{dT} \sim 4 \times 10^{-4},$$

when $T = 1300°\,\mathrm{K}$.

We have just drawn attention to the fact that, according to the Sommerfeld model, the temperature dependence of the work function, ϕ, can be formally related to the electronic contribution to the specific heat of the metal at the temperature concerned. It is an additional reason for satisfaction with this model that detailed thermodynamical arguments make it clear that these two quantities are not merely formally relatable (they are dimensionally homogeneous) but necessarily related the one to the other.

In considering our third point in detail, we have laid the foundation for the necessary comments on the second point, also.

Essentially, our second point was that equation (243) appears to indicate that the constant A' of equation (242) should be the same for all metals for which the former equation is valid—in particular, A' should not depend on the concentration of conduction electrons in the metal (represented by n in equation (201)). But we re-emphasise the fact that equation (242) should be regarded merely as the formal expression of an empirical result. The value of the emission constant A' is deduced from experiment, by use of this equation, in terms of the intercept on the axis of ordinates when experimental values of $\log (j/T^2)$ are plotted against $1/T$ and the 'best straight line' is drawn through the points. Now, we have just given reasons for the belief that these experimental points should realistically be represented otherwise than by the best straight line. Extrapolation to $1/T = 0$ implies a knowledge of the variation of ϕ with temperature at very high temperatures—and it is just in this range that significant variations are to be expected. It is not surprising, therefore, that we approach a comparison of the 'theoretical' and crude empirical values of A' with some scepticism: on close analysis we can discover no good reason why these values should agree better than as to an order of magnitude. In fact genuine comparison is not easy: only for one metal of group I is the empirical value of A' reliably known. For caesium, A' has been determined from experiment as $1\cdot6 \times 10^6$ A m^{-2} deg^{-2} K; the theoretical value ($4\pi mek^2/h^3$ of equation (243)) is $1\cdot20 \times 10^6$ A m^{-2} deg^{-2} K. For other pure metals, generally, empirical values of A' range from about $0\cdot4$ to $0\cdot7 \times 10^6$ A m^{-2} deg^{-2} K.

Our final conclusion must be that agreement between experiment and theory in this connection is at least as close as might be anticipated—and, we might add that we already begin to suspect that equation (243) gives a reasonably accurate account of the phenomenon for a wider variety of substances than the restricted class (of group I metals) for which the Sommerfeld model provides a satisfactory description of the kinetic energies of the conduction electrons.

Our last remark may be taken one stage farther—indeed to the conclusion of the matter so far as our present purpose is concerned. We have found in the Sommerfeld model a basis of calculation leading to 'theoretical' results in respect of thermionic emission for a particular group of metals which are entirely consistent with the more general conclusions derived from thermodynamical arguments. This consistency provides the essential theoretical justification for the belief that a more exact model capable of representing the conduction electrons in other metals, on the same general (quantum mechanical) basis, would lead to similarly acceptable results. In particular, we should expect that equation (242) would be valid for these metals, also, and that the empirically determined work function, kb', would represent the (negative) energy of the Fermi level in all cases. This is the assertion that we set out to justify in the beginning (p. 396). Having reached the end of our discussion of the theoretical ideas involved, we merely record the facts as experiment has revealed them: whenever it has been possible to surmount the many difficulties besetting independent determinations of the photoelectric threshold energy and the thermionic work-function energy for the same pure metal, under conditions ensuring adequate cleanliness of surface, these two energies have proved to be the same, as nearly as could be ascertained.

8.3. CIRCUITS CONSISTING OF DIFFERENT METALS IN CONTACT

We have already referred to Volta's discovery of the principle of the voltaic pile (p. 69), and to his earlier discovery of the steady difference of potential which is developed when dissimilar metals are in contact (p. 226). We have made reference to such 'contact potential differences' in other contexts—and in particular in relation to Millikan's determination of photoelectric threshold energies, in the last section (p. 393). Our first task, now, is to treat the problem of contact potentials systematically and in its own right.

Volta's two discoveries, it will be recalled, can be summarised (though not exhaustively) as follows: if a pile of disks of two different metals, A and B, is built up in the sequence ABAB . . . AB, then there is established a difference of potential between the first and the last disk which is independent of the number of pairs of disks in the pile; if electrolyte-moistened disks of cloth, C, are inserted in the pile so that the sequence eventually becomes ACBACB . . . ACB, the overall difference of potential increases linearly with the number of composite elements ACB which have been completed at any stage. It is the contact difference of potential which is not multiplied in the 'dry' pile of many elements: the other system when completed constitutes a sequence of similar voltaic cells connected 'in series' in which e.m.f's are additive.

For the present we are concerned with systems of the first kind, exclusively. We represent the contact difference of potential between the two metals A and B by $_AV_B$ (positive when the potential of the metal A is greater than that of B, according to conventional usage), implicitly assuming that this quantity is independent of the area of contact between samples of A and B, also that $_AV_B + _BV_A = 0$ (Volta's original results with the many-element dry pile of two metals would be unintelligible if these assumptions were groundless). In this notation the empirical results which Volta later obtained with dry piles of disks of several different metals, ACD . . . RSB, may be expressed formally (as we have already expressed them in equation (132)) in the statement

$$_AV_B = {_AV_C} + {_CV_D} + \ldots + {_RV_S} + {_SV_B}.$$

Noting that this formal expression may be written, alternatively,

$$_AV_C + {_CV_D} + \ldots + {_RV_S} + {_SV_B} + {_BV_A} = 0 \qquad (244)$$

—or, in words, that the overall change of potential in any complete path around a closed series circuit consisting of any number of components of different metallic constitution (at the same temperature) is zero—we have no difficulty in accepting the empirical results as valid: we cannot identify any source of available energy in such a circuit, and, this being the case, we have no reason to believe that any useful work could be extracted from the system by the circulation of charge in or around the circuit. Equation (244), then, is acceptable on thermodynamic grounds: our present aim is to understand its implications in terms of a theoretical model. We shall proceed by way of a more detailed consideration of experimental procedure and results.

One of the standard methods of determining contact potentials, which in its modern variants is capable, under strictly controlled conditions, of an accuracy of the order of 5×10^{-4} V, was first used systematically by Kelvin. The method is a 'null method', and for this reason success depended initially on the availability of an instrument of high sensitivity in relation to the detection of small quantities of electricity, or small differences of potential. Kelvin had developed such an instrument about the year 1860: his 'quadrant electrometer' remained the instrument of choice of many

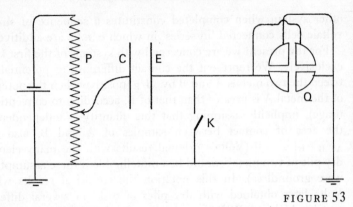

FIGURE 53

investigators over a wide field of electrical research for the next half century. Fig. 53 shows, schematically, how contact potentials were determined by its aid. Q represents the electrometer, and P a potentiometer arrangement by which, the key K being closed, an 'external' potential difference could be applied between E and C, oppositely mounted disks of the two metals under investigation. One pair of electrometer quadrants was permanently connected to earth, and when K was closed the other pair was earthed, also. In this situation, if the battery were disconnected from the potentiometer wire, equal and opposite 'free' charges would be developed on C and E sufficient in amount to maintain, between these disks, the contact potential difference $_cV_E$. If our previous statements are valid, the magnitude of these charges would be independent of the nature and composition of the wires connecting the one disk with the other. The aim of Kelvin's experiment was to annul the 'natural' charge on the disks by the application of an external potential difference equal and opposite to $_cV_E$—and the function of the electrometer Q was to enable this 'null' situation to be identified. The magnitude (and sign) of $_cV_E$ could then be obtained from the calibration of the potentiometer, according to standard procedure.

Let us consider the situation when the natural charge on the disks has not been completely annulled. K being closed, each of the circuits—that to the left of K in the figure, and that to the right—is in electrostatic equilibrium, the disk E and both pairs of electrometer quadrants are at earth potential, and no redistribution of charge would occur if K were opened. On the other hand, if K were opened and if the separation of the disks C and E were then changed, there would in general be a redistribution of charge. Some charge would be developed on the quadrants of the electrometer, and a deflection would be observed. Kelvin's criterion of identification of the null situation therefore was that there should be no deflection of the electrometer needle when the key K was opened and one of the disks was moved in relation to the other in the direction of their common axis.

It is worth while formulating the principle of this criterion more precisely, as an exercise in the application of Volta's equation (244). For this purpose we lose nothing in generality if we assume that all the connecting wires, and the quadrants of the electrometer, are composed of a single metal which we shall denote by M. We suppose that the contact point on the potentiometer wire has potential $-V$ with respect to earth, and that when K is closed the charges on disks C and E are q_1 and $-q_1$, respectively. Then, if C_1 is the capacitance of the condenser formed by the two disks in this arrangement,

$$q_1 = C_1(_\mathrm{C}V_\mathrm{M} - V + {}_\mathrm{M}V_\mathrm{E}) \tag{245}$$

When K is opened, and the capacitance of the condenser formed by the disks is changed to C_2, suppose that a quantity of charge $-q_3$ passes from the insulated quadrants to the disk E (and that the same amount of charge passes from C to the earthed quadrants of the electrometer). Then, if C_3 is the capacitance of the electrometer, we have, similarly,

$$q_1 + q_3 = C_2\left(_\mathrm{C}V_\mathrm{M} - V - \frac{q_3}{C_3} + {}_\mathrm{M}V_\mathrm{E}\right) \tag{246}$$

From equations (245) and (246),

$$\frac{q_3}{q_1} = \frac{C_3}{C_1}\frac{C_2 - C_1}{C_3 + C_2} \tag{247}$$

or, if we substitute from equation (244), alternatively,

$$\frac{q_3}{C_3} = (_\mathrm{C}V_\mathrm{E} - V)\frac{C_2 - C_1}{C_3 + C_2} \tag{248}$$

Equation (247) indicates that the fractional change of charge on the experimental disks is always less than the fractional change of capacitance, $(C_2 - C_1)/C_1$, being more nearly equal to this quantity as C_3 is the greater—but equation (248) shows that the difference of potential developed across the electrometer quadrants (being directly proportional to the absolute change of capacitance of the disks, and to the extent of departure from the null situation in respect of applied potential difference) is the greater as C_3 is smaller. For high sensitivity, therefore, a quadrant electrometer of small internal capacitance is desirable. It was the achievement of Kelvin's successors, particularly of F. Dolezalek (1901), to introduce significant improvements in this direction.

If we disregard the electrometer circuit, and consider the key K to be permanently closed, we can use fig. 53 for the consideration of the relevance of contact potential differences in Millikan's experiments on photoelectric threshold energies to which we have already referred (p. 404). We imagine E to be the emitter, irradiated by ultra-violet light of frequency v, C to be the collector, and the potentiometer P to provide the retarding potential difference, $-V_m$, necessary for the suppression of the photoelectric current to C. As we have previously noted (p. 393), Millikan would have avoided contact potential differences in his experiments altogether if he had used the same metal for collector and emitter in every case, but wisely he decided that the balance of advantage lay in using a common collector (of oxidised copper) with all the photoelectric emitters which he studied. Then, in order to 'correct' the externally measured retarding potential, $-V_m$, for the contact difference of potential between his electrodes, Millikan determined the latter quantity in each experiment (by Kelvin's method). Referring to fig. 53, we see that the 'true' retarding potential in this arrangement—the potential difference effective in the space between the electrodes—is $-(V_m - {}_cV_E)$, in terms of our previous notation. On this basis equation (237) becomes

$$(V_m - {}_cV_E)e = hv - \phi_E \tag{249}$$

and, v_0' being the 'corrected' value of the threshold frequency (the extrapolated value of v corresponding to the situation in which $V_m = {}_cV_E$), $\phi_E = hv_0'$. This, indeed, was the basis of Millikan's evaluation of ϕ for the photoelectric emitters which he studied (p. 396).

In our earlier discussion we stated that Millikan's use of the same collector with different emitters 'proved to be the source of further information' of some significance. Let us imagine experiments to be made with two emitters E and F using ultra-violet light of the same frequency ν. If $-V_{Em}$ and $-V_{Fm}$ are the externally applied retarding potentials necessary for the suppression of the photoelectric current to a common collector C in these experiments, then, in terms of equation (249), we have

$$(V_{Em} - V_{Fm} - {}_cV_E + {}_cV_F)e = \phi_F - \phi_E,$$

or $\qquad (V_{Em} - V_{Fm} + {}_EV_F)e = \phi_F - \phi_E \qquad (250)$

Millikan found empirically, in the conditions stated, that $V_{Em} = V_{Fm}$, in fact that for ultra-violet light of the same frequency, and with the same collecting electrode, the same externally applied retarding potential was required to reduce the collector current to zero, whatever material was used for the photoelectric emitter. If we accept this empirical result at its face value, we have, from equation (250),

$$e_EV_F = \phi_F - \phi_E \qquad (251)$$

In equation (251)—as consistently throughout this book—e represents the (positive) measure of the electronic charge, rather than the (negative) measure of the charge on the 'cathode-ray electron'. Thus we interpret the equation as follows: when two isolated metallic conductors are in contact the conductor for the material of which the photoelectric work function ϕ is the smaller becomes positive with respect to the other, and the measure of the contact difference of potential which is established is given by the difference of the two work functions divided by the measure of the electronic charge.

We are still merely accepting equation (251), tentatively, as summarising the results of experimental observations (later and more accurate observations than Millikan's have indeed provided increasing support for its validity)—for we have given no theoretical proof of its significance. Let us notice, then, that we have assumed the truth of Volta's equation (244) in deriving it, and that it is at least satisfactory that these two empirical results are mutually consistent. If equation (251) is valid absolutely, then equation (244) follows as a logical consequence. Earlier, we contented ourselves with the general argument that equation (244) represents a result which is acceptable on thermodynamic grounds: let us now apply the same criterion to the result represented by equation

(251). Remembering that the photoelectron is negatively charged, we first re-word the verbal interpretation of this equation, as given in the last paragraph, in more fundamental terms: we consider two photoelectrons, one 'just outside' the free surface of each of the two metals E and F, and we say that when these two metals are in contact the potential energy of the electron just outside the surface of metal E is less than that of the electron just outside the surface of the metal F by an amount $\phi_F - \phi_E$.

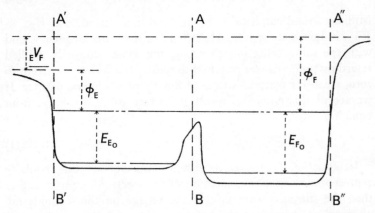

FIGURE 54

A situation such as we have just described is represented (on the basis of the Sommerfeld model, for two group I metals at the absolute zero of temperature) by the energy diagram of fig. 54. The heavy continuous line in the figure shows how the potential energy of a test electron varies with distance perpendicular to AB, the plane of contact of disks of the two metals in question. A′B″ and A″B″ represent the free surfaces of the disks, and E_{EO}, E_{FO} are the Fermi energies and ϕ_E, ϕ_F the photoelectric work functions characteristic of the two metals. As will be obvious from inspection, in order to validate equation (251), as we have just interpreted it, it has been necessary to draw the figure in such a way that the absolute energy of the Fermi level is the same for the two metals. We conclude, then, that Millikan's experimental results (and those of his subsequent corroborators) imply, on the basis of our model, that for two (group I) metals in contact there is transfer of charge (electrons) from one to the other, and that this transfer continues until such a difference of potential is established that the absolute energies of the two Fermi levels are the same. This situation is seen as the natural condition for electron transport equilibrium across the surface of contact, a condition which is entirely consonant with the general principles of thermodynamics.

We have been engaged in an attempt to exhibit the interrelations of the phenomena of contact potential and photoelectric emission using the Sommerfeld model as a guide to significant truth. As on a previous occasion (p. 403), when the interrelations of the thermionic and photoelectric emission phenomena were in question, we emerge with the general conviction that this simple model is as good a guide as any other more complicated model, for the purpose in hand. Certainly, the experimental results which are summarised by equations (244) and (251) do not refer only to the metals of group 1: we therefore conclude that, for all pairs of metals in contact isothermally, the absolute energies of the Fermi levels are the same—noting only the slight imprecision of this statement in relation to any temperature other than the absolute zero.

This general conclusion having been reached, there is just one point to be clarified before we proceed—and we return to the Sommerfeld model in order to focus discussion on it. On the basis of that model the magnitude of the Fermi energy E_0 is determined by the concentration of conduction electrons in the metal (p. 337), and the magnitude of $\phi + E_0$ (or, more directly, U_0) by the precise distribution of charge in the atoms of the surface layers (p. 386). Fundamentally, the significant values of these quantities are those relating to an isolated piece of metal carrying no excess charge of either sign. In the situation represented by fig. 53, as we have agreed, there has been transfer of charge from one disk to the other, and the question arises whether the consequent changes in the values of E_0 and $\phi + E_0$ for the metals in question are in any way significant. If they were, then the interpretation of equation (251), as a 'theoretical' rather than an empirical result, would be a matter of some delicacy. It can be stated at once that these energy changes are altogether insignificant in the practical situation. The redistribution of charge results essentially in the development of an 'electrical double layer' across the plane of contact AB (as indicated schematically by the potential energy curve in that figure). Macroscopically, this double layer may be represented by two charge sheets of surface density σ and $-\sigma$, respectively (the negatively charged sheet lying to the right in the figure), at a separation s. The effective field across AB is then σ/ϵ_0 (p. 36) and the potential difference ($_\mathrm{E}V_\mathrm{F}$) which the double layer introduces is $\sigma s/\epsilon_0$. Writing $\epsilon_0 = 9 \times 10^{-12}$ F m^{-1}, $s = 6 \times 10^{-10}$ m, if $_\mathrm{E}V_\mathrm{F} = 1$ V, $\sigma = 1\cdot5 \times 10^{-2}$ C m^{-2}, or approximately 10^{17} electronic charges m^{-2}. In an average metal the surface density of atoms in a principal lattice plane is of the order of $1\cdot5 \times 10^{19}$ atoms m^{-2}. We see, then, that the redistribution of charge, if it affected only a single layer of atoms on each side of the plane of contact between two metals, would not alter the free-electron concentrations in those single atomic layers by as much as 1 per cent. in the representative case that we have considered. Elsewhere the free-electron density would be unaltered.*

So far in this section we have been discussing the 'electrostatic' phenomena occurring in series circuits composed of different metals in contact at a single temperature. When the temperature is not the same throughout such a circuit, certain 'electrokinetic' effects are observed. These we must now consider. The simplest case is that of a circuit formed of two conductors, made of the pure metals A and B, respectively, in which a non-uniform distribution of temperature is maintained, the extremes of temperature, T_1 and T_2 ($T_2 > T_1$), occurring at the junctions between the conductors. Here we have specified an 'ideal' situation: the first observation of an electrokinetic effect in a real circuit approximating to that ideal was described by T. J. Seebeck (p. 123) in 1822. Seebeck constructed a shallow rectangular loop of two heavy conductors, one of bismuth and the other of copper, and with the loop set up in the plane of the magnetic meridian, with a compass needle pivoted at its centre, he observed a deflection of the needle when one of the junctions between the conductors was gently heated. When the other junction was heated, he found that the compass needle was deflected in the opposite sense. Oersted's

---

* It may be noted that even in this case the field in the double layer (approximately $1\cdot7 \times 10^9$ V m^{-1}) is more than 500 times greater than the 'breakdown field' for sparking in dry air under ordinary conditions. We conclude, therefore, that the maximum surface density of charge capable of retention by any conductor, in air, is of the order of one electron, in excess or in deficit, per 10^5 atoms in the first surface layer, in the region of greatest curvature of surface (p. 37). Moreover, we remember that the whole of the charge on such a conductor 'resides on the surface' (p. 33): if, therefore, the conductor is a sphere of radius r (metres), the total number of conduction electrons in the sphere may not be modified by more than about 1 part in $10^{14}\,r$ by charging the sphere in air.

discovery of the magnetic effect of the current from a voltaic pile had not long been made (p. 71): against the background of that discovery Seebeck's observations were naturally seen as providing an alternative source of current—less noxious perhaps than some of the early types of voltaic cell in which strong acids were employed—for experimental purposes generally. It is a fact of history that much of the pioneering work of Ohm, which led to precision in the concept of electrical resistance (p. 111), was carried out with 'thermoelectric couples' rather than voltaic cells as the source of current.

If this proved to be the first practical effect of Seebeck's discovery, its further investigation—almost equally naturally— proceeded in the direction of an attempt to establish some empirical correlation between this electrokinetic phenomenon and the electrostatic phenomenon of contact potential discovered by Volta. Volta had been able to arrange the metals in a single series, such that the sign of the contact difference of potential between any two metals (at room temperature) was correctly given in terms of the relative positions of the two metals in the series, any metal 'lower' in the series than any other acquiring a negative potential in respect of that other metal, contact between the two metals being established under the conditions stated. (We note that equation (251) provides sufficient basis for a 'theoretical' understanding of this empirical result.) Seebeck soon succeeded in showing that the phenomenon of the thermoelectric current was a general one—a two-component circuit formed of almost any pair of metals exhibited the effect to some degree—and, working in all cases with the junctions at the same two temperatures, he convinced himself that, in relation to this thermoelectric effect, also, a single serial order could be established. In respect of Seebeck's series, if a circuit were formed of any two metals, then the direction of current, say across the hot junction, was correctly given in terms of the relative positions of the two metals in the series, the temperatures of the two junctions being the 'standard' temperatures in question. It became immediately obvious, however, once this empirical regularity had been established, that Seebeck's serial order was not the same as Volta's: any simple correlation of the electrokinetic and electrostatic phenomena did not emerge from the comparison. In the following year (1823) a further complication was brought to light by James Cumming

(1777-1861), professor of chemistry at Cambridge. Cumming showed that the relative order of the metals in the 'thermoelectric series' changed when the temperature difference employed in the experiments on which the series was based was altered. Clearly, the Seebeck effect, at least with some pairs of metals, did not depend linearly on the difference of temperature between the junctions.

Once the concept of electromotive force in a current-carrying circuit had been made precise by the work of Ohm, it became evident that the essential character of the Seebeck phenomenon consists in the fact that there is a permanent source of e.m.f. in a circuit consisting of dissimilar conductors, when the junctions between the conductors are maintained at different temperatures. This thermoelectric e.m.f. was found to depend only on the materials of the conductors and on the junction temperatures, and not at all on the size and shape of the conductors employed (careful experiments carried out by Heinrich Gustav Magnus (1802-1870), professor of physics at the university of Berlin, in 1851, showed, in particular, that the distribution of temperature along the conductors in no way affects the resultant e.m.f., provided that the junction temperatures are fixed). We may formalise these conclusions by the following notation: we denote by $V_{AB}(T_2, T_1)$ the magnitude of the thermoelectric e.m.f., in a circuit of two metals A and B, tending to drive current from A to B across the junction at temperature T_2, T_1 being the temperature of the other junction.

By the early 1860s much work had been done on the determination of $V_{AB}(T_2, T_1)$ in respect of a wide variety of combinations of metals (and alloys) and over a considerable range of temperatures. Arising out of these determinations, M.P.Avenarius (1863) put forward an empirical rule having reference to circuits with one junction maintained at the ice-point, which we may quote in the form ($T_0 = 0°C$)

$$V_{AB}(T, T_0) = a(T - T_0) - b(T - T_0)^2 \qquad (252)$$

—and ten years later P.G.Tait (see *M L & T*, p. 78) enunciated the more general laws of 'intermediate temperatures' and 'intermediate metals'. The first of these laws can be expressed formally, in our adopted notation,

$$V_{AB}(T_3, T_1) = V_{AB}(T_3, T_2) + V_{AB}(T_2, T_1) \qquad (253)$$

The second law is more conveniently stated in words as follows: if one of the conductors forming a thermoelectric circuit is cut at any point, and an additional conductor is inserted there, the thermoelectric e.m.f. in the circuit is unaltered provided that the two points of junction of the additional conductor are at the same temperature.

If we accept Tait's first law, and consider two circuits involving the same two metals, A and B, with the cold junctions at different temperatures, T_1 and T_2, and the hot junctions at the same temperature T_3, we conclude that the rate of increase of thermoelectric e.m.f. with hot junction temperature is the same for each*: from equation (253), formally,

$$\frac{\partial}{\partial T_3}\left(V_{AB}(T_3, T_1)\right) = \frac{\partial}{\partial T_3}\left(V_{AB}(T_3, T_2)\right) \qquad (254)$$

Similarly, accepting Avenarius' equation (252), we have

$$\frac{\partial}{\partial T}\left(V_{AB}(T, T_0)\right) = a - 2b(T - T_0) \qquad (255)$$

Let us write

$$T_n - T_0 = a/2b \qquad (256)$$

then, on the basis of equations (254), (255) and (256), T_n is a temperature characteristic of the two metals A and B: if this is the temperature of the hot junction of a circuit involving these two metals, whatever is the temperature of the cold junction, there will be no first-order change in the thermoelectric e.m.f. in the circuit when the temperature of the hot junction is increased or decreased. T_n is referred to as the 'neutral temperature' characteristic of the metals A and B.

Having defined T_n, let us now use the law of intermediate temperatures (stated formally in equation (253)) to obtain an explicit expression for $V_{AB}(T_2, T_1)$ on the basis of Avenarius' equation (252). We have

$$\begin{aligned} V_{AB}(T_2, T_1) &= a(T_2 - T_1) - b\{(T_2 - T_0)^2 - (T_1 - T_0)^2\} \\ &= b(T_2 - T_1)\left(2T_0 - T_2 - T_1 + \frac{a}{b}\right), \end{aligned}$$

* In this sentence—and whenever the result which it embodies is repeated in later arguments—clearly, we may interchange the adjectives 'hot' and 'cold' without altering the truth of the statement.

or, substituting for a/b from equation (256),

$$V_{AB}(T_2, T_1) = b(T_2 - T_1)(2T_n - T_2 - T_1),$$

or, alternatively,

$$V_{AB}(T_2, T_1) = 2bT_n(T_2 - T_1) - b(T_2^2 - T_1^2) \qquad (257)$$

Let us now see where our argument has led. Equations (252) and (253) are formal expressions representing empirical generalisations so far unsupported by any background of theory. These two generalisations are basically independent: tentatively we have accepted both as valid, and, combining them, we have obtained an expression for $V_{AB}(T_2, T_1)$. Obviously, this expression, given by equation (257), is consistent with equation (253)—as it should be.

Equation (257) shows that, whatever the cold-junction temperature T_1, the thermoelectric e.m.f. in the circuit varies parabolically with T_2, the temperature of the hot junction (provided always that Avenarius' equation correctly describes this variation when the cold-junction temperature is the arbitrarily chosen 'standard' reference temperature T_0). The equation shows, moreover, that b is a constant for the pair of metals concerned. This is not the case with the parameter a in Avenarius' equation, the value of which depends on the cold-junction reference temperature (see equation (256)). Equation (257), in which both T_n and b depend only on the materials of the conductors, formalises Tait's empirical law (1870), generalising Avenarius' rule. Even though, at the present day, equation (257) has no more than the status of an empirical generalisation, it gives a surprisingly accurate description of the Seebeck phenomenon with pure metals—at least over ranges of temperature within which there is no 'phase transition' modifying the crystal structure of the solid materials concerned. And we may note, at this stage, that, if this equation is generally applicable, the early observations of Cumming (p. 413) on the 'inversion' of order in the thermoelectric series with change of temperature range represent a qualitative result which is a necessary consequence of the quantitative law.

So far we have been concerned only with Tait's first empirical generalisation. The form in which his second generalisation, the law of intermediate metals, was originally quoted (p. 415) gave it the appearance of having a practical rather than a theoretical relevance. In almost every case in which the Seebeck effect is employed in applied physics—or studied in pure physics research—the basic thermoelectric circuit is broken so that a galvanometer or other measuring instrument may be inserted in the circuit. Tait's second law provides the necessary assurance that the e.m.f. in the circuit will be unaltered, provided that any additional conductor so introduced (the galvanometer leads, or the coil of the instrument) has its two ends at the same temperature (if the two leads to the galvanometer are taken from the same sample of wire, it is clearly permissible that there should be the same difference of temperature, in the same sense, along each lead). We are now concerned to establish an alternative form of Tait's second law which shall have more obvious significance, theoretically: we wish to show that the 'law of the inserted conductor' (as we may call our first version) is equivalent to the formally expressed empirical law

$$V_{AC}(T_2, T_1) = V_{AB}(T_2, T_1) + V_{BC}(T_2, T_1) \qquad (258)$$

It is in the form of this equation, when it is set against equation (253), rather than in that of the verbal statement that we quoted originally, that Tait's second law takes on a character similar to that of his first law, justifying the similar designations, 'of intermediate metals' and 'of intermediate temperatures', by which they are generally known.

Suppose that a six-component series circuit is built up of pairs of conductors of three different metals A, B and C, arranged as indicated in fig. 55. The temperatures of the six junctions in the circuit (labelled 1-6 in the figure) are alternately T_1 and T_2. Let us calculate the total e.m.f. in the circuit on the basis of two independent 'thought experiments', each involving reliance upon Tait's second law as expressed in our original version. First, let us choose two points X and Y, one in each of the conductors of metal A, the two points being at the same temperature. Then if a voltmeter of effectively infinite resistance (electrostatic voltmeter) were connected between X and Y, and if the 'lower half' of the circuit were disconnected, the voltmeter would measure the thermoelectric e.m.f. in the 'upper half' of the circuit, namely $V_{CB}(T_1, T_2)$, tending to drive a clockwise current round the circuit. Similarly, if the upper half of the circuit had been disconnected, the voltmeter would have measured the e.m.f. in the lower half circuit, namely $V_{CB}(T_2, T_1)$ tending to drive current clockwise round the circuit. In the complete six-component circuit, therefore, the total thermoelectric e.m.f. is

$$V_{CB}(T_1, T_2) + V_{CB}(T_2, T_1),$$

on this reckoning.

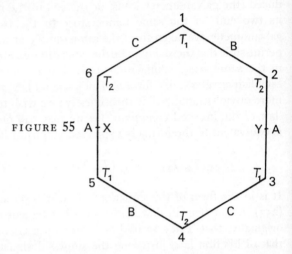

FIGURE 55

For our second thought experiment we imagine the electrostatic voltmeter to be connected successively between junctions 5 and 1, 1 and 3, and 3 and 5, in each case the larger of the two parts into which the whole circuit is thereby divided being disconnected. In this way we obtain the total e.m.f. in the whole circuit tending to drive current in the clockwise direction as the sum of three contributions, namely $V_{AC}(T_2, T_1)$, $V_{BA}(T_2, T_1)$ and $V_{CB}(T_2, T_1)$. Comparing the results of the two thought experiments, we then have

$$V_{AC}(T_2, T_1) + V_{BA}(T_2, T_1) + V_{CB}(T_2, T_1)$$
$$= V_{CB}(T_1, T_2) + V_{CB}(T_2, T_1).$$

Generally, according to our conventional notation (p. 414),

$$V_{AB}(T_2, T_1) = -V_{BA}(T_2, T_1) = -V_{AB}(T_1, T_2),$$

thus $$V_{AC}(T_2, T_1) = V_{AB}(T_2, T_1) + V_{BC}(T_2, T_1),$$

as we set out to prove.

We have said that the law of intermediate metals, in the form of equation (258), is clearly of 'obvious significance, theoretically'. It will be recalled that, in relation to contact potentials, the empirical law of Volta is expressible in a precisely similar general form (equation (244)). In that case, guided by the results of Millikan's experiments, we came to an understanding of the law on the basis of equation (251)—the more easily because a simple physical description could be given of the underlying equality. Equation (251) states that the energy that has to be expended in conveying a single electron from a position just outside the free surface of metal E to a position just outside the free surface of F, when these two metals are in contact, is equal to the excess of the energy necessary to remove an electron 'from the Fermi level of F' over that necessary to remove an electron 'from the Fermi level of E' (see fig. 54). For our present purposes, the details of this description are unimportant: we are concerned only to note that we came to an understanding of equation (244) in terms of an energy equation involving the difference of two quantities—one a quantity of energy characteristic of one of the two metals in contact, the other essentially the same quantity (generally of different magnitude) in respect of the other metal. The importance of Tait's second law is that, if it is accepted as a valid statement of fact, it virtually compels us to believe that, in a simple thermoelectric circuit, the energy which is somehow made available for the maintenance of the current is expressible as the difference of two precisely similar quantities, one calculable in terms of the properties of the one material (and the junction temperatures) and the other in terms of the same properties of the other material. Formally, therefore, we should expect to be able to identify a characteristic energy θ such that

$$eV_{AB}(T_2, T_1) = \theta_A(T_2, T_1) - \theta_B(T_2, T_1) \qquad (259)$$

It may be said, right away, that the identification of θ, in relation to any of the theoretical models that we have hitherto used, is a matter of some subtlety which we shall not be able to explore in depth: it is important, however, that we should discuss the energetics of the thermoelectric circuit in general terms, and this we now proceed to do, appealing first to the results of direct experiment for our basic material.

The first experimental discovery of relevance to our present discussion was made by Jean Charles Anathase Peltier (1785-1845) in 1834. Peltier found that, when a current was passed across the junction of two dissimilar conductors, the material in the immediate vicinity of the junction was heated or cooled, depending upon the direction of the current in the circuit. This effect was quite distinct from the general heating of a single homogeneous current-carrying conductor which, as far as was then known, was precisely the same whichever the direction of current flow—and it took place whatever the nature of the current source employed. From the limited observations which he made, Peltier concluded that if the only e.m.f. in a circuit of two dissimilar metals was the thermo-electric e.m.f., arising because of a difference of temperature between the junctions, then it was the material in the neighbour-hood of the hot junction which tended to be cooled and that in the neighbourhood of the cold junction which tended to be heated as a result of the natural flow of 'thermoelectric' current in the circuit. If, therefore, the temperatures of the junctions are to be main-tained constant in such circumstances (so we must conclude) heat must continually be supplied to the conductors in the region of the hot junction and abstracted from them in the region of the cold junction.

It was not until the early 1850s that accurate quantitative measurements were made of the Peltier effect. In 1853 von Quintus Icilius described an experimental arrangement in which he was able rapidly to 'switch out' a voltaic cell which had been sending current round a circuit of two dissimilar conductors, and 'switch in' a sensitive galvanometer in its place. On each repetition, the experiment was started with the whole circuit at the same temperature, then, during the period when the voltaic cell was supplying current to the circuit, a steady state was reached in which one junction became heated and the other cooled, through equal small ranges of temperature proportional to the rate of evolution (or absorption) of 'Peltier heat'. (The same current crossed the two junctions 'in opposite directions' at essentially the same temperature.) Finally, when the galvanometer was switched in instead of the cell, the initial deflection of this instrument, proportional to the initial value of the thermoelectric (Seebeck) current in the 'activated' circuit, was for all practical purposes proportional to the difference of temperature of the junctions—and so to the rate of evolution (or absorption) of Peltier heat in the previous phase of the experiment. In this way Icilius showed that the rate of appearance or disappearance of this heat at the junction was directly proportional to the first power of the activating current (provided that the original temperature of the conductors was the same throughout the various repetitions of the experiment). In the following year (1854) M. L. Frankenheim reported a similar conclusion derived from the results of a more comprehensive investigation. Using an auxiliary thermocouple, he measured the steady-state temperature change (and so, in arbitrary units, the rate of evolution of heat) in the neighbourhood of a junction through which the same current, i, was passed, first in one direction and then in the other. Repeating this determination for different values of i, he showed that the two rates of evolution of heat could be represented formally as $ai^2 \pm bi$. He interpreted the first term in this empirical result as representing the contribution, under his experimental conditions, from the Joule heat developed in the conductors; the second term he identified as representing the Peltier heat, evolved when the current was in one direction and absorbed when it was in the other.

If the rate of evolution (or absorption) of Peltier heat is proportional to the current passing across the junction, the absolute quantity of heat involved is proportional to the total quantity of electricity transported. On this basis, if we say that an amount of heat $q\pi_{AB}(T)$ is absorbed from the surroundings when a quantity q of electricity crosses, in the direction from A to B, a junction of two metals, A and B, at temperature T, we are thereby defining, conventionally, the Peltier coefficient $\pi_{AB}(T)$ for the two metals and the temperature concerned. As so defined, the Peltier coefficient is measured in joules per coulomb—or in volts (p. 157)— and, because this absorption of heat from the surroundings is the only effect that we have so far identified in which energy is drawn from an external source to maintain the thermoelectric current in the circuit, we are tempted to write, intuitively,

$$V_{AB}(T_2, T_1) = \pi_{AB}(T_2) + \pi_{BA}(T_1),$$

or $\qquad V_{AB}(T_2, T_1) = \pi_{AB}(T_2) - \pi_{AB}(T_1) \qquad\qquad (260)$

($\pi_{AB}(T_1)$, according to our convention, represents the amount of heat given up to the surroundings at the 'cold' junction, when unit quantity of electricity passes across the junction from B to A). However, this is only an intuitive reaction to the situation (it was, indeed, Joule's reaction in 1841), based largely on the recognition that the Peltier coefficient has been defined with the dimensions of a potential difference—and we should be well advised to examine the physical situation more closely before committing ourselves to any precise hypothesis.

First, let it be said that throughout our recent discussions, in the background of our intuition, there has been the tacit acceptance of the general law of conservation of energy. We must remind ourselves that this law in its modern form dates back no earlier than 1847 (see *M L & T*, §14.3): at the time of Peltier's discovery it was unknown. Even in its restricted form, having relevance only to quantities of heat and work (in which connection it may be referred to as the first law of thermodynamics), it had no secure basis of experimental justification before 1843 (*ibid.*, §14.2). Yet the strange fact of history is that the basic notions which later found expression in the second law (application of which, as we shall see, will significantly modify our over-hasty speculations), had already been formulated in 1824. In that year, Sadi Nicolas Léonhard Carnot (1796-1832), while serving as a lieutenant in the staff corps of the French army, published a memoir entitled *Réflexions sur la puissance motrice du feu*. In this memoir he put forward the view that the only reliable way to discuss the 'motive power of heat' was in terms of complete cycles of operations, in which a sample of 'working substance' was always returned, at the conclusion of any such cycle, to precisely the same physical state as that in which it existed at the beginning of the cycle. The simplest cycle, on this view, was one in which the working substance exchanged heat with its surroundings in two processes at different temperatures—and only if heat were taken in at the higher and rejected at the lower temperature would mechanical work be derivable over the cycle as a whole. Carnot further introduced the notion of a 'perfectly reversible process' (see *M L & T*, p. 290)—a process taking place in a system in which an equilibrium state is only infinitesimally disturbed, and in which, if such an infinitesimal disturbance were at any stage reversed in sense, the subsequent sequence of events in the system would be in every respect the reverse of the previous sequence. If an elementary cycle were entirely made up of such reversible stages, so Carnot maintained, the amount of mechanical work derivable over the whole cycle, for a given quantity of heat 'passing through' the working substance, from the higher to the lower temperature, would be as great as could possibly be obtained in any combination of processes in which the same amount of heat was involved, and the same two temperatures. In more modern parlance, 'the efficiency of a heat engine working on the basis of an elementary reversible cycle is independent of the nature of the working substance and a function only of the temperatures at which heat is exchanged'.

We have just stated, in modern terms, what is generally referred to as Carnot's principle. Carnot based this statement of qualitative 'law' on an intuitively accepted axiom which we have already written into our brief account of his overall point of view. We have represented him, in the last paragraph, as believing that 'only if heat were taken in at the higher and rejected at the lower temperature would mechanical work be derivable, over the cycle as a whole'.* In this axiom itself is to be found the germ of the second law of thermodynamics—but it remained unrecognised and neglected for a quarter of a century.

In 1848, W. Thomson (Kelvin) took the first step in rehabilitating the neglected principle. In the following year he published an extended *Account of Carnot's theory of the motive power of heat* in the *Transactions* of the Royal Society of Edinburgh. Thereafter it provided inspiration and challenge for the best theoretical physicists of the day. Within five years, through the work of W. J. M. Rankine (see *M L & T*, p. 228), Clausius (p. 207), and most particularly of Kelvin himself, there has been erected an imposing structure of deductive reasoning based on this principle alone. For our present purposes, the basic generalisation which emerged may best be expressed in words 'in a perfectly reversible cycle the net increase of entropy of the working substance is zero' —or, formally, in symbols

$$\Sigma \left(\frac{\Delta Q}{T} \right)_r = 0 \qquad\qquad (261)$$

* Carnot's 1824 memoir was his only scientific publication. In it he appears to have accepted a materialistic view of the nature of heat, but extracts from a number of unpublished manuscript works which had accumulated at the time of his death were published in 1878 (when his memoir was reprinted) and these show that he had at some stage so far adopted the contrary view, and anticipated the formulation of the first, as well as the second, law, that he was proposing detailed experiments for the determination of the mechanical equivalent of heat by methods essentially those which Joule devised for that purpose some twenty years later.

In equation (261), ΔQ represents the quantity of heat absorbed by the working substance in an elementary process occurring reversibly (hence the subscript r) at ('absolute thermodynamical') temperature T—and, in the previous form of words, Clausius' term 'increase of entropy of the working substance' denotes the physical magnitude $(\Delta Q/T)_r$ when an elementary process is concerned.

Over the years 1851 to 1854 Kelvin gave considerable thought to the question whether the new law—the second law of thermodynamics, which we have now formalised in equation (261)—could validly be applied in respect of the thermoelectric circuit. It was, of course, clear that the first law could be so applied, but in the conductors of any actual circuit there is the production of Joule heat by the current, also the transference, by conduction, of heat from the hot junction to the cold, and these are certainly not reversible effects. As far as the second law is concerned, at least in the form in which we have quoted it, the basic requirement is that all processes should be reversible. Kelvin was well aware of these considerations, but, driven by a conviction which he failed entirely to rationalise, he bequeathed his doubts to posterity and proceeded to apply the second law to the reversible processes alone, leaving the irreversible processes completely out of account. If this application should lead to results verifiable by experiment, Kelvin maintained, then later theorists would be faced with the problem of justifying his procedure.

Let us follow Kelvin in his speculations. We consider an elementary circuit of two metals A and B, with junction temperatures T and $T + \Delta T$. We suppose that a quantity q of electricity passes round the circuit in the direction from A to B across the 'hot' junction. If we assume that the only exchange of heat with the surroundings is in terms of the Peltier heat, then equation (260), suitably modified, is the appropriate expression of the first law. We have, to be precise,

$$qV_{AB}(T + \Delta T, T) = q(\pi_{AB}(T + \Delta T) - \pi_{AB}(T)),$$

or (see p. 415)*

---

* Here, and in the following pages, we are using the abbreviated notation $\dfrac{d}{dT}(V_{AB}(T))$ instead of the more cumbersome $\left\{ \dfrac{\partial}{\partial T}(V_{AB}(T, T_0)) \right\}_{T_0}$, reflecting our acceptance of the law of intermediate temperatures as interpreted by equation (254).

$$\frac{d}{dT}\left(V_{AB}(T)\right) = \frac{d}{dT}\left(\pi_{AB}(T)\right) \tag{262}$$

From the second law, applied only to the reversible heat effects, we have

$$q\,\frac{\pi_{AB}(T+\Delta T)}{T+\Delta T} - q\,\frac{\pi_{AB}(T)}{T} = 0,$$

or $\qquad \dfrac{d}{dT}\left(\dfrac{\pi_{AB}(T)}{T}\right) = 0,$

giving $\quad \pi_{AB}(T) = cT,$

where c is a constant. Substituting in equation (262), and integrating over a finite range of temperature from T_1 to T_2, we have, finally,

$$V_{AB}(T_2, T_1) = c(T_2 - T_1) \tag{263}$$

We observe the first result of our speculative exercise. If the Peltier effect is the only reversible effect in which heat is absorbed or evolved in the thermoelectric circuit, then the thermoelectric e.m.f., for a given pair of metals, should be directly proportional to the difference of temperature between the junctions. Already, in 1854, there was clear experimental evidence that this was not the case: even Cummings' results of 1823 were sufficient to dispose of this conclusion as a general law (see pp. 413, 416).

When Kelvin obtained equation (263) by the argument that we have followed, he did not immediately abandon his programme of enquiry, although its first result was in contradiction with experiment. Instead, he considered the possibility that there might be a second type of reversible heat exchange in a thermoelectric circuit, determined by the passage of electricity, in a single homogeneous conductor, 'through a range of temperature'. To this end he defined a hypothetical coefficient $\sigma(T)$ in terms of the amount of heat absorbed by the conductor from its immediate surroundings when unit quantity of electricity passes from a place in the conductor where the temperature is $(T-\frac{1}{2})$ to a place where it is $(T+\frac{1}{2})$. Then, in relation to the elementary thermoelectric circuit that we used previously, he could effectively write, applying the first law,

$$qV_{AB}(T+\Delta T, T)$$

$$= q(\pi_{AB}(T+\Delta T) - \pi_{AB}(T)) + q(\sigma_A(T) - \sigma_B(T))\Delta T,$$

that is $\quad \dfrac{d}{dT}(V_{AB}(T)) = \dfrac{d}{dT}(\pi_{AB}(T)) + \sigma_A(T) - \sigma_B(T) \qquad (264)$

and, applying the second law,

$$q\frac{\pi_{AB}(T+\Delta T)}{T+\Delta T} - q\frac{\pi_{AB}(T)}{T} + q\frac{\sigma_A(T)\Delta T}{T} - q\frac{\sigma_B(T)\Delta T}{T} = 0,$$

or $\quad \dfrac{d}{dT}\left(\dfrac{\pi_{AB}(T)}{T}\right) + \dfrac{\sigma_A(T) - \sigma_B(T)}{T} = 0 \qquad (265)$

Equation (265) may be re-written, after differentiation, in the form

$$\frac{d}{dT}(\pi_{AB}(T)) - \frac{\pi_{AB}(T)}{T} + \sigma_A(T) - \sigma_B(T) = 0,$$

then, on substitution in equation (264), we have

$$\pi_{AB}(T) = T\frac{d}{dT}(V_{AB}(T)) \qquad (266)$$

and, from equation (265), finally,

$$\sigma_A(T) - \sigma_B(T) = -T\frac{d^2}{dT^2}(V_{AB}(T)) \qquad (267)$$

Equations (266) and (267) are not obviously at variance with experiment. Indeed, if we accept Tait's equation (257) as adequately summarising experimental results in general, we have

$$\pi_{AB}(T) = 2bT(T_n - T),$$

$$\sigma_A(T) - \sigma_B(T) = 2bT,$$

and, as a necessary consequence,

$$\pi_{AB}(T) = (\sigma_A(T) - \sigma_B(T))(T_n - T).$$

Kelvin's suggestion of a new reversible thermal effect, characterised by the coefficient σ, was made at a time when the precise nature of the temperature-variation of $V_{AB}(T_2, T_1)$ had not been thoroughly explored, and certainly before there was any direct hint, from experiment, that an effect of the kind that he was postulating in fact occurred. Kelvin, therefore, set himself to examine the matter experimentally. He first obtained positive 'evidence' for the effect using the arrangement illustrated schematically in fig. 56. By means of the reversing key K, current from the battery S could be passed first in one direction and then in the other through the circuit A . . . G formed of coupled conductors all taken from a single sample of metal wire. The coupling elements B and F were maintained, by running water, at 'room' temperature

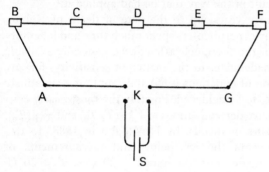

FIGURE 56

whilst D was maintained at a 'high' temperature (100°C). C and E were bored out so as to admit the bulbs of similar sensitive mercury thermometers. When no current was flowing in the circuit, which was designed as far as possible to be geometrically symmetrical about D, the two thermometers registered the same temperature within a small tolerance. When current was passed through the circuit, so that a steady state was reached, the temperatures registered by the thermometers were no longer the same —and the sense of the difference varied with the direction of the current. Clearly, a reversible heat effect had been established having the general character which Kelvin had postulated: the experimental arrangement ensured that current was passing, at one and the same time, both in the positive direction of the temperature gradient in a homogeneous conductor, and in the reverse direction, and a differential effect had been set in evidence, demonstrably related to the direction of current flow. Kelvin's first success was obtained using conductors of iron and copper— with which, as it happened, he found the sign of the heat exchange to be different: in terms of our conventional definition, it was as if the value of the coefficient σ was positive for copper and negative for iron, over the temperature range employed. Unperturbed by the fact that this coefficient, which, because of the way in which he had defined it (p. 425), he referred to as the 'specific heat of electricity', was not even of the same sign for all metals, Kelvin accepted his experimental success as demonstrating the soundness of his theoretical intuition: there must be some good reason why the second law of thermodynamics could validly be applied to the thermoelectric circuit in the way that he had applied it.

Over the next fifty years, up to the date of death of Kelvin, though a great many experimenters spent much time and ingenuity on investigations of the thermoelectric effects, generally available techniques were inadequate, in the matter of sensitivity, for any clear-cut verification of equations (266) and (267), of a rigorously quantitative nature, to be achieved. Possibly the most nearly convincing were extensive determinations of $V_{AB}(T, T_0)$ and $\pi_{AB}(T_0)$, for six different pairs of metals, by H. M. Jahn in 1888. In this notation T_0 represents the ice point, and measurements of $V_{AB}(T, T_0)$ were made over the range $-20°C < T < 20°C$. The object was to test the validity of equation (266), simply: in five cases out of six the numerical agreement was better than ± 20 per cent. It was another thirty years before more reliable measurements were made. Similarly, in relation to measurements of σ (the 'Thomson coefficient'), there was a very great volume of work, notably by F. P. le Roux (1867), Angelo Batelli (1886), H. L. Callendar (1886) and R. O. King (1898), but in respect of the precise verification of equation (267) the overall result was far from conclusive. Only within the past forty years has the situation been otherwise. We may summarise by saying that it now appears that Kelvin's equations (266) and (267) indeed represent the results of experiment to a high degree of accuracy—on the other hand, they had been accepted on trust, almost universally, from the time when Kelvin first obtained qualitative evidence for the 'Thomson effect' with iron and copper in 1855.*

---

* Speaking as President of the Royal Society of Edinburgh on 7 December 1874, in presenting the Keith Prize to P. G. Tait for his work on thermo-electricity, Kelvin said 'I am afraid the subject is somewhat involved; but I can only say that if the Fellows of the Royal Society diligently read their own *Transactions*, it would not be necessary for me to speak about it, because it was very minutely unfolded in a paper published a good many years ago. I chanced to be the author of that paper myself . . .'

Experimenters, then, have at last convincingly established the empirical validity of the formal results which Kelvin obtained by the 'doubtful' application of the second law of thermodynamics to the thermoelectric circuit. Also, over the same period, theorists have greatly clarified the prior issue of the justification of the procedure which Kelvin doubtfully employed. Basically, justification involves the acceptance of a further axiom, unknown to Kelvin. Boltzmann was almost certainly correct, when in 1887, he resurrected Kelvin's original doubts, and expressed the view that the thermodynamics of reversible processes, as it was then understood, could not properly be used as Kelvin had used it. The first sign of a new development came in the doctoral thesis of Niels Bohr (p. 269) in 1911. Bohr concluded that the validity of Kelvin's results 'was ultimately owing to the circumstance that the fundamental equations governing the motion of individual particles are symmetric with respect to past and future'. The 'principle of microscopic reversibility' became merged in the theory of irreversible thermodynamics of Lars Onsager in 1931. H. B. G. Casimir (1945), in particular, discussed the phenomena of thermoelectricity from the new point of view. According to this viewpoint the Thomson effect arises as an 'interference phenomenon', when external conditions are imposed involving two sets of 'forces' (an applied e.m.f. and a maintained difference of temperature) each of which in isolation results in a transport effect (electric current, or flow of heat) which is macroscopically irreversible in the context of the classical thermodynamics of Kelvin and Clausius. The previously unformulated axiom on which the general theory of such processes was based by Onsager is the quantitative expression of an inherent symmetry in the 'interference phenomenon'. We cannot here elaborate this statement, but the outcome of the matter is simply that there is a class of situations (the situation in the thermoelectric circuit being one of them) in which, pragmatically, a division may be made between the macroscopically reversible effects and the macroscopically irreversible effects in such a way that the validity of the second law of thermodynamics in respect of the reversible effects alone is ensured, once Onsager's axiom has itself been admitted as valid. The end of the story, then, is that, according to present-day views, Kelvin intuitively made the appropriate choice when, neglecting the other thermal processes involved, he considered only the entropy changes associated with the Peltier and (the then hypothetical) Thomson heats, in applying the second law to the thermoelectric circuit.

That is the end of the story in one of its aspects, it is true—but we are still left with the problem of attempting to understand, on the basis of some model with which we are familiar, something of the details of the transformation of the Peltier and Thomson heats into 'electrical energy'. We have already posed this problem, in terms of equation (259), and we have confessed that 'we shall not be able to explore it in depth'—but that is no reason why we should not take the first steps in exploration. Appropriately, according to its mode of definition, the Thomson coefficient, σ, has been termed the specific heat of electricity. It represents the heat absorbed by the conductor when unit quantity of (positive) electricity passes from a region of lower to a region of higher temperature, the temperature difference involved being one degree. On the basis of the Sommerfeld model the mean kinetic energy of the conduction electrons increases at a rate $(\pi^2 k/2)(kT/E_0)$ per electron per degree, at temperature T (p. 339). If the immediate fate of the Thomson heat were to provide for this increase of kinetic energy of the conduction electrons, then, in the first place, the sign of the coefficient σ would be uniformly negative for all metals (when a conventionally positive current flows in the direction of increasing temperature, in fact negative electrons are passing from regions of higher to regions of lower temperature in the conductor)—and, in the second place, the numerical magnitude of the coefficient would be given by $(\pi^2 k/2e)(kT/E_0)$, provided that Sommerfeld's model is applicable to the metal in question. Now, we have already drawn attention to the fact that the sign of σ is not the same for all metals (p. 428); on the other hand it is a remarkable circumstance that, sign apart, for good conductors, the Sommerfeld result gives a very fair order-of-magnitude estimate of the 'specific heat of electricity' as Kelvin defined it. For good conductors, at room temperature, kT/E_0 has been taken as of the order of $1/220$ (p. 348), and k/e has the value 8.6×10^{-5} joule per coulomb per degree K (p. 359). Thus the Sommerfeld specific heat of electrons (reckoned per coulomb of charge) is of the order of $2.0\ \mu\text{V deg}^{-1}\ \text{K}$, in a good conductor. Experimental values of σ, at room temperature, are as follows:

Na, -5.1; K, -11.3; Cu, $+1.3$; Ag, $+1.3$; Au, $+1.6$; Fe, -5.5

—the unit being μV deg^{-1} K, throughout. It would appear that the order of magnitude agreement, apart from the matter of sign, cannot possibly be fortuitous. We therefore take the view that our identification of the immediate fate of the Thomson heat is essentially correct, but that in respect of this non-equilibrium transport phenomenon there is a significant intervention of effects involving interaction between the conduction electrons and the lattice, whereby there is a second contribution to the 'specific heat' of the electrons—a contribution of the same order as that given by the calculation of Sommerfeld (which has reference to an equilibrium state)—which may be either positive or negative in sign. It would be beyond the scope of the present account to attempt to say more than that.

In respect of the Peltier heat, we start with the naïve view that if heat is absorbed from the surroundings when electrons cross the surface of separation of two conductors (in the direction from conductor B to conductor A, so that π_{AB} is a positive quantity according to the conventional definition), then the implication is that, at the temperature in question, the mean energy per conduction electron (under equilibrium conditions) is less for metal B than for metal A. The Peltier heat, on this view, goes to make good this deficit: formally, we suppose,

$$e\pi_{AB}(T) = \overline{W}_A(T) - \overline{W}_B(T) \qquad (268)$$

wherein $\overline{W}(T)$ represents the mean (total) energy of a conduction electron at temperature T. According to Kelvin's thermodynamical relations (equations (266) and (267)), the Peltier coefficient π_{AB} and the Thomson coefficients σ_A and σ_B, in general, must satisfy the equation

$$-T \frac{d}{dT}\left(\frac{\pi_{AB}(T)}{T}\right) = \sigma_A(T) - \sigma_B(T).$$

We have, therefore, on the basis of our present view,

$$-\frac{T}{e} \frac{d}{dT}\left(\frac{\overline{W}_A(T)}{T} - \frac{\overline{W}_B(T)}{T}\right) = \sigma_A(T) - \sigma_B(T) \qquad (269)$$

—and, consistently with the results of our previous analysis (see equation (259)), we conclude that for each metal separately

$$\frac{d}{dT}\left(\frac{\overline{W}(T)}{T}\right) = -e \frac{\sigma(T)}{T} \qquad (270)$$

Strictly, following only the logic of the formalism, we should have included a second term on the right-hand side of equation (270)— a contribution $c(T)$, the same for all metals, though possibly temperature-dependent—but there being no feature in our understanding of the physical situation which would justify such a term, we have omitted it intentionally. We have already discussed the predictions of the Sommerfeld model in relation to the value of σ: let us now continue that discussion in relation to the Peltier heat with the help of equations (270) and (268).

As a result of our previous discussion we were led to the simple result

$$\frac{\sigma(T)}{T} = -\frac{\pi^2 k^2}{2eE_0} \tag{271}$$

(see above). From equation (270), therefore, we have

$$\frac{d}{dT}\left(\frac{\overline{W}(T)}{T}\right) = \frac{\pi^2 k^2}{2E_0} \tag{272}$$

Now, according to equation (204), $\overline{E}(T)$, the mean kinetic energy of a conduction electron, at temperature T, on the Sommerfeld model, is given by

$$\overline{E}(T) = \tfrac{3}{5}E_0 + \frac{\pi^2 k^2 T^2}{4E_0} \tag{273}$$

and, if $\overline{U}$ is a potential energy term,

$$\overline{W}(T) = \overline{E}(T) + \overline{U} \tag{274}$$

We note that equations (272), (273) and (274) are not mutually consistent as they stand, but that if we were to take count only of the second term on the right-hand side of equation (273), and omit $\overline{U}$ in equation (274), writing $\overline{W}(T) = \pi^2 k^2 T^2/4E_0$, we should indeed have equation (272), but for a factor 2. Clearly, our naïve approach, with its basic assumption that results relative to equilibrium conditions can be taken over intact, is not adequate for our purposes (it ought to be possible to develop the Sommerfeld model so as to satisfy the general requirements of the thermodynamical relations), but it is at least sufficient to show that in any such development only the temperature-dependent part of the total energy of the conduction electrons will feature in the final result. Possibly we should have been prepared for this conclusion:

it is a basic characteristic of all quantum-theory models that the energy content of those electron states which, at any temperature, are, in effect, 'completely full', is 'frozen' in respect of interchange with the bulk material (lattice). We must leave the matter there, somewhat inconclusively as it must be admitted.

8.4. CIRCUITS INVOLVING ELECTROLYTES

In the introduction to chapter 5 the decision was taken not to consider in any detail the 'active' phenomena of the voltaic cell until the 'passive' phenomena of electrolysis had first been discussed, though it was pointed out that 'many physical systems [of the type in question] can act either actively or passively, according to the circumstances'. In this section, again, we shall be dealing with effects which are common to these two modes—in particular with the passage of charge from ions in solution to the solid electrodes—but now the reverse order of treatment will be appropriate. We have just concluded a discussion of the application of thermodynamics to the phenomena of thermoelectricity: it is appropriate that we should straightway apply the same principles to the more-than-formally related problem of the energetics of the voltaic cell, before the thread of the argument is lost.

The history of this particular application of the second law is strange indeed. As we have seen (p. 224), Kelvin was already deeply concerned with identifying the source of energy of the voltaic cell in 1851. Over the next few years (see p. 424) he was equally concerned with identifying the heat sources from which the energy of the thermoelectric current is derived. Basing his argument on imprecise knowledge concerning the temperature-dependence of the thermoelectric e.m.f., he concluded, tentatively at first —until his conclusions were buttressed by experimental observation—that there must be a second heat source, over and above the source of the Peltier heat, if the brute facts of experience were to be understood in terms of acceptable theory. But he did not look back, so it seems, over these years, and enquire what the conclusion would be if the e.m.f. of a voltaic cell were likewise temperature-dependent—not did he enquire, as far as we know, whether this were so. His calculations in respect of the Daniell cell appear to have satisfied him completely: in that case it seemed (p. 225) that, within the limits of experimental uncertainty, the dissipation of energy in Joule heating could be accounted for precisely in terms of the heat of the overall chemical reaction taking place in the cell. It remained for Helmholtz, some thirty years later (1882), to apply Kelvin's own arguments to this neglected problem, and to indicate the misfortune (if such it were) that Kelvin should have chosen the Daniell cell for his original calculations—for it so happens that at ordinary temperatures the temperature coefficient of e.m.f. of the Daniell cell is insignificantly small.

Before we continue with the argument from this point, there is one caution that must be entered. Classical thermodynamics deals with equilibrium situations through the device of the consideration of reversible processes. A general definition of a perfectly reversible process has already been given (p. 422). In this context a voltaic cell, of e.m.f. V, on open circuit, constitutes a system in equilibrium—and when connected in series with another (variable) source of e.m.f., of magnitude $-V'$, it passes current one way or the other depending on the sign of the resultant e.m.f. $V - V'$. If, for (positive and negative) values of $V - V'$ very small compared with V, the current through the cell varies linearly with $V - V'$ (in particular, provided that there is no discontinuity at $V' = V$, or no finite range of V' over which the current is zero), then we accept the flow of current in such a circuit, under these limitations, as a 'reversible' flow—and we classify the voltaic cell in question as a 'reversible cell'. The need for this caution arises from the fact that not all voltaic cells qualify for this classification. For example, if a gas is liberated from one of the electrodes when current is passed through the cell in the 'reverse' direction ($V' > V$), it is almost inevitable that the condition of thermodynamic reversibility will not be fulfilled. On the other hand, if the essential chemical process in a cell is metallic dissolution from one electrode and deposition on the other (as in the Daniell cell), then almost certainly the condition is satisfied. The necessary caution is that our further considerations have reference only to reversible cells. Even with this said, however, we have still to admit that in the ideal voltaic-cell circuit, as in the ideal thermoelectric circuit, there inevitably remain certain processes which are irreversible—the production of Joule heat, and possibly thermal conduction, in the connecting wires. Our justification for neglecting these processes is no more secure, on the basis of classical thermodynamics, in one context than in the other. Helmholtz's relation which we are now to derive, as well as Kelvin's which we have already obtained

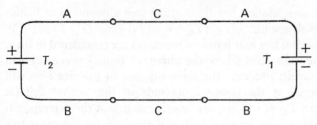

FIGURE 57

(equations (266) and (267)), alike require Onsager's axiom (p. 429) for their ultimate validation.

Suppose, then, that a reversible cell has electrodes of metals A and B, respectively. Let there be two such cells, similar in all respects, joined in opposition in a series circuit as represented in fig. 57. Let one cell be maintained at temperature T_1 and the other at temperature T_2. Connections to the external terminals are made in each case by wires of the same constitution as the respective electrodes. These external terminals are joined, as indicated, by wires of a third metal C. In this arrangement there is a difference of temperature $T_2 - T_1$ between the ends of these connecting wires —and there will be an exchange of Thomson heat with the surroundings (equal and opposite for the two wires) if current flows in the circuit. If these wires are broken at 'corresponding' points (points at the same temperature T, $T_2 > T > T_1$), then, according to Tait's law of intermediate metals (p. 416), the e.m.f. V_1 of the cell at temperature T_1 will be effective across one pair of free ends so produced, and the e.m.f. V_2 of the cell at temperature T_2 will be effective across the other pair. In other words, the e.m.f. which is effective in the complete circuit of fig. 57 is $V_2 - V_1$, acting in the direction in which the cell at temperature T_2 would send current spontaneously. Let us suppose that $V_2 > V_1$ (the argument would follow without essential change if $V_2 < V_1$), and let us consider a quantity q of electricity to pass round the circuit. We are to examine the suggestion that there must, of necessity, be exchange of heat between the cells and their surroundings, so that a quantity of heat qH_2 is absorbed by the cell at the higher temperature and a quantity of heat qH_1 emitted by the other, if the cells are to maintain the constant temperatures that we have assigned to them. We have already disposed of the question of Thomson heat in the connecting wires—that cancels to zero for the circuit as a whole—but there will be an absorption of Peltier heat in total amount $q(\pi_{AC}(T_2) + \pi_{CA}(T_1) + \pi_{BC}(T_1) + \pi_{CB}(T_2))$, as will be seen if the four terminal junctions are considered in turn. Within the cells themselves the chemical (ionic) processes will cancel in detail: precisely the same number of positive ions will be discharged at the positive electrode of the 'active' cell (at temperature T_2) as will acquire positive charge at the corresponding electrode of the 'passive' cell, and similarly for the other two electrodes. On balance these chemical (ionic) processes contribute no net energy accountable in relation to the 'reversible current flow' that we are considering.*

Having enumerated all the possibilities for the access of energy in the form of heat, we write the equation for the first law in the form

$$qH_2 - qH_1 + q(\pi_{AC}(T_2) + \pi_{CA}(T_1) + \pi_{BC}(T_1) + \pi_{CB}(T_2))$$
$$= q(V_2 - V_1),$$

and that for the second law as

$$\frac{q}{T_2}(H_2 + \pi_{AC}(T_2) + \pi_{CB}(T_2)) - \frac{q}{T_1}(H_1 + \pi_{AC}(T_1) + \pi_{CB}(T_1)) = 0.$$

In differential terms, therefore, if $T_1 = T$, $T_2 = T + \Delta T$, we have

$$\frac{dH}{dT} + \frac{d}{dT}(\pi_{AC} + \pi_{CB}) = \frac{dV}{dT} \tag{275}$$

and

$$\frac{d}{dT}\left(\frac{H + \pi_{AC} + \pi_{CB}}{T}\right) = 0 \tag{276}$$

Finally, from equations (265) and (276), we obtain

$$H + \pi_{AC} + \pi_{CB} = T\frac{dV}{dT} \tag{277}$$

If we had been considering a simple dissipative circuit, consisting of a single voltaic cell, operating isothermally at temperature T, and having its terminals connected by a resistor of metal

---

* Strictly, the circulation of charge that we have postulated is not an ideal cyclic process in the Carnot sense (p. 422): the initial and final states of the system are not indistinguishable, the total mass of metal A in the electrodes is the same at the end as at the beginning of the process but its disposition has changed—and the same is true of metal B and of the ions in solution in the electrolytes. We are ignoring these 'difficulties'.

C, application of the first law (in the way that Kelvin applied it) would have given

$$Q + H + \pi_{AC} + \pi_{CB} = V \qquad (278)$$

Q denoting the 'chemical heat' developed when unit quantity of electricity is passed by the cell. On this basis, substituting from equation (277), we should have

$$V = Q + T\frac{dV}{dT} \qquad (279)$$

which is Helmholtz's result—or, alternatively,

$$Q = -T^2 \frac{d}{dT}\left(\frac{V}{T}\right) \qquad (280)$$

Finally, if we accept the general interpretation of the phenomena of thermoelectricity as given in the last section—and, in particular, the formal result set out in equation (268), then equation (278) may be written

$$Q + H + \pi_{AB} = V \qquad (281)$$

We have consistently asserted (e.g. on p. 225) that 'the circumstances which determine the difference of potential between the electrodes [of a cell] on open circuit are those which obtain at the various surfaces of discontinuity in the cell, [one of these surfaces being] that effective as between the electrode materials themselves'. Equation (281) gives precision to this assertion, at least in relation to a reversible cell, on the basis of Helmholtz's analysis. We see that the electrical energy capable of delivery by such a cell is derived from the chemical heat of the overall cell reaction, represented by Q, the Peltier heat absorbed from the surroundings at the metallic junction between the electrode materials (or its equivalent), represented by π_{AB}, and heat similarly absorbed at the other surfaces of discontinuity within the cell, represented by H. According to equation (277), these contributions to the thermal energy from the 'surroundings' are, in total, negligible only in the exceptional case when the e.m.f. of the cell is independent of temperature over the significant range.

As with Kelvin's equations (266) and (267), so with Helmholtz's relation (equation (279)), detailed experimental investigations established the validity of the thermodynamical result, empirically,

long before modern developments of theory provided any satisfactory insight into the reasons why irreversible effects could be
disregarded with impunity in the analysis. No serious discrepancy
was ever substantiated, even though, in the extreme case, the
chemical heat might prove to be negative—still, equation (279)
was substantiated.*

The extreme case of negative Q values, to which we have just
referred, and of which an example has been given in the footnote,
emphasises again the difficulties of classification in this particular
field. In such a case thermal energy derived from the surroundings
provides the source not only for the heat dissipated in the circuit,
when the cell is functioning 'spontaneously', but also for the
chemical reaction taking place within the cell. It would appear
more appropriate, in these circumstances, to describe the complete
circuit as one in which electrolysis is taking place, occasioned by
there being a source of 'thermoelectric' e.m.f. in the circuit, rather
than as an external resistive load through which current is being
sent by a voltaic cell. Indeed, the role of the electrolyte in any
voltaic cell takes on a new aspect, once this possibility has been
recognised and discussed. R.W. Gurney (1898-1953) has put forward the view that in any voltaic circuit the essential function of
that portion of the circuit through which conduction is ionic rather
than electronic is merely to impose a barrier to the free passage of
electrons without significantly impeding the passage of charge. If
this element of the circuit also functions as a source of energy, so
much the better, but this function is subsidiary, rather than essential. We have already described the situation in a complete series
circuit consisting of conductors of different metals at a uniform
temperature (in which there is no resultant e.m.f. in any case) in
terms of redistributions of charge establishing contact differences
of potential across successive junctions—and we have interpreted
this situation through the statement that the absolute energy of the
Fermi level is the same in all the conductors concerned (p. 410).
If such a circuit is broken at any junction, and an additional ele-

---

* For example, a cell having mercury electrodes, the one in contact with a
paste of mercurous chloride in potassium chloride solution, and the other with
a paste of mercurous oxide in potassium hydroxide solution (the two solutions
making electrical contact through a capillary tube filled with the electrolyte)
has an e.m.f. of about 0·15 V at 20°C. The heat of chemical reaction (Q of
equation (279)) is $-0·07$ joules per coulomb and the total junction heat
$\left(T \dfrac{dV}{dT} \right)$ is 0·23 in the same units.

ment is inserted through which conduction is by the transport of ions rather than by 'free' electrons, then, since the concept of the Fermi level is inapplicable to the new circuit element, obviously there is no reason why the former equilibrium state should be maintained.

At the beginning of this section (p. 433) we decided to postpone any consideration of the physical phenomenon of 'the passage of charge from ions in solution to the solid electrodes' until we had investigated the more general theoretical problem of the energetics of the voltaic cell. We now take up the consideration that we previously postponed. The dual nature of the phenomenon was indicated very briefly in the introduction to chapter 7. We wrote there of 'negative electrons . . . released at [one] electrode, as a result of electrolytic effects occurring at its surface, . . . while . . . negative electrons in equal number . . . 'neutralise' positive ions arriving [at the other electrode]'. The description was brief, but the words were carefully chosen. Because in an external metallic circuit conduction is by electrons only, whereas in an electrolyte it is by ions of both signs, because negatively charged atoms (negative atomic ions) cannot exist permanently in a metal, the physical process cannot be the same at the two electrodes. For this reason we shall discuss the two situations separately: the one in which, macroscopically considered, positive charge passes from electrolyte to solid electrode—and the other, in which the direction of this conventional flow is from electrode to electrolyte. First, however, let us consider one aspect of the matter which provides a common background to both discussions.

Very crudely, an electrolytic ion in dilute solution may be represented by a charged conducting sphere situated in an 'infinite' dielectric medium. In this condition the electrostatic energy of the sphere is less than it would be 'in vacuum'. Taking infinite dispersion of charge as providing the reference configuration, if the electrostatic potential energy of the charged sphere in vacuum is U, it is U/K when the sphere is in an infinite dielectric of dielectric constant K (pp. 455, 117). To extract the charged sphere from an effectively infinite volume of the dielectric, therefore, requires the expenditure of work in amount $U(1 - 1/K)$; conversely, this amount of energy is released when the charged sphere passes from vacuum into the medium. When, in practice, physical chemists speak of the 'heat of solvation' of an ion, they are referring to the quantity that we have here roughly identified in relation to our model. To take the simplest example, when hydrogen chloride gas is dissolved in water (and ionised) the heat evolved, per molecule, is the excess of the combined heats of solvation of the positive and negative ions over the heat of dissociation of the gaseous molecule (into ions).

In defining the solvation energy, according to our model, we have, quite naturally, specified an 'infinite' volume of dielectric. If, instead, the charged sphere (of radius a) were assumed to be 'solvated' at the centre of a spherical 'drop' of dielectric of radius na, then, as it can easily be shown, the effective solvation energy would be $(1 - 1/n)$ of the standard value. For all practical purposes, therefore, an ion is 'fully solvated' once it is surrounded by solvent molecules providing a 'sheath' a few molecules thick. It is a fact of experience that those solvents which are important in relation to electrolytic effects are, without exception, pure liquids having dielectric constants very large compared with 1 (water, 80; methyl alcohol, 33; ethyl alcohol, 26; acetone, 21): the molecules of these substances are permanent electric dipoles (p. 380) of dipole moment of an order corresponding to the separation of positive and negative electronic charges through a distance equal to an atomic radius. A solvated ion, in such a solvent, becomes surrounded by a sheath of solvent molecules more or less orientated, the dipole axes tending to point towards the ion, or away from it, depending on the sign of its charge. As the ion moves through the electrolyte this general configuration is permanently maintained (though the actual solvent molecules making up the sheath may change). It is as if the 'effective ion' were a 'cluster'—a charged atom or radical at the centre, and a sheath of neutral (polar) molecules of the solvent surrounding it. To extract the charged component—the 'true ion'—from the cluster, work must be done equal to the solvation energy concerned.

Against this background of ideas, and before proceeding to the more complicated situations which obtain at the surface of the electrodes when current is passing through a cell, let us examine as prototype the situation in which a single piece of metal is dipped into a solution containing singly charged ions of the metal in question. We shall assume that, in the solid metal, the crystal lattice is likewise a lattice of singly charged ions. Initially, both the piece of metal and the electrolyte are uncharged. We have just seen that energy in amount equal to the solvation energy (let us denote it by W_S) is required to remove a (positively charged) metal ion from solution into vacuum. Let us calculate the corresponding energy (W_L) in relation to a lattice ion. We may imagine the process of removal of such an ion as follows: first, a lattice ion and an electron escape together as a neutral atom—this is the elementary act in the process of sublimation; second, the neutral atom is ionised in vacuum; third, the free electron returns to the metal. According to this analysis, obviously,

$$W_L = S + W_I - \phi,$$

S representing the energy of sublimation (per atom), W_I the first ionisation energy of the neutral atom, and ϕ the electronic work function (p. 396) of the metal concerned. All these quantities (as also W_S), for a singly charged ion, are of the order of magnitude of 10 eV (pp. 263, 269, 396) (because the energy of a charged sphere is proportional to the square of the charge, solvation energies of multiply charged ions are approximately 4, 9, . . . times as great as those of singly charged ions of similar size).

In relation to the situation that we are considering, then, energy in amount W_S is needed to remove a single charged metal ion from solution (into vacuum) and energy in amount W_L to remove a single charged lattice ion from the solid metal (into vacuum). If $W_S > W_L$, energy will be released by the passage of a lattice ion into solution; if, alternatively, $W_L > W_S$, the deposition of a positive ion from solution on the solid metal will result in the liberation of energy. In the first case the metal surface will be left with an unbalanced negative charge, in the second it will acquire an unbalanced positive charge in the spontaneous (exoergic) ion-transfer process concerned. In either case, the process will continue until the surface charge on the metal, holding an equal and opposite charge of ions in solution in its immediate neighbourhood, provides a 'potential energy step' between solution and metal which, for a single charged ion, just counterbalances the 'transfer energy' | $W_S - W_L$ |. We need add only one gloss to this result. For simplicity we have written as if the approach to equilibrium, in the situation which we have just considered, were a one-way process: to accept this literally would be altogether out of keeping with our understanding of molecular processes generally. Rather should we say that, finally, when equilibrium has been reached, as many positive lattice ions pass from the metal into solution, in unit time, as there are positive metal ions deposited from solution on the solid—and that, in the initial stages, it is the net transport of ions which is determined by the sign of $W_S - W_L$: at all stages positive ions cross the 'surface of discontinuity' between solid and liquid in both directions.

The situation at the cathode of an electrolytic cell (or the positive electrode of a voltaic cell) may be as simple as that that we have just considered, though in general it is not. It has this simplicity in the case of the Daniell cell, the positive electrode of which is a copper plate which dips into a copper sulphate solution. In such a case current is brought to the electrode by positive ions which on deposition occupy permanent lattice sites in the solid—and for a voltaic cell of this type the 'chemical' change at the positive electrode contributes a quantity $W_L - W_S$, per deposited (singly charged) ion, to the quantity eQ (p. 437), the overall chemical heat of the cell reaction (reckoned in relation to the fundamental electronic unit of charge, rather than the unit charge of orthodox definition). In any such case, each positive ion deposited from solution creates a 'vacancy' for one additional conduction electron in the electrode material, and it is the stream of negative electrons passing from the external circuit to the electrode to fill these vacancies which constitutes the conventional positive current flowing from the electrode into that circuit.

In general, at the positive electrode of a voltaic cell, or the cathode of an electrolytic cell, either deposition of metallic ions other than those of the electrode material takes place, or there is evolution of gas (generally hydrogen, when the electrolyte is an aqueous solution). In the former case there is nothing new in principle for us to discuss. The deposited ion remains permanently incorporated within the surface layers of the metal lattice and an additional conduction electron is required for its neutralisation, as before. Formally, care is required in defining the quantity analogous to W_L in this case: that is all. In the other case, however, the situation is different.

Let us consider the evolution of hydrogen gas at a platinum electrode when a dilute aqueous solution of a strong acid is electrolysed. The final product is molecular hydrogen, each molecule of the gas representing a stable association of two neutral atoms. The constituents of such a molecule are somehow assembled at the surface of the electrode, the electrons being derived from the platinum and the protons from the singly charged positive ions arriving at the surface of discontinuity between the solid electrode and the liquid electrolyte. Formally, again, we can evaluate the energy change involved by imagining the process of assembly to be a many-stage process. An amount of work $2W_S$ is required to remove two protons from a state of solvation in the electrolyte, and an amount of work 2ϕ to remove two electrons from the metal electrode. In vacuum, combination of these protons and electrons in pairs releases an amount of energy $2W_I$, W_I being the first ionisation energy of the hydrogen atom; finally, combination of the two neutral atoms to form a molecule releases a further amount of energy D, the dissociation energy of the molecule, in vacuum. On balance, the process is endoergic to the extent of $W_S + \phi - W_I - \frac{1}{2}D$, per singly-charged ion discharged. If a similar process were to be involved at the positive electrode of a voltaic cell, there would be a contribution of $W_I + \frac{1}{2}D - W_S - \phi$ to the overall chemical heat of the cell reaction (eQ) on account of this electrode process.

We have here given a formal account of the process of evolution of hydrogen gas at a metal electrode in terms of a sequence of 'fictitious events'. Clearly, the actual process follows a different course—though this does not invalidate our calculation. In the actual process there is no 'vacuum phase'; everything happens in the region of the surface of discontinuity separating the electrode and the electrolyte. There is good reason to believe that the positive 'hydrogen ions' arrive in this region as clusters of water molecules surrounding a stable ion of constitution $(H_3O)^+$ (an isolated proton, H^+, is a bare atomic nucleus—an entity smaller in radius than an atomic ion by a factor of 10^4). Neutral hydrogen atoms are released when conduction electrons from the solid electrode are captured by these hydrogen ions. Obviously a full understanding of the phenomenon can be achieved only through discussion of this process of capture in physical terms. This we are not in a position to do at this stage: it will be referred to again briefly in chapter 10 (p. 498).

At the negative electrode of a voltaic cell, or at the anode of an electrolytic cell, negative electrons leave the electrode through the external circuit either because positive ions pass into solution from the electrode or because negative electrolytic ions arriving at the electrode are there discharged, depositing solid material on the electrode or generating evolved gas. When positive ions pass from the solid electrode into solution, as at the negative electrode of a Daniell cell (a zinc rod in an acid solution of zinc sulphate), the process is the exact reverse of the simple process that we considered in relation to the positive electrode of the same cell. (For such a cell, in which the conditions at both electrodes are of this simplicity and when the processes occurring at the electrodes together consti- tute the overall chemical reaction in the cell, in a self-evident notation, we have, simply,

$$eQ = S_C - S_A + {}_CW_I - {}_AW_I + \phi_A - \phi_C + {}_AW_S - {}_CW_S \quad (282)$$

A denoting the metal of the negative electrode, and C that of the positive electrode, of the cell.) When negative ions are discharged at the solid electrode, in all cases an electron, or electrons, must pass from each ion, to be captured in the conduction band of the metal. The details of this process will obviously depend upon the ion-species concerned, but fundamentally we have the same diffi- culty in discussing the process, within the framework of classical ideas, as we noted in the similar context encountered above. Post- poning further comment, as before, we conclude our present discussion by considering a representative case of the generation of evolved gas, when negative ions are discharged in the process in question. We shall consider the evolution of oxygen at the platinum anode of an electrolytic cell in which the electrolyte is acidulated water, as in our previous example.

In the cell that we are considering there will be, in the immediate neighbourhood of the anode, when current is passing, negative ions formed in the dissociation of the molecules of the dissolved acid together with negative hydroxyl ions, $(OH)^-$, generally in much smaller concentration, formed in the dissociation of water molecules (the degree of dissociation of pure water is very small, but it is not negligible—see p. 213). In the quasi-steady state there will be dynamic equilibrium among the three species of ion: the hydrogen ions (provided largely by the dissolved acid), the hyd- roxyl ions, and the negative ions derived from the acid which we have mentioned. Taking the observed fact that almost pure oxygen is evolved at the anode (this is the case with dilute solutions of many acids and alkalis), we have to conclude that the discharge of hydroxyl ions at the platinum electrode is highly favoured in relation to that of the negative ions derived from the acid. Formally, then, we discuss the energy balance of the process in terms of the discharge of hydroxyl ions. Let W_S be the solvation energy of a hydroxyl ion, and W_I the energy required to remove the 'excess' electron from such an ion in vacuum. Suppose that four hydroxyl ions are removed from the electrolyte and caused to give up their excess electrons, these electrons then being captured from vacuum into the platinum electrode. At that stage work in amount $4(W_S + W_I - \phi)$ has been done, ϕ being the electronic work function for platinum, as before, and we have four neutral hydroxyl radicals in vacuum. Let these combine in pairs forming two molecules of hydrogen peroxide, H_2O_2; eventually let energy be supplied so that these two molecules dissociate, forming two molecules of water and a molecule of oxygen: $2H_2O_2 \to 2H_2O + O_2$. Let R_1 be the energy evolved in the formation of one molecule of hydrogen peroxide in the first reaction, and R_2 be the energy which has to be supplied in order that one molecule of oxygen is liberated in the second reaction. We complete our sequence of fictitious events by allowing the two molecules of residual water to 'recondense' in the electrolyte. In respect of this process, let L be the energy evolved when one molecule returns to the liquid. Then overall, for the discharge of one singly-charged hydroxyl ion, the adverse balance of energy is

$$W_S + W_I - \phi - \tfrac{1}{2}R_1 + \tfrac{1}{4}R_2 - \tfrac{1}{2}L.$$

Again, we have given no more than a purely formal account of an actual process of which the intermediate stages may be very different from those that we have postulated. Indeed, although the evolution of oxygen and hydrogen in the electrolysis of acidulated water has been studied since the time of Faraday, the precise details of the electrode processes are still the subject of argument —the details of the anode processes more particularly so. Some authorities have inclined to the view that molecules of hydrogen peroxide are in fact formed at the anode, as our formal scheme might suggest, others have considered it more likely that two electrons are captured from each negative hydroxyl ion, producing, at the electrode surface, a neutral atom of oxygen and a positive hydrogen ion which returns to the electrolyte: $(OH)^- \to O + H^+ + 2e^-$. Here we merely record these different viewpoints; it would be beyond the scope of this book to consider them further.

CHAPTER 9

MAGNETIC MATERIALS

9.1. INTRODUCTORY

Briefly expressed, the topic of this chapter is 'magnetism and matter'—and the aim the very limited one of setting that topic in perspective within the wider context, 'electricity and matter', which is the context of the book as a whole. To have sought a more ambitious aim would have been to distort the balance of our account unduly, and it would have presupposed a greater range of theory than we are able to command. For lack of space, and of a sufficient background of theory, then, we shall of necessity omit much that is known from experiment of this complex subject, and many details of interpretation. To repair these omissions, the unsatisfied reader must perforce turn to the specialist treatises: in doing so he will surely come to realise the root causes of our present limitations.

Already in this book we have discussed at considerable length effects which we have described as 'magnetic', and we have defined the field quantities B and H, in terms of which our experience of forces 'of magnetic origin', effective on current-carrying conductors, or on 'permanent' magnets, may formally be accounted for. We have also defined the magnetic permeability of 'the medium' (implicitly regarded, hitherto, as continuous) in which such effects are observed. In relation to permanent magnets, we have introduced the concepts of magnetic dipole moment and intensity of magnetisation—but only incidentally have we referred to the properties of any particular magnetic material. We have noticed the permanent magnetism frequently found in massive samples of the mineral magnetite, and the permanent magnetism that can be given to bodies made of iron and steel; on the other hand, we have not discussed the process of magnetisation, or the wide differences in the magnetic properties of iron which are occasioned by differences in the small amounts of other elements alloyed with, or 'dissolved' in, it. Indeed, we have so far mentioned no magnetic material (other than the natural magnetite) save 'iron' —and that of unspecified purity. In this chapter we must make good that deficiency.

The so-called Iron Age of the archaeologists' classification reaches back, in Egypt, in the countries of the Middle East, and in China, possibly to 4000 B.C. Throughout that period, at first by chance, later no doubt by design, pre-scientific man succeeded in producing samples of 'iron' which because of their relative purity, or the particular 'impurity' which they contained—or on account of the character of the heat treatment to which they had been subjected—exhibited specially desirable properties. Malleable, brittle and tough varieties of the metal came to be recognised, and these materials eventually found their characteristic uses—in the fabrication of vessels and the manifold implements of peace and war. At a relatively late stage in this historical process, the one specialist use developed which is of interest for us here. The needles which were used in the first crude forms of the mariners' compass (see p. 58)—whether they were the familiar domestic objects of circular section which were encased in hollow straws so that they might float on the surface of water, or flat strips of metal which could be pivoted horizontally in a vertical support—were made from the tough variety of the metal. Objects made of the other varieties, could not, it seemed, be made into 'permanent' magnets by 'touching with the stone' (*ibid.*). All varieties of iron were attracted to the poles of a magnet, but only the tough variety possessed the property of retaining some at least of the magnetisation which could be acquired in such circumstances.

The conclusions that we have just formulated represent the extent of the common knowledge of the instrument makers of Western Europe in the sixteenth century. Through careful experiment William Gilbert (p. 60) submitted this knowledge to critical scrutiny, and gave it the precision of scientific fact, but neither his investigations as they are described in *De Magnete* (1600), nor those of his successors for another hundred years and more, added any new substance to the small class of magnetic materials. It seemed that the phenomenon of magnetism was an attribute of the metal iron, and of some of its ores, exclusively.

When *De Magnete* was written, only twelve of the chemical elements as we know them today were recognised as such (according to the vague canons of the time). Only two more were added to the list during the seventeenth century, namely antimony (1604) and phosphorus (1669). In 1735, platinum and cobalt were so recognised, and nickel was the next, prepared in impure form by A. F. Cronstedt in 1751. When G. Brandt first isolated an impure specimen of cobalt in 1735, he reported that the metal was magnetic. First to obtain relatively pure samples of nickel (1775) and cobalt (1780) was Torbern Olof Bergman (1735-1784), professor of chemistry and mineralogy at the university of Uppsala. Bergman supported Brandt's claim that a lump of metallic cobalt would deflect a pivoted compass needle (to whichever pole it was approached), and reported that lumps of nickel showed the same effect. As the discovery of new elements proceeded (the total—according to modern criteria—was thirty-one by the end of the eighteenth century), it became standard practice to make the compass-needle test, and various positive results were prematurely reported. At first, manganese (discovered 1774) and chromium (1797) were thought to belong to the class of magnetic materials.

In the face of these results, Michael Faraday was the great sceptic. In 1836, and again in 1839, he reported that he had been unsuccessful in observing any magnetic action with pure cobalt, though he used a very sensitive ('astatic') magnetometer for the test. He had found no effect with chromium, and he was generally convinced that with manganese, and other materials which sometimes gave positive results, any apparent magnetic effect was due to iron impurity. As a chemist, he was acutely aware of the rudimentary state of the art of chemical purification, when the last refinement was required; therefore, at the time, he preferred to recognise only iron and nickel as truly magnetic, among the known elements. In June 1845, as a result of further experiments, he admitted his error in relation to cobalt, but he firmly maintained that no other element—and the total of the known elements had by then reached fifty-eight—should be classed with these three. Subsequent investigations amply demonstrated the soundness of Faraday's judgment in this matter: by the end of the century, in respect of magnetic properties, iron, cobalt and nickel were still in a class by themselves—they were the only 'ferromagnetic' elements then known. We shall be considering the characteristic properties of substances of this class in further detail in a later section of this chapter (p. 478).

If we have implied that the period from 1845 to 1900 saw no

further additions to the list of 'magnetic materials', we have grossly misled the (inattentive) reader. Indeed, at the very beginning of this period a major experimental discovery was made—and Faraday, alone, was responsible for making it. The discovery was made when powerful electromagnets were used for the first time, systematically, for the study of the magnetic properties of materials. Previously, permanent magnets were used—and generally, as we have mentioned, only small magnets disposed as compass needles (the advantage being that deflection of the magnet itself, rather than any movement of the specimen under test, provided direct evidence for the magnetic action which was sought). In November 1845 Faraday started a systematic investigation of the forces of magnetic origin brought into play when solid specimens, in the form of rods, cubes and spheres, were suspended in various positions between the soft-iron pole pieces of an electromagnet. He experimented with pole pieces of various shapes, finding conical pieces particularly advantageous, and later he extended the range of his investigations, examining specimens of a large variety of liquid substances and many gases. We may anticipate a more detailed summary of Faraday's results in the simple statement that he found all substances to be magnetic to a significant degree— and the nature of the effect with many was such that it could not possibly have resulted from an unsuspected trace of a ferromagnetic impurity.

Faraday early came to the conclusion—entirely empirically, on the basis of what he had observed—that the most significant feature of the action to which his suspended specimens were subject was a force related to the degree of non-uniformity of the magnetic field in which they were placed. For that reason, in particular, he found it advantageous to work with conical pole pieces. If the general disposition of such pole pieces is as shown in fig. 58, X'OX being the axis of symmetry, and the plane through O at right angles to X'OX a plane of symmetry, of the arrangement, then, ideally, the field direction at every point in this plane will be parallel to X'OX and the field strength will decrease monotonically with increasing distance from O in the plane.

If, in respect of Faraday's arrangement, the plane of fig. 58 represents the horizontal section through X'OX, the magnetic axis of the system, his method of experimenting was to suspend his specimens, by torsionless suspensions, so that their centres of

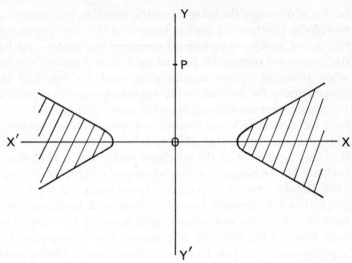

FIGURE 58

gravity lay in the line Y'OY. With this arrangement Faraday found that, whatever material was under test, either one or the other of two results was obtained. We shall describe these results by supposing simply that two separate experiments were made with each material. In the first experiment a uniform rod of the material under test, of length possibly one-half of the distance of separation of the pole tips, was suspended with its centre at O; in the second experiment a small spherical sample was suspended with its centre at P. In each case the sample was first brought into the desired position, then the electromagnet was activated to suitable strength.

The result of this double investigation, for many materials, was qualitatively the same as could be observed with samples of soft iron, or cobalt, or nickel, when the electromagnet was weakly activated. The elongated specimen having its centre at O took up a position of stable equilibrium with its length along X'OX, its centre remaining at O. The spherical specimen centred at P was drawn towards O, and, if the suspension was long enough, it would take up a position of (unstable) equilibrium in the neighbourhood of O. Slightly displaced from this position, it would tend to be attracted to the nearer pole tip. On the face of it, this general behaviour might be thought, by the sceptic, to indicate no more than the presence of small quantities of ferromagnetic impurity in the samples of material concerned, but Faraday did not take this view—and the results which he found to be characteristic of his other group of examined materials certainly could not be dismissed as adventitious in this simple fashion.

With this other group of materials, Faraday found that the elongated specimens centred at O took up positions of stable equilibrium with their lengths along Y′OY, when the electromagnet was activated—and the spherical specimens centred at P were repelled from O in the direction OY. Such repulsion, 'without reference to a particular pole of the magnet, for either pole will repel the substance, and both poles will repel it at once', was clearly a new* magnetic phenomenon—and Faraday rightly insisted on its novelty. In 1851, convinced that he was making a fundamental distinction based on a simple experimental test, Faraday introduced the term 'paramagnetic' to refer to those weakly magnetic substances of soft-iron-like behaviour, and the contrary† term 'diamagnetic' to refer to those others which, like bismuth, exhibited the new phenomenon that we have just described. As we shall see, the distinction remains valid today (§§9.3 and 9.4 are devoted to more detailed accounts of the magnetic properties of these two classes of substance)—and the terms which Faraday originally introduced are still retained in current use.

As we have already implied, the distinction between paramagnetic and diamagnetic behaviour, according to Faraday, is most directly made in terms of the action of a non-uniform magnetic field on a small sample of the material under test. If the material is paramagnetic, such a sample, arbitrarily placed in a non-uniform field, tends to move in the direction in which the field strength increases most rapidly; if the material is diamagnetic this tendency is in the opposite direction. Convinced that the distinction was a

---

* Not strictly so, however, for A.Bruygmans, in Leyden, in 1778, had placed a small piece of bismuth in a paper boat on the surface of mercury, and had noted its repulsion when either pole of a permanent magnet was brought near to it, and some fifty years later a similar effect had been observed by Lebaillif with both bismuth and antimony. But these were isolated observations, little noted at the time.

† The two terms are not strictly antithetic in derivation. 'Paramagnetic' refers to the setting 'parallel to the general field direction' of elongated specimens suspended with their centres mid-way between the pole tips in the arrangement illustrated in fig. 58. 'Diamagnetic', which had already been introduced by Faraday, in 1845, to refer to 'a body through which lines of magnetic force are passing, and which does not by their action assume the usual magnetic state of iron or loadstone', was taken over in 1851 and given the more precise—and more limited—connotation that we have indicated.

fundamental one, Faraday stressed the point that for the test to provide an unambiguous answer it should be conducted in vacuum. Consistently, Faraday had rejected the general notion of action at a distance, seeking always for an understanding of physical phenomena in terms of the relevant properties of the pervading medium (see p. 99). Therefore, he argued, if all material substances fall into one or other of two classes in respect of a particular phenomenon—and if the only formal distinction between the classes is the distinction of the 'sign' of the effect (we might reasonably characterise paramagnetic behaviour by a positive-valued, and diamagnetic behaviour by a negative-valued, parameter)—then only 'vacuum' can be entirely neutral in respect of the phenomenon concerned. This may appear to the reader to be a purely academic point of trivial significance, but when he came to investigate the behaviour of liquid materials, Faraday was able to demonstrate its practical importance. Enclosing solutions of ferrous sulphate in thin glass containers of appropriate shapes, Faraday found the suspended samples to exhibit paramagnetic behaviour, when tested in the standard arrangement. He then arranged that the same samples should be suspended inside an open vessel situated between the pole pieces of his magnet, when solutions of ferrous sulphate of different concentration were contained in the vessel. In this arrangement, when the concentration of ferrous sulphate in the suspended sample was greater than that in the surrounding solution, paramagnetic behaviour was observed; when the reverse was the case the sample behaved as if it were diamagnetic. Obviously, in this particular case it was the dissolved salt which was responsible for the paramagnetism of the solutions under test—and the general conclusion could be drawn that the force acting on a small sample of material in a non-uniform magnetic field is proportional to the difference of two quantities, one representing the effect of the field on the material of the sample and the other the effect of the field on the material of the surrounding medium. Only when the surrounding medium is vacuum is the second quantity strictly zero—and the direction of the resultant force on the sample unambiguously indicative of the class to which the material belongs.

We have stated—and accepted—Faraday's conclusion that the resultant force on a small sample of material arbitrarily placed in a non-uniform magnetic field is along the direction in which the field strength increases (or decreases) most rapidly with distance. If we try to formalise this conclusion, we recognise at once that we require a scalar quantity in order to be able to specify a vector in terms of its spatial derivatives (compare p. 29). H is not such a quantity. However, in relation to our present problem $\partial H^2/\partial s$ would represent a vector component in the direction of s—and, indeed, it represents the simplest specification of such a component that we can give within the general context of Faraday's views. Clearly, we must return later to attempt to justify our assumption (see footnote p. 454), but for the present let us take the bold step of assuming that the resultant force on a small sample of material of volume ΔS^* arbitrarily situated in a non-uniform magnetic field is in the line of maximum gradient of H^2 in its neighbourhood, that it is proportional to that gradient and to ΔS. On this assumption we may write, for ΔF, the resolved component of this resultant force in the direction of s, when the sample is in vacuum,

$$\Delta F = \tfrac{1}{2}\kappa\Delta S\,\frac{\partial H^2}{\partial s} \tag{283}$$

—and thereby define the magnitude of the 'magnetic susceptibility' of the material, which we denote by κ. The relevance of the factor $\tfrac{1}{2}$ in the expression for ΔF will appear as we proceed with the argument. If we accept equation (283) in respect of a sample in vacuum, then, in the light of what we have already concluded, we need only replace κ by $(\kappa - \kappa')$, κ' being the magnetic susceptibility of the surrounding medium, in order to represent the more general case in which a material medium is involved. Furthermore, we note that, on the basis of our defining equation, the magnetic susceptibility of a paramagnetic material is, by convention, positive, that of a diamagnetic material a negative quantity.

We are accepting equation (283), for the present, without further enquiry into its theoretical justification; it is appropriate to state, therefore, that when Faraday's non-uniform field arrangement with spherical specimens was developed for the purpose of precise quantitative measurements by Pierre Curie (see p. 241), the results of a long series of detailed investigations, involving a large variety

* Throughout this chapter we shall use the unconventional symbol S for the volume of a sample of magnetisable material to avoid confusion with e.m.f. (with which we shall also be involved later in the chapter) for which V is the standard symbol according to internationally agreed usage (see also, pp. 370-372)

of materials, over the period 1892 to 1895, effectively established the validity of the equation on an empirical basis.

In order to understand the significance of the new quantity, magnetic susceptibility, that we have defined in terms of equation (283), let us analyse this equation dimensionally, and, in particular, let us evaluate the dimensions of the quantity whose measure is given by κH. We have

$$[\kappa H] = L^{-2}\left[\frac{F}{H}\right],$$

or, if m is the measure of a magnetic pole strength, then (see equation (76)),

$$[\kappa H] = L^{-2}[m].$$

Magnetic dipole moment, M, being given by the product of pole strength and distance, finally,

$$[\kappa H] = L^{-3}[M].$$

Here we recognise κH as the measure of a physical quantity of the nature of magnetic dipole moment per unit volume. We have previously defined the intensity of magnetisation of a material in precisely this way (p. 63): we conclude, therefore, that the magnetic susceptibility of our earlier definition is the physical quantity,* characteristic of the material, which determines the intensity of magnetisation in any small sample of that material, situated in vacuum, in terms of the magnetic field strength at that point (in the absence of the sample). Indeed, if $\mathcal{J}$ represents the intensity of magnetisation of the sample under these conditions, equation (283), as a definition of κ, is consistent† with the alternative definition

$$\mathcal{J} = \kappa H \tag{284}$$

* Intensity of magnetisation ($\mathcal{J}$), as we have already shown (p. 121), is a physical quantity dimensionally homogeneous with magnetic flux density (B). According to our definition, therefore, magnetic susceptibility (κ) is dimensionally homogeneous with magnetic permeability (μ), as equations (65) and (284) confirm. Some authors adopt the convention of writing $\kappa\mu_0$ when we use κ. For these authors magnetic susceptibility is a pure number. This complication appears to be altogether unnecessary—and mildly obscurantist—and we shall have nothing to do with it (see footnote, p. 108).

† In 1847 Kelvin gave the first theoretical treatment of Faraday's observations in a paper 'On the forces experienced by small spheres [of substances *susceptible of magnetic induction*] under magnetic influence'. His final result (which he recognised as implicit in the general mathematical theory of Poisson—see p. 62) had precisely the form of our equation (283), $\kappa/2$ being represented by

In relation to equation (284) we note the implication that in paramagnetic materials (κ positive) the induced dipole moment has its axis in the same direction as that of the magnetising field, whereas in diamagnetic materials (κ negative) the reverse is the case. Clearly, in relation to either definition, certain assumptions are implicit. We have tacitly assumed that the material of the sample is magnetically isotropic—and we have assumed that the induced moment is accurately proportional to the magnetising field. The first assumption necessarily limits the generality of our considerations (more complicated effects are observed with specimens in the form of single crystals of a low order of symmetry, which we cannot enter into here); the wide validity of the second assumption may be regarded as abundantly demonstrated by the experimental investigations of Curie and others—at least if ferromagnetic materials are excluded (see p. 494).

In later sections of this chapter it will be our aim to give a general account, within the framework of present-day theory, of the magnetic properties of materials belonging to the three classes that we have now distinguished. First, however, it is appropriate that we should refer again to the well-nigh century-and-a-half-old view of Ampère, that the process of magnetisation generally is nothing more than the establishing throughout the sample in question of elementary current-loops having their axes in the

a constant 'depending on the capacity of the substance for magnetic induction'. Four years later, he introduced the term 'magnetic susceptibility' to denote this capacity, defining the physical quantity as follows: 'The magnetic susceptibility of an isotropic substance is the intensity of magnetization acquired by an infinitely thin bar of it placed lengthwise in a uniform field of unit magnetic force.' This is effectively our equation (284). (Kelvin's specification of 'an infinitely thin bar' was made so that his definition should be applicable equally to ferromagnetic materials and materials of relatively small susceptibility.) Finally, in 1872, in a recondite and very lengthy discussion of the problem of the energy of magnetisation, Kelvin obtained a general expression for what he called the 'mechanical value' attributable to a small specimen in a magnetic field, 'in space occupied by matter of zero susceptibility', from which the force acting on the specimen could be derived in terms of the space-rate-of-change of this energy in the direction of its steepest gradient. In this way the consistency of our equations (283) and (284) was formally verified.

A plausible, but non-rigorous, method of treating the problem of the energy of magnetisation, in this connection, is to follow, by analogy, the calculation of the energy of electrification of a small isolated conductor, using the concepts of magnetic pole and magnetic potential for the purpose. If C is the capacitance of such a conductor, then, when its potential is V, the charge is CV and the energy is $\frac{1}{2}CV^2$. In the case of a small sample of magnetisable material of volume ΔS, the induced dipole moment is $\kappa H \Delta S$ when the magnetising field is H—and it turns out that the energy of magnetisation is $-\frac{1}{2}\kappa\Delta S.H^2$. If this is accepted as the appropriate specification, then equation (283) follows directly (see also p. 495).

direction of the magnetising field (p. 83)—for we have previously implied (p. 91) that this speculative opinion has the ring of truth in it.

In modern terms an elementary current-loop would naturally be pictured as an electron revolving in a circular orbit. There would be both circulation of charge and circulation of mass. Inescapably, magnetisation, on this interpretation of Ampère's view, would involve the generation of angular momentum about the axis of magnetisation. Before considering the properties of magnetic materials of the three classes separately, therefore, we devote the next section to the specific question of the reality or otherwise of rotational effects associated with magnetisation.

9.2. MAGNETIC MOMENT AND ANGULAR MOMENTUM

We have already shown that associated with a plane current loop of area A, situated in vacuum and carrying a current i, there is a magnetic field which at distant points is indistinguishable from that of a magnetic doublet, of dipole moment $\mu_0 iA$, located within the loop and having its axis at right angles to the plane of the loop (see equations (56) and (93)). If the loop is circular and of radius r the associated dipole moment is thus $\pi\mu_0 ir^2$. Suppose now that the current in the loop is made up of electrons of charge e and mass m moving with drift velocity v. Let there be N such 'free' electrons per unit length of the conductor forming the loop. Then $i = Nev$, and the expression for the magnetic dipole moment becomes $\pi\mu_0 Nevr^2$. The total angular momentum of these free electrons about the axis of the loop is obviously $2\pi rN \cdot mvr$, that is $2\pi Nmvr^2$. Comparing these results, we see that the ratio of the measures of the angular momentum and the magnetic moment associated with the circulating electrons is given numerically by $2m/\mu_0 e$—and we note that this quantity is independent of N and of the radius of the loop. On this basis we conclude that for a single electron revolving in a circular orbit the same ratio would apply, nor is it difficult to show that for a general 'central' orbit the same is true. Accepting this conclusion, we designate $2m/\mu_0 e$ as the 'gyromagnetic ratio' for an orbiting electron, assuming only that the electron itself is a 'point' mass devoid of rotation.

Basically, there are two variants of Ampère's original view (recalled at the end of the last section) which merit separate consideration, since each has its relevance to present-day theory. Divesting ourselves, at the outset, of preconceived notions of twentieth-century provenance, we might assume either that Ampère's current loops are generated within the magnetisable material by the action of the applied field, or that they are present, but with random orientations, in the unmagnetised specimen and that the action of the field is to cause their partial alignment in the field direction. According to either assumption it would appear that, in the process of magnetisation, the ensemble of current carriers in a specimen would acquire angular momentum about the axis of magnetisation. This conclusion was first given formal expression by O. W. Richardson (see p. 180) in 1908. Richardson assumed that there could be no overall torque on the specimen as a whole, about the axis of the field, when the field was applied, so he predicted that angular momentum of opposite sign and equal amount would be acquired by the solid specimen when it was magnetised. Accepting the electron-orbit representation of the Ampère current loops, as we have done, Richardson predicted that the specimen would acquire 'gross' angular momentum of amount $2mM/\mu_0 e$ at the same time as it acquired a total magnetic dipole moment M.

According to our second assumption—that Ampère's current loops are present, but randomly orientated, in an unmagnetised material—we may make certain predictions which are not necessarily valid on the basis of the first assumption. Always assuming that we associate mass with the carriers of these currents, we effectively have a population of elementary gyrostats distributed throughout a solid specimen, and, when we rotate this specimen about any axis, the tendency will be for the axes of the gyrostats to align themselves with the axis of rotation. That being precisely the tendency which results from the application of a magnetising field, according to our present assumptions, we predict that rotation of any body must produce the same overall effect as would a magnetising field of appropriate intensity applied along the axis of rotation. This prediction was first made by S. J. Barnett in 1909. Later, Barnett developed the theory of this hypothetical process of 'magnetisation by rotation', and showed that the effect of changing the angular velocity of rotation by an amount Ω was equivalent to that of changing the magnetising field by $2m\Omega/\mu_0 e$. As before, e/m represents the specific charge of the material carriers of the Ampère currents, which Barnett assumed to be negative point-electrons as Richardson had done. We note that in relation to this process, as with Richardson's process of 'rotation by magnetisation', the factor of equivalence is simply the gyromagnetic ratio that we have already defined.

The suggestions of Richardson and Barnett were not the first to be made in relation to possible gyromagnetic phenomena. Adopting, as it seems, a version of Ampère's view more nearly akin to our first variant than to our second, Maxwell, in 1861, had examined the consequences of supposing that the Ampère currents in a magnetised body involve the motion of matter as well as of electricity. In that case, so Maxwell said, the magnetised body itself might be expected to show gyroscopic behaviour, and if it were rotated about an axis passing through its centre of mass and inclined to its axis of magnetisation it might be possible to detect the movement of the latter axis towards closer alignment with the former. Maxwell attempted the experiment but with negative results.

The first positive results in a gyromagnetic experiment were reported by Barnett in 1915. Barnett observed the magnetisation of a soft iron rod by rotation. The direction of magnetisation was that to be expected if the carriers of the Ampère currents were negative electrons, but the magnitude of the effect was something less than one-half of that predicted by theory. In spite of the smallness of the effect (a rate of rotation of several million revolutions per second would have been required to produce the same magnetisation as that produced by the earth's magnetic field in the laboratory, if the theory were to be believed), this discrepancy was regarded as outside the limits of possible experimental uncertainty.

In the following year A. Einstein and W. J. de Haas reported positive results of a qualitative nature using the method suggested by Richardson (to whose original suggestion, however, no reference was made). Later, E. Beck, in 1919, and G. Arvidsson, in 1920, independently, greatly improved the experimental procedure, and obtained for the first time reliable quantitative results by this method. In respect of both iron and nickel the rotation by magnetisation which they observed was approximately one-half the expected value. The discrepancy was in the same sense as that which Barnett had found—and the explanation was equally elusive. The only secure conclusion concerned the sign of the charge on the carriers: that was negative, as everyone believed.

The possibilities of a rational explanation of these perplexing results began to emerge from the work of the theorists in the period 1925 to 1928. In 1925 George Eugene Uhlenbeck (b. 1900), at that time tutor to the sons of the Netherlands ambassador in Rome, and Samuel Abraham Goudsmit (b. 1902), pupils of Ehrenfest at Leyden, attempted to provide a physical interpretation of a formal scheme, which Goudsmit had devised, by which the complexities of the Zeeman effect (see p. 237) and the finer details of the optical spectra of atoms appeared to be successfully correlated. They suggested that such an interpretation could most simply be based on the assumption that the electron itself possesses intrinsic angular momentum, and an intrinsic magnetic moment, of unique value. Three years later, Dirac (see p. 337) produced massive support for this point of view. Elaborating a general theory of electron behaviour on the basis of the then recently formulated wave mechanics, and imposing the condition that the theory should be consistent with the principle of special relativity, he showed that without further assumption there appears in the general expression for the total energy of the particle a term which is most naturally interpreted as arising from an intrinsic magnetic moment associated with 'spin'. According to Dirac's theory, the magnitude of this intrinsic magnetic moment is $\mu_0 eh/4\pi m$, and that of the intrinsic angular momentum is $h/4\pi$. Here h, of course, is Planck's constant. For a 'Dirac electron', therefore, the 'intrinsic' gyromagnetic ratio is $m/\mu_0 e$—one-half the 'classical' value for an orbiting electron.

The final contribution from theory, at this stage, arose when the possible energy states of an electron in the field of an atomic nucleus were first evaluated using the new mechanics. On the quasi-classical theory of Bohr, the simplest such state was that in which the electron moved in a circular orbit with angular momentum $h/2\pi$ (p. 272): according to the wave-mechanical model the simplest state proved to be a spherically symmetrical state of zero 'orbital' angular momentum. According to the new model, therefore, the gyromagnetic ratio for an electron in a spherically symmetrical atomic state should be $m/\mu_0 e$; for an electron in a non-spherically symmetrical state it could have certain values between $m/\mu_0 e$ and $2m/\mu_0 e$. The fact that, in 1925, all the experimental evidence pointed to the conclusion that, for ferromagnetic substances generally, the gyromagnetic ratio is very closely $m/\mu_0 e$, led naturally to the view that the magnetism which these substances exhibit is 'electron-spin magnetism', exclusively.

It is a matter of history that evidence for this view had already been adduced from careful experiment by A. H. Compton (see p. 315) and O. Rognley in 1920. These authors had attempted to observe a change in the intensities of the Bragg reflections of X-rays (p. 276) from a crystal of magnetite when the latter was magnetised. They argued that a significant change should have been observed if magnetisation involved the alignment of atoms within the crystal lattice, or even if it involved the alignment of the axes of individual electron orbits within the atoms of the lattice. Because they were unable to detect any change of intensity, they concluded that, for this ferromagnetic material at least, magnetisation most likely involves the alignment of single electrons having the attribute of intrinsic magnetic moment and spin. No one, at the time, appears to have taken this suggestion seriously, though Uhlenbeck and Goudsmit made reference to it when they revived the suggestion of the 'spinning electron' in 1925.

At this point we have taken the matter of the association of angular momentum and magnetic moment as far as is profitable for the purposes of this book; even so, it may not be altogether superfluous to add a brief postscript. Possibly because the experimental investigation of gyromagnetic phenomena poses such a manifold challenge to the resourcefulness of the investigator, pursuit of perfection appears to have become more obsessive in this field than in most. Almost thirty years after he made his first successful attack on the problem, S. J. Barnett returned to its investigation, and along with his collaborators reported many refinements of technique and many new determinations over another nine years (1944-1953). Similarly, G. G. Scott (see p. 354), having published a long series of determinations of the gyromagnetic ratios of iron, cobalt and nickel, and their alloys, over the period from 1951 to 1957, in the latter year took over a new laboratory built specifically for the purpose and continued his investigations with improved equipment, repeating and extending his earlier work. We may fittingly end by quoting Scott's most recent values of the gyromagnetic ratios of the three classical ferromagnetic metals, taken from a review which he published in 1962. The values here quoted are those of the so-called g' factors, the numbers by which Richardson's ratio for the orbiting point-electron, $2m/\mu_0 e$, must be divided to match the results of experiment. They are as follows:

Fe, 1.919 ± 0.002; Co, 1.850 ± 0.004; Ni, 1.837 ± 0.002.

9.3. DIAMAGNETIC MATERIALS

In describing the results of his first experiments which established the diamagnetic behaviour of bismuth and other substances, Faraday drew attention to the fact that the induction of currents in conducting circuits, which he had investigated fourteen years previously (p. 126), is a macroscopic phenomenon of the same general character as diamagnetism. During the time in which the magnetic flux through such a circuit is increasing there is an induced current in the circuit in such a direction that the magnetic field due to the current, along the axis of the circuit, is opposite in direction to the increasing 'applied' field (p. 127). Two years later (1847), Weber (p. 80) took this observation a stage farther. In conformity with Ampère's view, he supposed that there exist, in atoms and molecules generally, 'perfectly conducting paths' around which electric charge may circulate indefinitely without dissipation of energy. These paths are the paths of the Ampère currents in the atoms of those substances which are paramagnetic or ferromagnetic in behaviour, but they exist in all atoms. When any material is placed in a magnetic field, on this view, currents are induced in these paths, whether there are pre-existing currents circulating or not. As long as the field is maintained the induced currents persist, because there is no dissipation, but they disappear 'reversibly' when the field is reduced to zero. Naturally, the induced currents confer diamagnetic behaviour on the material concerned. On Weber's view, all matter is intrinsically diamagnetic; when any material exhibits paramagnetic (or ferromagnetic) behaviour, it is merely that its intrinsic diamagnetism is masked by the presence of permanent Ampère currents in its atoms or molecules which suffer partial (and generally temporary) alignment when a magnetising field is applied. Weber's detailed appreciation of the situation was far in advance of his time; as we shall see, translated into modern terminology, it represents very closely the presently accepted interpretation of the facts.

New facts giving support for Weber's distinction, that diamagnetism has its origin within the atom whereas paramagnetism involves the mutual interaction between one atom and another ('partial alignment' requiring that some interatomic mechanism should 'resist' the directive action of the magnetising field), were provided by the investigations of Curie to which we have already referred (p. 453). Curie found that for diamagnetic substances, generally, the magnetic susceptibility is independent of temperature; for paramagnetic substances the susceptibility is temperature-dependent. A temperature-dependent quality, by definition, is one for which the thermal motion of the atoms is relevant; a quality which has its origin in processes occurring within individual atoms may be expected to be uninfluenced by temperature changes. Having made this point, let us now attempt to translate Weber's ideas into modern terminology, as we suggested should be done.

In an earlier chapter, when discussing the Lorentz interpretation of the Zeeman effect (p. 233), we considered the effect of a magnetic field on the motion of an electron moving in a circular orbit under a central force. The direction of the applied field being at right angles to the plane of the orbit, we found that the angular velocity of the electron about the centre of force was changed by an amount $\Delta\omega$, proportional to the magnetic flux density of the applied field. Numerically the change is given (equation (137)) by

$$| \Delta\omega | = \frac{Be}{2m}.$$

If we consider the electron orbit to be in vacuum (a sufficiently good approximation to the situation in all but ferromagnetic materials), we may write, instead,

$$| \Delta\omega | = \frac{\mu_0 e}{2m} H \qquad (285)$$

H being the magnitude of the applied field. Whatever the sign of the electron charge, or the sense of rotation, this change in angular velocity is in such sense as to superpose on H an 'induced field' component of direction opposite to H. With the change of angular velocity, there is a change in the effective magnetic dipole moment of the orbiting electron. Before the magnetic field was applied the dipole moment associated with the orbit was $\pm \mu_0 evr/2$ (p. 456), that is $\pm \mu_0 e\omega r^2/2$; when the field is applied it becomes

$$\tfrac{1}{2}\mu_0 er^2(\pm\omega - | \Delta\omega |).$$

In this expression (e representing a positive quantity in all cases) the positive sign denotes a dipole moment having its axis in the direction of H, and *vice versa*. The induced dipole moment, ΔM, then, is a diamagnetic moment, invariably, and we may write

$$\Delta M = -\tfrac{1}{2}\mu_0 e r^2 \mid \Delta\omega \mid,$$

or
$$\Delta M = -\frac{\mu_0^2 e^2 r^2}{4m} H \qquad (286)$$

Let us now consider the simplest possible model of an atom of a diamagnetic substance. Let us suppose that the atom contains two coaxial orbits of the same radius in which electrons rotate with the same angular velocity but in opposite senses. In the classical context, in which the possibility of electron spin is ignored, such an atom would have no permanent magnetic dipole moment. Under the influence of an axially applied magnetic field H it would acquire a (diamagnetic) moment $2\Delta M$, according to equation (286). If the field were applied in an arbitrary direction, at an angle θ to the atomic axis, the orbits would precess (in the same sense) about the field direction with angular velocity $\mid \Delta\omega \mid$ (p. 237). It is not difficult to show that, in these circumstances, the effective diamagnetic moment developed by the atom would be $(1 + \cos^2 \theta)$ ΔM. For an assembly of such atoms, therefore, having their axes randomly orientated, the average dipole moment may be specified as

$$\overline{\Delta M} = \frac{\Delta M}{2} \int_0^\pi (1 + \cos^2 \theta) \sin \theta \, d\theta \qquad (287)$$

(the probability of the atomic axis lying between θ and $\theta + d\theta$ to the field direction being given by $\tfrac{1}{2} \sin \theta \, d\theta$). On evaluation of equation (287) we obtain

$$\overline{\Delta M} = \tfrac{4}{3}\Delta M;$$

hence, on the basis of this particular atom model, we have, finally,

$$\overline{\Delta M} = -\frac{\mu_0^2 e^2 r^2}{3m} H \qquad (288)$$

The atom of helium, as we know, in fact consists of a nucleus and two extranuclear electrons—and we know that helium is monatomic in the gaseous form. Also, helium gas is diamagnetic.

Let us assume, then, that equation (288) refers directly to this particular case. If the density of the gas to which the magnetising field H is applied is ρ, if the chemical atomic weight of helium is A, and if N denotes the value of Avogadro's constant, the number of helium atoms in unit volume of the gas under the conditions of the experiment is $\rho N/A$, and the intensity of magnetisation is $\overline{\Delta M} \rho N/A$. We have, therefore,

$$\frac{\rho N}{A} \overline{\Delta M} = \kappa H \tag{289}$$

or, substituting for $\overline{\Delta M}$ from equation (288),

$$\frac{\kappa}{\rho} \frac{A}{N} = -\frac{\mu_0^2 e^2 r^2}{3m} \tag{290}$$

According to equation (290) κ/ρ should be constant (and, in particular, should be independent of temperature)—as experiment shows it to be—and, if this is so, then the equation may be used for the evaluation of r. Experimentally, the magnitude of the left-hand member of equation (290) is -0.49×10^{-40} henry m^2 for helium gas; inserting the known values of μ_0, e and m in the other member, we have, therefore, $r = 0.57 \times 10^{-10}$ m.

Having regard to the extreme simplicity of our model this is a very satisfactory result. The effective radius of the helium atom, as deduced from measurements of gaseous viscosity—which on the basis of kinetic theory yield the mean free path and so the atomic cross-section—is 1.3×10^{-10} m, and (for comparison) the radius of the electron orbit in the normal hydrogen atom according to the Bohr theory (equations (162) and (170)) is 0.53×10^{-10} m.

TABLE 3

	He	Ne	A	Kr	Xe
$-\dfrac{\kappa A}{\rho N}$ (10^{-40} H m^2)	0·49	1·71	5·02	7·20	10·9
a (10^{-10} m)	1·29	1·40	1·71	(1·9)	(2·2)
Z	2	10	18	36	54

Encouraged by the results of our calculations in the case of helium, let us now consider the experimental facts in respect of the inert gases generally. In table 3 experimental values of $\kappa A/\rho N$ are given, together with values of a, the 'gas-kinetic radius', and

Z the atomic number (that is, the number of extranuclear electrons in the atom). On the basis of equation (290) we should expect that the significant parameter determining the 'atomic susceptibility' $\kappa A/\rho N$ would be the sum of the areas of all the electron orbits (assumed circular) in the neutral atom. According to the evidence from the a-values listed in the table, the overall size of the atom does not increase very markedly with the number of extranuclear electrons (Z), and the atomic susceptibility of these inert gases increases less rapidly with Z in the range $Z > 18$ than it does for $Z < 18$. This is generally what we should expect on any theory of atomic constitution: the gas-kinetic size of the atom is fixed by the radius of the outermost electron orbit; as Z increases an increasing fraction of the electrons, being more tightly bound, occupy inner orbits of smaller radius than this. For the diamagnetic susceptibilities of the inert gases, therefore, we conclude that classical theory is able to give an account of the results of experiment which is broadly satisfactory—and we may note in passing that the modification which wave mechanics introduces, that of replacing well-defined orbits by volume distributions of effective charge and current (p. 286), is in the direction of postulating values of the mean square distance, represented by r^2 in equation (290), which are generally smaller than the classical values. This was the sense of the discrepancy between the value of r, which we calculated on the basis of this equation in the case of helium, and the gas-kinetic radius of the helium atom.

TABLE 4

	P	As	Sb	Bi
$-\dfrac{\kappa A}{\rho N}$ (10^{-40} H m^2)	7·32	6·13	27·8	74·2
Z	15	33	51	83

There is no other group of diamagnetic elements for which the situation is as simple as it is with the inert gases. In table 4 we give the experimental values of $\kappa A/\rho N$ for the elements of group VB of the periodic classification. Obviously, there is the same general trend, the mass susceptibility increasing with Z as before, but the increase is less regular, and the values for antimony and bismuth —particularly the latter—are considerably higher than we should expect if we based our predictions on the inert-gas values. The fact is that in solid substances generally—and the results in table 4 refer to the solid state—except in perfect insulators, the ultimate structural units are not neutral atoms, exclusively. In respect of magnetic properties, the conduction electrons (or 'holes'—see §7.3) have a contribution to make, and the theory of the effect becomes complicated in consequence. We shall not attempt to follow these complications here, merely indicating, as a measure of the difficulties which face the theorist who seeks to provide a full interpretation of all the facts, that with bismuth (the least representative element amongst the diamagnetics) the magnetic susceptibility is not only temperature dependent to a significant degree but also (at low temperatures) magnetic-field dependent, as well.

If we do not find the simplicity of inert-gas behaviour with other elements, in the solid state, there is one group of chemical compounds which, even though its members are solids at ordinary temperatures, follows the same simple pattern. The structural units in crystals of the alkali halides, are the singly charged ions of metal and halogen, respectively (p. 219). Both positive and negative ions in this case have electron configurations of the inert-gas type: $_3Li^+$ the same as $_2He$, $_{11}Na^+$ the same as $_{10}Ne$, $_9F^-$ the same as $_{10}Ne$, $_{17}Cl^-$ the same as $_{18}A$, and so on, correspondingly, for the other members of the group. For the positive ions, the nuclear charge being one unit greater than that of the corresponding neutral atom of an inert gas, the radii of equivalent electron orbits will be less, and the diamagnetic susceptibility will consequently be expected to be less than that of the inert gas concerned. For the negative ions, conversely, the diamagnetic susceptibility should be greater than the appropriate inert-gas value. This is essentially what is found. The (cubic) crystals of the alkali halides are found to be magnetically isotropic and to be diamagnetic. On the general assumption that the ionic constituents contribute independently to the overall effect, the experimental values of magnetic susceptibility can be accounted for satisfactorily. We should only add, with the discussion of the next section in mind, that the alkali metals themselves are uniformly paramagnetic in behaviour.

9.4. PARAMAGNETIC MATERIALS

We have already adopted the point of view, inherited from Ampère and Weber, and supported by the circumstantial evidence of Curie's experiments, that paramagnetism results when the 'carriers'—atoms, or molecules, or ions, as the case may be—possess permanent magnetic dipole moments of electronic origin. Gyromagnetic effects, observed with ferromagnetic materials, lead us to suspect that the electron itself carries an intrinsic moment of this type—and we should naturally anticipate other contributions from the orbital motions of the electrons in an atom (or molecule or ion). If this view is correct, the very fact that many substances are diamagnetic, with no sign of temperature dependence of susceptibility at ordinary temperatures, indicates clearly that complete cancellation of these electronic contributions obtains in many atomic systems. That this should be so was a matter of surprise in the early years of this century; it became less surprising as soon as Bohr's principle of quantisation of angular momentum (p. 270) came to be accepted; nowadays it is seen as a general consequence of the tendency to 'pairing' of electron motions that has already been noted in another connection (p. 336).

It has been said that Curie's experiments of 1895, showing that paramagnetic susceptibilities decrease as the temperature increases —in many cases in inverse ratio with the (absolute) temperature —generally support the view that the carriers in such substances possess permanent dipoles. The measure of this support, qualitative and circumstantial at first, was provided by the theoretical work of Langevin in 1905. Paul Langevin (1872-1946) was a pupil of Curie, and later succeeded him in his professorship at l'École de Physique et de Chimie in Paris. Basing his treatment on the result of Larmor (p. 237), Langevin was the first to set out clearly the theory of diamagnetism as we have given it in the last section, and, more originally, to develop the theory of paramagnetism that we are now to describe. The former theory, as we have seen, involved a precise calculation in relation to a particular model; the latter theory was statistical in nature.

We start from the expression for the couple acting on a permanent magnetic doublet, of dipole moment M, when its axis is inclined at an angle θ to the direction of a magnetic field H. We have (equation (45)),

$$G = -MH \sin \theta \tag{291}$$

In this expression the negative sign implies that the sense of the couple is such as to tend to the decrease of θ. If $W(\theta)$ represents the magnetic potential energy of the doublet in the field, and if, conventionally, we take $W(\pi/2) = 0$, we have, therefore,

$$W(\theta) = \int_{\theta}^{\pi/2} G \, d\theta,$$

or $\qquad W(\theta) = - MH \cos \theta \qquad\qquad (292)$

The statistical aspect of the theory enters when equation (292) is used in conjunction with Boltzmann's result (p. 356) concerning relative probabilities in a system in thermal equilibrium. In a paramagnetic gas, in thermal equilibrium, in the absence of a magnetic field, there is no difference of potential energy associated with different orientations of the magnetic axes of individual atoms or molecules of the gas. Such orientations are energetically indistinguishable and, in consequence, all are 'equally probable'. If we consider a sample of gas consisting of a very large number, n, of molecules, in thermal equilibrium the number of molecules having their magnetic axes inclined at an angle between θ and $\theta + d\theta$ to any arbitrarily chosen direction will be $\tfrac{1}{2}n \sin \theta \, d\theta$. Obviously, there will be no resultant magnetisation of the gas. When a magnetic field is applied, directional differences of magnetic potential energy are introduced in accordance with equation (292), and, states of lower potential energy being favoured states, there will be a redistribution of orientations, which the collisions resulting from thermal motion will maintain, in favour of the smaller values of θ. Formally, the effect is specified in terms of the Boltzmann factor $e^{-W(\theta)/kT}$ (in which T is the absolute temperature and k is Boltzmann's constant): the probability that the magnetic axis of a molecule is inclined to the field direction at an angle lying between θ and $\theta + d\theta$ is now given by $P(\theta)d\theta$, where

$$P(\theta) = ae^{-W(\theta)/kT} \sin \theta \qquad\qquad (293)$$

In equation (293), a is a numerical 'normalising' constant, introduced so that

$$\int_{0}^{\pi} P(\theta)d\theta = 1 \qquad\qquad (294)$$

On the basis of equation (293), the distribution of the molecular magnetic axes being axially symmetrical about the field direction, the resultant moment of induced magnetisation is along the direction of the field and, for a sample of n molecules, is given by

$$\mathcal{J}S = n \int_0^\pi P(\theta) M \cos \theta \, d\theta \qquad (295)$$

Here S is the volume of the sample of gas concerned, and $\mathcal{J}$ is the intensity of the induced magnetisation. Clearly, from equations (293), (294) and (295), we have

$$\mathcal{J} = \frac{n}{S} \frac{\int_0^\pi e^{-W(\theta)/kT} M \cos \theta \sin \theta \, d\theta}{\int_0^\pi e^{-W(\theta)/kT} \sin \theta \, d\theta} \qquad (296)$$

Let us write $MH/kT = \alpha$, $\cos \theta = x$, then equation (296) becomes

$$\mathcal{J} = \frac{nM}{S} \frac{\int_{-1}^{+1} e^{\alpha x} x \, dx}{\int_{-1}^{+1} e^{\alpha x} \, dx}.$$

Integrating by parts, we obtain

$$\mathcal{J} = \frac{nM}{S} \left\{ \frac{[e^{\alpha x} x]_{-1}^{+1}}{[e^{\alpha x}]_{-1}^{+1}} - \frac{1}{\alpha} \right\},$$

that is, $\quad \mathcal{J} = \frac{nM}{S} \left(\frac{e^\alpha + e^{-\alpha}}{e^\alpha - e^{-\alpha}} - \frac{1}{\alpha} \right) \qquad (297)$

In equation (297) the quantity nM/S represents the arithmetical sum of the dipole moments of all the molecules in unit volume of the sample. On the basis of our model the intensity of magnetisation could not possibly be greater than this quantity, however great the magnetising field. This conclusion is confirmed by the form of the equation: as α tends to infinity, the term in brackets in the equation tends to one. On the other hand, when $\alpha \ll 1$, the bracketed term takes on the value $\alpha/3$: for $H \ll kT/M$, therefore,

$$\mathcal{J} = \frac{nM^2}{3SkT} H \qquad (298)$$

According to equation (298), in these circumstances our theory predicts simple paramagnetic behaviour—and, for the paramagnetic susceptibility κ, it gives the value

$$\kappa = \frac{nM^2}{3SkT},$$

varying inversely as the absolute temperature, as Curie's empirical law, in its simplest form, requires. Taking over the formalism that we used in the last section (and using A for the atomic or molecular weight, as is appropriate to the case), we have $n/S = \rho N/A$, so that, finally, for a paramagnetic gas, on Langevin's theory,

$$\frac{\kappa}{\rho}\frac{A}{N} = \frac{M^2}{3kT} \tag{299}$$

Among the common gases, oxygen and nitric oxide provide the most obvious examples of simple substances in relation to which the predictions of equation (299) may be tested. The values of the quantity $\kappa A/\rho N$ for these gases at $20°C$ are found to be $8 \cdot 93 \times 10^{-38}$ and $3 \cdot 72 \times 10^{-38}$ H m², respectively. With $k = 1 \cdot 38 \times 10^{-23}$ J deg⁻¹ K, we obtain for M, the permanent molecular dipole moment, the values $3 \cdot 29 \times 10^{-29}$ and $2 \cdot 12 \times 10^{-29}$ Wb m, in the two cases concerned. These values may profitably be compared with the value of the intrinsic magnetic moment of the electron on Dirac's theory, $\mu_0 eh/4\pi m$ (p. 459); this quantity, the so-called Bohr magneton (because it is also the magnetic moment associated with the ground-state orbit of the electron in the neutral hydrogen atom according to Bohr's theory), turns out to be $1 \cdot 16 \times 10^{-29}$ Wb m. The order-of-magnitude agreement is impressive—indeed, the over-optimistic reader might be tempted to carry the comparison farther, and to conclude that with nitric oxide the molecular dipole moment is precisely two Bohr magnetons, with oxygen precisely three. Rather than give way prematurely to such speculation, let us examine more critically the basis of the Langevin calculation.

In the first place we remind ourselves that in 1905 Langevin's avowed aim was to provide a 'modern' version of the older ideas of Ampère and Weber, based upon the discovery of the negative electron as a common constituent of atoms generally—and the broad (though not detailed) understanding of the Zeeman effect which that discovery had made possible. On the other hand, we note that Langevin introduced into his theory a unique magnetic moment (for atoms of one kind). It is perhaps not a criticism to say that in this he was ahead of his time, but what can be said with assurance is that there was no justification, in any then-accepted theory of atomic constitution, for such an assumption, when Langevin made it basic for his calculations.* The assumption is clearly equivalent to that of a unique electron angular momentum, of which there was no hint before it appeared 'from nowhere' in the first quantum theory of Bohr in 1913.

A second more difficult matter concerns Langevin's use of equation (292) for the magnetic potential energy of his carriers. It is true that a permanent magnet of dipole moment M is subject to an aligning couple of magnitude $MH \sin \theta$ when its axis is inclined at an angle θ to the direction of a uniform field H—and that, therefore, equation (292) is valid for such a body, however small. It is also true that a plane loop of current-carrying conductor is subject to a couple in similar circumstances, tending to align its axis with the field direction (p. 129)—and that this couple can be represented by assigning a magnetic dipole moment to the current loop (equation (93)) and treating it formally as if it were a permanent magnet to which equation (291) applies. Again, there is no limitation in size, except that implied by the condition that a material conductor is involved. Both these statements are undoubtedly true, but, unfortunately, they are also irrelevant. Langevin was not dealing with small permanent magnets, or small current loops in 'real' conductors. He was concerned with electrons, imagined to be moving in orbits within individual atoms. 'Classically', the theory of diamagnetism contains the whole story of the effect of an applied magnetic field on the motion of such electrons, provided that the condition of central forces is fulfilled: the orbits precess about the field direction, and nothing more. Moreover, within the framework of the classical description, there can be no doubt that this dia-magnetic (Larmor) precession occurs as a universal effect—the Zeeman phenomenon and the phenomena of diamagnetism admit of no other description in traditional terms: the only doubt is whether, within the same frame of reference, we can justify the use of equation (292), from which it appears impossible to separate

---

* It was shown by J. H. van Leeuwen, in 1921, that if Langevin had not made this assumption, but had instead accepted the 'classical' view that atomic electron orbits might be modified in thermal collisions, his calculations would have failed completely.

the assumption of the reality of the aligning couple G of our previous argument.

Some authors, affecting to retain the classical framework, boldly make the separation that we have just declined to make, accepting equation (292) but denying reality to the aligning couple. They assert that intermolecular collisions arising from thermal motion (concerning which we have merely written that they are the means by which the Boltzmann energy distribution is maintained) provide the only mechanism by which molecular orientations may be changed. Clearly, there is a difficulty for either point of view: it is difficult to see in detail how an aligning couple arises, in classical terms; on the other hand, it is difficult, in logic, to accept the expression for the potential energy without at the same time accepting the reality of the couple. Let us offer the following comment. The same basic result (equation (105)) may be made the starting point for two separate calculations. Applied to a single electron moving in a central orbit in a uniform magnetic field, it predicts the Larmor precession. Applied to the conduction electrons uniformly distributed around a circular loop of wire, it predicts that there will be an unbalanced couple acting on the wire loop when current is flowing. These are two different results, but the physical situations are also very different, in the two cases. The conduction electrons are constrained to an effectively one-dimensional (curvilinear) solid body, and are uniformly distributed throughout its finite length. The orbiting electron can occupy only one 'point' at any time, but it has available a three-dimensional domain of possible motion. If we were to consider an atomic electron as occupying all points around its orbit all the time, we might have a quasi-classical model which predicted alignment by the field as well as the diamagnetic precessional effect which we have accepted as fundamental. After all, in the precessional motion, the orbit behaves essentially as if the electron were constrained, by the central field of the nucleus, in a 'current loop' of invariable dimensions. As gloss on this comment, we merely remind the reader that on the wave-mechanical view of atomic structure (pp. 286, 465) each extranuclear electron is pictured as 'spread over the whole volume of the atom' according to a characteristic pattern. It is not implausible, then, to believe that the difficulty that we have been discussing discloses one of the more subtle instances in which classical theory is strictly inadequate as a basis of explanation just because it involves the clear-cut, spatio-temporal description of submicroscopic processes which the wave-mechanical theory disallows.

After this close-knit discussion, it is salutary to return to direct experiment—for, even before the new theory was adumbrated, experiment had something definite to contribute to the solution of the problem. In 1922, Otto Stern (b. 1888) and Walter Gerlach (b. 1889) published the results of an experiment in which individual silver atoms had been subjected to the action of a strong, inhomogeneous, magnetic field. This field was established in a

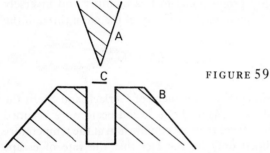

FIGURE 59

long channel between soft-iron pole pieces, A and B, whose section at right angles to the length of the channel was as illustrated in fig. 59. The silver atoms entered the channel, in a vessel in which the best possible 'vacuum' was maintained, as a parallel beam, having passed through a series of narrow collimating slits the projection of which on the plane of the figure is represented by C. The beam of silver atoms originated in an electrically heated oven having a suitable orifice, and was received at the other end of the evacuated vessel on a plate cooled in liquid air. In this way, eventually, a visible trace of deposited silver could be obtained on the collecting plate. When the pole pieces were unmagnetised, the trace on the collector revealed the strip-like character of the atomic beam, as was expected. When the field was applied, the trace was as indicated in fig. 60. There was a central clear space in the symmetrical pattern—which was not expected, at least on the basis of classical theory.

Obviously, on the basis of any theory of atomic structure, the mere fact of the deflection of the paths of individual silver atoms under the influence of the field, in the conditions of the experiment, provides evidence for a field-dependent potential energy. This conclusion is inescapable once it is accepted as an empirical result that the magnitude of the deflection is directly correlated with the degree of inhomogeneity of the field to which individual atoms are subjected. If we accept Langevin's theory of the paramagnetic gas, overlooking the difficulties that we have been discussing, equation (292) specifies this magnetic potential energy explicitly. On this basis, the deflecting force on a given atom, in the direction at right angles to both the length of the channel and the length of the colli- mating slits, may be written as $-\partial W/\partial y$, and the ultimate linear displacement of the point of arrival of this atom on the collecting plate will be directly proportional to this quantity and inversely proportional to the square of the velocity of the atom through the

FIGURE 60

field. In the experimental arrangement of Gerlach and Stern the velocities of the silver atoms in the deflected beam were assumed to be those characteristic of thermal equilibrium at the temperature of the oven (modified only by the fact that the rate of escape through an orifice is itself proportional to the velocity). Classically, therefore, at any point across the pattern on the collecting plate, we should expect to find transverse displacements the spread of which is determined by the range of velocities represented in the beam, and the range of values of θ, the inclination of the magnetic axis of an atom to the field direction during its passage through the field. If we accept the reality of an aligning couple due to the field (there can be no question of the intervention of molecular collisions under the conditions of the experiment), then $\theta = 0$ for all atoms, and deflections should be in one sense only, with a diffuse trace bearing witness to the distribution of velocities amongst the atoms in the beam. Alternatively, if we believe that only precession of the magnetic axes of individual atoms occurs, then, since we have no reason to suppose that the atoms enter the field with other than randomly orientated axes, we should expect a symmetrical pattern of 'positive' and 'negative' deflections, most dense in the middle (the deflection being proportional to $\cos \theta$, and the probability distribution in θ being as $\frac{1}{2} \sin \theta \, d\theta$). As we have seen, neither expectation is fulfilled: there is a symmetrical pattern of diffuse traces, but very definitely the density in the centre of the pattern is indistinguishable from zero. Clearly, the classical picture has failed—whichever variant of it we choose.

Being denied the possibility of interpreting the experimental results of 1922, either on the assumption that the magnetic axes of the atoms are aligned with the field uniformly, or on the supposition that they are randomly orientated and precessing, let us take the bold step, as Stern and Gerlach did, of accepting the form of the deflection pattern at its face value, and supposing that, for some reason or another, every silver atom passes through the field having magnetic potential energy either MH or $-MH$. (This is equivalent, on a classical basis, to the assumption that in a magnetic field H the magnetic axis of an atom of dipole moment M sets either antiparallel or parallel to the field.) In this case the diffuseness of the deflected trace will be due exclusively to the distribution of velocities among the atoms (account having been taken of the finite width of the collimating slits)—and we can at least derive a value for M, once the magnetic field has been accurately surveyed, the effective temperature of the oven determined and the deflection itself measured between points of maximum density in the double trace. In the 1922 experiments, the then-available techniques had been pushed to the utmost, precision being still an unattainable ideal, but Stern and Gerlach carried out the procedure that we have outlined and concluded that the magnetic moment of the silver atom was 1 Bohr magneton with a possible uncertainty of some 10 per cent. This was, indeed, an encouraging result.

In the following years similar experiments were performed with atomic beams obtained with other metallic elements of conveniently low melting point. With the alkali metals, lithium, sodium and potassium, precisely similar patterns were obtained as with silver, and these permitted similar interpretation; on the other hand atomic beams of zinc, cadmium and lead were undeflected. (Silver and the alkali metals are all odd-numbered elements possessing an 'unpaired' electron (see p. 357), zinc, cadmium and lead are even-numbered; so this feature of the results, at least, was expected.) Very soon massive improvements in technique became possible, and a whole new field of atomic spectroscopy was opened up which we cannot here explore. For our purposes only one of these later investigations is immediately relevant: in 1933 W. Meissner and H. Scheffers repeated the earlier experiments with lithium and potassium. In each case they demonstrated conclusively that the distribution of intensity in the deflected trace was precisely as Stern and Gerlach had supposed: assuming a unique value for the atomic magnetic moment, they analysed their direct measurements of trace density and in each case obtained a velocity spectrum in good agreement with the modified Maxwellian distribution characteristic of the oven temperature concerned. The previously unverified assumption having thus been confirmed, they were able to calculate atomic magnetic moments from the observed most probable deflections on a more secure foundation. The values which they obtained coincided with the then-accepted value of the Bohr magneton to within a few parts in a thousand.

Here we must leave the results of the atomic beam experiments, though they have much more, in the matter of detail, to contribute to an understanding of paramagnetic behaviour generally. For our purposes it is enough that we have elicited the answer that they give to the vexed question of field-induced orientation, which constituted our major difficulty in relation to Langevin's theory. Let it be said at once that the experiments do not answer the question whether, or even whether it is significant to enquire if, an isolated atom having a permanent magnetic moment orientated at an arbitrary angle to an applied field experiences an aligning couple due to the field. What we can justifiably conclude from them is rather than any arrangement which provides a measure of the field-dependent potential energy in such circumstances will always exhibit that energy as having one of a small number of discrete values—as if, on a classical interpretation, the magnetic axis of the atom was constrained to take up one of a small number of allowed orientations with respect to the field. Within the classical idiom, this conclusion is frequently expressed using the term 'space quantisation', but it should be stressed that the direct evaluation of the experimental results is in terms of forces, or their associated potential energies, rather than dipole orientations.

The notion of space quantisation (we use the term primarily because of its convenience) arose, as we have seen, out of experiments performed before the advent of wave mechanics, or the emergence of the concept of quantised electron spin. Already, in terms of the Bohr theory, specifications were devised giving the 'allowed orientations' in terms of the resultant angular momentum associated with the electron orbits in the atom. It was supposed that the component of angular momentum along the field direction was itself restricted to quantised values. With the introduction of wave mechanics and the acceptance of the 'spinning electron', these specifications were translated into the new formalism and given a more logical foundation. In 1927 Léon Brillouin (b. 1889) revised the Langevin calculation from this point of view. In the upshot the expression for the paramagnetic susceptibility (equation (299)), appropriate for values of $H/T \ll k/M$, was essentially unchanged, but predictions concerning the high-field/low-temperature behaviour were somewhat modified, the expression within brackets in equation (297) being replaced by another expression, having a different limiting value for $H/T \gg k/M$. Experiments with high magnetising fields, at liquid helium temperatures, have latterly confirmed Brillouin's predictions with considerable accuracy.

Fundamentally, the Langevin-Brillouin calculations refer only to paramagnetic materials in the gaseous state; on the other hand, it is found, empirically, that Curie's law, in a slightly generalised form, provides a satisfactory account of the low-field behaviour of many solid substances, and of the aqueous solutions of certain salts. The generalised version of Curie's law valid in such cases,

$$\frac{\kappa}{\rho} = \frac{C}{T - T_0} \tag{300}$$

involves two constants for each material. T_0 (equation (300)) represents a characteristic temperature (the value of which may be positive or negative) and C is proportional to the square of the molecular dipole moment, as equation (299) would suggest. For paramagnetic gases, and for a few solid materials, $T_0 = 0$, as nearly as experiment can decide; for most other paramagnetic substances it has a non-zero value. When the value of T_0 is not positive then it is possible to carry out significant investigations of simple paramagnetic behaviour at the lowest available temperatures (and the highest attainable fields). It was, indeed, with solid materials of this type that W. Henry in 1953 found agreement with the Brillouin—rather than the Langevin—formula for the 'saturation' magnetisation, as we have mentioned above. The materials that were studied in these experiments were potassium chromium alum, ferric ammonium alum and gadolinium sulphate octahydrate. Structurally, these three substances have much in common: all are sulphates, and all contain water of crystallisation (the alums, twelve molecules of water for every trivalent ion in the molecule). The paramagnetism is believed to be due exclusively to the trivalent ion (Cr^{3+}, Fe^{3+} or Gd^{3+}) in each case. In the solid state, therefore, these substances are 'magnetically dilute'—the magnetic carriers being widely separated in the crystal lattice. It appears to be a general—and generally understandable—rule that the predictions of the Brillouin formula should be most nearly realised in the case of paramagnetic solids that are magnetically dilute in this sense: in relation to magnetic effects, such solids more nearly resemble gases than do other solids in which the concentration of magnetic carriers is greater.

At this point, having introduced the reader to some of the simpler aspects of the subject, we conclude our survey of the phenomenon of paramagnetism: as we indicated at the beginning of this chapter, to go farther would merely be to expose the inadequacies of the basic theoretical notions that we have been able to develop in earlier sections of the book.

9.5. FERROMAGNETIC MATERIALS

In the introduction to this chapter we stated that iron, cobalt and nickel were still, at the end of the nineteenth century, in a class by themselves, magnetically—they were the only ferromagnetic elements then known. These elements and their alloys were the only substances, so it seemed, out of which permanent magnets could be made. Their magnetic susceptibilities (measured at very low field strengths) were several orders of magnitude greater than those of paramagnetic substances generally—and at easily attainable fields, and ordinary temperatures, saturation of magnetisation could be achieved. Earlier, before Faraday had discovered the susceptibility of magnetisation of all materials, it was believed that these three elements also become non-magnetic at high temperatures. In 1822, Barlow (see p. 124) had found that a bar of soft iron ceased to affect a compass needle when it was heated to a medium red heat, and Faraday himself confirmed a similar effect with nickel (at a lower temperature), in 1836, and (at a higher temperature) with cobalt, in 1845. Afterwards, when he had established the universality of magnetic behaviour, Faraday showed that this apparent loss of magnetism with the three ferromagnetic elements was not complete: above the transition temperature, each of these metals exhibited the normal behaviour of a paramagnetic solid.

Later, the transition temperature came to be called the 'Curie temperature', its approximate identification with T_0 in equation (300) providing a satisfactory formal description of the paramagnetic behaviour of the material over a considerable range of higher temperature. Presently accepted values of the Curie temperatures of the three metals are: Fe, 770°C; Co, 1130°C; Ni, 360°C.

In 1836, at the time when he admitted only iron and nickel as magnetic elements (see p. 448), Faraday speculated whether all metals might possibly show similar transitions from non-magnetic to magnetic behaviour if they were cooled to sufficiently low temperatures. Using 'sulphurous acid' (and later, in 1839, ether and solid carbon dioxide) as a 'freezing mixture', he made a systematic search for such an effect, but with a negative result. In the upshot it was a hundred years before Faraday's speculation was in any way vindicated. Arising from the investigations of S. Legvold and F.H.Spedding and others, in the years since 1953, we now know that the rare-earth metals gadolinium* $(Z = 64)$, terbium $(Z = 65)$, dysprosium $(Z = 66)$ and holmium $(Z = 67)$ —and possibly europium $(Z = 63)$ and erbium $(Z = 68)$—become ferromagnetic when sufficiently cooled. The respective Curie temperatures are: Gd, 16°C; Tb, −55°C; Dy, −188°C; Ho, −253°C.

So far, except through reference to the alloys of iron, cobalt and nickel, we have been concerned only with the ferromagnetic elements. In 1903, F. Heusler found that an alloy of the three 'non-magnetic' elements manganese, aluminium and copper, in proportions given approximately by the stoichiometric formula $MnAlCu_2$, exhibits ferromagnetic properties. Later he found similar behaviour with two alloys containing manganese, tin and copper, mixed in the atomic proportions $MnSnCu_2$ and Mn_3SnCu_6, respectively. In relation to saturation intensity of magnetisation these Heusler alloys compare favourably with nickel.

For nearly thirty years the Heusler alloys remained as magnetic curiosities. Then, with the gradual emergence of a better theoretical understanding of the phenomenon, and the awakening of some technological interest, a more systematic search was undertaken. In 1931 H.H.Potter described the ferromagnetic properties of a

* The first report that gadolinium is ferromagnetic, was made by G.Urbain, P.Weiss and F.Trombe in 1935.

silver-rich alloy of approximate composition Ag_5MnAl; in 1952 E. Adams produced a binary alloy of bismuth and manganese (74% Bi, 26% Mn) suitable for the production of small permanent magnets; and in 1960 another such alloy, of composition 72% Mn, 28% Al, was discovered by A. J. J. Koch and his collaborators in Eindhoven. In 1960, also, F. A. Hames identified two ferromagnetic alloys of palladium, of atomic composition approximately represented by the formulae Pd_2MnSb and $PdMnSb$, as well as three alloys, two of nickel and one of cobalt, which proved to be ferromagnetic, although the atomic concentration of the ferromagnetic element was no more than 50 per cent. of the total. Overall, now, the class of ferromagnetic materials contains many more members than the three 'transition elements' iron, cobalt and nickel.

The three classical ferromagnetic elements are referred to as 'transition elements' because they are of neighbouring atomic numbers ($Z = 26, 27, 28$), they have closely similar chemical properties, and together form a natural sub-group separating the 'A-group' elements from the 'B-group' elements of the first 'long period' of the periodic classification. (Other similar groups of transition elements are ruthenium, rhodium and palladium, $Z = 44, 45, 46$, and osmium, iridium and platinum, $Z = 76, 77, 78$.) Already, in the second decade of the nineteenth century, Johann Wolfgang Döbereiner (1780-1849), professor of chemistry at Jena, was pointing to the chemical similarity of iron, cobalt and nickel—and osmium, iridium and platinum—as significant for a deeper understanding of the relationships of the elements generally: these groups were two of his 'triads' of elements that were specially related. Nowadays we believe that the structural feature in common in these cases is that, as between one member of such a triad and the preceding one, the 'last added' electron is not the least-tightly-bound electron, as is generally the case when any neutral atom is compared with the atom of the element standing next lower in the periodic table; there is an unfilled shell 'lying deeper' in the atom into which successive electrons are incorporated (as Z is increased) before there is any further increase in the number of 'valency' electrons in the 'outermost' (incomplete) shell. Herein, according to present views of the matter, is the natural explanation of the similarity of chemical properties among members of the transition-group triads.

Whilst it is certain that Faraday and his contemporaries must have pondered the question what significance there could be in the fact that the three ferromagnetic elements of their experience were the members of a particular Döbereiner triad, when they finally disclosed a correlation which they considered significant it associated the property of ferromagnetism with the close-packing of atoms rather than with any chemical behaviour. Describing the loss of ferromagnetic properties at high temperatures, de la Rive (p. 73) wrote (1854) '[these effects] have led several physicists to believe that [magnetism] arises in these bodies, from the small distance apart of the atoms of which they are formed. In fact, iron, cobalt and nickel are among those bodies which, volume for volume, contain the greatest number of atoms, and, in consequence, for which the atoms are the closest together. Increase of temperature results in an increase in the distance of the particles one from another; now since this increase in separation, when it exceeds a certain measure, causes these bodies to lose their magnetic properties, one may conclude that [other] substances in which the atoms are ordinarily farther apart cannot possess these properties at all.' In one sense, as we shall see, there was a remarkable prescience in this early correlation, but, set in its place in history, it is perhaps more soberly seen as foreshadowing the wider generalisation of Julius Lothar Meyer (1830-1895), professor of chemistry at Tübingen from 1876 until his death, who, when he was *Privatdozent* at the university of Breslau, in 1864 published his *Modern theories of chemistry* and exhibited the essential periodicity of atomic volume as a function of atomic weight. We now know that, apart from the light elements beryllium, boron and carbon, iron, cobalt and nickel have the smallest atomic volumes amongst all the elements—and we know that in the general periodic variation of this quantity (with atomic number, as we should now insist) the other significant minima are those 'occupied' by the corresponding transition-group triads of the second and third 'long periods' of the table. Smallness of atomic volume is correlated with the filling of incomplete inner electron shells: it remains to be seen (p. 488) whether the one or the other circumstance is particularly favourable to the appearance of ferromagnetism.

The first formally successful theory of ferromagnetism was given by Pierre Ernest Weiss (1865-1940) in 1907. Weiss extended Langevin's theory of paramagnetism (and the extension can equally well be applied to the later theory of Brillouin) by assuming that the effective magnetising field is not simply the 'applied' field arising from the external sources, but that this is increased, in the solid material, by an internal field arising from the induced magnetism and proportional to its intensity. If we write H' to denote the value of the effective magnetising field according to this assumption, we have

$$H' = H + \lambda \mathcal{J} \tag{301}$$

where λ is a quantity characteristic of the material concerned (and of which the unit of measurement is the metre per henry). Also, in shortened form, we have the Langevin (or Brillouin) equation (see equation (297))

$$\mathcal{J} = \frac{nM}{S} f\left(\frac{MH'}{kT}\right) \tag{302}$$

If we take an initially unmagnetised specimen (of such shape that its magnetisation will prove to be uniform), then, on the basis of this formalism, if it is placed in an externally applied field H, it will develop magnetisation of intensity $\mathcal{J}$ given by the elimination of H' from equations (301) and (302).

We can examine the various possibilities most simply by exhibiting the simultaneous equations for $\mathcal{J}$ and H' graphically, as in fig. 61. OA represents the form of the expression for $\mathcal{J}$, as given by equation (302). As it is plotted ($\mathcal{J}$ versus H'/T) it is essentially temperature-independent, for a given solid substance, apart from an insignificant effect due to changes of density (proportional to n/S).* According to the Langevin formula the slope at the origin is $(\rho N/A)(M^2/3k)$—see equations (298) and (299). Since equation (301) can be re-written in the form

$$\mathcal{J} = \frac{T}{\lambda}\frac{H'}{T} - \frac{H}{\lambda} \tag{303}$$

any arbitrarily drawn straight line, such as BC in fig. 61, must refer to a particular value of the externally applied field and a particular temperature. A little consideration will show that, on the scale of the diagram, H/T is represented by the intercept OD, and H/λ by the intercept OB.

---

* λ might depend sensitively on the density of the material, and so on the temperature, but in the simple Weiss theory such a possibility is not envisaged.

We consider first the case when the slope of BC is greater than the slope of OA at the origin, that is when the internal field is relatively small and we have

$$\lambda < \frac{A}{\rho N} \frac{3kT}{M^2} \tag{304}$$

or, say, $\lambda < \lambda_0(T)$.

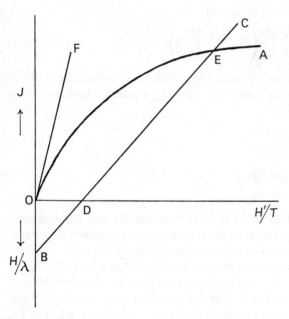

FIGURE 61

The process of magnetisation is represented by taking a straight line such as OF, of appropriate slope and drawn through the origin, and moving this line parallel to itself, 'downwards' in the figure. The ordinate of the point of intersection with OA gives the intensity of magnetisation at any stage of the process. Obviously, the whole process is reversible: if the applied field is removed, the magnetisation returns to zero. The possibility of permanent magnetisation is excluded, and the substance is paramagnetic. For not-too-large fields, the intensity of magnetisation is given by solution of the equations

$$H' = H + \lambda \mathcal{J},$$

$$\mathcal{J} = \frac{\rho N}{A} \frac{M^2}{3kT} H' \quad H' = \frac{H'}{\lambda_0}$$

(provided that we adopt the Langevin form of $f(\alpha)$ in equation (302)). On this basis we have

$$\frac{\kappa}{\rho} \equiv \frac{\mathcal{J}}{H\rho} = \frac{1}{\rho(\lambda_0 - \lambda)},$$

or $\qquad \dfrac{\kappa}{\rho} = \dfrac{N}{A} \dfrac{M^2}{3k} \left(T - \dfrac{\rho N}{A} \dfrac{M^2}{3k} \lambda \right)^{-1}$ $\hfill$ (305)

Finally, comparing equation (305) with the empirical form of the modified version of Curie's law given by equation (300), we obtain the identifications

$$C = \frac{N}{A} \frac{M^2}{3k},$$

$$T_0 = \frac{\rho N}{A} \frac{M^2}{3k} \lambda = \rho C \lambda.$$

We conclude that, if T_0 is truly constant for any paramagnetic substance, then, insofar as density changes are regarded as insignificant, λ is constant—which was our initial assumption.

Let us now repeat our analysis for the case in which $\lambda > \lambda_0$. As before, we start from the assumption that $\mathcal{J} = 0$ when $H = 0$. However, we see, at once, that this represents an unstable situation. The 'field line' now intersects the magnetisation curve OA at E_0, as well as at O (fig. 62). If the applied field is increased infinitesimally, the induced magnetisation increases discontinuously to a value appropriate to E_0 (the magnetisation curve has been reflected through the origin in fig. 62 so that reversal of the applied field may be considered, and the process of demagnetisation). Further increase of the applied field ultimately results in saturation of magnetisation, the representative point E_1 moving along OA 'to infinity'. If the field is now decreased to zero, the magnetisation of the specimen does not decrease beyond the value appropriate to E_0. The field must be reversed in direction, and 'increased' to a value corresponding to $\lambda . OB_2$, before the induced magnetisation is reversed in direction. According to our model, that reversal will

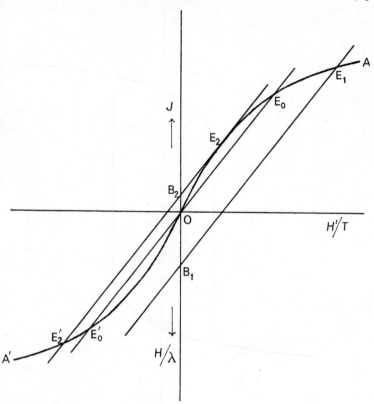

FIGURE 62

again be by a discontinuous process, the magnetisation changing abruptly from a value appropriate to E_2 to one appropriate to E_2' on the curve. Clearly, if the applied field is made to vary cyclically through a range lying between limits corresponding to $\pm \lambda . OB_1$ (fig. 62), the magnetisation of the specimen will also vary cyclically, and in a manner represented diagrammatically in fig. 63.

The representation which we have achieved in fig. 63 is immediately recognisable as predicting the phenomenon of 'hysteresis', which is the primary distinguishing feature of ferromagnetic behaviour. Obviously, our model has fulfilled the original purpose for which it was devised: it has pointed the way to an understanding of ferromagnetism as a special case of paramagnetism, occurring in substances in which magnetisation gives rise to a significant

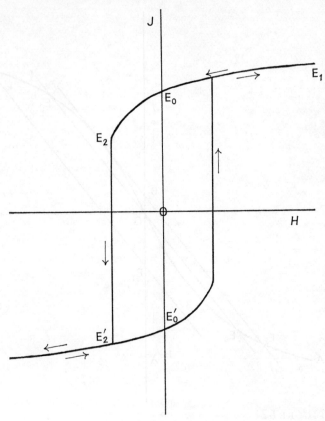

FIGURE 63

internal magnetising field, and favoured at relatively low temperatures when the magnetic potential energy of a single atom aligned in opposition to the internal saturation field is considerably greater than the characteristic thermal energy of the atom at the temperature concerned.*

Having reached this stage, we are left with two major problems. One of these Weiss was able to 'solve' when he first put forward

---

* Inequality (304), with the sign reversed, as is appropriate in the ferromagnetic case, may be written

$$M \left(\frac{\lambda \rho N M}{A} \right) > 3kT.$$

The term in brackets will be recognised as giving the magnitude of the internal magnetising field at saturation, according to our model.

the formal theory in 1907 (he 'solved' the problem by means of an additional assumption which has since been shown to be essentially valid); the other he was in no position to deal with—it remained unsolved until it was possible to treat it by the methods of wave mechanics. The first problem arises from the fact that the simple model has, in one sense, been too successful. Because of the essential instability of the 'configuration' $H = 0$, $\mathscr{J} = 0$, there is no clear reason, according to the model, why samples of ferromagnetic materials should ever be found in the unmagnetised state. Weiss accepted the challenge of this conclusion, and asserted, in effect, that they are indeed never so found. The iron bar, which to macroscopic test appears to be unmagnetised, is on Weiss's view constituted of a very large number of micro-'domains', each 'spontaneously' magnetised to near saturation, only the magnetic axes of the individual domains are randomly orientated. Gross magnetisation appears through changes of orientation of the domain axes, or through encroachment of one domain at the expense of another. This solution of the problem, as we have already implied, is now supported by much direct experimental evidence. In consequence, the domain-concept has in recent years become central to the experimenter's approach to the phenomenon—though we cannot follow it farther here.

The second problem arising from the Weiss model, according to any classical estimate, is much more intractable. We must obviously attempt to provide a physical interpretation of the internal field, and in this attempt we immediately encounter difficulties of an 'absolute' kind: the fields, whose origin is to be identified physically, are so large. According to the last footnote, the internal saturation field in a ferromagnetic material at temperature T must be larger than $3kT/M$, M being the atomic magnetic moment. If the atom is regarded as an ideal doublet of moment M, the field on the axis at a distance r from the centre of the doublet is $M/2\pi\mu_0 r^3$ (p. 57). Let us write, then, as the basis of an exploratory calculation,

$$\frac{M}{2\pi\mu_0 r^3} > \frac{3kT}{M}.$$

On this basis we obtain formally

$$r < \left(\frac{M^2}{6\pi\mu_0 kT}\right)^{\frac{1}{3}}.$$

If $M = 10^{-28}$ Wb m (a generous assumption—see p. 470), and $T = 300°$ K, inserting the standard values of μ_0 and k, we have numerically,

$$r < 4 \cdot 7 \times 10^{-11} \text{ m}.$$

This value is an order of magnitude smaller than an atomic radius: our exploratory calculation fails, therefore, in that it provides no support for the view that the 'internal magnetising field' can be of 'magnetic' origin, in the classical sense of the term.

In 1928 Werner Heisenberg (b. 1901) put forward a non-classical theory of the internal field which in its fundamentals is the presently accepted theory of the phenomenon. On the assumption that the atomic magnetic moment, in ferromagnetic materials, is exclusively an electron-spin moment (p. 459), the potential energy difference which favours the alignment of spin axes in neighbouring atoms turns out to be of electrostatic rather than magnetic origin. The effect is non-classical in that this energy difference would be zero if the restriction which the Pauli principle (p. 336) enshrines were not effective. The magnitude of the effect is strongly structure sensitive (in relation both to structural symmetry and to absolute size of the unit cell of the crystal lattice). In this sense, at least, the century-old speculations which de la Rive reported (p. 481) are reflected in the modern theory. Finally, in relation to elementary ferromagnetics, only those atoms with inner electron shells which are incomplete provide internal fields of sufficient magnitude to meet the requirements of the situation. In this connection, the rare earth elements (p. 479) qualify for inclusion along with the transition-group triads (although their atomic volumes are not particularly small), as experiment shows to be the case.

Obviously there is much that we have left undescribed—and much still to be discovered—with regard to the detailed properties of ferromagnetic substances, but it appears that the basis of a theoretical understanding of this complicated subject has at last been achieved.

9.6. SUSCEPTIBILITY AND PERMEABILITY

In previous sections we have defined two quantities, the magnetic permeability, which we have denoted by μ, and the magnetic susceptibility, denoted by κ, each of which has reference to a magnetic property of matter in general. Formally, the magnetic permeability is defined (equation (65)) as the magnetic flux density at a point in a material medium per unit magnetic field established at that point: $B = \mu H$. Correspondingly, the magnetic susceptibility is defined (equation (284)) as the intensity of magnetisation at a point in a sample of material per unit magnetic field established at that point: $\mathcal{J} = \kappa H$. Provided that we restrict our consideration to isotropic materials, magnetic permeability and susceptibility are scalar quantities relating the magnitudes of pairs of vector quantities of which the directions are the same. As we have stated, these scalar quantities have reference to magnetic properties of matter in general: they are different in one respect however—whilst we must insist that the magnetic susceptibility of vacuum is zero (p. 452), we find it necessary to concede that the magnetic permeability of vacuum is finite (p. 107). On the other hand, there is more than formal similarity in the definitions of the two quantities. We have decided that magnetic flux density and intensity of magnetisation are dimensionally homogeneous (pp. 121, 454); so also, therefore, are magnetic permeability and magnetic susceptibility. They are measured in terms of the same unit, the henry per metre (p. 134). Having reached this conclusion, we are naturally led to search for some necessary relationship between the two quantities, which did not immediately appear in the course of their definition, but which the reality of the situation requires none the less. It is our first concern, in this section, to derive that relationship by the process of considering an ideal experiment.

In section 3.7 we described the classical experiments, made with a soft-iron ring wound with two coils of copper wire, by means of which Faraday discovered the phenomenon of electromagnetic induction in 1831—for which he and others later formulated the empirical rules and buttressed them with acceptable theory. We have already considered sufficient of that theory (pp. 127, 130) to be familiar with the empirical rules. For our ideal experiment, let us now refine Faraday's arrangement: let us take a circular ring ('torus') of ferromagnetic material of circular cross section A ($\equiv \pi a^2$) and radius of revolution r ($r \gg a$), uniformly and closely wound with a 'primary' coil containing n turns per unit length of the ring axis. Let there be a 'secondary' coil of a single turn and of radius slightly greater than a. When a current i_0 is reversed in the primary coil, a quantity of electricity will pass around the secondary coil determined by $2\Phi_0$, the overall change in the magnetic flux

EM 21

through that coil, and R, the total resistance of the secondary coil and any galvanometer or other instrument with which it is in circuit.*

In relation to this particular situation we may evaluate Φ_0 as follows. We imagine the torus of solid material to be removed from the primary coil (possible in an ideal experiment!) and the coil to be placed in vacuum. With a current i established in the coil we apply Ampère's formula (equation (99)) to calculate H, the magnitude of the magnetic field at any point on the ring axis of the coil. Clearly, the direction of the resultant field is along the tangent to this axis at every such point. We have, in this way,

$$H \cdot 2\pi r = 2\pi r n i,$$

or $$H = ni \tag{306}$$

For any point outside the coil, in our ideal arrangement, a similar application of Ampère's law shows that there is no component of magnetic field parallel to the plane of the ring axis and perpendicular to the radius drawn from the point to the axis of revolution of the toroidal coil. Indeed, a little consideration shows that the resultant field is identically zero everywhere outside the coil, in this ideal arrangement. Inside the coil, for points not on its ring axis, the magnitude of the field differs insignificantly from that given by equation (306) provided that $a \ll r$—and the magnitude of the magnetic flux density differs insignificantly from $\mu_0 ni$. If, now, the torus of ferromagnetic material is replaced in the coil, H, as we have just calculated it, is the value of the magnetising field, and the magnetic flux density is given by μH, μ being the permeability of the material. As before, the magnetic flux density is effectively uniform over the right section of the torus, and is zero everywhere else. We have, then, irrespective of the precise area of the secondary coil in the arrangement that we have described,

$$\Phi_0 = \pi a^2 \mu n i \tag{307}$$

Suppose that, before replacing the solid torus in the primary coil as we have just assumed, we cut out a thin slice leaving an effectively parallel-faced gap at right angles to the ring axis. We

* At any instant, the current in the secondary coil is given numerically by $(1/R)(d\Phi/dt)$ (see equation (78)); the total charge carried by this current during the period of reversal of the primary current is, therefore, $2\Phi_0/R$, Φ, the flux through the secondary coil having changed from Φ_0 to $-\Phi_0$ in the interval.

imagine the experiment of reversing a primary current i, and observing the throw of a ballistic galvanometer included in the single-turn secondary circuit, to be repeated with this arrangement. We postulate that the width of the gap cut in the torus is small compared with a. In the first place it will be found that the ballistic throw is somewhat smaller than previously recorded—obviously the change of magnetic flux through the secondary coil is now smaller than $2\Phi_0$ as given by equation (307); but more important, from our point of view, is the observation that the galvanometer deflection is almost exactly the same whether the secondary coil is located in the mid-plane of the gap or in any position in which it is 'threaded' by solid material. We conclude that when a steady current is passing in the primary coil, in the ideal arrangement that we have described, the magnitude of the magnetic flux density is the same at all points inside that coil—the same, that is, within the solid material as in vacuum in the (narrow) gap.

Now, it is a simple matter to calculate the magnitude of the magnetic flux density in the gap. Realistically, the total magnetic flux across the gap arises from two 'sources': the current in the primary coil and the induced magnetism in the (incomplete) torus. We have already calculated the first contribution: it is given by $\pi a^2 \mu_0 n i$. Here, however, we shall merely denote its magnitude by $\pi a^2 \mu_0 H$. The second contribution can most simply be calculated by making use of the artificial concept of the magnetic pole—which we have agreed is a rational procedure when convenience is served (p. 120). If the intensity of magnetisation of the incomplete torus is $\mathcal{J}$, this is also the measure of the magnetic pole strength per unit area of the opposing surfaces of the gap.* The magnetic flux across the gap arising from the plane distributions of opposite poles on its two bounding surfaces is then given simply by $\pi a^2 \mathcal{J}$ (see p. 122). Thus, when the gap is sufficiently narrow, so that the bounding surfaces are effectively infinite planes with relation to any intervening point, and the magnetic flux density B is uniform throughout the gap as we have supposed,

$$B = \mu_0 H + \mathcal{J} \tag{308}$$

Equation (308) gives the magnitude of the magnetic flux density

---

* The reader will find it instructive to compare this view of the situation with that which we adopted in considering the phenomenon of dielectric polarisation in an earlier chapter (p. 373).

in the gap. B is, also, as we have agreed, the magnitude of the magnetic flux density in the material of the incomplete torus. If we interpret (308) in that sense, and proceed to the limit in which the gap is completely closed (it was opened only for didactic purposes) then, by definition, $B = \mu H$, and $\mathcal{J} = \kappa H$, so that, finally,

$$\mu = \mu_0 + \kappa \tag{309}$$

In equation (309) we have the necessary relation between the magnetic permeability and the magnetic susceptibility that we set out to derive.

In deriving this relation, it will be recalled, we specified a torus of ferromagnetic material for our ideal experiment. This was not because equation (309) itself is limited in applicability to substances of this class—indeed, it is valid for isotropic materials generally—but rather because otherwise a real experiment of a similar character would in fact be inconclusive. With diamagnetic substances, and with most paramagnetic substances under ordinary conditions, it is a fact of experience that $|\kappa| \ll \mu_0$. With such materials, therefore, the ideal experiment that we devised would be altogether too insensitive to provide a convincing demonstration of the effects upon which our argument was founded. It is necessary to maintain a sense of reality, even in relation to ideal experiments.

There are other considerations that we can profitably enter into on the basis of the ideal experimental arrangement that we have just employed in the last investigation. For this purpose we dispense with the single-term secondary coil and its associated galvanometer, and we suppose, specifically, that current for the primary coil is provided by a battery of simple cells of e.m.f. V. We denote the resistance of the primary coil by R, and we investigate the energy relations characteristic of the build-up of the current, i, in this coil, from zero to its steady value V/R, when the coil is wound on a toroidal sample of material of magnetic susceptibility κ. The method is precisely the same as that which we have already used in section 3.8. If Φ is the instantaneous value of the total magnetic flux through the multi-turn coil, we have (compare equation (85))

$$V - \frac{d\Phi}{dt} = Ri.$$

Substituting for Φ, as $2\pi rn \cdot \pi a^2 B$, in terms of equation (308), from which

$$\Phi = 2\pi^2 ra^2 n(\mu_0 H + \mathcal{J}),$$

and noting that $2\pi^2 ra^2$ is essentially S, the total volume of the material 'specimen' under consideration, we obtain

$$V = Ri + Sn \frac{d}{dt}(\mu_0 H + \mathcal{J}).$$

Multiplying throughout by i, replacing ni by H (equation (306)), and integrating with respect to t, as before, we then have

$$\int_0^t Vi \, dt = \int_0^t Ri^2 \, dt + S\mu_0 \int_0^{H_0} H \, dH + S \int_0^{J_0} H \, d\mathcal{J} \qquad (310)$$

If we interpret equation (310) as we previously interpreted equation (87), we shall conclude that the three terms on the right-hand side of the equation represent the various ways in which the energy supplied by the battery in time t is redistributed. The first term represents the energy dissipated as heat in the circuit, the second term the amount of energy which would have been stored in the medium (vacuum) whether the specimen had been present in the coil or not, and the third term the amount of energy (proportional to the volume of the specimen) which is stored (or dissipated in the specimen) because, in fact, the specimen is in position in the coil. We note, in passing, that the second term is explicitly given by $S\mu_0 H_0^2/2$, and that the form of it suggests that we may regard this part of the energy as uniformly stored in that part of the medium which is contained within the volume of the coil—the only region where the magnetic field is different from zero—with volume density $\mu_0 H_0^2/2$. By the same token we can consistently regard the third term as representing energy localised within the specimen.

Suppose, now, that we repeat our calculation, taking as initial conditions $i = i_0$, $H = H_0$, $\mathcal{J} = \mathcal{J}_0$, and that we increase the resistance in the circuit in such a way that it becomes infinite after a time T (compare p. 141). We have

$$\int_0^T Vi \, dt = \int_0^T R(t)i^2 \, dt + S\mu_0 \int_{H_0}^0 H \, dH + S \int_{J_0}^0 H \, d\mathcal{J} \qquad (311)$$

According to equation (311), the energy dissipated as heat in the circuit during this time is greater than that which the battery has supplied by an amount

$$S\mu_0 \int_0^{H_0} H\, dH - S \int_{J_0}^0 H\, d\mathcal{J}.$$

Clearly, the energy which was 'stored in vacuum', when the magnetic field H_0 was established in the primary coil, is restored to the matter of which the coil is made when the current in the coil, and with it the magnetic field, is reduced to zero. Furthermore, provided that the material of the toroidal specimen is not ferromagnetic, the same is true of the rest of the magnetic energy: there is no hysteresis, but a one-to-one correspondence of $\mathcal{J}$ and H at all times, so that

$$-S \int_{J_0}^0 H\, d\mathcal{J} = S \int_0^{J_0} H\, d\mathcal{J}$$

in the context of equations (310) and (311). The third term in equation (310) under these conditions, is validly described as representing energy stored (rather than dissipated) in the specimen: when the magnetising field is reduced to zero this energy, also, is restored to the matter forming the conductor of the primary coil to be dissipated as heat in the coil. For a paramagnetic or diamagnetic material under ordinary conditions the one-to-one correspondence of $\mathcal{J}$ and H is simply represented by the defining relation $\mathcal{J} = \kappa H$ (equation (284)), with κ constant. In these circumstances, it will be noted, the third term in equation (310) reduces to $S\kappa H_0^2/2$.

For a ferromagnetic specimen, in our ideal arrangement, subjected to a recurring cycle of changes in which the current in the primary coil is slowly varied from an initial value i_1 to i_2 and back again to i_1, repeatedly, on balance a non-zero amount of energy equal to

$$S \oint H\, d\mathcal{J}$$

is removed from the battery and not restored from the specimen to the coil in each cycle. In practice this quantity is always positive (see fig. 63). It represents a 'hysteresis loss' of $\oint H\, d\mathcal{J}$ per unit volume of specimen per cycle—and experiment shows that it is dissipated as heat in the specimen.

In the last paragraph but one, we concluded that when a specimen of an isotropic paramagnetic or diamagnetic material for which the susceptibility is constant is magnetised by the creation of a magnetic field H in the region in which it is situated, energy of magnetisation in amount $\kappa H^2/2$ per unit volume is derived from the current-source producing the field. In the magnetised state unit volume of the specimen also possesses magnetic potential energy in amount

$$- \Sigma\, MH \cos \theta,$$

in the notation of equation (292), the summation extending over all the magnetic carriers in the volume concerned. Since, by definition,

$$\mathcal{J} = \Sigma\, M \cos \theta = \kappa H,$$

the magnetic potential energy per unit volume is simply $-\kappa H^2$. The total energy of magnetisation per unit volume of the specimen is thus $-\kappa H^2/2$. This is a more satisfactory—though still not completely rigorous—derivation of this result than the one which we sketched at an earlier stage (footnote, p. 454).

CHAPTER 10

NON-CLASSICAL EFFECTS INVOLVING POTENTIAL BARRIERS

10.1. INTRODUCTORY

In chapter 8 we made considerable use of potential energy diagrams in discussing the phenomena of photoelectric and thermionic emission of electrons from metal surfaces in vacuum, and we continued to employ this direct method of representation, as appropriate, when the phenomena of contact potential difference and the thermoelectric circuit were involved. We did not, however, persevere with its use in the last section of that chapter, when we were concerned with the problem of the discharge of electrolytic ions at metallic electrodes—that is, with the problem of the passage of a negative electron from its state of binding in the conduction band of the metal to an external ion, or *vice versa*. To that extent our treatment of the passage of current 'across surfaces of discontinuity' was inconsistent, overall, though there was a good reason for our inconsistency. We admitted at the time (pp. 443, 444) that there was a non-classical feature of the process of electron transfer in the ion-discharge phenomenon that we could not profitably discuss without first introducing certain fundamental ideas that we had not previously elaborated. Indeed, our discussion of the formation of the electrical double layer across the surface of contact of two metals in section 8.3 (p. 410) was likewise less than complete (though we did not there draw attention to its shortcomings)—and for the same reason. In this chapter we must develop the ideas that we previously neglected, and exhibit their importance, by considering in some detail two phenomena, 'field emission' of electrons from metals, and alpha-particle emission from atomic nuclei, which are quite incomprehensible, theoretically, without their aid. First of all, however, let us review briefly the use that we have already made of the 'potential barrier' concept in our earlier discussions.

The potential energy curve of fig. 49, which refers to a hypothetical 'test electron' approaching the surface of separation of a lump of metal from vacuum, and passing into the bulk of the solid material, discloses a finite 'potential step' across the physical boundary of the metal, and exhibits the character of an 'infinite' potential barrier—effectively infinite, that is, in spatial extent on the vacuum side. In the same figure, the position of the horizontal line EF on the scale of ordinates represents the greatest total energy of a conduction electron at the absolute zero of temperature—the ('absolute') Fermi energy for the metal concerned. In fig. 52 the distribution of conduction electron energies at some higher temperature is indicated schematically. In this connection we used the potential barrier concept as a basis for an understanding of the process of thermionic emission. We concluded, in effect, that a strictly equilibrium state, in relation to the distribution of energy amongst the conduction electrons in the metal, could not obtain at any temperature other than the absolute zero. Under any other conditions strict thermal equilibrium would require that there should be some electrons present in the metal having total energies greater than zero (on the basis of the convention that the potential energy of an electron at an infinite distance from the metal surface in vacuum is zero). Such electrons, arriving at the physical boundary of the metal with their velocities appropriately directed, would pass through, and escape 'over the top of the potential barrier'.

This use of the potential barrier concept, which was generally successful, was founded in classical mechanics. It involved attention to the particle aspects of the electron motion, exclusively, disregarding the wave aspects of that motion. But we have to remember that the Sommerfeld model, in relation to which fig. 49 has been regularly employed, is a wave-mechanical model (albeit the simplest such) and that the fundamental notion of a well-defined Fermi energy is incomprehensible except in wave-mechanical terms. In dealing with the conduction electrons we have been operating all along with a hybrid assortment of concepts, as we have admitted from time to time (see, for example, p. 343), and we must be prepared for surprises if we lose sight of the insecurity of such a procedure. Here we state categorically that, whilst there are certain situations in which the predictions of particle mechanics and wave mechanics are essentially identical (as when the total particle energy is negative and a step barrier of infinite spatial extent is involved), there are others in which this is far from the case. When the potential barrier is of finite height and small 'thickness', and the total particle energy is less than the energy height of the barrier, the two predictions are utterly different.

We leave justification of our last assertion to the following sections of this chapter. Meanwhile we reflect that the two situations that we mentioned above—that of the electrolytic ion about to be discharged at a metal electrode, and that of the electrical double layer across the surface of contact of two dissimilar metals—are of the latter type. Such was the reason for our previous caution in discussing them. If a line be drawn from the centre of the electrolytic ion normally to the surface of the adjacent electrode, the curve of electron potential energy along this line will exhibit a local potential barrier 'impervious', on a classical basis, either to a conduction electron in the metal (if the ion is a positive ion) or to an electron belonging to the ion (if it is a negative ion). And, in relation to the problem of the electrical double layer, fig. 54 already indicates, schematically, the existence of such a local barrier centred on the plane of contact AB. If this figure had been drawn in respect of two metal disks separated, in vacuum, by a distance equal to a few atomic diameters, rather than for two disks making intimate contact, this local barrier would have been both higher and of greater thickness, and, on a classical basis, it would have been effectively impervious to the conduction electrons of either metal at all ordinary temperatures.

In detail, this is the analysis of these two situations according to classical particle mechanics, yet we know that electrolytic ions are discharged at metallic electrodes—and that dissimilar metals exhibit their characteristic contact potential differences even though no great care is taken to ensure that contact is perfect down to atomic dimensions (indeed it is very difficult in air to maintain a clean metal surface, and contamination tends to be by oxides, or organic substances which in bulk are non-conductors of electricity). In the following sections we shall be dealing with more obvious cases in which it will be necessary to conclude that a local potential barrier which is classically 'impervious' is not, in fact, the absolute barrier which we might have supposed it to be. As we shall see, wave mechanics provides the formalism for a consistent description of all such effects.

10.2. FIELD EMISSION OF ELECTRONS

During the half-century from 1860 (when Kelvin made the first systematic observations of the potential difference necessary to cause sparking between spherical electrodes in air) to 1910, a very considerable amount of work was done on the whole subject of the spark discharge. Towards the end of that period, when the more spectacular aspects of the phenomenon had been thoroughly investigated, attention was turned to the less spectacular—the almost invisible very short sparks which may be obtained over distances of 5×10^{-6} m and less, using differences of potential of the order of 100 V (and less, in proportion as the spark length is smaller). R. F. Earhart was the first to recognise, in 1901, that on this miniature scale the phenomenon is different in character from the normal insulation-breakdown phenomenon which is the spark of everyday experience. This conclusion became more clear-cut with the work of C. Kinsley and G. M. Hobbs, of the university of Chicago, in 1905. Hobbs, in particular, showed that, in these extreme conditions, the effect is independent of the pressure and the nature of the gas surrounding the electrodes, and the sparking potential is proportional to the spark length, so that a critical field strength is implied—the value of this critical field (of the order of 10^8 V m^{-1}) depending on the material of which the electrodes are made.

Already in 1903 Thomson had expressed the view, in relation to Earhart's experiments, 'that the spark is carried in this case by carriers dragged by the electric field out of the metal and not out of the gas'. The experiments of Kinsley and Hobbs confirmed him in this view: if their results could be taken at face value, precisely similar results would be obtained in a perfect vacuum. In such a case the carriers must be conduction electrons, 'field-extracted' from the negative electrode. Indeed, Thomson had written (1903) 'Let us now suppose than an external electric force F acts on the corpuscle, tending to make it move away from the metal; then if Fe is comparable with $e^2/4r^2$, the external field will give appreciable assistance to the corpuscle in escaping from the metal, and will allow corpuscles to leave the metal, whose kinetic energy is too small to allow them to escape in the absence of an external field.' The reader will recognise here the image-force concept which we have been using consistently throughout our discussions. Twenty years after Thomson, W. Schottky gave a detailed account of this view of the matter (see below). Meanwhile, at the university of

Chicago, R. A. Millikan and his students attempted, over many years, to reproduce, under 'vacuum' conditions, and using greater inter-electrode distances, results similar to those of Hobbs and Earhart with only partial success.

The first convincing results, under vacuum condictions, were reported in 1926, by Millikan and C. F. Eyring from the California Institute of Technology, and B. S. Gossling and others from the Research Laboratories of the General Electric Company in England. In each case electron currents were observed, from fine metal wires or sharp points, rapidly increasing with applied voltage (when the nominal field at the emitting surface was of the order of 10^8 V m^{-1}), in a way which was independent of temperature, at least from room temperature up to $700°$ C. In each case there was strong evidence that the currents arose from specially active 'spots', occupying only a very small fraction of the total cathode area when wire cathodes were employed—and that these active spots tended to become modified through continued emission, or by heat treatment of the cathode, so that the precise characteristics of any emitter varied unpredictably. However, there was enough of stability in the phenomenon for the two groups of investigators to reach very similar conclusions, independently, regarding the underlying regularities.

By 1926, Schottky's attempt to give a general theoretical account of the emission process had already been published (1923): in this connection the two groups of experimenters agreed, without reservation, that the attempt was very far from successful—at least in relation to the particular effect that they had been studying. In view of this result it might be thought that we are merely confusing the issue by referring to Schottky at all in the present context, but it will appear that this is not so: we digress, therefore, to formulate Schottky's equation precisely, so that the matter may be clarified. When this has been done we shall be the better placed to appreciate the peculiar characteristics of the phenomenon of 'field emission'—and we shall discover that although Schottky's equation has no direct relevance to that phenomenon it gives a very accurate description of another, that of 'field-enhanced' thermionic emission. Ultimately we shall find that conditions may be realised in practice such that the two phenomena are exhibited simultaneously, the distinction becoming a conceptual rather than an operational distinction, the electron current in such a case being temperature-and-field dependent. Operationally, the designation 'T—F emission' has been employed to describe such a situation (see p. 511).

As we have stated, Schottky generalised and carried forward a suggestion that Thomson first made in 1903 (see above). Let us consider an effectively plane surface of discontinuity separating metal from vacuum. Let $eV(x)$ be the potential energy of a test electron at a distance x from this plane (x positive in vacuum) when the external ('accelerating') field is zero. For our present purposes we adopt the Sommerfeld model in relation to the internal field of the metal, and take the constant value of $eV(x)$ throughout the bulk of the metal as the reference zero of potential energy. Then, in the notation of fig. 49, the value of the potential energy of the electron 'at infinity' in vacuum is $-U_0$. Now suppose that we apply an electron-accelerating field, the strength of which, in vacuum, in the immediate neighbourhood of the surface of discontinuity is X. This field does not penetrate into the bulk of the metal, and we imagine that it terminates abruptly at the effective surface of discontinuity that we have specified. Then, on the vacuum side of this surface, the potential energy of a test electron is $eV(x) - eXx$. This quantity is everywhere less than $-U_0$ (which is a positive quantity), and is a maximum when

$$\frac{dV(x)}{dx} = X \tag{312}$$

If the maximum occurs at a distance x_m, then the maximum potential energy of the test electron is less than $-U_0$ by an amount $\Delta\phi$, where

$$\Delta\phi = e\{Xx_m - V(x_m)\} - U_0 \tag{313}$$

$\Delta\phi$ is the amount by which the height of the potential barrier 'preventing the escape' of the conduction electrons in the metal is lowered by the application of the accelerating field; by the same token it is the measure of the decrease in the work function in relation to electron emission—either thermionic emission or photo-electric emission, as the case may be.

Interpreting equation (312) geometrically on the basis of fig. 49, we see that x_m decreases as X increases, so that over a range of values of X less than some critical value only the image-field component of $V(x)$ need be considered in our calculations. When this is the case, we have, simply,

$$eV(x) = -U_0 - \frac{e^2}{16\pi\epsilon_0 x};$$

then, in terms of equation (312),

$$\frac{e}{16\pi\epsilon_0 x_m{}^2} = X,$$

and, from equation (313),

$$\Delta\phi = \left(\frac{e^3 X}{4\pi\epsilon_0}\right)^{\frac{1}{2}} \tag{314}$$

or, alternatively,

$$\Delta\phi = \frac{e^2}{8\pi\epsilon_0 x_m} \tag{315}$$

Let us now write Richardson's (second) thermionic equation (equation (242)) in the form

$$j_0 = A'T^2 e^{-\phi/kT},$$

using the subscript to denote current density under limiting conditions of effectively zero accelerating field. Then, in view of our interpretation of equation (313), if j is the thermionic current density when the accelerating field is X, we have, in general,

$$j = j_0 e^{\Delta\phi/kT} \tag{316}$$

and, substituting from equation (314), for not-too-large values of X,

$$\log_e (j/j_0) = \left(\frac{e^3 X}{4\pi\epsilon_0}\right)^{\frac{1}{2}} /kT \tag{317}$$

Equation (316) taken together with equation (313), and equation (317), are the general and particular forms of Schottky's result that we set out to derive.

We have said that the experimental observations of Millikan and Eyring, and Gossling, gave no support for Schottky's suggestion that equation (316) should provide the basis of a satisfactory explanation of the phenomenon of field emission (when trustworthy results came to be obtained). In the first place, these authors' agreement that the currents which they observed originated in 'active spots' on the surface of a wire cathode in itself introduced the need for caution in attempting to apply Schottky's equation to the practical situation. Equation (316) specifies the degree of enhancement of the normal thermionic emission as a result of the application of the field. If there is any measurable current 'at zero field', this must come from the whole wire: in the 1926 experiments the 'enhanced' current came predominantly from a very much smaller area. Schottky had been aware of this difficulty: indeed, he had postulated that in the practical situation field-emission currents would first develop from small areas of local irregularity on a wire cathode, where the surface field might be as much as ten times greater than the value calculated from the macroscopic dimensions of the system. In this, certainly, he was correct. However, the real reason why equation (316) failed in relation to the field-emission phenomenon was that the field-dependence of the current should, according to the equation, be more pronounced at low temperatures than at high—and this was shown not to be the case. Explicitly, when equation (317) is applicable, we should expect to have

$$\frac{1}{j}\frac{dj}{dX} = \left(\frac{e^3}{\pi\epsilon_0 X}\right)^{\frac{1}{2}}/4kT.$$

No such variation was observed.

In 1928, Millikan and C. C. Lauritsen, leaving theory aside, proposed an empirical equation for field emission to which their temperature-independent experimental results (up to temperatures of 1000°C) appeared to conform. They wrote, for the emission current i,

$$i = Ae^{-b/X} \tag{318}$$

Here A is a constant for a given experimental arrangement, b depends on the metal of the cathode, and X is the accelerating field as before. About the same time, what has since proved to be an acceptable theory of the phenomenon was put forward, independently, in two publications, entirely different in character. In the first, under title 'Three notes on the quantum theory of aperiodic effects', J. Robert Oppenheimer (1904-1967) established certain general theorems and devoted two or three sentences towards the end of his paper to the application of his ideas to the problem of field emission. It was sufficient for his purposes—and sufficient to establish full priority for him as originator of the basic notions employed. The second publication, by Ralph Howard Fowler (1889-1944) and L. W. Nordheim, devoted entirely to the single problem, took the simplest possible model (simpler even than the model we have hitherto been using) and evaluated its consequences in detail.

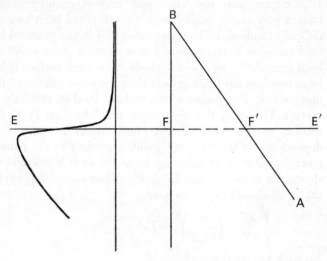

FIGURE 64

Allowing ourselves the wisdom of hindsight, let us delineate, at this stage, the general features of the problem which the theorists had to solve. Fig. 64 represents the situation, schematically, according to the model of Fowler and Nordheim. Basically, the Sommerfeld picture is accepted, but the potential step across the physical boundary of the metal is assumed to be abrupt—and the potential gradient representing the accelerating field X, to become discontinuously effective at the step. The figure has been lettered according to the scheme already adopted for fig. 52, with which it should be compared. EF represents the Fermi level of the conduction electrons, as before, and the 'vertical' distance FB the effective work function, which we shall denote by ϕ'. The model is not sufficiently detailed to provide an explicit specification of ϕ' as a function of X, but we shall assume, if the question arises, that ϕ' decreases smoothly as X increases, essentially as Schottky's calculation predicts.

Fundamentally, as we have seen, the problem in 1928 was to explain the lack of any marked temperature-dependence of the field-rate-of-increase of electron emission, under the experimental conditions that had been realised. Naïvely, we might suppose that there was little chance of a satisfactory explanation, unless it was postulated that the emitted electrons had their origin, within the metal, in energy states the population of which was itself independent of temperature, or nearly so—unless, in fact, the emitted electrons originated 'from below the Fermi level', according to the conventional jargon. From this point of view, Schottky's attempted explanation, assuming that only the 'high-energy tail' of the electron energy spectrum was involved, was doomed to failure from the outset.

If we accept this evaluation, then there are two possibilities. Either, in the experimental situation the accelerating field at the 'active spots' was sufficiently high so that ϕ' was zero, or negative (this might form the basis of a 'classical' explanation, carrying Schottky's ideas one stage farther than he did himself), or, if this could not have been the case, then some non-classical effect that we have not yet encountered must be invoked as a basis of explanation. In the 1926 experiments, with tungsten wire cathodes, nominal fields at the wire surface were of the order of 10^8 V m^{-1}: immediately outside the active spots effective fields might have been ten times greater than this (see p. 503)—they could hardly have been more than a hundred times greater, as would have been necessary if the first possibility were to be admissible. (The normal work function of tungsten is 4·5eV, and equations (314) and (315) can be used, at least to give the order of magnitude of the necessary field conditions.) Hard facts force us back, then, on the alternative of a non-classical explanation.

The explanation provided by the work of Oppenheimer, and Fowler and Nordheim, was essentially non-classical, though it may be introduced through the consideration of effects belonging strictly to classical physics. According to classical ideas, and on the basis of the model of Fowler and Nordheim (fig. 64), an electron belonging to the Fermi level, if it approached the physical boundary of the metal, would be 'totally reflected' at F. Here, we use the term 'totally reflected' deliberately—though in classical physics its use is, nowadays, conventionally restricted to the description of wave phenomena. The phenomenon of total reflection of light at the boundary between an optically denser and an optically rarer medium was known to Ptolemy (V & W, p. 141). Newton discovered that this 'internal' reflection was no longer total if (with glass as the denser, and air as the rarer medium) a second slab of glass were placed very close to the first. In such an arrangement some of the light is able to traverse the thin layer of optically rarer medium (air) and pass forward into the second denser medium (glass). Mistakenly, as we now believe, Newton regarded this effect as providing strong support for his view that light is corpuscular in nature.* Although the explanation on the wave theory was more subtle, the germ of it was already present (1826) in the original work of Fresnel (see V & W, §8.6): over the next fifty years, as successive hypotheses were advanced as bases for a physically acceptable wave theory (V & W, §9.1), the true nature of the effect became clear to the theorists. For a period of fifty years more, in its various aspects, it received close attention from experimenters, also; Elmer E. Hall, in particular, in 1902, described an extensive series of experiments which confirmed prediction in all essential respects.

Broadly speaking, the effect is a general one, having its origin in the fact that, for all types of wave motion, the values of certain macroscopically defined field quantities ('displacements') describing the motion must be mathematically 'continuous' through the physical boundary at which reflection occurs. In the ideal case in which only two 'semi-infinite' media are concerned, when plane waves are incident on the boundary at the critical angle, the whole

---

* Newton wrote (*Opticks*, 2nd edn., 1717, Book III, Query 29), 'The Rays of Light in going out of Glass into *Vacuum*, are bent towards the Glass; and if they fall too obliquely on the *Vacuum* they are bent backwards into the Glass, and totally reflected; and this Reflexion cannot be ascribed to the Resistance of an absolute *Vacuum*, but must be caused by the Power of the Glass attracting the Rays at their going out of it into the *Vacuum*, and bringing them back. . . . And this is still more evident by laying together two Prisms of Glass, or two Object-glasses of very long Telescopes, the one plane the other a little convex, and so compressing them that they do not fully touch, nor are too far asunder. For the Light which falls on the farther Surface of the first Glass where the interval between the Glasses is not above the ten hundred thousandth of an Inch, will go through that Surface, and through the Air or *Vacuum* between the Glasses, and enter into the second Glass. . . . But if the second Glass be taken away, the Light which goes out of the second Surface of the first Glass into the Air or *Vacuum*, will not go forwards, but turns back into the first Glass, and is reflected; and therefore is drawn back by the Power of the first Glass, there being nothing else to turn it back.'

of the energy is indeed returned to the denser medium in the 'totally reflected' wave—but not without some of it penetrating a short distance into the rarer medium (as Newton imagined all his light corpuscules to penetrate), before returning to contribute to the reflected beam. In the rarer medium, in such a case, the disturbance has the character of a quasi-stationary wave, parallel to the surface and to the plane of incidence, in which the displacement amplitude decreases exponentially, in a direction normal to the surface, with characteristic decrement-length $\lambda/2\pi$, λ being the wavelength of the disturbance in that medium.*

Though there is no net transport of energy (over times very long compared with the period of the wave) through any element of area in the 'disturbed' surface region in the rarer medium in the ideal case that we have just described, when small particles of absorbing material are introduced into this region—or another surface of discontinuity bounding a second semi-infinite piece of the denser medium is introduced—the situation is different. Hall coated a plane glass plate with gelatine containing silver bromide in suspension, and found that when light was incident on the glass-gelatine interface at the critical angle silver bromide grains situated within a wavelength's distance from the interface were rendered photographically developable. As to the other effect, we have Newton's original observation—and many other later and more precise confirmations of the result—that a very thin stratum of a rarer medium is not a perfect barrier to the transport of energy from one piece of denser medium to another, when a homogeneous wave disturbance is incident, at the first interface, at the critical angle for 'total reflection'. In the latter situation the conditions of continuity have to be satisfied at each of the two boundaries—and the result is a progressive ('transmitted') wave in the second denser medium, the reduction in intensity through the intervening layer being by a factor of $e^{-4\pi d/\lambda}$, if d is the layer thickness (and the intensity is proportional to the square of the displacement amplitude, as is regularly the case).

Here then, is the classical analogy, if with Oppenheimer, and Fowler and Nordheim, we are to regard field emission as a

---

* In another place (V & W, §§7.2, 7.3) we considered the problem of standing waves on the surface of deep water, and, applying the principle of continuity as appropriate to that case, concluded that the wave amplitude decreases with increasing distance, z, from the surface as $e^{-2\pi z/\lambda}$. $\lambda/2\pi$ is again the decrement-length in this case.

'nonclassical' phenomenon in which the wave aspects of electron motion are all-important. Let us consider a conduction electron belonging to the Fermi level. In the bulk of the metal its kinetic energy is E_0 (at the absolute zero of temperature), and its momentum is $(2mE_0)^{\frac{1}{2}}$. Correspondingly, the de Broglie wavelength (Λ) is $h/(2mE_0)^{\frac{1}{2}}$, h being Planck's constant and m the mass of the electron (see pp. 340, 387). When there is no external accelerating field, that is when conditions are as represented in fig. 52, the de Broglie waves of the Fermi-level electrons approaching the surface are 'totally reflected' at F—but not without there being established, on the vacuum side of the boundary, over a small distance normal to the surface, the quasi-stationary wave system which the imposition of continuity conditions would require. If the potential step at the boundary is abrupt (rather than as represented in the figure) —and if ϕ is the work function—then, classically, if a Fermi-level electron were to be found on the vacuum side of the boundary, its kinetic energy would be negative $(-\phi)$, and its momentum would be imaginary $(-2m\phi)^{\frac{1}{2}}$. Now, a de Broglie wavelength which is imaginary is not devoid of physical significance in wave mechanics, and, in relation to the potential barrier problem that we are discussing, it turns out that the quantity $h/(2m\phi)^{\frac{1}{2}}$—the modulus of the imaginary de Broglie wavelength—determines the decrement-length, $|\Lambda|/2\pi$, in respect of amplitude, of the quasi-stationary waves on the vacuum side of the boundary, for a Fermi-level electron.

Let us consider, first of all, two different conductors A and B brought together in vacuum until their proximate surfaces are separated by a small distance d. Let ϕ_1 and ϕ_2 be the respective work functions and let us suppose that $\phi_1 < \phi_2$. In the crudest approximation, fig. 65 represents the 'initial' potential energy barrier opposing the passage of conduction electrons from one metal to the other, E_1F_1 denoting the Fermi level for the conduction electrons of conductor A and F_2E_2 the corresponding level for B. Note that $F_1'E_1'$, the level in B which has the same total energy as E_1F_1 in A, is initially a vacant level in B. However, it cannot remain vacant indefinitely—for in that case the conditions of continuity in respect of the de Broglie waves would not be satisfied at F_1'. If conductor A were an infinite 'source' of conduction electrons and conductor B an infinite 'sink', a steady state would be reached in which, in relation to the gap separating the conductors, there would be built up, in B, a 'progressive' de Broglie wave of intensity $e^{-4\pi d / |\Lambda|}$, that is $e^{-\frac{4\pi d}{h}(2m\phi_1)^{1/2}}$, of the intensity of the 'incident' wave in A. We interpret this result in the statement that, in this situation, each Fermi-level electron in A, when it approaches the surface of A adjacent to B, has a chance $e^{-\frac{4\pi d}{h}(2m\phi_1)^{1/2}}$ of passing across the gap into the second conductor with its total energy unchanged. In fact, of course, two finite conductors do not constitute an infinite source and sink in relation to conduction electrons. As we have previously described (p. 411),

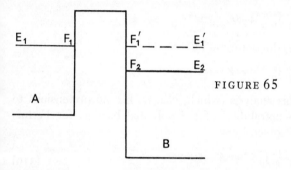

FIGURE 65

the transfer of a totally insignificant fraction of the conduction electrons from one conductor to the other is sufficient so to modify the relative potentials of the conductors that further net transfer of electrons is halted. The Fermi levels of the two conductors come to have the same total energy (p. 410), and fig. 65 no longer represents the potential energy barrier across the gap. Fig. 54 was drawn for two conductors in intimate contact, representing the final state with the contact potential fully established. Where there is a significant vacuum gap between the conductors a longer time is required—very much longer when $d > |\Lambda|$—for this equilibrium state to be achieved, but ultimately it is achieved, essentially by the non-classical process of the 'passage of electrons through the potential energy barrier between the conductors'.

We are now in a position to revert to the problem of field emission, with the help of fig. 64. For this purpose we may consider the emitter to be an infinite source, for the emitted electrons are continuously removed by the accelerating field. At any point within the potential barrier, at a distance x from BF, the classical kinetic energy of a Fermi-level electron would be $-(\phi' - eXx)$.

We have, therefore,

$$| \Lambda | = h/\{2m(\phi' - eXx)\}^{\frac{1}{2}},$$

and, for the decrease in amplitude of the de Broglie waves between x and $x + dx$, the attenuation factor

$$e^{-\frac{2\pi}{h}\{2m(\phi' - eXx)\}^{1/2} dx}.$$

Across the whole barrier (from F to F', in fig. 64), the accumulation of these factors of attenuation amounts, overall, to an amplitude-reduction ratio of

$$1 : e^{-\frac{2\pi}{h} \int_0^{\phi'/eX} \{2m(\phi' - eXx)\}^{1/2} dx},$$

or an intensity reduction ratio of

$$1 : e^{-\frac{4\pi}{h} \int_0^{\phi'/eX} \{2m(\phi' - eXx)\}^{1/2} dx}.$$

According to this analysis (which, clearly, has no pretensions to rigour!), the 'penetrability' of the potential barrier, for Fermi-level electrons is given by

$$P = e^{-\frac{4\pi}{h} \int_0^{\phi'/eX}\{2m(\phi' - eXx)\}^{1/2} dx} \qquad (319)$$

Simple evaluation of equation (319) then gives us*

$$P = e^{-\frac{8\pi}{3h}(2m)^{1/2}\frac{\phi'^{3/2}}{eX}} \qquad (320)$$

—and, as before, we interpret P as the probability that a Fermi-level electron, 'incident on the potential barrier' within the metal, will pass through into vacuum under the influence of the accelerating field.

Equation (320) contains the central result of the Fowler-Nordheim calculation. When this result is elaborated, taking count of the distribution of conduction electrons 'below the Fermi level', following these authors, we have

$$j = A'X^2 e^{-\frac{8\pi}{3h}(2m)^{1/2}\frac{\phi'^{3/2}}{eX}} \qquad (321)$$

In equation (321), if j represents the current density, the value of the constant A' is given explicitly on the basis of the model. We recognise at once that, apart from the multiplying factor X^2,

---

* It will be noted that e is used here to denote both the measure of the electronic charge and the base of Napierian logarithms—without, it is hoped, introducing unnecessary confusion.

equation (321) has precisely the form of the empirical relation of Millikan and Lauritsen (p. 503). That this relation had been put forward entirely independently of theory, as the best representation of the experimental results, provided the strongest possible support for the new ideas which were involved in the theoretical approach: indeed no one has since doubted the essential correctness of those ideas in this particular context.

Having reached this conclusion, it remains now only to refer briefly to later work—and to certain questions that have been left in suspense in the course of our discussion. It is quite clear that on the theoretical side, once the 'correct' approach had been discovered, it was merely a matter of refinement to introduce the image field into the calculations (and so, in our notation, to take count of the variation of ϕ' with X). Also, the extent to which the final result is model-dependent could be investigated. No new principle was involved. These refinements have been carried through, and the theory made more secure thereby.

On the experimental side, as we have seen (p. 500), purely practical considerations severely limited the generality of the situations that the earlier workers were able to investigate. The great advance came when methods were found of so fabricating emitters that they did not develop 'active spots' under the action of intense accelerating fields. Already, in 1928, N. A. de Bruyne and W. S. Pforte, independently, had achieved this result with tungsten wire cathodes, up to surface fields of 10^8 V m^{-1}, and had verified Schottky's relation (equation (317)), giving the enhancement of thermionic emission, accurately, over this range. Much later (1953-1955), W. P. Dyke and his collaborators succeeded in subjecting tungsten cathodes to surface fields ranging from $2 \cdot 5 \times 10^9$ V m^{-1} to 7×10^9 V m^{-1} whilst still obtaining uniform surface emission at all temperatures from room temperature to 1700° C. In this way they were able to study 'temperature-and-field' emission (see p. 501) systematically, and to verify the predictions of the refined theory that we have mentioned.

In '$T - F$ emission', when the collecting field and the cathode temperature are both high, the energy spectrum of the emitted electrons comprises essentially two components, according to our accepted picture of these processes, the energy separation of the centroids of the component spectra being ϕ', or thereabouts. The electrons of higher energy are those which are 'thermionically' emitted 'over the top of the potential barrier'; those of lower energy are the 'field-emitted' electrons which have 'passed through the barrier'. Already in the period from 1931 to 1940 J. E. Henderson and his co-workers had demonstrated conclusively the correctness of this picture. Using essentially a triode arrangement of cylindrical symmetry, these authors showed that whatever the accelerating potential applied to the 'grid', no field emission current passed to the 'anode' unless this electrode were made positive with respect to the filament of the 'valve' by ϕ'/e or some greater voltage. When conditions were those of thermionic emission, on the other hand, some anode current passed even when the anode was slightly negative with respect to the filament (p. 180).

10.3. ALPHA-PARTICLE EMISSION FROM NUCLEI

The phenomenon of α-radioactivity—the emission of α-particles from atomic nuclei—provides an even more clear-cut example of the need for a non-classical explanation than does the phenomenon of 'cold electron emission', which we discussed in the last section. In the α-particle case the classical paradox can be stated quite simply: an α-particle incident on a heavy nucleus 'from outside' can be scattered through 180°, having been instantaneously brought to rest in the repulsive field of the nucleus, and return with more kinetic energy than is possessed by the α-particle which that nucleus emits spontaneously. Let us elaborate this general statement, describing briefly the experiments on which it is based, and examining its implications.

In section 6.4 we described the experiments of Geiger and Marsden, and Chadwick, by which the predictions of the Rutherford scattering formula (equation (156)) were verified, in detail, in respect of α-particle scattering in thin foils of various metallic elements, in particular platinum ($Z = 78$) and gold ($Z = 79$). In 1925 Rutherford and Chadwick extended these investigations, examining the scattering in uranium ($Z = 92$) and obtaining essentially similar results. The experiments were carried out using α-particles of approximately 7·7 MeV energy, and the natural conclusion, taking all the results into account, was that for heavy nuclei in general (say, for atomic numbers from 78 to 92 inclusive) the whole of the positive charge of the nucleus is concentrated within the closest distance of approach of a 7·7 MeV α-particle to the nucleus, in a head-on collision. More than that, it appeared that outside this distance the only force of nuclear origin to which an α-particle is subject is the coulombian repulsion arising from the nuclear charge. These conclusions being accepted (on the basis of a classical analysis of the situation), we can use the results of the scattering experiments to plot the potential energy of an α-particle (of charge $2e$) in the field of a heavy nucleus (of charge Ze) as a function of the radial distance of separation, r. To be precise, the potential energy is given by

$$U(r) = \frac{Ze^2}{2\pi\epsilon_0 r} \tag{322}$$

—at least for values of r greater than a limiting value corresponding to $U(r) = 7\cdot7$ MeV, the maximum energy of the α-particles employed in the investigation.

Let us now consider a particular case. Let us suppose that AB (fig. 66) represents that portion of the potential energy curve of an α-particle in the radial field of the heavy nucleus $^{234}_{90}$Th, the form of which is given by equation (322), as attested by the scattering experiments. If an α-particle incident on such a nucleus (with sufficient energy) were to penetrate into the nuclear structure, it might well give up its additional energy and be captured. In that event the nucleus $^{238}_{92}$U would be formed. This is a 'well-known' nucleus, belonging to the long-lived parent species of the uranium-radium series of radioelements. There is nothing intrinsically impossible in its being formed in this way—and in any case we know that $^{238}_{92}$U is an α-emitting species. Naïvely, we suppose that, in the 'quiescent' state, such a nucleus contains an α-particle 'ready to be emitted', and we may imagine that the incident α-particle is captured into this state. As long as it remains within the nucleus this 'nascent' α-particle is subject to the attractive forces arising from the other nuclear constituents (which together make up the nucleus $^{234}_{90}$Th). In terms of fig. 66, therefore, immediately 'inside the nuclear surface' the potential energy of the captured α-particle rapidly decreases; and we suppose that it becomes negative in the central region of the 'core'. The dotted line CD, in the figure, represents this conclusion schematically; and the portion BC (concerning the form of which no precise assumptions are made) is added to complete the picture.

Completed in this way, fig. 66 provides a generalised representation of the profile of the spherically symmetrical potential barrier

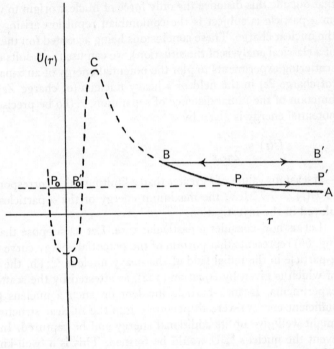

FIGURE 66

which opposes the (radial) entry of an α-particle into a $^{234}_{90}$Th nucleus—or the (radial) exit of an α-particle from a $^{238}_{92}$U nucleus (leaving a $^{234}_{90}$Th nucleus as residue). The 'horizontal' line BB' represents the head-on collision of a 7·7 MeV α-particle with a $^{234}_{90}$Th nucleus, the 'vertical' distance between BB' and AB being a measure of the kinetic energy of the α-particle at successive points along its path. In the particular case that we are considering, the point of paradox is that the kinetic energy of the α-particle spontaneously emitted from a $^{238}_{92}$U nucleus in the act of disintegration is only 4·2 MeV, as measured 'at infinity'. Classically considered, there is a double paradox here. If the horizontal line PP' is drawn, in the figure, to represent the motion of such a particle after it has left the 'residual' nucleus, then, classically considered, the emitted particle cannot have had its origin closer to the centre of the nucleus than is represented by the point P in the diagram. This conclusion is doubly unacceptable. In the first place, the resultant force on an α-particle at P is repulsive: it is unacceptable to have to conclude that the α-particle ultimately emitted from a $^{238}_{92}$U nucleus, which remains bound in the nucleus, on the average, for some $6\cdot5 \times 10^9$ y before it is emitted, is located in a region of repulsive force. In the second place, the scattering experiments, as we have seen, classically interpreted, indicate that the whole of the positive charge of the nucleus is concentrated within a distance from the centre less than that corresponding to the point B in the figure. It is unacceptable that we should have to conclude that some of this charge—that of the nascent α-particle—is in fact situated at the distance of P.

Classically, then, we reject these two unacceptable conclusions— and we insist that the nascent α-particle must be contained within the nucleus, where the resultant central force is attractive, until the moment of disintegration. Adopting the 'single particle model' of fig. 66, in which this disintegration particle is already regarded as conceptually distinct from the residual nucleus from which it is ultimately to separate, we imagine that there exists in the initial nucleus a bound state of appropriate energy, and we assign the α-particle to that state. Accordingly, we add P_0P_0' to the figure (characterised by the same total energy as PP') to represent the bound state of the disintegration α-particle of $^{238}_{92}$U in the field of the residual nucleus $^{234}_{90}$Th. Classically, or otherwise, we could hardly have come to any other description of the pre-disintegration state of the nuclear system (in the zero-order approximation)— but we have not resolved the basic paradox simply by insisting on this description: we have merely identified more clearly the real point of breakdown in the classical interpretation. According to the principles of classical physics, the 'nascent' α-particle occupying the bound state P_0P_0' could never become the 'emitted' α-particle in the unbound state PP'. For sake of concreteness, we have considered the particular case of the α-disintegration of $^{238}_{92}$U to lead us to this conclusion, but there is nothing significant in our choice of example. The difficulty is a perfectly general one: the problem of α-disintegration is fundamentally the problem of understanding 'the passage of the α-particle through the barrier of potential energy which surrounds the nucleus'—that is all.

It is tempting to believe, when it is exhibited in this way, that the problem of α-disintegration, in its formal aspects at least, is essentially the same as that of field emission which we have already discussed. In a sense this is true, but there is a real difference that we should recognise from the outset. α-disintegration is a 'catastrophic' process, happening 'once for all'; field emission, on the other hand, is a continuing process, depending only on the maintenance of the field. In that case, as we pointed out previously (p. 509), the emitting cathode is effectively an infinite source of electrons; in the other, the radioactive nucleus is a source of but a single α-particle. Empirically, in the field-emission case, we are not primarily concerned with the distribution in time of the emitted electrons; in the α-particle case the temporal aspect of the phenomenon is its essential feature. From these points of view, then, the two effects are indeed quite different; it is a measure of the generality of the basic notion of barrier penetration, as Oppenheimer originally conceived it, that, theoretically considered, the two problems should have so much in common.

Oppenheimer did not himself suggest, in his general theoretical paper of 1928, to which we have already referred (p. 503), that the problem of α-disintegration provided an obvious field of application of his original ideas. That suggestion was made, later that year, by Gurney (see p. 438) and Edward Uhler Condon (b. 1902), and about the same time the same method of approach was adopted, independently, by George Gamow (b. 1904), who was the first to carry through a detailed calculation based on a simplified model.

In general terms, if E denotes the total energy of the nascent α-particle (of mass M) in the radioactive nucleus of charge number Z (that is, the kinetic energy with which the α-particle is eventually found 'at infinity' after the disintegration), and $U(r)$ the potential energy of this α-particle in the field of the residual nucleus (of charge number $Z - 2$), and if $U(r) > E$ over the range of radial distance from r_1 to r_2, we may take over the calculation of barrier penetrability from the last section (p. 510) and, instead of equation (319), obtain in this case

$$P = e^{-\frac{4\pi}{h}(2M)^{1/2}\int_{r_1}^{r_2}(U(r)-E)^{1/2}\,dr} \tag{323}$$

According to Gurney and Condon, and Gamow, we interpret equation (323), simply, as follows. Inside the nucleus, the nascent α-particle, in continual motion, 'strikes the inside of the potential barrier', say, with frequency f. On each occasion P represents the probability that the α-particle will 'pass through the barrier' and escape. The overall probability per unit time, then, that the α-particle will escape from the nucleus is fP, but this is the measure of the radioactive disintegration constant, λ, appropriate to the nuclear species concerned. Thus

$$\lambda = fP \tag{324}$$

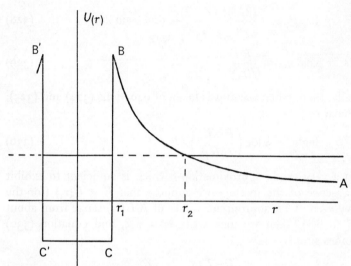

FIGURE 67

The simplified model that Gamow employed in the evaluation of α-disintegration constants, essentially through the use of equations (323) and (324), is represented schematically in fig. 67. In radial profile the potential energy barrier is considered as made up of a central 'rectangular well' (BCC'B') of inner potential U_0 (a negative quantity) and breadth $2r_1$, and an outer slope (BA) of strictly coulombian form and extending from r_1 to infinity (on each side). According to this model, in which all motion is considered to be radial motion, we have

$$f = \left(\frac{E - U_0}{2Mr_1^2}\right)^{\frac{1}{2}} \tag{325}$$

$$U(r) = \frac{(Z-2)e^2}{2\pi\epsilon_0 r} \tag{326}$$

$$r_2 = \frac{(Z-2)e^2}{2\pi\epsilon_0 E} \tag{327}$$

Obviously, the model was chosen intentionally so that equation (323) should yield an explicit expression for P. In fact, integration proceeds smoothly by change of variable ($E = U(r) \cos^2 u$), once substitution is made from the model-sensitive equations (326) and (327). We obtain, explicitly,

$$\log P = -\frac{(2M)^{\frac{1}{2}}}{h} \frac{(Z-2)e^2}{\epsilon_0 E^{\frac{1}{2}}} (2u_0 - \sin 2u_0) \tag{328}$$

with

$$\cos^2 u_0 = \frac{E}{U(r_1)} \tag{329}$$

Finally, then, when account is taken of equations (324) and (325), we have

$$\log \lambda = \tfrac{1}{2} \log \left(\frac{E - U_0}{2Mr_1^2} \right) + \log P \tag{330}$$

In a very crude approximation—which is sufficient to exhibit the essence of the matter—we suppose that $E \ll U(r_1)$ (for the heavy α-emitters, appropriate values of $E/U(r_1)$ range from about 0·15 to 0·3); then we may write $u_0 = \pi/2$, and equation (330) becomes simply

$$\log \lambda = \tfrac{1}{2} \log \left(\frac{E - U_0}{2Mr_1^2} \right) - \frac{2\pi}{h\epsilon_0} \frac{(Z-2)e^2}{v} \tag{331}$$

v being the velocity with which the emitted α-particle is found 'at infinity' after the disintegration. We see, at once, that essentially only two factors determine relative values of λ, according to the model. The second term in the expression for $\log \lambda$ is overwhelmingly the dominant term, thus the velocity (or energy) of emission of the α-particle and the nuclear charge number Z are all-important; the nuclear radius r_1, and the inner potential U_0 are involved in equation (331) only in the first term, and the value of this is little different over the whole range of our interest (the heavy α-emitters, as we have already indicated).

Let us pursue this last statement to a numerical comparison, for in so doing we shall best demonstrate the extraordinary success which attended the wave-mechanical theory of α-disintegration from the outset. In 1928, the experimental facts regarding α-disintegration were generally regarded as being reasonably well represented by the empirical rule of Geiger and Nuttall. This rule, first adumbrated by the two authors (John Michael Nuttall (1890-1958)) in 1911, and buttressed by more precise measurements by Geiger (see p. 251) in 1921, may be formulated, for our purposes, in the equation

$$\log \lambda = a + b \log v \tag{332}$$

Referring specifically to the α-emitting members of the three 'classical' radioactive series ($83 \leqslant Z \leqslant 92$), equation (332) contains two constants a and b. The former of these appeared to have somewhat different values for the α-emitters of the three series; the latter was given the same value for each. By and large, in 1921, all the available information could be subsumed under equation (332), with $b = 160$, or thereabouts. Let us accept this empirical result, and conclude that, for the heavy α-emitters generally,

$$v \frac{d \log \lambda}{dv} = 160 \tag{333}$$

(on the basis of equation (332), the left-hand member of equation (333) is precisely equal to b).

According to our crudely approximate theoretical result (equation (331), with only the second term considered),

$$v \frac{\partial \log \lambda}{\partial v} = \frac{2\pi}{h\epsilon_0} \frac{(Z-2)e^2}{v} \tag{334}$$

In the right-hand member of equation (334) let us write $v = \beta c$, c denoting the velocity of light in free space, then, 'theoretically',

$$v \frac{\partial \log \lambda}{\partial v} = 4\pi(Z-2) \frac{\alpha}{\beta} \tag{335}$$

where $\alpha = \dfrac{e^2}{2\epsilon_0 hc}$.

The left-hand member of equation (335) represents a pure number, thus α is non-dimensional, as β is. In fact, the value of α is very closely 1/137*, so we may write, numerically, according to theory,

$$v \frac{\partial \log \lambda}{\partial v} = 0.092 \frac{Z-2}{\beta} \tag{336}$$

* In the theory of atomic spectra, the number which we have denoted by α is referred to as the 'fine-structure constant'.

Among the heavy α-emitters known to Geiger, the extreme values of $(Z-2)/\beta$ were 1940 (for $^{238}_{92}$U) and 1200 (for $^{212}_{84}$Po). According to Gamow's theoretical equation (336), therefore, the extreme values of $v\,\dfrac{\partial \log \lambda}{\partial v}$ are 178 and 110. Comparing this range of values with the value 160 from the Geiger-Nuttall relation (equation (333)), we need seek no further evidence for the 'extraordinary success' that we have mentioned. By the end of 1927 no one was any nearer a theory of α-disintegration than he had been in 1913 (when the nuclear origin of the particles was first recognised); by the end of 1928 there was crude numerical agreement, on the basis of a well-founded theory of general relevance.

Since 1928, experiment has revealed previously unsuspected complexity in the phenomenon of α-disintegration, and the simple theory of Gamow has been correspondingly modified and greatly refined. However, the basis of the theory remains unscathed, and it would be unprofitable to follow its developments here. It is appropriate, rather, that we should end where we began. Gurney and Condon concluded their first brief announcement of their novel point of view with the pertinent remark 'Much has been written of the explosive violence with which the α-particle is hurled from its place in the nucleus. But from the process pictured above, one would rather say that the α-particle slips away almost unnoticed.' Much has been written in this book: it is now for the writer, like the α-particle, to slip away, through the prison wall of his long confinement, almost unnoticed in the end.

INDEX OF NAMES

Short **biographical details**, or references to them, are to be found on pages indicated in **heavy type**. Page references followed by f indicate footnotes.

INDEX OF SUBJECTS